DICTIONARY OF TECHNICAL TERMS

DICTIONARY
OF TECHNICAL TERMS

Containing Definitions of Commonly Used Expressions in Aeronautics, Architecture, Woodworking and Building Trades, Electrical and Metalworking Trades, Printing, Chemistry, Plastics, etc.

▸

FREDERIC SWING CRISPIN, C.E.

(Ninth Edition — Revised)

THE BRUCE PUBLISHING COMPANY
MILWAUKEE

Library of Congress Catalog Number: 61–15639

© 1961 THE BRUCE PUBLISHING COMPANY
MADE IN THE UNITED STATES OF AMERICA

(Eleventh Printing — 1961)

PREFACE

This Dictionary, for the use of students, draftsmen, mechanics, builders, electricians, and for workmen generally, has been prepared for the purpose of assisting them in securing an understanding of the technical terms with which they come in daily contact.

While many handbooks contain glossaries of the terms mentioned in their texts, the authors, in most cases, assume that those interested should be so familiar with the articles described that definitions should not be needed, and they therefore proceed with their descriptions of the application, instead of prefacing their remarks with understandable definitions.

Definitions of many of the terms listed here will not be found in any technical text nor in the average dictionary even though they are, almost without exception, terms which are in use in all sections of the United States.

No attempt has been made to include all the technical terms in any field of endeavor, but the purpose has been to make the scope broad enough to give the workman that knowledge of trade nomenclature which will be extremely useful to him in the pursuit of his vocation.

F. S. CRISPIN

F. S. CRISPIN

Philadelphia, Pa.

PREFACE TO THE NINTH EDITION

The favorable manner in which THE DICTIONARY OF TECHNICAL TERMS has been received makes an even further expansion of its content seem warranted. This new edition, therefore, contains many terms and definitions not found in the earlier editions: particularly in relation to aeronautics, auto mechanics, electricity, plastics, radio, television, and welding.

Acknowledgment of assistance in bringing this book up to date is made to the following: National Aeronautics and Space Administration for permission to make free use of the definitions prepared by them; Mr. Elmer Briggs, Vice Principal of the Dobbins Vocational School, Philadelphia; Prof. Richard Hartmann of the University of Pennsylvania, for his assistance in suggesting a list of electrical definitions; Mr. Alexander F. Bick for preparing a list of plastic definitions; the Sherwin Williams Company for supplying valuable technical information on paints and lacquers; Dr. Harold Abrams and Mr. Burnell Kinkler for many helpful suggestions; Mr. Robert Hesse as an expert in the field of printing; the International Nickel Company for authoritative words on metallurgy; the Plastic Catalog Corporation, and Modern Plastics for generous assistance in the field of plastics; the Shell Oil Co.; the American Welding Society; the General Electric Co. and the National Broadcasting Co. for their courtesy in permitting the use of a new list of television definitions; the Manufacturing Chemists Association, Inc.; the American Institute of Electrical Engineers for permission to quote from their "American Standard Definitions of Electrical Terms."

ABBREVIATIONS USED IN THIS BOOK

Adv.	Advertising
Aero.	Aeronautics
Agric.	Agriculture
Algebra	Algebra
Arch.	Architecture
Arith.	Arithmetic
Art	Art
Art Met.	Art Metal
Auto.	Automotive
Auto. Mech.	Automobile Mechanics
Bldg.	Building
Bookbndg.	Bookbinding
Bot.	Botany
Cabwk.	Cabinetwork
Carp.	Carpentry
Ceram.	Ceramics
Chem.	Chemistry
Chem. Plast.	Chemical Plastics
Color	Color
Concrete	Concrete
Draft.	Drafting
Draw.	Drawing
Dyeing	Dyeing
Elec.	Electricity
Elec. Plast.	Electrical Plastics
Engin.	Engineering
Fdry.	Foundry
Fine Arts	Fine Arts
Forg.	Forging
Furn.	Furniture
Gear.	Gearing
Geol.	Geology
Geom.	Geometry
Jewelry	Jewelry
Leather.	Leathercraft
Lumber	Lumber
Mach.	Machinery
Man. Arts	Manual Arts
Masonry	Masonry
Math.	Mathematics
Mech.	Mechanics
Mech. Arts	Mechanical Arts
Mech. Drg.	Mechanical Drawing
Mech. Engin.	Mechanical Engineering
Metal.	Metallurgy
Metal Fin.	Metal Finishing
Metalwk.	Metalwork
Min.	Mining
Mineral.	Mineralogy
Mold.	Molding
Naut.	Nautical
Paint.	Painting
Paint and Lacquer	Paint and Lacquer
Papermkg.	Papermaking
Patmkg.	Patternmaking
Phys.	Physics
Piping	Piping
Plast.	Plastics
Plaster.	Plastering
Plast. Art	Plastic Art
Plumb.	Plumbing
Pot.	Pottery
Print.	Printing
Rad.	Radio
Rivet.	Riveting
Sheet Metal	Sheet Metal
Sheet-Met. Wk.	Sheet-Metal Working
Shopwk.	Shopwork
Steam Fit.	Steam Fitting
Steam Heat.	Steam Heating
Steel	Steel
Surv.	Surveying
Tel.	Television
Textile	Textile
Uphol.	Upholstery
Weld.	Welding
Wood	Wood
Wood Fin.	Wood Finishing
Wood Patmkg.	Wood Patternmaking
Wood Turn.	Wood Turning
Woodwk.	Woodwork
Woodwkg.	Woodworking

A

A bat′ter-y (*Elec.*) The source of supply for filament power in a battery-operated radio set.

ab′a-cus (ăb′*a*-kŭs) (*Arch.*) The upper part of the capital of a column, either square or curved. (*Math.*) A calculating table with sliding balls on wires or sticks.

Grecian Doric Abacus
Corinthian Abacus

ab-ra′sion. The process of reducing material by grinding instead of cutting with tools.

ab-ra′sive. Grinding material such as sandstone, emery, carborundum, etc. The natural abrasives include the diamond, emery, corundum, sand, crushed garnet and quartz, tripoli, and pumice. The artificial abrasives are in general either silicon carbide or aluminum oxide, and are marketed under many trade names.

ab-ra′sive pa′per. Paper or cloth upon which flint, garnet, emery, or corundum has been fastened with glue or some other adhesive.

ab-scis′sa (ăb-sĭs′*a*) (*Math.*) The length of an axis at right angles to the axis of ordinates.

ab′so-lute (*Mech.*) A term frequently used in the trades to indicate a thing as being perfect or exact.

ab′so-lute al′ti-tude (*Aero.*) The height of an aircraft above the earth.

ab′so-lute an′gle of at-tack′ (*Aero.*) The angle of attack of an airfoil measured from the attitude of zero lift.

ab′so-lute ceil′ing (*Aero.*) The maximum height in a standard atmosphere at which a given airplane under specified operating conditions can maintain horizontal flight.

ab′so-lute mo′tion (*Phys.*) Records successive changes of position with respect to a point in space which is regarded as ideally fixed.

ab′so-lute ze′ro (*Phys.*) −273 degrees Centigrade. −459.2 degrees Fahrenheit.

ab-sorb′ent. A substance that absorbs.

ab-sorb′ent cot′ton (*Textile*) Natural cotton with the fatty and waxy matter removed in order to increase its absorbing qualities.

ab-sorp′tion dy′na-mom′e-ter (*Elec.*) A form of dynamometer in which the measured energy is absorbed by frictional resistance and is not transmitted to other machines to perform useful work.

ab′stract de-sign′. Design based on geometric lines and shapes.

a-but′ment (*Arch. and Engin.*) The support of an arch, beam, or bridge, which sustains the reaction due to the load. Abutment

a.c. (*Elec.*) The common expression for alternating current.

ac′a-cine gum (ăk′*a*-sĭn) Same as gum arabic.

a-can′thus (*Arch. and Furn.*) A Greek conventional leaf ornament used as a decorative feature of carved furniture, and a characteristic of the Corinthian capital. Acanthus

---

sāle, surfâce, grăm, humăn, màsk, solàr, bär, bâre; mē, ĕdition, lĕnd, momĕnt, bakẽr; kīnd, fĭt; lōde, ômit, ŏlive, cŏnsume, sôrt; dūty, ûtility, nŭt, alŭm, bûrn.

ac-cel′er-at′ed mo′tion (ăk-sĕl′ēr-āt′ĕd) (*Mech.*) Motion in which velocity is not constant. The term is used in reference to both increased and decreased velocity, although, when decreased, it is known as "negative accelerated motion."

ac-cel′er-at′ing jet (*Auto Mech.*) The carburetor jet through which the accelerating charge is injected into the incoming air charge.

ac-cel′er-at′ing pump (*Auto. Mech.*) A plunger-type pump attached to the carburetor for the purpose of increasing the richness of the mixture and to give a quick "pickup" under load.

ac-cel′er-at′ing–pump pis′ton (*Auto Mech.*) The small leather cup washer or hollow brass piston in the cylinder of the accelerator pump.

ac-cel′er-a′tion (*Mech.*) The rate at which the velocity of a moving body increases.

ac-cel′er-at′or (*Auto. Mech.*) A mechanical device for regulating the amount of gas mixture which is fed to the engine, usually operated by the foot. (*Plast.*) In plastics, a chemical that hastens reaction, particularly one that speeds resin hardening. Also called promoter.

ac-cel′er-om′e-ter (*Aero.*) An instrument for recording, measuring, or indicating accelerations.

ac′cent (*Math.*) A mark or marks to distinguish the order or value of similar symbols, as a′ (read "a prime"), etc.

ac-ces′si-bil′i-ty. The degree of convenient arrangement of parts to permit easy adjustment, repair, assembling, disassembling, etc.

ac-ces′so-ry (ăk-sĕs′ô-rĭ) A mechanical part or attachment not necessarily a part of the machine with which it is to be used but does make possible a wider range of work or better performance.

ac-cor′di-on (*Arch.*) A type of door or partition, which can be folded, or opened and closed, in a manner like the operation of the bellows of the musical instrument.

ac-cu′mu-la′tor (*Mech.*) A cylinder into which water is forced in order to furnish the motive power in hydraulic machines of various kinds. (*Elec.*) A storage battery.

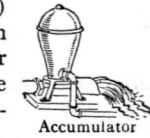
Accumulator

ac′cu-rate. Without error; precise; correct; conforming exactly to a standard.

a′ce-tate, cel′lu-lose (*Plast.*) Plastic used as a base for magnetic recording tape.

a-ce′tic ac′id (ă-sē′tĭk) (*Chem.*) A colorless, pungent liquid ($HC_2H_3O_2$) usually obtained by the destructive distillation of wood or by the oxidation of alcohol with ferments. Vinegar is an impure acetic acid.

ac′e-tone (ăs′ê-tōn) (*Chem.*) An inflammable liquid (CH_3COCH_3) with a bitter taste, obtained by the destructive distillation of certain wood, acetates, and various organic compounds.

a-cet′y-lene gas (à-sĕt′ĭ-lēn) (*Chem.*) An illuminating gas (C_2H_2) resulting from the action of water on calcium carbide. Also used for oxyacetylene welding.

a-cet′y-lene gen′er-a′tor (*Weld.*) A container from which there can be supplied, under uniform pressure, the acetylene gas produced by the action of water on calcium carbide.

a-cet′y-lite (*Chem.*) Calcium carbide treated with glucose to give a slower and more uniform production of acetylene gas than can be had from the untreated calcium carbide.

ach′ro-mat′ic (ăk′rô-măt′ĭk) Without color. A lens which refracts light of all colors equally is said to be achromatic.

ac′id. (1) A substance which produces hydrogen ions when dissolved in water. (2) Acid is a hydrogen compound whose aqueous solution contains hydrogen ions and no other positive ions.

ac′id bath (*Elec.*) Pickle used for cleansing metal objects in preparation for electroplating; usually by dipping.

ac′id–blast etch′ing (*Print.*) A process for the mechanical etching of photo-engraved plates.

ac′id col′or (*Dyeing*) Artificial organic dyestuff, so named from the fact that acid is used as an assistant for creating an affinity of the fiber for this dyestuff. About 75 per cent of all wool dyeing is accomplished by its use.

ac′id cure (*Auto.*) The use of sulphur chloride for repairing tires by rapid vulcanization without heat.

ac′id-proof paint (*Elec.*) Paint which resists the action of acid.

a-cid′u-lat′ed wa′ter (*Elec.*) Any acid solution which is diluted with water.

ac′i-er-al (ăs′ĭ-ēr-ăl) (*Metal.*) A lightweight alloy, 6.4 per cent copper, 0.4 per cent zinc, 0.9 per cent nickel, 0.1 per cent iron, 0.4 per cent silicon, and the balance aluminum. It was formerly used extensively for automotive parts.

ac′me thread (ăk′mê) (*M e c h.*) A screw thread, the section of which is between the square and V threads. Used extensively for feed screws. The included angle of space is 29 deg. as compared to 60 deg. of the National Coarse or U.S. thread.

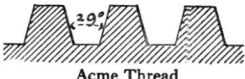

Acme Thread

a-cous′tics (à-kōōs′tĭks) (*Phys.*) The science of sound; the study of the effects of sound upon the ear. The acoustics of a room are said to be "good" or "bad" according to the ease or clearness with which sounds are perceived by the hearers.

a′cre. A measure of land equal to 160 sq. rods, 4840 sq. yd., 43,560 sq. ft.

ac′ro-te′ri-a (ăk′rô-tē′rĭ-à) (*Arch.*) Small pedestals placed at the apex and at the extremities of a pediment, usually without bases or plinths.

a-cryl′ic res′ins (*C h e m. P l a s t.*) Methyl-Methacrylate resin. The familiar Plexiglas and Lucite (British Perspex). These resins are clearer than glass, and are used in aeronautical domes, in light diffusers, special windows, outside displays, etc. One of their uses is in instrument lenses, and in contact lenses, and the resin will pipe light around corners. (See PLASTICS.)

ac-tin′ic rays (ăk-tĭn′ĭk) The light rays which act on photographic emulsions.

ac′tive con-duc′tor (*Elec.*) One through which an electric current is passing.

ac′tive cur′rent (*Elec.*) In alternating current that part in the phase with the voltage, or the effective energy as differentiated from the wattless or useless energy.

ac′tive ma-te′ri-al (*Elec.*) In a storage battery it is referred to as the paste of the positive (grid) plate of the cell.

ac′tive pres′sure (*Elec.*) In alternating current the effective voltage which produces a current, as distinguished from impressed voltage of the circuit.

ac′tu-ate. To move, cause to move, or bring into action. Automobile engine valves are actuated by motion of the camshaft.

a-cute′ an′gle (*Math.*) One which is less than 90 deg., or less than a right angle.

ad (*Print.*) A common abbreviation for advertisement.

Ad′am (*Furn.*) An English furniture style introduced by Adam brothers (1728–1792), usually decorated with Roman classic ornaments.

a-dapt′a-bil′i-ty (*Phys.*) Suitability; the degree of ease of adjustment to existing conditions.

a-dapt′er. A device by means of which objects of different size are made interchangeable.

a-dapt′er plate (*Plast.*) In injection molding, the plate-holding mold which fits press or platen.

ad-den′dum (*Gear.*) The point or portion of the tooth of a gear wheel lying outside the pitch circle.

ad-den′dum cir′cle (*G e a r*) The outer circumference of a gear wheel.

a d - d i′t i o n pol′y-mer-i-za′tion (*Plast.*) A chemical reaction in which molecules combine through interaction of unsaturated groups without the splitting off of any by-products.

ad-her′ence. The quality of clinging or sticking together of unlike particles.

ad-he′sion or ad-he′sive pow′er (*Mech.*) The friction existing between a driving wheel and the surface with which it is in contact. (*Mech. Arts*) The property which enables one surface to adhere or stick to another, as in glue practice. (*Plast.*) In plastics, a state in which two faces are held together by a plastic adhesive, or by the plastic itself, after its faces have been softened by a solvent.

ad-ja′cent an′gles (*Math.*) Angles in which one leg is common to both.

ad-just′. To bring about a proper arrangement of parts as regards relation, position, fit, etc.

ad-just′a-ble bor′ing tool (*Mach.*) A tool in which the cutter can be set for different jobs, avoiding the necessity of changing both cutter and holder.

ad-just′a-ble con-dens′er (*Elec.*) A condenser in which the capacity may be varied to suit changing needs, by means of movable plates.

ad-just′a-ble par′al-lels (*M a c h.*) Wedge-shaped bars of iron placed with the thin end of one on the thick end of the other. The top face of the upper and the bottom face of the

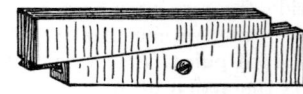

Adjustable Parallels

lower remain parallel, but the distance between the two faces can be increased or decreased, and the bars locked in position by means of a screw to prevent shifting.

ad-just′a-ble pitch pro-pel′ler (*Aero.*) One whose blades are so attached to the hub that they may be set to any desired pitch when stationary.

ad·just′a·ble ream′er (*Mach.*) A reamer which can be increased in size, usually by means of a central bolt or screw, the tightening of which causes an expansion of the reamer.

ad·just′a·ble re·sist′ance (*Elec.*) Also called variable resistance. A resistance which admits of increase or decrease.

ad·just′a·ble speed mo′tor (*Elec.*) A motor whose speed can be varied over a wide range and when once adjusted remains constant regardless of load.

ad·just′a·ble tap (*Mach.*) Taps, usually made with inserted blades or chasers capable of radial adjustment.

ad·just′ing screw (*Mach.*) A setscrew, by the use of which the position of machine parts is adjusted or regulated more accurately than would be possible by the mere setting to dimensions.

ad·just′ment (*Mach.*) The placing and setting of engine or machine parts in related position.

ad·just′ment strips (*Mech.*) Wedge-shaped strips of metal by means of which the exact bearing of sliding surfaces is accurately adjusted, correct contact being obtained by the use of set or adjustment screws.

ad′man′ (*Print.*) One who prepares advertising material.

ad·mit′tance (*Elec.*) The opposite of impedance. A unit, measured in ohms, used in alternating-current circuits.

a·dul′ter·a′tion. Making impure by the addition of baser ingredients or foreign substances.

ad·vance′ (*Auto. Elec.*) To adjust the timing of the spark to occur earlier with regard to time of top dead center of piston position. (*Metal.*) A copper, nickel alloy used for electrical-instrument work.

ad′ver·tis′ing. The act of preparing and circulating public announcements.

adz. A cutting tool with the blade set at right angles to the handle; used for rough-dressing timber.

adz–eye ham′mer (*Woodwk.*) Usually the claw-type nail hammer in which the eye is extended to give a longer bearing on the handle than is the case with other hammers.

Adz-Eye Hammer

a′er·at′ed water (*Chem.*) Water purified by passing air through it.

a′er·a′tion (*Chem.*) The passing of air through water or other liquid to effect purification; exposure to the chemical action of air. (*Plumb.*) A secondary tank in a sewage disposal plant in which the sewage is raised, by a mechanical device, from the bottom of the tank and discharged over the retained liquid. The circulation of the sewage and the consequent exposure to the atmosphere reduces the sewage to a stable effluent.

a·e′ri·al (*Elec.*) A term used in wireless. It consists of a single conductor or group of conductors. Usually suspended between two high points, on buildings, towers, or poles, for the purpose of receiving or radiating into space the electromagnetic waves conveying the signal. It is also called an "antenna."

a-e′ri-al met′al (*M e t a l.*) A very strong alloy of aluminum and lithium. It is very light, weighing only about 100 pounds per cubic foot.

ac′ro-bat′ics (*Aero.*) Voluntary evolutions with an aircraft other than those required for normal flight.

a′er-o-dy-nam′ic bal′anced sur′face (*Aero.*) A control surface that extends on both sides of the axis of the hinge or pivot, or that has auxiliary devices or extensions connected with it in such a manner as to effect a small or zero resultant moment of the air forces about the hinge axis.

a′er-o-dy-nam′ic cen′ter, wing sec′-tion (*Aero.*) A point located on or near the chord of the mean line, approximately one quarter of the chord length aft of the leading edge and about which the moment coefficient is practically constant.

a′er-o-dy-nam′ics (*A e r o.*) That branch of science which treats of the motion of air and other gaseous fluids, and of the forces on solids moving in such fluids.

a′er-o-dy-nam′ic vol′ume (*A e r o.*) The total volume of an aerostat, including its projecting parts.

a′er-o-dyne (*Aero.*) A generic term for aircraft that derive their lift in flight chiefly from aerodynamic forces.

a′er-o-lite′ (*Metal.*) An aluminum alloy containing about 96 per cent aluminum. Specific gravity 2.74. Used for airplane and automotive parts.

a′er-o-nau′tics. The art and science relating to the flight of aircraft.

a′er-o-stat (*Aero.*) A term applied to any "lighter than air" craft, as airship or balloon.

a′er-o-stat′ics (*A e r o.*) The science which treats of the equilibrium of gaseous fluids and bodies immersed in them.

a′er-o-sta′tion (*A e r o.*) The art of operating aerostats.

Af′ri-can ma-hog′a-ny (*W o o d*) *Khaya senegalensis.* A remote member of the mahogany family found principally in Africa. The very large tree produces exceptionally fine figured timber of unusual lengths and widths. Used for fine furniture.

aft′er-damp (*Chem.*) Carbon dioxide left in a mine after the explosion of mine gases.

aft′er-im′age (*Color*) That impression which remains of a visual object after the direct stimulation has been withdrawn from the retina.

ag′ate (*M i n.*) A variegated quartz in which colors are usually in bands; a gem. (*Print.*) A type size about 5½ points.

ag′gre-gate. A mass formed by the union of similar particles.

ag′ing of in′can-des′cent lamp (*Elec.*) A gradual lessening of the brightness of an incandescent lamp, due to oxidation of the filament and the coating on the inside of the bulb.

ag′ing of mag′net (*Elec.*) Subjecting a magnet to the process of increasing its magnetic permanency.

ag′i-ta′tor (ăj′ĭ-tā′tẽr) (*Mech.*) A mechanical stirring device, commonly used in mixing ingredients in large vats or tanks.

a-gon′ic lines (å-gŏn′ĭk) (*Aero.*) Lines on a map or chart, connecting points on the earth's surface where magnetic variation is zero.

ag′ri-cul′tur-al bolt (*Shopwk.*) A bolt, the body of which has a series of helical bands and grooves which are formed by a rolling process; used in farm machines and appliances.

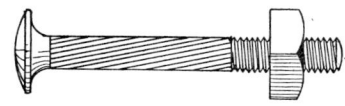

ag'ri-cul'ture. The art and science relating to the production and raising of plants and animals.

ai'le-ron (ā'lê-rŏn) (*Aero.*) An auxiliary surface usually hinged or pivoted to the trailing edge of a wing, the primary function of which is to impress a rolling moment on the airplane.

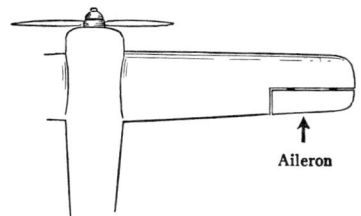
Aileron

ai'le-ron an'gle (*Aero.*) The angular displacement of an aileron from its neutral position. It is positive when the trailing edge of the aileron is below the neutral position.

ai'le-ron roll (*Aero.*) A roll in which the motion is largely maintained by forces arising from the displacement of the aileron.

air. The atmosphere. (*Chem.*) The mixture of gases that forms the apparent blue envelope of the earth, although technically the term "air" is usually applied to a limited portion of the atmosphere.

air–a-cet'y-lene weld'ing. A gas-welding process wherein the welding heat is obtained from the combustion of air and acetylene.

air–blast trans-form'er (*Elec.*) A transformer which is prevented from overheating by the forced circulation of air around its windings.

air bleed (*Auto. Mech.*) A small manually adjusted air valve by which the amount of air in fuel mixture can be varied.

air bound. When action of any parts or part is prevented by an air pocket.

air brake (*Auto. Mech.*) The conventional style of mechanically applied brake set by air pressure instead of foot pressure. The pressure of the hand or foot operates an air valve, permitting a flow of air, from cylinders in which it has been stored under pressure, to set the brakes.

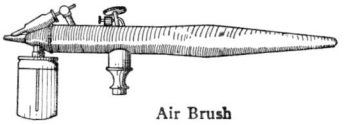
Air Brush

air–brush let'ter-ing (*Art*) Lettering finished or shaded with an air brush, which is an implement for spraying inks or paints by compressed air.

air cell (*Elec.*) A primary cell of the depolarizer type in which oxygen is extracted from the air by a special carbon electrode which is used as a depolarizer.

air cham'ber (*Engin.*) A vessel installed on piston pumps to minimize the pulsating discharge of the liquid pumped. The chamber contains air under pressure and is fitted with an opening on its underside into which some of the liquid from the pump is forced upon the delivery stroke of the piston. The air acts as a cushion to lessen the fluctuation of the liquid flow between the suction and delivery strokes of the piston.

air clamp (*Mach.*) Any type of clamping device operated by pneumatic pressure.

air clean′er (*Auto. Mech.*) A device designed to separate dirt and other foreign substances from the atmosphere before it enters the combustion space.

air com-pres′sor (*Auto.*) A machine for supplying air under pressure for inflating tires and for many industrial uses. (*Mach.*) A machine in which air is compressed for motive power.

air con-dens′er (*Elec.*) A form of condenser in which air spaces between the disks serve to insulate the charges from one another.

air con-di′tion-ing. Relates to three different operations — air washing, humidifying, and dehumidifying.

air con-trol′ (*Aero.*) The means employed to operate the control surfaces of the aircraft.

air–cooled en′gine (*Auto. Mech.*) A blower at the front of the engine forces air up over the cylinders into an enclosed space; from there it is forced down past the cylinders and other parts. The cylinders are arranged individually, and are cast each with a series of fins around the circumference in order to present maximum radiating surface.

air–cooled trans-form′er (*Elec.*) A transformer in which the heating of the coils sets up a ventilating draught.

air–core so′le-noid (*Elec.*) A solenoid which has a hollow rather than a solid core.

air′craft (*Aero.*) Any weight-carrying device designed to be supported by the air, either by buoyancy or by dynamic action.

air′craft car′ri-er (*Aero.*) A ship designed to carry aircraft and to permit their landing and take-off.

air cush′ion. Usually an air-filled cylinder so constructed as to serve as a shock absorber or as a device for regulating or arresting motion.

air–dried (*Lumber*) Lumber seasoned by drying in the air as opposed to kiln-dried.

air drill (*Mach.*) A drill operated by compressed air.

air duct (*Aero.*) A tube, usually of fabric, supplying air for filling or for maintaining pressure in air-filled parts of an aerostat.

air flow (*Auto. Mech.*) Refers to the passage of air over certain types of automobiles, so designed that air friction is reduced to a minimum.

air′foil (*Aero.*) Any surface designed to be projected through the air to produce a useful dynamic reaction.

air′foil pro′file (*Aero.*) The outline of an airfoil section.

air′foil sec′tion (*Aero.*) A cross section of an airfoil made by a plane parallel to a specified reference plane. A line perpendicular to this plane is called the axis of the airfoil.

air–fu′el ra′ti-o (*Auto.*) The quantity of gasoline and air, expressed as a ratio of their respective weights that go to make up the fuel mixture of an internal-combustion engine.

15–1 by weight
9600–1 by volume

air fur′nace (*Fdry.*) A type of furnace used in the production of malleable iron castings.

air gap (*Elec.*) Applied to a space in

a circuit which is solely occupied by air, as an air gap in a spark plug.

air ham′mer (*Mach.*) A tool in which a hammer head is activated by means of compressed air. The air is conducted to the tool through a hose. A trigger starts or stops the admission of air to the hammer.

air hard′en-ing (*Mech.*) Hardening of high-speed steels by air blast.

air hoist (*Mech.*) A hoisting device operated by compressed air.

air line (*Aero.*) (1) An established system of aerial transportation, its equipment, or the company owning or operating it. (2) The great circle route between two points.

air lock (*Auto.*) A stoppage in a water or gas line caused by a bubble of air being pocketed somewhere along the line.

air log (*Aero.*) An instrument which measures the linear travel of an aircraft with relation to the air.

air-om′eter. An instrument for measuring the rate of air flow.

air′plane (*Aero.*) An aircraft heavier than air, fitted with fixed wings and power driver.

air′plane dope (*Aero.*) The liquid material applied to the fabric surfaces of airplanes to increase their strength, to produce tautness by shrinking, and to act as a filler for maintaining airtightness.

air′plane tail (*Aero.*) The rear part of an airplane, usually consisting of a group of stabilizing planes, or fins, to which are attached certain controlling surfaces such as elevators and rudders; also called "empennage."

air pock′et (*Aero.*) More accurately described as a downdraft.

air′port (*Aero.*) A place regularly used for receiving or discharging passengers or cargo by air travel, or a place on land or water provided with taking-off or landing accommodations, and which offers facilities for shelter, repair, and conditioning of aircraft.

air′port bea′con (*Aero.*) A beacon light of high candle power, located at or near an airport for the purpose of indicating the general or specific location of the airport.

air scoop (*Aero.*) A scoop or hood to catch the air and maintain the air pressure in ballonets, internal-combustion engines, ventilators, etc.

air′ship (*Aero.*) A lighter-than-air craft provided with a power and control system, e.g., dirigible. When its power plant is not operating it acts as a free balloon.

Airship

air′ship sta′tion (*Aero.*)(1) The complete assembly of sheds, masts, gas plants, shops, landing fields, and other equipment required to operate airships and supply their needs. (2) The base from which airships are operated.

air–slaked lime (âr-slākt) (*Chem.*) Lime converted into hydroxide and carbonate by exposure to the air; it is worthless for many of the purposes for which water-slaked lime is used.

air space (*Elec.*) The open space in a dynamo or motor between the polar faces of the field magnet and the surface of the armature.

air speed (*Aero.*) The speed of an aircraft relative to the air.

air′–speed head (*Aero.*) An instrument which, in combination with a gauge, is used to measure the speed of an aircraft relative to the air. It usually consists of a pitot-static tube or a pitot-venturi tube.

air′-speed in′di-ca′tor (*A e r o.*) An instrument for indicating the speed of an airplane relative to the air.

air spring (*Auto. Mech.*) Another name for the most efficient type of shock absorber. A plunger operates in a cylinder which contains oil and air.

air′tight′. So constructed or sealed as to prevent any inlet or outlet of air.

air′way (*Aero.*) An established air route.

air′way bea′con (*Aero.*) A beacon light of high candle power, other than an airport or landmark beacon, located on or near an airway for the purpose of indicating the location of the airway.

air′wor′thi-ness (*Aero.*) The quality of an aircraft denoting its fitness and safety for operation in the air under normal flying conditions.

aisle (*Arch.*) A passageway, as in a church or assembly room, by which the pews or seats may be reached.

al′a-bas′ter (*Min.*) A white or delicately tinted fine-grained gypsum.

al′bert-ite (*Min.*) A jet-black, brittle, natural asphalt found in Nova Scotia. Yields mineral oils and coke.

al′bum. A book for holding photographs or the like. A blank book for holding stamps, autographs, etc.

al′che-my (ăl′kĕ-mĭ) (*Chem.*) Chemistry as it was practiced in the Middle Ages. Its purpose was largely to discover the transmutation of metals and the universal cure of diseases.

al′co-hol (*Chem.*) C_2H_5OH. Ethyl hydroxide, made from grain. Not to be confused with methyl hydroxide or methanol.

al′cove (*Arch.*) Any large recess in a room, usually separated by an arch.

al′de-hyde (*Chem.*) The first oxidation product of a primary alcohol. CH_3CHO.

al′ge-bra′ic sym′bols (*Math.*) Conventional signs, letters, brackets, etc., by which certain processes and calculations in mathematics are indicated.

a-lign′ (*Auto.*) To bring parts into proper position in relation to one another.

a-lign′ment (á-līn′mĕnt) (*M a c h .*) Linear accuracy, uniformity, or coincidence of the centers of a lathe. Also applied to the axial continuity of shafting and shaft bearings; a straight line of adjustment through two or more points.

a-live′ (*Elec.*) A term applied to a carrying circuit, or to two adjacent contacts of different potential. (*Print.*) Standing type matter not to be distributed.

a-liz′a-rin (á-lĭz′á-rĭn) (*Chem.*) A yellow to orange crystalline coloring compound used to dye cotton, wool, and silks.

al′ka-li (*Chem.*) A strong base. A base is a substance which produces hydroxyl ions when dissolved in water.

al′ka-net (ăl′ká-nĕt) (*Chem.*) A dye-producing plant, native of the Mediterranean region, Hungary, and western Asia, yielding a red coloring matter.

al′kyd res′ins (*Chem. Plast.*) The name is derived from the first two letters of the word alcohol and "cid" of the word acid. This type of resin is used principally for lacquers, paints, and metal finishes.

Al'len screws (*Mach.*) Cap screws and setscrews having hexagonal socket in the head. Such screws are adjusted by means of a hexagonal key.

Allen Setscrew

all–geared drive (*Mach.*) The transmission of power for feeds and speeds on a machine by means of gears instead of by belts and pulleys.

al'li-ga'tion (*Arith.*) The method or rule for finding the relation between the prices of the ingredients in a mixture, their proportions, and the price of the mixture.

al'li-ga'tor-ing (*Paint and Lacquer*) Cracks in the surface layer only, which widen due to contraction, caused by a sudden change in temperature, lack of binder, not sufficient drying time between coats, poor penetration, or applying a hard film over a soft undercoat.

al'li-ga'tor wrench (*Plumb.*) A wrench with toothed V-shaped jaws fixed in position.

al'lo-trop'ic (*Chem.*) Different form of the same substance, e.g., diamond and coal as forms of carbon.

all'o'ver pat'tern (*Art*) A pattern repeated over an entire surface.

al-low'ance (*Mach.*) The minimum clearance or maximum interference intentionally permitted between mating parts.

al-loy' (*Metal.*) White metal. Babbitt metal. (*Metalwk.*) A homogeneous combination of two or more metals, usually a fine and a baser metal. (*Plast.*) In plastics, a blend of synthetic resins.

al-loy' steel (*Metalwk.*) A steel which is alloyed with one or more of the following metals: manganese, nickel, tungsten, molybdenum, vanadium, and chromium. These alloy steels are strong, tough, and hard.

all–row'lock wall (*Masonry*) A wall built with two courses entirely of stretchers on edge alternating with one course of headers on edge.

al'man-dite (*Mineral.*) A variety of mineral garnet, used for abrasive coating on paper and cloth.

al'mery (*Arch.*) Same as ambry.

al'nic (*Metal.*) An alloy, a combination of aluminum, nickel, and cobalt, used to make small permanent magnets. This combination gives the alloy its high retentivity.

al'pha. The first letter of the Greek alphabet (A) (a). (*Chem.*) A form which is combined. Distinguishing one of two or more isomers or modifications.

al'pha par'ti-cle (*Chem. and Phys.*) A high velocity electrically charged particle thrown off by many radioactive materials; has two neutrons and two protons.

al'pha rays (*Chem. and Phys.*) One of the three types of rays emitted by radioactive substances.

al'tar (*Arch.*) In present-day use, commonly applied to the communion table in churches. Originally, a raised platform on which sacrifices or offerings were made to the gods.

al'ter-nat'ing cur'rent or a.c. (*Elec.*) An electric current which reverses in direction at rapid, regular intervals, usually 120 times per second.

al'ter-nat'ing–cur'rent arc (*Elec.*) An arc produced by an alternating current. In such an arc the carbons assume tapered points instead of cratering, which permits a more horizontal spreading of the light.

al′ter-nat′ing–cur′rent arc weld′ing. An arc-welding process wherein the supply at the arc is alternating current.

al′ter-nat′ing–c u r′r e n t   m o′t o r (*Elec.*) An electric motor of either single or polyphase type operated by an alternating current.

al′ter-nat′ing–cur′rent trans-form′er (*Elec.*) A device used to raise or lower the voltage of an alternating circuit. It consists of an induction coil having a primary and secondary winding and a closed iron core.

al′ter-nat′ing–cur′rent trans-mis′sion (*Elec.*) The transmission of power by the use of alternating current.

al′ter-na′tion (*Elec.*) The changes undergone by an alternating current in rising from zero to maximum positive pressure, falling to zero, then rising to maximum negative pressure, then back to zero. The two complete changes are referred to as one cycle wave or period. (One complete set of values.)

al′ter-na′tor (*Elec.*) An electric generator which produces alternating current.

al′ti-graph (*Aero.*) An altimeter equipped with a recording mechanism. Present instruments are of the aneroid type. The chart, driven by clockwork, is usually graduated in feet or meters. It is a barograph whose scale is designed to read heights.

al-tim′e-ter (ăl-tĭm′ē-tēr)(*Aero.*) An instrument for recording altitudes.

al′ti-tude. Vertical elevation. A high or the highest point.

al′um (*Chem.*) An astringent mineral salt. Usually a double sulphate of aluminum and potassium.

alumen (*Metal.*) A very strong aluminum alloy which can be forged and machined. It consists of 88 per cent aluminum, 10 per cent zinc, and 2 per cent copper. It is heavier than aluminum.

a-lu′mi-na, or ox′ide of a-lu′mi-num (*Chem.*) An important constituent of all clays, determining their suitability for firebrick and furnace linings; also used in the preparation of paints called "lakes," and in dyeing and calico printing. Al_2O_3. Widely used in granular form for abrasive purposes, in grinding or cutting materials of high tensile strength such as alloy and high speed steels, annealed malleable iron, tough bronze, etc.

a-lu′mi-num (*Min.*) A very light silvery-white metal used independently or in alloys with copper.

a-lu′mi-num al-loys′. The combination of aluminum and other metals, such as copper, nickel, tungsten, etc., to produce castings and sheets where strength and lightness are required. These alloys are more valuable than pure aluminum.

a-lu′mi-num bronze. An alloy of copper with aluminum, in various and widely different proportions.

a-lu′mi-num bronze pow′der(*Paint.*) Aluminum finely powdered by beating in stamp mills. When mixed with light varnish or banana oil, it is used as a metallic paint.

a-lu′mi-num hy-drox′ide (*C h e m .*) $Al(OH)_3$. White gelatinous solid used in water purification and as a mordant in dyeing.

a‑lu′mi‑num ste′a‑rate (*Paint and Lacquer*) Used in the manufacture of lacquers to produce a flat finish.

al′um leath′er. Leather tanned by the use of alum.

a‑mal′gam (*Min.*) An alloy or union of mercury with one or more metals.

a‑mal′ga‑ma′tion (*Elec.*) The application of a coating of mercury to the zinc plate of a voltaic cell, thereby forming an alloy which prevents the local action liable to arise from impurities in the zinc.

am′ber (*Elec.*) A yellowish or reddish brown translucent fossil resin which becomes electrified through friction when rubbed against another object.

am′bo (*Arch.*) In early Christian churches, a raised pulpit-like platform stand, or desk, where parts of the service were read or chanted.

Am‑boi′na; var.: **amboyna** (*Wood*) *Lingoum indicum.* An East Indian tree which produces what is commonly considered the most beautiful and most expensive of cabinet woods and veneers.

am′broin. An insulating material made from fossil copal and silicates. It is strong, heat resistant, and non-hygroscopic. It is used for molded insulations, and is cheaper than ebonite.

am′bry (ăm′brĭ) (*Arch.*) A closet near the altar for sacred vessels. A cupboard.

A‑mer′i‑can bond (*Masonry*) Same as common bond. This bond is in very general use as it is quickly laid and is as strong as other bonds. Every fifth or sixth course consists of headers, while the other courses consist of stretchers.

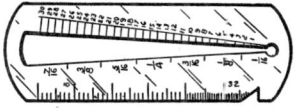

American Screw Gauge

A‑mer′i‑can screw gauge (*Metalwk.*) A standard gauge for checking the diameter of wood screws and machine screws.

A‑mer′i‑can Stand′ard Pipe Threads. (Formerly known as Briggs Pipe Thread Standard.) Is the thread used on wrought iron or steel, steam, gas, and water pipes.

am′e‑thyst (ăm′ê‑thist) (*Min.*) Quartz with a clear purple or violet color. A precious stone.

a‑mi′no (ă‑mē′nō) (*Plast.*) Combining form in name of chemical compound indicating presence of NH_2 group, derived from ammonia.

am′i‑no‑plast (*Chem. Plast.*) General term for synthetic resins from amino or amido compounds. A typical example is urea-formaldehyde resin.

am′me′ter (ăm′mē′tĕr) (*Elec.*) The instrument used in measuring the density of flow of the current in an electric circuit.

Ammeter

am′me′ter shunt (*Elec.*) See SHUNT.

am‑mo′ni‑a (*Chem.*) A colorless, pungent, suffocating gas (NH_3), obtained chiefly by the dry distillation of nitrogenous bodies such as coal. The most important source of ammonia is the union of nitrogen and hydrogen with increased pressure and temperature in presence of iron.

am-mo′ni-um chlo′ride (*Chem.*) Commonly known as sal ammoniac. When dissolved in water it is used as an electrolyte for some primary cells.

a-mor′phous. Without definite form; unorganized. (*Chem. Plast.*) Devoid of crystalline structure.

am′pere (ăm′pēr) (*Elec.*) The unit of measurement of electric current strength. A pressure of one volt will force one ampere through a resistance of one ohm.

Am-père (äm′pâr′) **André Marie.** French physicist and scientific writer — 1775–1836, whose name is given to the unit of measurement of electric-current strength (the ampere).

am′pere hour (*Elec.*) (ăm′pēr) Used in rating storage batteries, representing a current of one ampere flowing for one hour.

am′pere me′ter. (*Elec.*) Same as ammeter. A meter to register the density of flow of current.

am′pere turns (*Elec.*) The product obtained by multiplying the number of turns in a magnetic coil by the current strength in amperes.

am′per-sand "&" (*Print.*) The abbreviation for "and."

am-phib′i-an (*Aero.*) An airplane built to arise from and alight on either water or land.

am′phi-bole (ăm′fĭ-bōl) Short fiber asbestos.

am′pli-fi′er (*Elec.*) A device for increasing the strength of weak currents or sounds.

am′pli-tude (ăm′plĭ-tūd) (*Math.*) An angle upon which the value of some mathematical f u n c t i o n depends. (*Phys.*) The distance covered by a particle in making a complete vibration.

a-nal′o-gous col′ors (*á*-năl′ô-gŭs) Closely related colors, e.g., red-orange, and yellow-orange, etc.

a-nal′y-sis (*Chem.*) The resolution of a compound into its parts or elements. (*Math.*) A tabulated statement; the process of resolving a problem into its first elements.

an′a-lyt′i-cal ge-om′e-try (*M a t h.*) The study of geometric figures by the process of algebraic analysis.

an′chor (*Arch.*) The pointed ornament forming an element of the egg-and-dart molding. (*Bldg.*) That bolt or fastening device which attaches to the anchorage. (*Fdry.*) A metal support for holding a core in place.

an′chor-age. That permanent placement to which the lower members of a structure may be attached in order to secure greater stability for the entire structure.

and′i′ron. A metal support for wood in an open fireplace. Sometimes called a "firedog."

an′e-mom′e-ter (ăn′e-mŏm′-e-tēr) An instrument for measuring the velocity of an air current.

an′er-oid al-tim′e-ter (ăn′-ēr-oid ăl-tĭm′ê-tēr) (*Aero.*) Anemometer An altimeter, the indications of which depend on the deflection of a pressure-sensitive element. The graduations of the dial correspond to an empirical or arbitrary pressure-temperature-altitude formula.

an′er-oid ba-rom′e-ter. Shows the pressure of the atmosphere by the movements of the elastic top or diaphragm of an exhausted metallic box. Indicates weather changes and height above sea level.

an′gle (*Math.*) The difference in

direction of two straight lines; the space between two straight lines that do or would meet. Angles are used for measuring circular movement or rotation.

an'gle bead (*Arch.*) A molded strip used in an angle; usually where two walls meet at right angles.

an'gle brack'et (*Arch.*) A form of support having two faces generally at right angles to each other. A web is often added to increase strength.

an'gle di-vid'ers (*Woodwk.*) A tool for bisecting angles; also can be used as a try square.

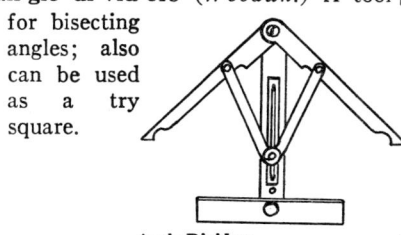

Angle Dividers

an'gle i'ron (*Mech.*) A strip of structural iron, the section of which is in the form of a right angle.

an'gle of at-tack' (*Aero.*) The acute angle between the chord of an airfoil and its direction of motion relative to the air.

an'gle of dead'rise (*Aero.*) The angle with the horizontal made by a transverse line joining the keel of a hull with the chine.

an'gle of dec'li-na'tion (*Elec.*) The angle of variation. The angle between the geographic meridian of a place and the magnetic meridian.

an'gle of dip (*Elec.*) The angle which a magnetic needle makes with the horizon when the vertical plane in which it turns corresponds with the magnetic meridian.

an'gle of heel (*Aero.*) The angle between a horizontal plane and the lateral axis of a seaplane on the water.

an'gle of in'ci-dence (*Aero.*) Same as angle of wing setting.

an'gle of in'cli-na'tion (*Mach.*) The angle formed by a screw thread with relation to its axis.

an'gle of lag (*Elec.*) The angle which shows the amount by which the phase of the active component falls behind the total current in the alternating-current circuit.

an'gle of lead (lēd) (*Elec.*) The angle through which commutator brushes are moved out of the normal plane to avoid sparking.

an'gle of pitch (*Aero.*) The acute angle between two planes, defined as follows: One plane includes the lateral axis of the aircraft and the direction of the relative wind; the other plane includes the lateral axis and the longitudinal axis. In normal flight the angle of pitch is the angle between the longitudinal axis and the direction of the relative wind.

an'gle of re-pose', or **an'gle of fric'tion** (*Mech.*) The angle of a plane surface, inclined relatively to the horizon, upon which a body will, under specific conditions, just begin to slide. It varies with the nature of the particular materials placed in contact.

an'gle of roll (*Aero.*) The acute angle through which an aircraft must be rotated about its longitudinal axis in order to bring its lateral axis into a horizontal plane. Also called "angle of bank."

an'gle of sta'bi-liz-er set'ting (*Aero.*) The acute angle between the line of thrust of an airplane and the chord of the stabilizer.

an'gle of thread (*Mach.*) The angle included between the sides of the thread measured in an axial plane.

an'gle of wing set'ting (*Aero.*) The acute angle between the plane of the wing chord and the line of thrust. It may differ for each wing.

an'gle of yaw (*Aero.*) The acute angle between the direction of the relative wind and the plane of symmetry of an aircraft. It is positive when the aircraft has turned to the right.

an'gle plate (*Mach.*) Used in setting up work, generally for machinery; made of cast iron, being formed of two plates of metal at right angles with each other, and pierced with holes or slots for the reception of bolts.

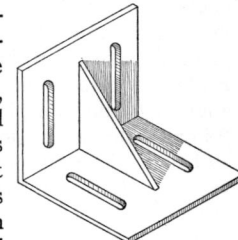
Angle Plate

an'gu-lar cut'ter (*Mach.*) A milling cutter on which the cutting face is at an angle with regard to the axis of the cutter.

an'gu-lar gears (*Mach.*) Bevel gears designed to run at angles other than a right angle.

an'gu-lar ve-loc'i-ty (*M e c h.*) The ratio which the arc described in one second, by a body or point rotating about a center, bears to the radius.

an-hy'dride (ăn-hī'drĭd) (*C h e m.*) The product left when water is removed from a compound. H_2SO_4— $H_2O=SO_3$.

an-hy'drous (ăn-hī'drŭs) (*C h e m.*) Destitute of water; dried up; withered.

an-hy'drous am-mo'ni-a (*Chem.*) Purified ammonia gas liquefied by cold and pressure. Used for organic preparations and refrigeration.

an'i-line (ăn'ĭ-lĭn) (*Chem.*) A colorless, oily compound ($C_6H_5NH_2$), the base from which many of the coal-tar dyes are made; also used in the rubber industry.

an'i-mal-ized cot'ton (*Textile*) Cotton coated with protein material to give it the nature of animal fibers toward silk or wool dyes.

an'i-on (ăn'ī-ŏn) (*Elec.*) The nonmetallic radical which appears at the anode, or positive electrode, in an electrolytic cell.

an-neal' (*Metal.*) To heat to a critical temperature and cool slowly in order to soften metal, reduce brittleness, and make it more workable.

an-nealed' tub'ing (*Metal.*) Metal tubing is commercially supplied hard, partially annealed, and fully annealed. When bending is required, full-annealed tubing should be used.

an-neal'ing (*Metal.*) The gradual heating and the gradual cooling of glass, metals, or other materials to reduce brittleness and increase flexibility, etc.

an'nu-al ring(*Lumber*) The circumferential layer of wood seen in a cross section of timber, which represents the yearly growth.

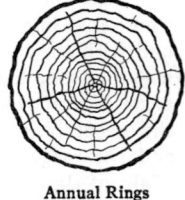
Annual Rings

an'nu-lar ball bear-ing (ăn'ŭ-lăr) (*Mach.*) A bearing in which the balls are contained in a ringlike holder.

an'nu-lar vault (*Arch.*) A vault rising from two parallel walls; same as barrel vault.

an'nu-lar wheel (*Gear.*) A ring gear with teeth fixed to its internal circumference; called also an internal gear.

an'nu-lat'ed col'umns (ăn'ū-lāt'ĕd) (*Arch.*) Columns clustered together by rings or bands; much used in English architecture.

an'nu-let (ăn'ū-lĕt) (*Arch.*) A small square molding used to separate others.

an-nun'ci-a'tor (ă-nŭn'shĭ-ā'tēr) (*Elec.*) A device for indicating, by visual and auditory means, a closed circuit or an activity which closes a circuit at a predetermined station or place.

an-nun'ci-a'tor wire (*Elec.*) Soft copper wire wound with two layers of cotton thread in opposite directions and coated with paraffin.

an'ode (*Elec.*) Opposite of cathode The point where, or path by which a voltaic current enters an electrolyte; the positive voltaic pole or the plate constituting it.

an'o-diz-ing (*Metal.*) The forming of a hard surface film of aluminum oxide on aluminum parts by an electric process in a chromic-acid solution. This film acts as a protective coating and serves as a good paint base.

an'ta (*Arch.*) A pilaster opposite another, as on a door jamb.

an'te-fix' (ăn'tē-fĭks') (*Arch.*) An upright ornament fixed to the corners of bed cornices.

an-ten'na (*Rad., Tel.*) The common aerial, either indoor or outdoor, for receiving or sending out "radio" waves.

Anthemion

an-the'mi-on (ăn-thē'mĭ-ŏn) (*Arch. and Art*) The palm-leaf pattern as used by the Greeks in ornamental design.

an'thra-cene (ăn'thrá-sēn) (*Chem.*) Obtained by the distillation of coal tar; used in the manufacture of dyestuffs.

an'thra-cite (*Min.*) A medium hard, glossy mineral substance, commonly known as hard coal.

an'ti-bi-ot'ic (*Chem.*) A mold or fungus, which kills, retards, or completely represses the growth of other organisms, usually without harming higher orders of life. This substance can be synthetized chemically or produced by a microorganism.

an'ti-drag' wire (ăn'tĭ-drăg') (*Aero.*) A wire designed primarily to resist forces acting parallel to the chord of the wing of an airplane and in the same direction as the direction of flight. It is generally enclosed in the wing.

an'ti–freeze mix'ture (*Auto Mech.*) Alcohol, glycerin, or any of the chemical preparations mixed with the water of the cooling system to prevent freezing.

an'ti-fric'tion met'al. Babbitt's metal or white metal, used for lining the steps and bearings of shafts and axles, and similar moving parts; inexpensive and efficient.

an'ti-knock (*Chem.*) A substance

which brings about uniform expansion of the products of combustion.

an'ti-log'a-rithm (ăn'tĭ-lŏg'á-rĭth'm) (*Math.*) The number corresponding to a given logarithm.

an'ti-mo'ni-al lead (*Metal.*) An alloy of from 4 to 10 per cent antimony with 90 to 96 per cent lead. Used for storage-battery plates.

an'ti-mo-ny (ăn'tĭ-mô-nĭ) (*Min. and Chem.*) A silver-white, hard, crystalline metallic element related to arsenic and tin. Frequently used in alloys of tin and lead to give hardness (Sb).

an'ti-node' (*Phys.*) Midway point, maximum amplitude, of a vibrating body between two nodes.

an-tique' (ăn-tēk') (*Papermkg.*) A bulky paper of low finish similar to "eggshell." (*Print.*) A moderately bold type face both **Roman and** *italic*, in which all lines are of nearly the same thickness as shown in the words Roman and italic.

an'ti-si'phon (*Plumb.*) A type of water seal trap in which the outlet leg is increased in diameter to contain a sufficient volume of liquid to prevent a siphoning action which would break the seal.

an'vil (*Forg.*) A steel or iron block upon which forging is done.

an'vil block (*Forg.*) A massive block of cast iron which is placed beneath the anvils of steam and other heavy hammers, for the absorption of the vibration due to the blow. It is often embedded in masonry or concrete.

an'vil vise (*Forg.*) A vise having an anvil cast as a part of the stationary jaw.

ap'er-ture. An opening, orifice, or hole. (*Elec.*) An opening through which an electronic beam can pass.

a'pex (*Math.*) The top or peak of a cone, pyramid, or conical figure generally.

a-poth'e-car-ies' flu'id meas'ure.
60 minims (min.) = 1 fluid (or liquid) dram
(fl. dr.)
8 fluid drams = 1 fluid (or liquid) ounce
(fl. oz.)
16 fluid ounces = 1 pint
8 pints = 1 gallon

ap-par'ent E.M.F. (*Elec.*) Voltage as indicated by the pressure drop caused by current passing through resistance.

ap-par'ent pow'er (*Elec.*) In an inductive A.C. circuit, the product of the amperes $\times$ volts (KVA) as distinguished from the true power as shown by a wattmeter.

ap-par'ent watts (*Elec.*) Volts times amperes in an a.c.-current circuit.

ap-pend'age. Something appended to or accompanying a principal or greater thing, but not necessary to it.

ap-pen'dix (*Print.*) An addition or supplement to the subject matter of a book, usually following the last chapter.

ap-pli'an-ces (*Elec.*) A general term used in speaking of household electric laborsaving devices, such as toasters, mixers, sweepers, etc.

ap'pli-ca'tion. The act of applying; putting into practice; the practical demonstration of a principle.

ap-plied' de-sign' (*Fine Arts*) Design used to beautify or make useful objects more attractive.

ap-plied' me-chan'ics (*Phys.*) Treats

of the laws of mechanics as applied to construction in the useful arts.

ap-plied' mold'ing (*Furn.*) Molding placed to give the effect of paneling; Jacobean ornament of the seventeenth century.

ap-pren'tice. A learner in a trade. Usually one, who, by contract or indenture, is taught the rudiments of the trade during the term of the agreement.

ap-pren'tice-ship. That period of time agreed upon between employer and employee, during which the employer promises to teach the employee the rudiments of his trade In the U. S. it is usually three or four years; in many foreign countries, five years or more.

ap-proach' light (*Aero.*) A light usually green, designed to indicate a favorable direction of approach for landing an aircraft.

ap-prox'i-mate-ly (*Mech.*) Nearly, frequently used when speaking of the capabilities of machines, their measurements, and near shipping weights.

a'pron (*Aero.*) A hard-surface area of considerable extent immediately in front of the entrance of a hangar or aircraft shelter which is used for the handling of aircraft or for repair in clear weather. (*Arch.*) A plain or molded piece of finish below the stool of a window, put on to cover the rough edge of the plastering. (*Furn.*) That board immediately under the top of a table, which fastens the legs together, gives support to the top, and improves the appearance of the table; the width of the board or strip is used vertically. (*Mech.*) The vertical plate in the front part of the carriage of a screw-cutting lathe to which the split nut is attached.

apse (ăps) (*Arch.*) The altar end of a church; a recess.

aq'ua am-mo'ni-a (*Chem.*) Solution NH_4OH. Ammonium hydroxide commonly called ammonia water. Used as a household cleanser.

aq'ua dag (*Chem.*) A colloidal suspension of graphite in water.

aq'ua for'tis (*Chem.*) HNO_3. Nitric acid.

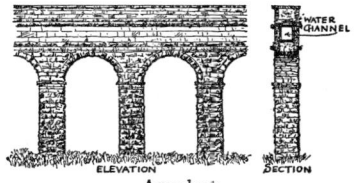

Aqueduct

aq'ue-duct (ăk'wê-dŭkt) A water conduit of channels, steel pipes, syphons, or tunnels, etc., through which a community is supplied.

a'que-ous. Watery.

ar'a-besque' (ăr'à-bĕsk') (*Arch.*) An ornament, painted, inlaid, or carved in low relief, the pattern consisting of plants, fruits, and figures of men and animals interlaced in fantastic devices.

Arabesque

(*Furn.*) An ornament, painted, inlaid, or carved in the Arabian manner.

Ar'a-bic num'bers. The commonly used numerals, 1, 2, 3, 4, 5, 6, 7, 8, 9, 0, as distinguished from the Roman I, II, III, IV, etc.

ar'bor (*Arch.*) Detached latticework; a bower; a nook. (*Mech.*) A short shaft or spindle on which an object may be carried while being machined. (See MANDREL.) On a milling machine, an arbor may have a tapered shank with a straight body for carrying rotary cutters.

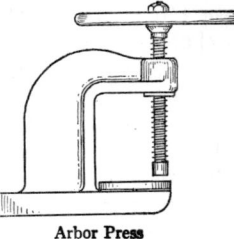
Arbor Press

ar′bor press (*Mach.*) A device for pressing an arbor, or shaft, into the bore, or hole, of an article to be turned on a lathe and for removing same when work is finished.

arc (*Elec.*) Any flashing occurring between the terminals of an electric circuit when the circuit has been interrupted. (*Math.*) Any portion of the circumference of a circle.

ar′ca (är′kà) (*Furn.*) A chest for storing treasures.

ar-cade′ (*Arch.*) A range of arches supported either on columns or on piers, and attached to or detached from the wall. An arched passageway.

Arcade

arc braz′ing. An electric brazing process wherein the heat is obtained from an electric arc formed between the base metal and an electrode, or between two electrodes.

arc cut′ting. A group of cutting processes wherein the severing of metals is effected by melting with the heat of an arc between an electron and the base metal.

arc fur′nace (*Elec.*) A furnace in which the heat is generated by an electric arc.

arch (*Arch.*) A curved or pointed structure supported at the sides or ends only, used to span openings or spaces.

Arch

arch bar (*Arch.*) A flat bar or strip of iron used as a support for a flat arch.

arch bricks (*Arch.*) Wedge-shaped bricks made to conform to the radius of an arch.

arch but′tress (*Arch.*) Same as flying buttress, an arch springing from a buttress or pier.

Ar′chi-me′de-an prin′ci-ple (är′kĭ-mē′dē-ăn) A body wholly or partly immersed in a fluid is buoyed up by a force equal to the weight of the fluid displaced.

ar′chi-tect (*Arch.*) One skilled in methods of construction and in designing and planning buildings. Also one skilled in the supervision of their construction.

ar′chi-tec′ture. The art and science relating to building.

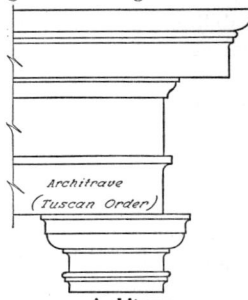
Architrave

ar′chi-trave (är′kĭ-trāv) (*Arch.*) The lowest member of an entablature; also a door molding.

ar′chi-trave cor′nice (*Arch.*) An entablature of two members only, an architrave and a cornice, the frieze being omitted.

ar′chives (är′kīvz) A repository for the preservation of documents or records.

ar′chi-volt (är′kĭ-vōlt) (*Arch.*) An ornamented or adorned band or frame running over the face of the arch stones of an arch, and bearing upon imposts; also a collection of members forming the inner contour of an arch.

arch′way′ (*Arch.*) The space or passage under an arch.

arc′ing (är′kĭng) (*Elec.*) Forming an arc, as at the brushes of a dynamo or in a broken circuit.

arc–lamp car′bon (*Elec.*) One of the carbon rods between which the arc occurs in an arc lamp.

arc of con′tact (*Mech.*) In tooth gearing, the space included between those two points where the contact of a single pair of wheel teeth begins and ends.

arc weld′ing. The piece to be welded is usually made the positive terminal. Direct current is used. The welding rod is the negative. The work is touched with the rod and withdrawn slightly causing an arc.

a′re-a (*Arch.*) An open space or court; an uncovered space. (*Math.*) The measured content of a surface.

a′re-a drain (*Plumb.*) A drain placed in the floor of a basement areaway, a depressed or basement entry way, a loading platform, or a cemented driveway which cannot otherwise be drained. Such a drain is usually made of 4-in. or larger cast-iron pipe leading into a running trap with cleanout and into the house drain.

a-re′na (*Arch.*) The oval central space in a Roman amphitheater. The name frequently applied to any scene of athletic contest.

ar′gon (är′gŏn) (*Chem.*) A colorless, inert gas resembling nitrogen; present in ordinary air to the extent of 0.9 per cent. Obtained by fractional distillation of liquid air, and used for filling electric incandescent lamps.

ar′ma-ture (*Elec.*) The revolving member of a dynamo.

ar′ma-ture coil (*Elec.*) That portion of an armature winding passed over, in following the course of the winding from one commutator segment to another. Or, a section of armature winding prepared on a form to the exact shape required to fit into the slots of the armature core.

ar′ma-ture core (*Elec.*) A core of metal surrounded by a coil of wire or the like, rotating near the poles of a magnet.

ar′ma-ture cur′rent (*Elec.*) See CURRENT.

ar′ma-ture disks (*Elec.*) See LAMINATED CORE.

ar′ma-ture of a mag′net (*Elec.*) or "keeper." A bar of iron or steel placed across the poles of a horseshoe magnet for the preservation of magnetization, or the movable iron or steel piece controlled by an electromagnet, as the armature of a bell.

ar′ma-ture re-ac′tion (*Elec.*) Certain reactions against the magnetic circuit of a dynamo which are established by the rotation of the armature.

ar′ma-ture shaft (*Elec.*) A shaft on which the component parts of the central member of a motor or generator are assembled.

ar′ma-ture slots (*Elec.*) Armature

pockets or chambers which admit the windings of a coil.

ar′ma-ture spi′der (*Elec.*) The radial armed frame which supports the armature of a motor or generator on its shaft.

ar′ma-ture var′nish (*Elec.*) An insulating varnish used for coating the armature windings as a protection against moisture.

ar′ma-ture wind′ing (*Elec.*) See COIL.

ar′moire′ (àr′mwär′) (*Furn.*) A large wardrobe or cupboard during and after the Renaissance.

ar′mored ca′ble (*Elec.*) Insulated wires within a flexible metallic covering; commonly called B.X.

ar′ras (ăr′ăs) A tapestry. A screen or hangings of heavy cloth for the wall of a room.

ar-rest′er (ȧ-rĕs′tẽr) (*Mech.*) Any mechanical contrivance or device used to stop or slow up motion.

ar-rest′ing gear (*Aero.*) The gear incorporated in aircraft and in the landing area to facilitate landing in a limited space.

ar-rest′ing hook (*Aero.*) A hook attached to an aircraft which engages the arresting gear in landing.

ar′ris (ăr′ĭs) (*Arch.*) The ridge between two channels of a Doric column. An external angle, edge, or ridge.

ar′row-heads′ (*Draft.*) The tips at the extremities of dimension lines to indicate the exact location to which the measurement refers.

ar′se-nal proc′ess (*Metal.*) This hot-dip process for tinning is as follows: The steel plate to be tinned is first pickled in a bath of sulphuric acid and water, then washed clean. It is next dipped in a flux of zinc and hydrochloric acid, and then dipped in a molten mixture 80-per-cent lead and 20-per-cent tin until well coated.

ar′se-nic (*Chem.*) A silvery, crystalline metalloid, sometimes found native. It is obtained by the distillation of roasted arsenic ores. It is used for medicines, insecticides, arsenic salts, and metallurgy.

ar-tic′u-lat′ed–type con-nect′ing rod (*Auto. Mech.*) A type of rod used on V, Y, X, or radial engines in which the crank end of the rods is joined to a master rod.

ar-tif′i-cer. A workman of inventive mind skilled in the use of hand tools.

ar′ti-fi′cial. Not genuine or natural; unreal.

ar′ti-fi′cial ho-ri′zon (*Aero.*) (1) A device that indicates the attitude of an aircraft with respect to the true horizon. (2) A substitute for a natural horizon, such as a liquid level, pendulum, or gyroscope, incorporated in a navigating instrument.

ar′ti-fi′cial mag′net (*Elec.*) A magnet which has an acquired magnetism, as distinguished from a natural magnet.

ar′ti-fi′cial stone. A manufactured product made to resemble stone. A common type is made from pulverized quarry refuse mixed with cement.

ar-til′ler-y–type wheel (*Auto.Mech.*) The commonly used wood-spoke wheel with metal hub and felloe.

ar′ti-san. One who works with his hands and manufactures articles in metal, wood, etc.

art met′al. Metal shaped into artistic forms.

as-bes′tine (ăs-bĕs′tĭn) (*Paint.*) A silicate of magnesium much used in paint. It serves as an aid in holding paint pigment in solution and in binding paint films together. Also marketed under such names as "French chalk" and "talc."

as-bes′tos. A fibrous variety of amphibole distinguished by its ability to resist high temperatures and the action of acids, and capable of being spun and woven. Most of the commercial asbestos comes from Canada. It is used for fireproof clothing, theater curtains, building materials, brake linings, etc.

as-bes′tos shin′gles (*Bldg.*) A fireproof roof covering made in the form of shingles; asbestos is the principal part of its composition.

as-cend′er (*Print.*) That part of a lower-case letter which extends above the body of the letter as in b, d, h, etc.

ash. That portion of the mineral substances in coal which remains after the combustible has been burned; it is the inorganic substance in the coal and has no heating value. (*Wood*) *Fraxinus.* A light-colored, coarse-grained wood used frequently for the spokes in and felloes of wheels, for hammer handles, and generally in work requiring flexibility combined with moderate strength.

ash′ing (*Plastics*) A grinding process

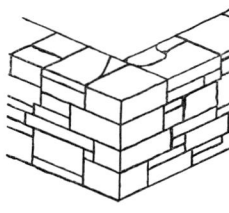

Random Ashlar

accomplished by means of a buffing wheel coated with a coarse abrasive.

ash′lar (*Carp.*) Plaster studs between floor beams and rafters of a garret. (*Masonry*) Dressed stone used for the outside facing of a wall.

as′pect ra′ti-o. The ratio of span to mean chord of an airfoil; i.e., the ratio of the square of the maximum span to the total area of an airfoil.

as′pen (*Wood*) *Populus tremuloides* or *P. grandidentata.* A common tree in many parts of the United States. The wood is of little commercial importance except for making paper pulp in which it ranks next to spruce and hemlock. Grows to height of 40 to 50 ft.; wood light in color; brittle; weight 25 pounds per cu. ft.

as′phalt (*Min.*) Mineral pitch; a bituminous composition used for paving, flooring, roofing, etc.

as′phalt oil (*Chem.*) Oil containing asphalt or having an asphalt base, as distinguished from oil having a paraffin base.

as-phal′tum (*Min.*) A mineral pitch. It is a form of bitumen, black or brown in color, brittle and glossy. Asphalt and asphaltum are interchangeable terms. Principal sources are Trinidad and Venezuela. "Gilsonite" is the name applied to that asphaltum, similar in appearance to coal, which is mined in Utah.

as-phal′tum var′nish. The best quality is known as "gilsonite"—black in color and comparatively expensive. It is used where quick drying is essential giving an effect similar to a Japan finish. Common asphaltum varnish used principally for its heat and acid-resisting qualities, is black in color if used on an absorbent surface such as wood, but appears slightly brownish on a metal surface. The largest users are battery manufacturers.

as-say′. To analyze ores for the purpose of determining the amount of precious metal contained therein.

as-sem′ble (*Shopwk.*) To collect or put in place the different parts of a machine or other manufactured article.

as-sem′bled car (*Auto.*) One for which a car manufacturer buys engines, axles, steering gear, body, and perhaps other items from individual parts manufacturers, and completes the assembly in his own plant.

as-sem′bling. The putting together in correct relation of the parts which comprise a piece of mechanism.

as-sem′bly line. A method of progressive assembly introduced early in automobile manufacture but applied to many lines of production. Usually, but not always, the line is kept in continuous motion, workmen remaining at their stations and adding parts to the partially completed mechanism as it passes by.

as′sets. Money or convertible property such as could be made available for payment of debts, etc.

as-sume′. Take for granted.

A-stage res′ins (*Plast.*) Thermosetting resins reacted only to the initial stage where they are soluble and fusible. The normal stage of a resin used for impregnation.

a-stat′ic gal′va-nom′e-ter (*Elec.*) A very sensitive galvanometer which neutralizes the effect of the earth's magnetism by the use of astatic needles.

as′tra-gal (ăs′trȧ-găl) (*Arch.*) A small semicircular molding, either plain or ornamented, frequently used to cover the joint between doors.

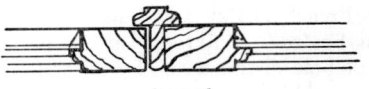

Astragal

as′ymp-tote (ăs′ĭm-tōt) (*Math.*) A straight line which continually approaches a curve without touching it.

at′mos-pher′ic pres′sure (*P h y s.*) The pressure extended due to the weight of the air above the earth. At sea level this pressure is about 14.7 pounds per square inch. The atmospheric pressure of 14.7 pounds will support or balance a column of mercury 29.92 in. high.

at′om. An atom may be considered the smallest particle of an element that takes part in a chemical change. It has a nucleus of one or more positive charges of electricity called "protons." Revolving around its protons are charges of negative electricity called "electrons." The atom is electrically neutral.

a-tom′ic en′er-gy. See NUCLEAR ENERGY.

a-tom′ic hy′dro-gen weld′ing. An alternating-current arc-welding process wherein the heat is obtained from an arc produced between two suitable electrodes in an atmosphere of hydrogen.

a-tom′ic num′ber (*Chem.*) The number of planetary electrons in an atom.

a-tom′ic the′o-ry (*Chem.*) The theory which asserts that all substances are composed of infinitesimally small particles or atoms.

a-tom′ic weight (*Chem.*) The weight of the atom of any element as compared with another as a standard; usually hydrogen is taken as 1.

at′om-ize. To divide a stream or jet of any liquid into a fine spray resembling smoke or dust in appearance.

at′om-iz′er (ăt′ŭm-īz′ẽr) A device for breaking a liquid into fine particles or a spray.

a′tri-um (*Arch.*) A large hall or lobby with galleries on three or more sides at each floor level.

at-tach′ment (*Mach.*) Any device used in connection with a machine in order to give a wider range or better quality of work.

at-tach′ment plug (*Elec.*) A small plug which may be fastened to the end of a flexible cord, and is attachable to socket or baseboard outlet to carry current to some appliance.

Attachment Plug

at′tic (*Arch.*) In modern structures, that space between the roof and the ceiling of the upper story. In classical structures, that part which extends above the level of the cornice.

at′ti-tude (*Aero.*) The position of an aircraft as determined by the inclination of its axes to some frame of reference. If not otherwise specified this frame of reference is fixed to the earth.

at-trac′tion (*Elec.*) Pull or force acting between two unlike (N and S) magnetic poles; or between two unlike (+ and —) static charges.

au′di-o (I hear) (*Tel.*) A synonym for the word "sound," or the electrical impulses which carry aural intelligence.

au′di-o-fre′quen-cy (*Elec.*) Rate of change of current in electrical circuits audible to the human ear. The range is between 16 and 16,000 vibrations per second.

au′ger (*Carp.*) A wood-boring tool of large size with attached handle at right angles to the tool line. Several types are made for different purposes.

au′ger bit. An auger without a handle, to be used in a brace.

au-rif′er-ous. Bearing or containing gold.

aus′ten-it′ic al-loy′ steels (*Metal.*) Austenitic steels are those composed wholly or largely of austenite which is a solid solution of carbon in iron of the gamma (crystal) type. Such steels are of low tensile strength, soft, ductile, and nonmagnetic. They were named after Sir Roberts-Austen, an eminent British metallurgist.

au-tog′e-nous weld′ing (*Shopwk.*) A type of welding in which metals are united by fusing, without compression or hammering, and without the use of flux; although the term also applies to gas welding in which both flux and welding rod are used.

au′to-gi′ro (ô′tô-jī′rō) (*Aero.*) A type of rotor plane whose support in the air is chiefly derived from airfoils rotated about an approximately vertical axis by aerodynamic forces, and in which the lift on opposite sides of the plane of symmetry is equalized by the vertical oscillation of the blades.

au′to-mat′ic. Self-regulating or self-adjusting. A movement is automatic when it is effected without the direct intervention of the hand.

au′to-mat′ic cen′ter punch (*Mach.*) A center punch so constructed that, when pressure is applied, a spring-controlled hammer contained within the handle is released with sufficient force to cause the point to leave its mark on metal.

au'to-mat'ic choke (*Auto. Mech.*) An electrically controlled device by which the choke is automatically operated on starting the car.

au'to-mat'ic cir'cuit break'er (*Elec.*) An automatic device for breaking the circuit when the strength of current exceeds a predetermined proper limit.

au'to-mat'ic clutch (*Auto. Mech.*) A clutch operated by vacuum from the intake manifold and controlled by the accelerator pedal.

au'to-mat'ic cut'out (*Elec.*) An electrical adjustment for automatically removing any electrical part or connection from a circuit at the proper moment.

au'to-mat'ic pi'lot (*Aero.*) A group of units which, when combined electrically and mechanically, form a system capable of automatically controlling the flight of an aircraft.

au'to-mat'ic pro-pel'ler (*Aero*) A propeller whose blades are attached to a mechanism that automatically sets them at their optimum pitch for various flight conditions.

au'to-mat'ic screw ma-chine'. A machine for the rapid and accurate production of small parts such as screws, bolts, bushings, etc. Material in the form of a bar is fed into position to permit the necessary machining operations. After being "set up," its operation is automatic.

au'to-mat'ic shift (*Auto. Mech.*) A transmission-gear control by which gears are shifted from one speed to another usually by simply depressing the clutch pedal.

au'to-mat'ic spark con-trol' (*Auto. Mech.*) A governor controlled either by vacuum, electrical, or mechanical means by which a spark to each cylinder is properly timed.

au'to-mat'ic sta-bil'i-ty (*Aero.*) Stability dependent upon movable control surfaces automatically operated.

au'to-mat'ic switch (*Elec.*) A switch which opens and closes by itself at required times.

au'to-mat'ic tel'e-phone (*Elec.*) A type of telephone which permits the completion of a connection by means of automatic switches without the assistance of an operator.

auto-ma'tion. An industrial technique of mass production using self-directing, self-correcting, self-evaluating machines as a replacement for human effort.

au-tom'a-ton. Any device or mechanism which automatically imitates the actions of the living.

au'to me-chan'ics. The practical science of repair and maintenance of automobiles.

au'to-mo'bile. A vehicle propelled by steam, gasoline, or electrical power. The term, as generally used, includes pleasure and business cars, delivery cars, and trucks.

au'to-mo'bile bat'ter-y (*Auto. Elec.*) A storage battery used to operate the starting and lighting systems of an automobile or to supply the current for an electrically operated vehicle.

au'to-mo'tive en'gi-neer'. One skilled in the design, construction, and development of the automobile. Technically, the term might be extended to cover mechanically propelled mediums generally.

au'to-plate' (*Print.*) A machine which

casts, shaves, trims, and delivers curved stereotype printing plates ready for use.

au'to-pulse mag-net'ic fu'el pump (*Auto.Mech.*) An electrically operated device for maintaining the gasoline level in the carburetor.

au'to trans-form'er (*Elec.*) A variable compensator in which a choking coil is introduced across the alternating-current supply circuits so that the varying currents can be obtained from different points on its windings. A single-coil transformer tapped to provide primary and secondary.

aux-il'ia-ry. Giving or furnishing aid or support, generally in a subordinate or secondary manner; supplementary; as an auxiliary view in drawing.

aux-il'ia-ry air in'take (*Auto.*) An opening to permit the admission of additional air to the carburetor when the car is being operated at high speed.

aux-il'ia-ry air'port bea'con (*Aero.*) A beacon light, usually of lower candle power than the main airport beacon light. It is placed on the airport site to indicate the specific location of an airport that has a separate airport beacon which is visible at a greater distance to indicate the general location of the airport.

aux-il'ia-ry air–valve car'bu-ret'or (*Auto. Mech.*) A carburetor with an air valve designed to control the richness of the mixture.

aux-il'ia-ry air'way bea'con (*Aero.*) A beacon light, usually of lower candle power than the principal airway beacon lights, marks special features of the terrain along an airway, or otherwise supplements the principal airway beacons.

av'er-age. A medial sum; a median; a mean proportion of many cases.

a'vi-a'tion (*Aero.*) The art or science of airplane operation.

a'vi-a'tor (*Aero.*) The pilot of aircraft heavier than air.

a-vo-di-re' (a-vō-dē-rā') (*Wood*) *Turraeanthus africana.* A fine cabinet wood native to the west coast of Africa. Introduced into the United States about 1925 and has become very popular. Color dull white to golden cream with beautiful grain effects.

av'oir-du-pois' weight.

27 11/32 grains (g.)	= 1 dram (dr.)
16 drams	= 1 ounce (oz.)
16 ounces	= 1 pound (lb.)
25 pounds	= 1 quarter
4 quarters	= 1 cwt.
2000 pounds	= 1 short ton
2240 pounds	= 1 long ton

A.W.G. (*American wire gauge*) Adopted as a standard for gauging the size of wires used for electrical purposes.

awl. A small pointed tool for making holes for nails or screws.

awl haft. An awl handle.

ax'es of an air'craft (*Aero.*) Three fixed lines of reference, usually centroidal and mutually perpendicular. The horizontal axis in the plane of symmetry, usually parallel to the axis of the propeller, is called the longitudinal axis; the axis perpendicular to this in the plane of symmetry is called the normal axis; and the third axis perpendicular to the other two is called the lateral axis. In mathematical discussions, the first of these axes, drawn from rear to front, is called the X axis; the second drawn downward, the Z axis; and the third, running from left to right, the Y axis.

ax′i-al force (ăk′sĭ-ăl) (*Engin.*) A force which acts uniformly over the section of a prismatic body so that its resultant coincides with the axis of the body.

ax′i-al pitch (*Mach.*) More commonly referred to as "pitch"; may be described as the amount of advance per revolution of a single screw thread.

ax′i-al–type en′gine (*Aero.*) An engine having its cylinders equidistant from and parallel to the main shaft. Power is transmitted to the shaft through a wabble plate, swash plate, or gears.

ax′i-om (*Math.*) Self-evident truth, universally accepted.

ax′is (*Math.*) A central line considered in relation to certain geometrical or mechanical relations. A point or line about which or on which a body revolves.

ax′is of sym′me-try (*Geom.*) An imaginary central line around which a symmetrically developed body is formed, and in which the center of gravity is found.

ax′le. A shaft or device which carries the driving, traveling, or truck wheels of a vehicle, such as a locomotive, wagon, trolley, automobile, etc.

Ayr′ton gal′va-nom′e-ter shunt (âr′tŭn găl′vȧ-nŏm′ê-tēr) (*Elec.*) A shunt in which the coils are so arranged that their relative multiplying power is always the same; the universal shunt.

az′i-muth of a line (ăz′ĭ-mŭth) The angle which the vertical plane containing it makes with the plane of the meridian.

B

B bat′ter-y (*Elec.*) A battery of high voltage and low amperage; in radio keeps the plate of an electron tube positive in relation to its filament.

B e-lim′i-na′tor (*Elec.*) A device for producing the necessary "B" voltage for operation of a battery radio set, replacing the B battery.

B.X. (*Elec.*) A trade name for a flexible armored cable.

Bab′bitt met′al. An alloy of 50 parts of tin, 2 parts of copper, and 4 parts of antimony, used for lining the bearings of engines and machines which are subjected to much friction.

back (*Bookbndg.*) The binding edge of a book. (*Leather.*) That which comes from the back of an animal; the better quality.

back band (*Arch.*) The molding or strip covering the joint between a masonry wall and the outer face of a window or door casing.

backed-up (*Print.*) Sheets properly printed on two sides; "backed-up wrong" indicates misprinting.

back e-lec′tro-mo′tive force (*Elec.*) A term sometimes used for counter-electromotive force. It refers to that electromotive force which opposes or tends to set up a current in the reverse direction to the impressed current.

back fill′ing (*Arch.*) Fill of broken stone or other coarse material outside a foundation or basement wall to provide drainage.

back′fire (*Auto. Mech.*) An incomplete explosion taking place in the intake of a gas engine, produced by faulty valves, late timing, or lean fuel mixture. The vacuum produced causes fire to travel back in the manifold.

back flow (*Plumb.*) Flow of water or sewage opposite to the normal direction of flow.

back′flow′ valve (*Plumb.*) A device inserted in the drain of a house or other building to prevent a reversal of the flow of sewage. Its main function is to prevent a flood, and consequent damage, which might be caused by the overloading of a combination type of public sewer.

back gear (*Mach.*) An arrangement of gear wheels by which the power of the driving belt is proportionately increased, as on the head of a lathe.

back′ing (*Bookbndg.*) Shaping and preparing the back of a book for reinforcement and to fit the cover. (*Print.*) In electrotyping, filling the copper shell with metal to make it solid.

back′ing brick (*Arch.*) The inner part of a brick wall, often of cheaper and less perfect brick than is used for the face of the wall.

back′ing lamp (*Auto. Mech.*) A lamp usually combined with the rear and stop lamps, but which lights only when the car is placed in reverse.

back′ing of a joist or raft′er (*Carp.*) Owing to the variation in widths of joists, it is necessary, in order to obtain even floors or roofs, to block up the narrower pieces until all the upper surfaces are at the same level.

back′ing of a wall. The rough inner

---

sāle, surfâce, grăm, humᵃn, màsk, solᵃr, bär, bâre; mē, êdition, lĕnd, momĕnt, bakēr; kīnd, fīt; lōde, ômit, ŏlive, cŏnsume, sôrt; dūty, ûtility, nŭt, alᵘm, bûrn.

face of a wall. The fill deposited behind a retaining wall.

back′ing off (*Shopwk.*) Removing metal behind the cutting edge to relieve friction in cutting, as in taps or reamers.

back′ing out (*Metalwk.*) The running back of a tap or die after a thread has been cut.

back′ing plate (*Plast.*) In injection molding, a plate supporting cavity blocks, guide pins, bushings, etc.

back′ing-up (*Masonry*) The using of bricks of a cheaper grade for the inner face of a wall. (*Print.*) Printing the second side of a sheet.

back′lash (*Auto. Mech.*) The backward movement of a pair or train of gears when the driving pressure is variable. It equals the amount of clearance between the flanks of the teeth.

back light (*Tel.*) Illuminating a subject from a point to the rear of its plane.

back lin′ing (*Bookbndg.*) The material used on the inside surface of the back of a book cover to improve the finish, strength, and appearance.

back pres′sure (*Auto. Mech.*) An opposing atmospheric force built up in the cylinders of an engine due to faulty timing, carbon deposits, dirty or fouled muffler, which prevents an engine from delivering its full power. (*Plumb.*) Air pressure in pipes greater than atmospheric pressure.

back rest (*Mach.*) Serves as a support for slender work during turning or grinding operations. Such a rest does not surround the work as does a steady rest but is open at the front.

Backsaw

back′saw (*Woodwkg.*) Any saw whose blade is stiffened with a metallic back. Tenon and dovetail saws are backsaws.

bad col′or (*Print.*) The appearance caused on the printed sheet by ink, too much or too little used.

bad cop′y (*Print.*) Manuscript which cannot be easily read.

badg′er (*Art*) An artist's brush made of badger's hair. (*Carp.*) A wide rabbet plane having a skew mouth.

baf′fle plate. A diaphragm or thin plate used to deflect or retard the flow of gases.

ba·gasse′ (bȧ-gȧs) (*Plast.*) Fibrous by-product from sugar cane. It is much used as a building board.

bag mold′ing (*Plast.*) A commercial method of producing large, three dimensional synthetic resin laminations, smooth on both sides. Example: Fiberglas-resin boat molding. A flexible rubber or resin bag is lowered and clamped into the mold, and this is pressed against the rigid mold, either by air pressure or by vacuum, forcing the resin up through the glass fiber.

bail. A half hoop or horseshoe-shaped piece for supporting something.

bail out (*Aero.*) To jump from a plane, depending on a parachute for support.

Ba′ke-lite (Bā′kĕ-līt) (*Plast.*) A trade name for a plastic made by chemical condensation of phenol and formaldehyde.

bal′ance (*Aero.*) A condition of steady flight in which the resultant force and moment on the airplane are zero. (*Art*) A piece of artwork is in balance when its parts are so arranged as to give the most pleasing effect to the eye. (*Print.*) When type composition has its various parts so grouped that they are equalized in mass. (*Mech.*) A sensitive instrument for weighing.

bal'anced back'flow' valve (*Plumb.*) A valve with a counter-balanced gate.

bal'anced cir'cuit (*Elec.*) An electrical circuit so adjusted with respect to near-by circuits as to escape the influence of mutual induction. A three-wire circuit having the same load on each side of the neutral wire.

bal'anced core (*Fdry.*) A core which is supported only at one end.

bal'anced pul'ley. A pulley which has been weighted and tested for balance, at rest and in motion, to prevent excessive wear on bearings.

bal'anced sur'face (*Aero.*) A control surface which extends on both sides of the axis of the pivot in such a manner as to reduce the movement of the air forces about the pivot.

bal'ance, dy-nam'ic or run'ning (*Shopwk.*) Securing the proper distribution of weight so that shafts or pulleys will run without vibration.

bal'ance, stat'ic or stand'ing (*Shopwk.*) Distributing the weight of pulleys or shafts so that, when placed on knife edgeways, they will stand in any position. If unbalanced, the heavy side rolls to the bottom.

bal'ance weight. The weight placed on the inner edge of a wheel to effect perfect balance. A weight slid over the end of a lever and attached thereto to counterbalance a moving part.

bal'ance wheel. A flywheel. Its purpose is to insure smooth and regular motions in an engine or machine.

bal'anc-ing ma-chine'. A machine which measures the "out of balance" of a revolving piece and indicates the amount and location of the necessary correction.

bal'anc-ing way (*Shopwk.*) Level strip or sharp-edge disk for testing shafts or pulleys for standing balance. The disks are usually mounted on ball bearings.

bal'co-ny. A platform or gallery projecting from the wall of a building, enclosed by a balustrade or parapet.

balk (bôk) (*Carp.*) A squared beam or timber.

balk ring (*Auto. Mech.*) A friction regulated pawl or plunger used to facilitate the engagement of gears.

ball and claw foot (*Furn.*) A carved foot representing a ball grasped by a claw.

bal'last (băl'ɑ̆st) Gravel or broken stone for a railroad bed.

ball bear'ing (*Auto. Mech.*) Any one of the various bearings consisting of hardened steel balls in some sort of retainer, so constructed that the load is carried by the balls.

ball check valve. The active part of such a valve consists of a ball resting on a seat. Under pressure, the ball rises from the seat and permits flow in one direction; when pressure is removed or reversed, the ball returns to its closed position.

ball clay (*Pot.*) The lump of clay which a potter places in the center of his revolving table and from which he forms pottery shapes.

ball cock (*Plumb.*) A faucet opened or closed by the fall or rise of a ball on the surface of the water.

ball'ing (*Metal.*) Forming wrought iron into balls in the furnace, preparatory to their passage through the squeezer.

bal-lis'tics. The science which treats

of the characteristics and performance of firearms, guns, cannon, etc.

bal′lon-et′ (băl′ô-nĕt′) (*Aero.*) A compartment, constructed as a unit or partitioned off, inside a balloon or airship, to maintain gas pressure by blowing in or letting out air.

bal-loon′ (*Aero.*) An aerostat without a propelling system.

bal-loon′ fram′ing (*Bldg.*) Studs extended in one piece from the foundation to the roof; the joists, in addition to being supported by a ledger board, are nailed to the studs.

bal-loon′ tire (*Auto. Mech.*) A relatively large, flexible, thin-walled tire designed for low air pressures. The flexible wall and low pressure provide "easy-riding" qualities.

Ball-Peen Hammer

ball–peen ham′mer (*Metalwk.*) The type of hammer commonly used by machinists; one end of the head is rounded or ball shaped for riveting or peening; the surface of the other end is flat and is used for striking a chisel, or in other such work.

ball race (*Mach.*) In a ball bearing, the grooves in which the balls run.

ball ream′er (*Mach.*) A hemispherical rose reamer used in finishing the recess for a ball joint.

Ball Stake

ball stake (*Sheet Metal*) A mushroom-shaped stake used for shaping and working curved objects.

ball tool (*Leather.*) A small straight tool, the end of which terminates in a ball. Used for producing raised relief designs in leatherwork.

Bal-op′ti-con (*Tel.*) A trade name for a projector used for charts, pictures, or anything not transparent. Also called balop or telop.

bal′sa (*Wood*) *Ochroma lagopus*. A common, second-growth tree in the West Indies and in Central America. Its structure somewhat resembles basswood and poplar. Its extreme lightness combined with good strength make it a desirable wood for use in airplane construction.

bal′sam fir (*Wood*) *Abies balsamea*. A medium-sized evergreen tree reaching 40 to 50 ft. in height; wood is brittle and not durable. Has little commercial use except for wide sale as Christmas trees.

bal′sams (*Chem. Plast.*) Natural vegetable exudations consisting of resins mixed with volatile oil. The name is also applied to products having the physical characteristics of the natural balsams but produced by reactions which normally lead to resinous materials.

bal′us-ter (*Arch. and Bldg.*) The supports usually of wood, of the handrail of an open stair. (*Furn. and Woodwk.*) A small pillar or column; one of the units of a balustrade. A splat with the outline of a baluster.

bal′us-trade′ (*Arch.*) A series of small columns or pilasters surmounted by a top rail or coping.

Balustrade

bam-boo′ (*Furn.*) A tropical, tree-like grass used in making furniture, canes, fishpoles, etc.

ba-na′na oil (*Wood Fin.*) "Amyl acetate." A product which gets its name from its odor, used for mixing finishes for wood and metal.

Ban′ca tin. A high grade of tin from Malacca and Banca.

band (*Arch.*) A flat frieze or fascia running horizontally around a tower or other parts of a building; it usually has a projecting molding at upper and lower edges, the flat portion, between, being ornamented. In furniture, a narrow inlay of contrasting color or grain used to embellish a surface.

band′ing (*Arch., Bookbndg., and Furn.*) To decorate with a band, strip, or stripe.

band i′ron. Thin ribbon of iron often used to protect packing cases in shipment.

band saw. An endless saw running on revolving pulleys, used for cutting work in wood.

band twist′ing (*Shopwk.*) A peculiar twist given to a band saw in order to make it coil to advantage for storing.

band′width (*Tel.*) The number of cycles per second in the band of frequency required to transmit the visual or aural signal. Present television is transmitted in channels six megacycles wide, which accommodate both picture and sound signals.

ban′dy leg (*Furn.*) A curved or bowed leg. A cabriole leg.

ban′is-ter (*Furn.*) A baluster.

ban′is-ter back (*Furn.*) The back, as of a chair, built in a manner to resemble a banister; i.e., with upright slats or bars surmounted by a top rail.

bank (*Aero.*) To cause an airplane to incline laterally in order to accomplish a turn or change of course. Right bank is to incline the airplane with the right wing down. (*Furn.*) A long seat or bench of the Middle Ages.

bank′er. A stonecutter's workbench.

bank′ing trans-form′ers (*Elec.*) The grouping of transformers to form a group or "bank."

bank of lamps (*Elec.*) A number of electric lamps mounted on a single base. Often used to indicate the voltage of a generator which is about to be switched into a circuit.

bar (*Forg.*) In forging, the long pieces of metal are usually referred to as bar stock. (*Print.*) The piece of metal used across the center of a book chase to prevent the chase from spreading.

bar clamp. A clamp consisting of a long bar and two clamping jaws, used by woodworkers for clamping large work.

bare′faced ten′on (bâr′făst tĕn′ŭn) (*Carp.*) A tenon shouldered on one side only.

bar fold′er (*Sheet Metal*) A machine for folding or edging strips or sheets of metal, for forming angles, locks, and square joints, and to turn round edges for wire.

barge′board (*Arch.*) Same as verge board. A board suspended from the verge of a gable. During the last quarter of the nineteenth century such boards were frequently very ornate.

bar i′ron (*Shopwk.*) Lengths of iron which are used in forging and in the shops; generally applied to that which is flat or rectangular in section.

ba′rite (bā′rīt) (*Chem.*) A mineral

occurring in white crystals, in granular form, and in compact massive form resembling marble. It is often called heavy spar (BaSO₄).

ba′ri-um (bā′rĭ-ŭm) (*Chem.*) A silvery white, slightly lustrous, somewhat malleable metal; used in barium salts and in alloys (Ba).

bark tan′nage (*Leather.*) The tanning of leather through the use of bark, as of chestnut oak.

bar′ley twist (*Furn.*) Spiral turning.

bar mag′net (*Elec.*) (1) A straight permanent magnet. (2) A permanent magnet made in a bar shape.

bar′o-graph (*Aero.*) A barometer which registers automatically.

ba-rom′e-ter. An instrument for indicating atmospheric pressure; used for forecasting the weather and for measuring elevations.

ba-roque′ (bȧ-rōk′) Fantastic in style, grotesque, irregularly shaped. A style of architecture common in the first half of the eighteenth century. In furniture it was exemplified by such period styles as Louis XIV, Italian, late Jacobean, and William and Mary.

bar′rel–type en′gine (*Aero.*) An engine having its cylinders arranged equidistant from and parallel to the main shaft.

bar′rel vault (*Arch.*) An arched ceiling consisting of one or more arches of concave cylindrical shape.

bars (*Metal.*) Lengths of iron or steel of rectangular sections. (*Fdry.*) The ribs across the cope of a flask.

ba-ry′tes or **bar′i-um sul′phate** (*Paint.*) See BLANC FIXE.

ba-salt′ (bȧ-sôlt′) An igneous rock of dark color, used for road beds, ballast, etc.

bas′cule bridge (bȧs′kūl) One in which the leaf or leaves are pivoted on a horizontal shaft and lift vertically.

Bascule Bridge

base (*Chem.*) (1) A substance that produces hydroxyl ions when dissolved in water. (2) A substance whose aqueous solutions contain (OH) ions and no other negative ions. (3) A compound capable of so uniting with acids as to neutralize their acid properties and form salts. (*Furn.*) The bottom of a piece of furniture; the plinth in carcase work; also the valances around the lower part of a bed.

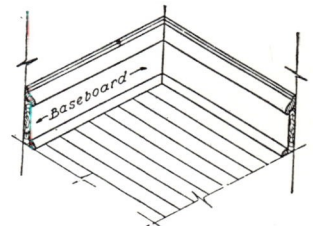
Baseboard

base′board (*Arch.*) The finishing board which covers the plaster wall where it meets the floor.

base cir′cle (*Gear.*) In gear drawing, the circle on which the involute tooth is constructed.

base course (*Masonry*) The first course or foundation course on which the remainder rests.

base line (*Arch. and Man. Arts*) A definite line from which measurements are taken in laying out work.

base′ment (*Arch.*) The finished portion of a building below the main floor.

base mold′ing (*Arch.*) The molding immediately above the plinth of a wall, pillar, or pedestal.

base of a col′umn (*Arch.*) That part between the shaft and the pedestal.

base plate or bed plate (*Mach.*) The foundation plate or support of a piece of machinery.

base trim (*Arch.*) A board or molding used for finishing off the base of a piece of work, as on a baseboard.

bas′ic load (*Aero.*) The load on an aircraft when it is at rest or in a condition of unaccelerated rectilinear flight. The basic load is needed for purposes of stress analysis.

bas′ic steel. Steel produced by the "Basic-Bessemer" or by the basic open-hearth process, i.e., the means by which sulphur, phosphorus, silicon, manganese, and carbon can be removed from the molten charge. During the past twenty years the Bessemer process has been giving way to the basic open-hearth process, owing to the fact that low phosphorus ore is being exhausted.

ba′sil (*Mech.*) The beveled edge of a drill or chisel.

ba′sis weight (*Print.*) The standard weight per ream for any given paper of given size.

bas′ket (*Aero.*) The car suspended beneath a balloon for carrying passengers, ballast, etc.

bas′-re-lief′ (bä′rė-lēf′) A form of low relief sculpture in which the design or pattern is but slightly raised from the background.

bas′set ta′ble (*Furn.*) A Queen Anne period card table.

bas′si-net (*Furn.*) A basket-shaped baby's bed or cradle, originally made of wicker.

bass′wood (*Wood*) *Tilia americana.* The name given American Linden. A large tree which usually grows to a height of from 60 to 70 feet. Wood: diffuse porous; rays: distinct but colorless, light, soft, compact, moderately strong; light brown to nearly white, fine in texture; weight: 29 pounds per cu. ft.; uses: paper pulp, woodenware, cheap furniture, panels, carving, and to some extent in airplane manufacture. Easy to work.

bast (*Shopwk.*) A strong, woody fiber obtained from trees, used in the manufacture of ropes, cordage, and matting. It is of excellent quality in the linden.

bas′tard (*Mech.*) A term frequently applied to anything which does not conform to accepted standards. (*Metalwk.*) A course-cut file but not as rough as a first cut. (*Print.*) Type with a face larger or smaller than the size proper to the body.

bat (*Ceram.*) A term applied to a slab of fired clay and to a lump of moist clay. (*Masonry*) A broken brick or a part of a brick.

batch. A quantity of anything considered as a whole, as a batch of castings. A quantity of a mixture, as a batch of concrete.

ba′tik (bä′têk) (*Textile*) A method of resist dyeing in which wax is used to cover that part of the fabric which is not to take the dye.

bat′ten (*Furn.*) A strip of wood placed across a surface of one or more boards to prevent warping, to strengthen, etc. A cleat is also termed a batten. (*Plaster.*) A strip used for attaching laths where studs are not accessible.

bat′ten door (*Arch.*)
A door made of sheathing, secured by strips placed crossways, and nailed with clinched nails.

bat′ten down(*Naut.*) To fasten down as with tarpaulin and strips or battens.

bat′ten-ing (*Plaster.*) The application of battens or strips to which laths or other material may be attached. (*Textile*)

Batten Door

The driving up in close order of the filling threads in weaving.

bat′ter (*Arch. and Masonry*) The slope of the face of a wall that is out of plumb. The backward and upward slope of a retaining wall. (*Print.*) A breakage or marring of type or a plate so that it will not print perfectly.

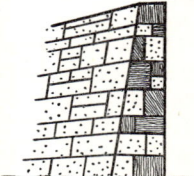
Batter

bat′ter-y (*Elec.*) A number of primary or storage cells, condensers, or dynamos, grouped together as a single source of electricity. The term is incorrectly used when applied to a single cell.

bat′ter-y ac′id (*Elec.*) The acid used in forming the electrolyte of a storage battery. Sulphuric acid is commonly used.

bat′ter-y ca-pac′i-ty (*Elec.*) The number of ampere hours that can be obtained from a storage battery.

bat′ter-y charg′er (*Elec.*) An electrical device for charging a battery. It usually converts alternating current to direct current for charging purposes.

bat′ter-y con-tain′er or bat′ter-y case (*Elec.*) The hard rubber or plastic composition casing into which the elements and the electrolyte are placed.

bat′ter-y ig-ni′tion sys′tem (*Auto. Mech.*) The ignition system in which the initial current is supplied by the battery.

bat′ter-y volt′age (*Auto. Elec.*) Electric pressure across terminal poles of a battery as measured by a voltmeter.

bat′tle-ment (*Arch.*) A parapet with a series of notches in it. The raised parts are "merlons"; the notches, "crenels." (*Furn.*) The indented or notched wall of a parapet, the design of which is used as a decorative feature on furniture.

Bau′me′ scale (bō′mā′ skāl) A device for determining specific gravity of liquids, particularly petroleum products. It has to a great degree been superseded by the American Petroleum Institute scale.

baux′ite (bō′zīt) (*Mineral.*) A white to red earthy aluminum hydroxide; the principal source of the metal aluminum. It is largely used in the preparation of aluminum and alumina, and for the lining of furnaces which are exposed to intense heat.

bay (body parts) (*Aero.*) The portion of a face of a truss or of a fuselage, between adjacent bulkheads or adjacent struts or frame positions. (*Arch.*) A space between two piers or columns.

bay′o-net sock′et (*Elec.*) A lamp

socket having two lengthwise slots in its sides. These slots take a right-angled turn at the bottom, so that a lamp with two pins may be connected by pushing it into the socket and giving it a slight turn.

beach'ing gear (*Aero.*) An arrangement of wheels to be attached to the hull of a seaplane to permit handling ashore.

bea'con (*Aero.*) A light, group of lights, or other signaling device, indicating a location or direction.

bead (*Arch.*) A thin molding, usually half round in section. (*Shopwk.*) Almost any small circular molding. The cut down the middle of a piece of fencing causes it to be called a beaded board.

bead'ing (*Sheet-Met. Wk.*) The forming of a bead on a piece of work for ornamenting or stiffening.

bead'ing ma-chine' (*Sheet Metal*) A machine, which, by means of rolls of different shapes and sizes, impresses in the metal a bead corresponding in shape to the particular rolls used. The beading serves to ornament and strengthen the vessel.

bead plane (*Woodwkg.*) A special form of plane for cutting beads.

beak'er (*Chem.*) A cylindrical vessel, generally of glass, with a lip for pouring.

beak'head (*Arch.*) A sort of drip mold used on the extreme lower edge of the lowest member of a cornice.

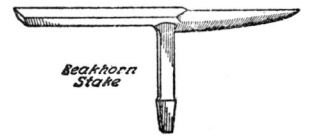

beak'horn stake (*Sheet Metal*) A stake having one end rounded and tapered, the other end long and rectangular in section; used for bending and shaping square and conical objects.

beam (*Aero.*) (1) A radio-directional aid to air navigation. (2) The main spar of a wing. (3) The plan view of the side of an aircraft. (*Arch.*) A piece of timber or other material, or a built-up structure whose length is greater than its width or depth and whose strains are those due to leverage, tension, or compression.

beam ceil'ing (*Arch.*) A ceiling in which beams, either false or true, usually in a horizontal position, are exposed to view.

beam com'pass (*Draw. and Shopwk.*) A large compass with adjustable points which are attached to a beam or bar of wood or metal; used in drafting rooms and shops for describing large circles or arcs.

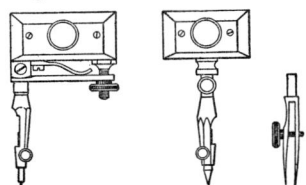

Beam Compasses

beam drill (*Mach.*) Similar to a radial drill except the arm is supported at both ends as is the crossrail on a planer.

beam pat'tern (*Auto. Mech.*) The shape or spread of the light area from the head lamps.

bear'er (*Print.*) Excess metal within or around the printing area of a plate; also strip of metal sometimes placed at side of a plate when hand inking and proofing.

bear′ing (*Arch.*) That portion of a beam, truss, etc., which rests on the supports. (*Mach.*) The support or carrier for a rotating shaft.

Bearing

bear′ing cap (*Mach.*) The top half of a journal bearing. See CAP.

bear′ing met′al (*Metal.*) Antifriction and white metals, brass, gun metals, and the various alloys used for making or lining the bearings of journals.

bear′ing par-ti′tion (*Bldg.*) A partition that carries the floor joists and other partitions above it.

bear′ing plate (*Engin.*) A plate of the thickness and area required to distribute a given load, such as a plate under a beam flange resting on a wall. If the plate is 2 in. or more in thickness, it is called a slab.

bear′ing pro-jec′tor (*Aero.*) A fixed directional projector used in conjunction with a landmark beacon to indicate the direction toward a landing area by means of the direction of its beam.

bear′ing sur′face (*Engin.*) The surface over which a load is distributed.

bed (*Mach.*) That part of a lathe which supports the headstock, tailstock, and carriage. (*Masonry*) In bricklaying and masonry, the horizontal surfaces on which the bricks or stone of the wall lie in courses. (*Print.*) The support for the type form on a platen press or a cylinder press.

bed charge (*Fdry.*) The deep load of coke in the bottom of a cupola. The first charge of iron is also called a bed charge.

bed′ding (*Fdry. and Patmkg.*) A molding operation which consists of filling the drag flask with sand and forcing the pattern down to the desired position. The sand is then firmly tucked and rammed about the pattern.

Bed′ford lime′stone. One of the finest and best known building stones to be found in the United States. It gets its name from its shipping point, Bedford, Indiana.

bed mold′ing (*Arch.*) Molding used as a finish underneath an overhang; e.g., the finish molding at the joining of eaves and outside wall.

bed plate (*Arch.*) A metal plate used as a rest or support of some structural part. (*Mach.*) A metal plate used as a foundation of a machine.

beech (*Wood*) *Fagus*. A large tree which sometimes grows to 100 ft. in height with a diameter of 2 to 3 ft. Wood is hard, strong, and tough but not durable. Excellent for fuel, but has little other commercial use.

bees′wax. The wax from the cells of the honeycomb. Has many uses in the arts; used to coat metal patterns to facilitate their withdrawal from the sand.

bel′fry (*Arch.*) An attached or detached tower containing bells.

Belfry

bell (*Elec.*) An electric signaling device operating through the use of an electromagnet, clapper, and gong.

bell–and–spig′ot joint (*Plumb.*) Each length of cast-iron pipe is made with an enlarged or bell end and a plain or spigot end. The spigot end of one length fits into the bell end of the next length. The joint is made tight by calking.

Bell Crank

bell crank. A lever or crank having two arms which meet at an angle of 90 deg.

bell metal. A hard, brittle, sonorous alloy of copper and tin.

bell′mouthed. Having a bell-shaped opening at the end.

bell or hub (*Plumb.*) That portion of a pipe which, for a short distance, is sufficiently enlarged to receive the end of another pipe of the same diameter for the purpose of making a joint.

bel′lows (*Fdry.*) An instrument with an air chamber and flexible sides,

Bellows

used for directing a current of air. In a foundry, small hand bellows are used for blowing parting sand away from the faces of patterns, etc.

bell–ring′ing trans-form′er (*Elec.*) A small transformer which steps down the voltage of the ordinary house circuit to supply current for bell ringing.

bell switch (*Elec.*) A switch for cutting a bell in or out of a circuit.

bel′ly (*Furn.*) A protruding surface caused by buckling, warping, etc.

(*Leather.*) The inferior leather which comes from the underneath part of an animal. (*Print.*) A gradual depression in the center of a line of type.

belt (*Masonry*) A projecting band course or courses, or a course of a different kind of brick. (*Mech.*) A band or strap of leather, canvas, or other material, flexible enough to act as a transmitter of power over smooth pulleys, acting by friction only.

belt clamp (*Mech.*) A device for holding the two ends of a belt together while they are being connected.

belt con-vey′or. A wide belt running over pulleys, transporting materials laid upon it.

belt dress′ing. Any of the various compounds used on machinery belting to prevent slipping.

belt hook (*Shopwk.*) A device used for shifting belts manually. It usually consists of a long pole or stick with a projecting pin, hence the name *hook*.

belt lac′ing (*Mach.*) A narrow strip of rawhide used for lacing the ends of a belt together. Wire hooks and other types of fasteners are sometimes incorrectly spoken of as "belt lacing."

belt sand′er (*Woodwkg.*) A motor-driven machine equipped with a belt of sandpaper for finishing woodwork.

belt shift′er (*Shopwk.*) Usually a flat strip of wood 4 or 5 ft. long having shifter fingers or arms attached to it; used for shifting a belt from tight to loose pulleys and vice versa on overhead shafting.

bench (*Shopwk.*) A strong table equipped with vise and other implements to facilitate the work performed on it.

bench as-sem′bly (*Shopwk.*) The process of fitting and putting together, two or more parts on a bench. The fitting may require filing, scraping, tapping, reaming, soldering, drilling, fastening with screws, and the like.

bench dog (*Shopwk.*) A peg of wood or metal inserted in a slot or hole near the end of a bench; used to prevent a piece of work from slipping. Different from bench stop.

bench hook (*Woodwkg.*) A flat piece of wood with cleats on both sides, one at each end, used to prevent injury to the bench top during certain operations.

Bench Hook

bench lathe (*Mach.*) A small lathe mounted on a workbench for handling light work.

bench plane. Plane kept on the bench, being in constant use, as jack, trying, and smoothing planes.

Bench Plane

bench stop (*Woodwkg.*) An adjustable metal device, usually with a notched edge, set into a bench top near its end. Work is placed against it while being planed.

Bench Stop

bench vise (*Mach.*) The ordinary machinist's vise, either plain or swivel.

benchwork (*Woodwkg. and Sheet-Met. Wk.*) Term used to distinguish work carried on at the bench or vise from machine work.

bend (*Leather.*) The half of a butt or hide containing the best quality of sole leather.

Ben Day proc′ess (*Print.*) Invented by Ben Day, used by photo-engravers. Designs are transferred from gelatin films to metal plates and then etched.

bend′ing mo′ment (*Engin.*) Bending moment for a section of a loaded beam is the algebraic sum of all the loads, including weight of the beam, and reactions to the left or right of the section with respect to any point in the section.

bend′ing pin or i′ron (*Plumb.*) A tool used for straightening or expanding lead pipe.

Ben′dix drive (*Auto. Mech.*) That portion of a particular starting system which consists of a pinion gear running loose on a threaded shaft which has stops at both ends, and a heavy spring to absorb the shock. When the starting circuit is completed, the pinion runs into mesh with the gear on the flywheel and turns the engine over. When the foot is removed from the starter, the starting motor stops and the pinion is thrown out of mesh.

bend test (*Engin.*) The bending of a test specimen through 90 deg. or around a pin to determine its liability to fracture.

bent (*Engin.*) A section of a steel-frame building. A portion of the framework of a scaffold put together and placed in position instead of being constructed in position. A truss or beam carried at the ends on columns.

bent gouge (gouj) (*Woodwkg.*) A gouge curved in the direction of its length, used by patternmakers for hollowing out the concave portions of core boxes.

bent le′ver (lē′vẽr) (*Mech. Engin.*) A lever having an offset in it.

ben′zene (*Chem.*) C_6H_6. Derived from coal tar and is the mother substance of carbolic acid, aniline dyes also quinoline dyes, etc. It should not be confused with "benzine" which is a petroleum product.

ben′zine (*Chem.*) A mixture of several of the lighter constituents of petroleum. Obtained by fractional distillation of petroleum. Used as a solvent.

ben′zol (*Chem.*) A coal-tar product (C_6H_6). A colorless, inflammable, volatile liquid; used principally as a solvent; also for motor fuel, paint and varnish removers, etc. (same as benzene).

be-ryl′li-um (bė-rĭl′ĭ-ŭm) (*Metal.*) One of the lightest and hardest metals known. Ideal for airplane use except for its high cost. It readily alloys with aluminum.

Bes′se-mer steel. The mild steel produced directly from the pig in the Bessemer converter.

be′ta par′ti-cle (*Chem.*) An electron, negative or positive, thrown off by many radioactive materials.

be′ta ray (bē′tȧ) (*Chem.*) One of the three types of rays emitted by radioactive substances.

be′ta-tron (*Elec.*) An electric device in which electrons revolve in a vacuum enclosure in a circular or a spiral orbit normal to a magnetic field and have their energies continuously increased by the electric force resulting from the variation with time of the magnetic flux enclosed by their orbits.

Be′ton (bȧ′tôn) (*Print.*) The name of a type family which originated in Germany.

bev′el (*Furn.*) A sloping edge; also a tool similar to a square. (*Shopwk.*) Any surface not at right angles to the rest of the piece. When at 45 deg., the bevel is frequently called a "miter." The name is also given to the tool for measuring or laying off bevels. When combined with a scale of degrees, it is called a "bevel protractor." (*Woodwk. and Metalwk.*) A tool used for testing the accuracy of work cut to an angle or bevel.

bev′eled rule (*Print.*) A rule which has its face on a beveled surface.

bev′eled sticks (bĕv′ĕld) (*Print.*) Pieces of wood or metal, which when used with wedges or quoins, hold type securely in a galley.

bev′el gears (*Engin.*) Gear wheels which transmit power between two shafts which meet at an angle. If at right angles, and the wheels are of the size, they are called "miter gears."

bev′el-ing in weld′ing. The flattening or tapering of the ends of pieces to be welded in order to make a smoother looking job.

bev′el pro-tract′or. An adjustable tool for measuring angles.

bev′el wash′er. Used frequently in structural work to give a flat bearing for the nut when a threaded rod passes through a beam at an angle.

bez′el. The metal ring around the dial glass of a clock. (*Jewelry*) The metal rings which hold a jewel. (*Mach.*) The bevel on the edge of a cutting tool.

bib (*Plumb.*) A spigot or faucet.

bi′ble pa′per (*Paper*) A thin, opaque, relatively strong book paper.

bi-chlo′ride of mer′cu-ry (*Chem.*) $HgCl_2$. Also called corrosive sublimate — antiseptic used for washing wounds, etc., and in surgery. It is virulent poison. The antidote is albumen (white of an egg).

bi-chro′mate of po-tas′si-um (*Chem.*) $K_2Cr_2O_7$. Orange-colored crystals used in photography, blueprinting, and as an oxidizing agent in analytical chemistry.

bid (*Arch.*) A proposal to furnish supplies or equipment, to carry out or to perform certain work for a specified sum.

bi-en′ni-al-ly. Occurring every two years.

bi-lat′er-al tol′er-ance. Plus or minus tolerance. Allowable variation above or below basic dimension, e.g., $5.250 \pm .002$ in.

bil′let (*Plast.*) A large cake, usually cylindrical, placed in the pressing chamber of a hydraulic extrusion press. (*Steel*) Short rectangular length of bar or scrap iron used for producing the smaller sections of finished iron in the rolling mill.

bill′head (*Print.*) A form of office stationery on which bills are made out.

bil′lion. In United States a thousand millions and in England a million millions.

bill of ma-te′ri-al. A list of parts and quantities of those parts required on a certain operation or machine.

bi′na-ry al-loys′ (*Metal.*) An alloy made up of only two metals.

bi′na-ry dig′its (*Math.*) Integral members, used by digital computers.

bind′er (*Fdry.*) Material used to bind core sand to give strength to cores. Linseed oil, molasses, and a number of trade preparations are used.

bind′ers board (*Papermkg.*) A heavy board made of mixed papers; used for book covers.

bind′er-y. Workplace where books, folders, and pamphlets are folded, assembled, and bound.

bind′ing post (*Bookbndg.*) Metal posts used in loose-leaf covers which pass through slots or holes punched in the paper filler leaves and thus form a binding medium. (*Elec.*) A metal post furnished with a screw for fastening an electric wire.

Binding Posts

bin-oc′u-lars. A double telescope or spyglass adapted to both eyes.

bi′o-chem′is-try. Biological chemistry, i.e., the chemistry of living organisms.

bi′plane (*Aero.*) An airplane having two main supporting planes, one above the other.

bi-po′lar (bī-pō′lẽr) (*Elec.*) Having two magnetic poles of opposite polarity.

bi-po′lar re-ceiv′er (*Elec.*) A double-pole or two-pole telephone receiver in which both poles act on the diaphragm.

bird's–eye ma′ple (*Wood*) *Acer saccharum.* The very beautiful effect obtained with boards or veneers cut from maple burl.

bird's'-mouth' (*Carp.*) The notch cut in the underside of a rafter to give it bearing on the wall plate. Used when the rafter has a tail extension for cornice.

Bird's-Mouth

Bir'ming-ham or Stubs wire gauge (*Mach.*) Designates Stubs soft wire sizes. Used for gauging iron wire, and hot- and cold-rolled sheet steel. Differs from the Stubs steel wire gauge.

bis'cuit (bĭs'kĭt) (*Ceram.*) Unglazed ware after the first firing.

bi-sect'. To cut or divide into two equal parts.

bi-sec'tor. A line which bisects another line or angle.

bis'muth (bĭz'mŭth) (*Chem.*) A metallic element used for making alloys which have low melting points. Widely used for safety plugs in steam boilers, electrical fuses, automatic sprinklers, fire alarms, etc. A rise in temperature due to fire will melt the alloy, starting a water sprinkler, etc.

bit brace. A device for holding bits, so constructed that good leverage is had for the turning thereof.

Bit Brace

bite. Trade term for etching on metal plate.

bit file (*Patmkg.*) A file designed for sharpening auger bits.

bit gauge. The correct term for the commonly used name "bit stop."

bit stop. A device attached to a bit to control the drilling or boring to a desired depth.

bi-tu'mi-nous coal. Ordinary soft coal.

black an-neal'ing (*Metal.*) A method used to anneal sheets or other products when it is not essential that the product be free from scale and discoloration.

black bean (*Wood*) *Castanaspermum australe.* An Australian tree which produces wood similar to teak. It is becoming popular for fine interiors.

black birch (*Wood*) *Betula nigra.* This tree usually grows to a height of 50 to 60 ft. with a diameter of 1 to 3 ft. The wood is hard and strong. Used for interior trim and as a substitute for mahogany and cherry in furniture construction.

black cop'per. Contains about 75 per cent copper. It is obtained by resmelting low-grade copper.

black'damp (*Chem.*) A term applied to carbon dioxide found in the atmosphere of mines. (See CHOKEDAMP or AFTERDAMP.)

black gum (*Wood*) *Nyssa sylvatica.* Also known as sour gum. Tree of medium size. Wood not hard but cross grained and hard to split. Used for wooden kitchenware, excelsior, baskets, and crates.

black'ing (*Fdry.*) Ground charcoal, coal or coke dust, or plumbago dusted over the surface of a mold; prevents burning of the sand.

black lead (*Fdry.*) Used for coating patterns and the faces of cast-iron chilling molds.

black let′ter (*Print.*) A black-faced type usually called "text."

black′smith′. A smith who forges metal by hand.

black′smith drill (*Metalwk.*) A drill made with a shank ½ in. in diameter, to fit a certain kind of holder. The shank has a flat for a setscrew.

black spruce (*Wood*) *Picea mariana.* Found in the northern states and Canada; lightweight; reddish in color; easy to work, though tough in fiber.

black var′nish. Ordinary shellac to which lampblack has been added. Used by patternmakers.

black wal′nut (*Wood*) *Juglans nigra.* Heavy, hard, porous wood of a brownish color; durable. Used for small cabinetwork, gun stocks, and interior decorating.

blade. The flat, active working part of a tool, instrument, or device, as the blade of a knife, the blade of an oar, the blade of a propeller, etc.

blade an′gle (*Aero.*) The acute angle between the chord of a section of a propeller, or of a rotary wing system and a plane perpendicular to the axis of rotation.

blade back (*Aero.*) The side of a propeller which corresponds to the upper surface of an airfoil.

blade face (*Aero.*) The surface of a propeller blade which corresponds to the lower surface of an airfoil. Sometimes called "thrust face" or "driving face."

blade-width ra′ti-o (*Aero.*) The ratio of the developed width of a propeller blade at any point, to the circumference of a circle whose radius is the distance of that point from the propeller axis.

blanc′ fixe′ (blän′ fēks′) (*Paint.*) Barium sulphate used in the manufacture of paints, made by grinding barytes to a fine powder. When artificially made, the pigment is of finer texture and is known as blanc fixe.

blank (*Sheet metal*) A piece cut from a flat sheet before any forming operation has taken place.

blank and cen′ter-punch die (*Sheet Metal*) A die which, in one operation, cuts a blank and center punches the positions where holes are to be punched or drilled.

blank and pierce die (*Sheet Metal*) A compound die which, in one operation, cuts a blank and pierces one or more holes in it.

blank book (*Bookbndg.*) A book which is wholly or partly free from writing or print.

blank case (*Print.*) A type case without sectional divisions.

blank cut (*Print.*) The blank part of the last page of a chapter.

blank′ing die (*Shopwk.*) The most commonly used of all the varieties of press tools. The strip of sheet metal is fed under the stripper and is prevented by that member from lifting with the punch upon the upstroke, following the punching out of the blank. Where several punches are combined in one hole for blanking many pieces simultaneously, they are known as "multiple blanking tools."

blank′out (*Tel.*) A term used in tuning a receiver when the picture on the cathode ray tube is "erased" or blanked out while adjusting the receiver for picture reception.

blast (*Fdry.*) The volume of air forced into furnaces where combustion is hastened artificially.

blast fur′nace (*Fdry.*) A furnace used for the smelting of iron from its ores.

blast gate (supercharger) (*Aero.*) A device for controlling the pressure in the nozzle box of a turbosupercharger by discharging into the free atmosphere a portion of the exhaust gases that would otherwise pass through the turbine wheel.

blast'ing. The discharge of an explosive for the loosening of material; as rock in a quarry.

blast'ing pow'der (See DYNAMITE.)

Blau'gas (blou'găs) (*Chem.*) An oil gas, made by the destructive distillation of petroleum, used for lighting, heating, and for cutting steel. Impure propane, C_3H_8, used for filling Zeppelins and for operating their engines.

bleach'ing (*Wood Fin.*) Cleansing or whitening by the use of oxalic acid or some similar substance.

bleed (*Auto.*) To drain off, as, the fluid from a hydraulic brake system. (*Bookbndg.*) A book is said to bleed when it has been trimmed so closely as to cut into the print.

bleed'er. A small drain cock. Also a by-pass valve.

bleed'ing (*Wood Fin.*) A term usually applied in connection with the use of mahogany and red dye stains. Unless the finishing coat is of some quick-setting material such as shellac, the undercoat may partially dissolve and "bleed" through the top coat.

blem'ish. Any scar or mark which tends to deface a surface.

blend'ing (*Plast.*) Mechanical mixing of various ingredients of a molding composition to assure uniform distribution of all particles: called dry blending or wet blending, depending on conditions. (*Wood Fin.*) The toning of a finish when applied to a surface to give a desired color effect.

blimp (*Aero.*) A name applied to small nonrigid airships. (*Tel.*) A soundproofing cover for a motion-picture camera which prevents motor sounds from spilling into the microphones on a sound stage.

blind. Something that obstructs light or vision as a screen or shutter.

blind hole. A hole which does not pass completely through a piece, as distinguished from a "through hole."

blind mor'tise and ten'on (*Woodwk.*) A short tenon fitted to a mortise which does not pass completely through the piece, therefore does not show on the opposite side.

blind tool'ing (*Bookbndg.*) Teetering or ornamentation impressed on book covers without gilding or coloring.

blink'er light (*Aero.*) A light flashing more than 20 flashes per minute.

blis'ter (*Aero.*) A sheet of clear water raised by the motion of a float or hull and separated from the free-water surface by an air space. (*Plaster.*) Small air pocket or scablike spot on a plastered surface. It occurs only in the top coat and is caused by too rapid working. (*Plast.*) Rounded elevation of the surface of a plastic, with boundaries more or less sharply defined, somewhat resembling a blister on the human skin; it may burst and become flattened.

blis'ter-ing (*Paint and Lacquer*) Blisters or air pockets are generally the result of sealing in moisture, hand smears, or differences in temperature of surface and finishing materials.

blis'ter steel (*Metal.*) Raw steel bars made by the cementation process.

block (engine) (*Auto. Mech.*) The cylinder casting of a multiple cylinder gas engine. It includes the cylinder bores and provision for cooling; either water jackets or cooling fins.

block (*Ceram.*) A mold made from the original pattern.

block and tack'le. One or more sheaves or pulley blocks and the rope, chain, or cable used in connection with same.

block chain (*Mach.*) A chain as used on bicycles, consisting of unit blocks connected by side links.

block'ing con-dens'er (*Radio*) A condenser used in a radio circuit between two points of opposite D.C. potential to prevent a short circuit.

block'ing course (*Masonry*) A course of stones placed on the top of a cornice crowning the walls.

block let'ter (*Print.*) Heavy, sansserif letter. (See GOTHIC.)

block plane (*Woodwkg.*) A small plane from 5 to 7 in. in length, used chiefly in working end grain. It differs from other planes in that it has no cap iron and in having the cutting bevel placed up instead of down.

Block Plane

blocks, "Jo" (*Shopwk.*) Shop name for Johannssen measuring blocks They are extremely accurate and are used for testing the accuracy of other measuring devices.

block tin (*Plumb.*) Pure tin.

bloom (*Metal.*) In the manufacture of wrought iron, the pasty mass of iron is put through a squeezer or is hammered with a steam hammer to remove a portion of the slag, after which it is known as a "bloom." (*Masonry*) The appearance of efflorescence on the surface of a brick wall. (*Tel.*) The condition of bright illumination in a picture or a portion of a picture on the picture tube obscuring picture details. This occurs when an area of white bounces light; for instance, the white bosom front worn by a man with his black tuxedo may cause the picture to bloom and obscure the details of his face.

blow'er (*Mech. Engin.*) A device for increasing draft; used for ventilation or the production of blast.

blow'hole (*Fdry.*) Hollow cavity in a casting caused by the presence of air or gas in the mold.

Blowhorn Stake

An implement used by metalworkers, **blow'horn stake** (*Sheet-Met. Wk.*) consisting of an upright post, at the top of which arms project on either side; one of these arms is long and slightly tapered; the other, short with a very abrupt taper.

blow'ing (*Ceram.*) The breaking of ware due to the formation of steam in too rapid firing.

blow mold'ing (*Plast.*) A method of producing plastic bottles and hollow ware, by blowing air through a plastic extruded tube or blob against the cool surfaces of a metal mold.

blown fuse (*Auto. Mech.*) A burned-out fuse.

blow'off' (*Engin.*) A valve or drain connection on a steam or hot-water boiler so arranged to draw off water and steam with any accumulated oil, grease, and dirt.

blow'out (*Auto.*) A rupture of both inner tube and outer casing of a tire of such nature as to almost instantaneously exhaust the air.

blow′out coils (*Elec.*) Electromagnetic coils in the line circuit of a magnetic switch to cause magnetic stress to extinguish the arc between contacts when the switch is opened.

blow′out patch (*Auto.*) A piece of canvas and rubber inserted in a tire casing to reinforce a weak spot.

blow′pipe. A tube by which air or gas is blown through a flame for the purpose of heating, fusing, or melting something.

blow′torch (*Shopwk.*) A portable device for securing intense local heat. Used by plumbers and painters.

blub (*Plaster.*) A swelling or bulging out.

blue an-neal′ing (*M e t a l.*) A method of annealing by which a bluish-black finish is given to steel sheets.

Blowtorch

blueprint. A drawing transferred to chemically treated paper by exposure to electric light or sunlight. Process known as "blueprinting."

blue stain (*Wood*) Caused by a fungus growth in unseasoned lumber. While objectionable in appearance, it does not have any great effect on the strength of the wood.

blue′stone or cop′per sul′phate (*Chem.*) Blue, poisonous crystals slowly efflorescing in the air. ($CuSO_4 5H_2O$) Obtained by the action of dilute sulphuric acid on copper oxide in large quantities, with evaporation and crystallization. Used in the textile industry, electric batteries, etc.

blung′ing ma-chine′ (*Pot.*) A pottery machine used for mixing clays.

blush′ing (*Paint and Lacquer*) A blooming that appears as a white or gray cloud in the film on hot humid days. Caused by condensation of moisture due to the rapid evaporation of the solvents.

board. Thin timber as distinguished from planks or strips. Long pieces less than 2 in. thick and more than 4 in. wide are called boards.

board feet. The unit of measure for lumber. One foot square and one inch or less in thickness.

board meas′ure (*Woodwkg.*) The term in which quantities of lumber are designated and prices determined.

board rule (*Woodwk.*) A graduated scale used in checking lumber for quantity.

boast′ing (*Furn.*) Rough carving.

bob′bin (*Plast.*) A formed core upon which the coil of a magnet is wound.

bod′kin (*Print.*) A long, sharp-pointed, tapered instrument for removing type from a line while making corrections.

Bo-do′ni (bô-dō′nē) (*Print.*) The designer of the first modern Roman-faced type; Bodoni type.

bo′dy (*Aero.*) The fuselage of an airplane with its cowling, covering, and the nacelle and nacelle mounting. (*Ceram.*) A piece of ware exclusive of any finish, such as glaze or decoration. (*Mech.*) The main portion of a pattern, casting, forging, or machine. (*Plast.*) A term used in the plastic industry to indicate viscosity in a fluid, either resin or other material; viz. "light body," or "heavy body."

bod′y-ing in (*Furn.*) A process in

French polishing executed before the finishing stage; literally, filling in the grain of the wood.

bod′y mat′ter (*Print.*) That part of an advertisement set in body type, not display.

bod′y type (*Print.*) That kind of type generally used for reading matter in books, etc.

bog ore. A soft iron ore found in swampy places.

boiled oil (*Paint.*) Linseed oil which has been heated to 400 to 500 deg. F. and while hot has added to it a small quantity of litharge or manganese dioxide. Used to promote the quick drying of paint. Serves as an excellent polish for antique furniture

boil′er. The term is of wide application. (1) That part of a furnace in which steam is generated for heating or for the production of power as in industrial plants or on ships, for household heating, etc. (2) The closed container in which a supply of heated water is stored for domestic use. In general, any closed liquid-containing vessel to which heat is applied. Distinguished from tanks or open containers. (3) According to use and construction boilers for heating and power purposes are classified as (*a*) cast-iron sectional, (*b*) steel fire tube, (*c*) steel water tube, and (*d*) special. (See: CAST-IRON BOILER, HORIZONTAL RETURN TUBULAR BOILER, FIRE-TUBE BOILER, STEEL BOILER, etc.)

boil′er horse′pow-er (*Engin.*) In a boiler, the evaporation of 34.5 lb. of water per hour from and at 212 deg. F. Equivalent to 33,471.9 B.T.W. per hour.

boil′er mak′er. One skilled in the various operations incidental to the manufacture of tanks and boilers.

boil′er plate (*Metal.*) Steel sheets or plates rolled for use in the construction of tanks or boilers.

boil′er room (*Engin.*) The part of a factory or other building in which the boiler and accessories for heating and power are placed.

boil′er scale. Deposit caused by precipitation of carbonates and sulphates of calcium and magnesium and other suspended matter on the inside of a boiler.

boil′ing point of wa′ter. The temperature at which water begins to boil, under ordinary conditions; 212 deg. F. or 100 deg. C.

bold (*Print.*) Heavy-faced type. Anything standing out prominently.

bold′face (*Print.*) Type heavier than the text with which it is used. Used to give prominence to headings.

bole. A fine, compact, unctuous or plastic clay usually colored yellow, brown, or black by iron oxide; formerly used as a pigment.

bo-lec′tion (bô-lĕk′shŭn) A molding around the edge of a panel and projecting beyond the surface of the casing which holds the panel.

bol′lard. A post of cast iron or wood, on a dock used in mooring vessels. Also used on the decks of vessels.

bo-lom′e-ter (bô-lŏm′ê-tẽr) (*Elec.*) A thermal balance. (*Phys.*) A very sensitive instrument for measuring minute quantities of heat energy by changes of electrical resistance.

bol′ster (*Arch.*) The lateral part of the volute of an Ionic capital; a crosspiece on an arch centering, running from rib to rib; the bearing place of a truss bridge upon a pier; a cap or top piece on a post to lengthen the bearing of a beam, etc. (*Shopwk.*) A block sometimes called the "die block," in which a punch-press die is held. It is attached to the head by bolts at either end.

bol'ster. (*Verb*) To bolster up. To strengthen a support. (*Noun*) In general, a block or support; also a long pillow.

bolt (*Mech.*) A fastening; commonly a piece of metal with head and threaded body for the reception of a nut.

bolt cut'ter or bolt shear. Usually hand-operated shears for cutting bolts, links of chain, etc.

bombe' (*Arch. and Furn.*) Puffed, rounded, or bulged.

bond (*Masonry*) The arrangement or placing of bricks in a wall so as to tie together the face and backing. (*Mech.*) A binding agent, e.g., material used to hold particles of abrasive together in a grinding wheel.

bonded lining (*Auto. Mech.*) The lining cemented to brake shoes or bands to eliminate the use of rivets.

bond pa'per (*Papermkg.*) Name originally given to paper made entirely from rags, animal sized; used for bonds and stock certificates. Also hard-sized paper used for letterheads, etc.

bond stone (*Masonry*) Stone running through the thickness of a wall at right angles to its face, serving to bind it together.

bone black (*Chem.*) Animal charcoal, obtained by the destructive distillation of bones. Used as a decoloring agent, filtering medium, sugar refiner, and as a paint pigment.

bon'net (*Plumb.*) A cover used to guide and enclose the tail end of a valve spindle.

book'bind'ers' wire (*Print.*) Tinned openhearth steel wire, made in 18 to 30 gauge round shapes and 18 by 20- to 26 by 32-gauge flat shapes. Sold in 5-lb. spools or paper cones.

book'bind'ing. Fastening book sections and placing a cover over same.

book pa'per. Coated or uncoated paper used for general printing purposes, as distinguished from wrapping, bond, ledger, and cover paper.

boom. The movable arms of a derrick by which weights are lifted and shifted from one position to another.

boost (*Aero.*) To supply an engine with more air or mixture than it would normally induct at sea level.

boost con-trol', au'to-mat'ic (*Aero.*) An automatic regulator of boost pressure.

boost'er (*Elec.*) A generator connected in series with a circuit for the purpose of increasing the voltage of that circuit. Generally used in connection with a system where a storage battery carries part of the load. The booster increases the voltage to a point where it becomes necessary to charge the battery.

boost'er brake (*Auto. Mech.*) An auxiliary air chamber operated from the intake manifold vacuum, connecting with regular brake pedal and increasing braking effects with less pedal pressure.

boost'er coil (*Elec.*) An induction coil utilizing direct-current supply to provide energy to the spark plugs of an (aircraft) engine during its starting period.

boost'er mag-ne'to (*Aero.*) An auxiliary magneto used for starting.

boost'er pump (*Auto.*) An auxiliary pump, built integral with the fuel pump, providing vacuum to continue operation of the windshield wiper and similar devices when the vacuum of the intake manifold will not maintain their operation.

boot. A covering serving as a protection against dirt and weather.

bo'rax (*Chem.*) ($Na_2B_4O_7$) A white crystalline compound found native as "tincal," used as an antiseptic, for welding mixtures in iron and steel, for brazing gun metal and copper, and for softening water.

Borcher's met'al (*Metal.*) Alloy valuable for its acid-resistant and corrosion-resistant qualities. The principal ingredient is chromium.

bor'der (*Furn.*) An outer-edge design of especially assembled veneer patterns. (*Print.*) Any line or ornamentation enclosing printing.

bore. The internal diameter of a pipe, cylinder, or hole for shafting, whether it be rough or machined. (*Mech. Drg.*) Indicates that hole is to be finished by boring.

bo'ric ac'id (*Chem.*) A colorless crystalline compound (H_3BO_3), made by treating borax with an acid; used in medicines and as a preservative.

bor'ing (*Mach.*) The operation of making or finishing circular holes in wood or metal.

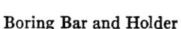

Boring Bar and Holder

bor'ing bar (*Mach.*) A stiff cylinder bar provided with a cutterhead; used on lathes, drill presses, and other machines for boring cylinders, etc.

bor'ing ma-chine' (*Mach.*) A machine especially constructed for boring cylinders, bosses, bed rings, and the like.

bor'ing mill (*Mach.*) An upright machine tool with revolving table which carries the work. The tool rest is carried on a crossrail as on a planer. Many kinds of work are more easily "set up" on a boring mill than on a lathe.

bor'ing tool. Brace bit and similar tools for wood; cutters for metal, including a large number of types.

bo'ron (bō'rŏn) (*Chem.*) Obtained by electrolysis. Resembles silicon. Used to give hardness to steels and in compounds as fluxes and deoxidizing agents.

bo'ron car'bide (*Chem.*) A fine, black, crystalline powder of hardness nearly equal to that of the diamond. Used as an abrasive.

bort. A name applied to diamonds that are used for abrasive purposes.

boss (*Arch.*) An ornament usually carved, forming the keystone at the intersection of the ribs of a groined vault. (*Mech.*) (1) The center or hub of a wheel; (2) a circular disk cast on or attached to some mechanical part.

Boss

boss'ing stick (*Plumb.*) A wooden tool for shaping lead for tank lining.

Bos'ton hip roof (*Arch.*) Formed by laying a double row of shingles or slate lengthwise along the hip; joints must be securely made to obtain a watertight job.

bot′a-ny. The science of plant life.

botch. To do a poor job in a slovenly and unworkmanlike manner; also, a spoiled job.

bot′tled (*Print.*) Type which is wider at the bottom than at the top, due to an imperfect casting, is said to be "bottled."

bot′tom-an′chored core (*Fdry.*) A core anchored to the bottom of a mold to prevent any tendency to float when the mold is poured. Its use should be avoided if possible.

bot′tom board (*Fdry.*) The board or plate that is placed on top of the drag and fastened there before rolling it over. It then serves as the bottom of the mold during the remaining molding and casting operations.

bot′tom clear′ance (*Gear.*) The difference between dedendum and addendum which provides for the clearance between the top and root of gear teeth when in mesh.

bot′tom rail (*Arch.*) The lowest horizontal member of a door or of a window sash.

bot′tom stake (*Sheet-Met. Wk.*) An upright bar with the working edge at the upper end.

bott stick (*Fdry.*) A light iron rod 5 or 6 ft. long with a disklike expansion at one end. A stopping bar on which a lump of clay is gathered to be used in stopping the flow of metal from the cupola.

bound′a-ry. A limiting or dividing line or mark.

bound′a-ry light (*Aero.*) Any one of the lights designed to indicate the limits of the landing area of an airport or landing field.

bound′a-ry mark′er (*Aero.*) A painted cone, solid circle, disk, or other device used to mark the boundary of the available landing area on an airport or landing field.

Bour′don′ tube (Bōōr′dôn′) (*Auto. Mech.*) A sealed tube containing a highly volatile gas, the expansion of which controls a registering needle on a graduated dial.

bour-geois′ (bûr-jois′) (*Print.*) An old designation of a type size equivalent approximately to 9 point.

bow (bō) (*Arch.*) Any projecting part of a building in the form of an arc or of a polygon.

bow com′pass (*Draft.*) A small compass used by draftsmen. Positive adjustment is obtained by means of a screw which connects the two legs.

bow-heav′y (bou) (*Aero.*) The condition of an airship which, when at rest in still air, trims with its axis inclined down by the bow. The term "bow-heavy" is preferred to "nose-heavy" in describing airships.

bow pen (bō) (*Draft.*) A compass used for inking small arcs or circles; as in other bow instruments adjustment is made by means of a screw connecting the legs.

bow pen′cil (*Draft.*) A drawing instrument used in penciling small arcs or circles. (See BOW COMPASS and BOW PEN.)

bow saw (*Carp.*) A saw with a thin narrow blade held in tension by the leverage obtained through the twisting of a cord, or by means of rods and turnbuckle.

bow win′dow (*Arch.*) A window placed in a bow, i.e., any projecting part of a building which is in the shape of an arc or of a polygon.

box an-neal'ing (*Metal.*) A method of annealing steel by heating it in a closed metal box.

box'board' (*Papermkg.*) A thick cardboard with folding qualities used for making boxes.

box col'umn (*Arch.*) A built-up hollow column usually of square section used in porch construction.

box con-nec'tor (*Elec.*) A kind of hollow ferrule with nut, used to attach ends of cable to a box.

box frame (*Arch.*) A window frame containing boxes for the sash weights.

box gir'der (*Engin.*) A built-up girder consisting of two parallel I beams with plates joining them riveted upon top and bottom.

box'wood (*Wood*) *Buxus*. A hard, tough, close-grained wood of pale-yellow color, used for rules, scales, and small tools and tool handles. Before being used, it should undergo several years of seasoning. Flowering dogwood also is known as boxwood.

Boyle's law (*Phys.*) The temperature remaining constant, the volume of a gas varies inversely as the pressure.

brace (*Carp.*) An inclined piece of timber used as a support or stiffener. (*Furn.*) A support used to help hold together parts of furniture, giving durability and strength to the whole structure. (*Mech.*) A holder for bits.

Braces

brace bit (*Woodwkg.*) Ordinary bit used for wood boring, and having square, tapered shanks to fit in the socket of a common brace.

brace frame (*Arch.*) Framework of a building in which the corner posts are braced to sills and plates

brace jaws (*Woodwkg.*) Those parts of a bit brace which clamp about the tapered shank of a bit.

brac'ing (*Arch.*) The staying or supporting with rods and ties for the strengthening of a structure.

brack'et (*Furn.*) A projecting part of furniture used to support a shelf or ornament. (*Patmkg.*) Usually consists of two pieces at right angles, or otherwise, connected by a web.

brack'et cor'nice (*Arch.*) A cornice supported by a series of exposed brackets.

brack'et-ing (*Plaster.*) The wooden skeleton pieces to which the lath and plaster forming the surface of a cornice are fastened.

brad (*Woodwk.*) A long slender wire nail with a very small head.

brad'awl (*Woodwkg.*) A short non-tapering awl, with cutting edge on the end.

Bradawl

brake band (*Auto. Mech.*) A flexible band of metal to which the brake lining is fastened.

brake drum (*Auto. Mech.*) Usually steel stamping varying in diameter from 10 to 18 in. and from 2 to 3 in. in width. It is attached to the wheels of the car to receive the braking action from the brake shoes or brake bands and lining.

brake flu'id (*Auto.*) A mixture of glycerin, oils, and additives of such composition that it will retain proper fluidity in the braking system under varying weather conditions, and will withstand excessive heating.

brake horse-pow'er (*Engin.*) The horsepower of a machine taken off a brake attached to it and registered by a dynamometer.

brake lev′er (*Auto. Mech.*) A lever to which brake rods are attached in a mechanical braking system.

brake lin′ing (*Auto. Mech.*) Woven material of cotton, asbestos, and fine copper wire, or the like, applied to brake bands.

brake ped′al (*Auto. Mech.*) The foot pedal which controls the application of the brakes.

brake ratch′et (*Auto.*) Usually a notched quadrant which engages a pawl attached to the brake lever thus permitting a setting of the brake lever in a fixed position.

brake rod (*Auto. Mech.*) A rod terminating with an eye or clevis, forming a part of the linkage in a mechanical braking system.

brake shoe (*Mech.*) A metal casting fitted to the curve of a wheel and pressed against the wheel to secure braking action.

brak′ing sur′face (*Auto.*) The area of contact between the stationary and moving parts of a brake. (*Mech.*) The area of the face of contact of surfaces through which braking friction is obtained.

brak′ing tin (*Sheet-Met. Wk.*) The turning or bending of the edges of tin sheets on the machine known as a "brake."

brak′ing with com-pres′sion (*Auto. Mech.*) On steep grades the car may be placed in first or second gear and the foot removed from the accelerator; the speed of the car will then be retarded by the braking effect of the engine compression. The brakes should be used only for snubbing the speed by intermittent application in case the "braking with compression" is not sufficient.

branch (*Plumb.*) Outlet or inlet of pipe fitting, set at angle with the run.

branch cir′cuit (*Elec.*) That part of a wiring system which extends beyond the final overcurrent device or fuses protecting the circuit.

branch cut′out (*Elec.*) Cutout branching out from main supply circuit to various load devices.

branch ell (*Plumb.*) An elbow having a back outlet in line with one of the outlets of the "run." Also called a "heel outlet elbow."

branch pipe (*Plumb.*) A general term used to designate a pipe, either cast or wrought, that is equipped with one or more branches.

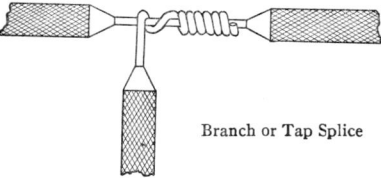

Branch or Tap Splice

branch splice (*Elec.*) The connection where a wire or conductor taps off from another wire or conductor.

branch wire (*Elec.*) A subordinate wire leading from a main conductor.

brass. An alloy of copper and zinc, or copper, zinc, and lead. The latter is not common.

brass foil. Same as Dutch metal. A very malleable alloy of copper and zinc, sold in the form of thin leaves, and used extensively in book bindings.

brass rule (*Print.*) A strip of brass, type high, one long edge of which is used as a printing surface.

bray′er (*Print.*) A small hand roller used for spreading ink.

brazed joint (*Metalwk.*) Made by brazing, as distinguished from soldered, welded, riveted, or screwed joint.

braz′ing (*Metalwk.*) Joining two or more pieces of metal with an alloy. The joints are cleaned, bound with wire, and sprinkled with borax, then heated until the alloy melts.

braz′ing clamps (*Shopwk.*) Clamps for holding the ends of a band saw or other work while being brazed.

braz′ing met′al. An alloy of 2 parts tin and 98 parts copper.

braz′ing sol′der (sŏd′ẽr) (*Metal.*) Or brazing spelter, contains 50–52 per cent copper, 0.55 per cent lead, iron 0.10 per cent, and the remainder zinc. It melts at between 1560 and 1600 deg. F.

break (*Bldg.*) A term meaning any projection from the general surface of a wall or building. (*Mech. Drg.*) The indicated omission of a uniform part of a long object without using a smaller scale.

break′er (*Auto. Elec.*) A mechanical device consisting of a movable arm and stationary post, both faced with metal contacts which interrupt the current passing through, at properly timed intervals.

break′er arm (*Auto.*) Shaped flat metal bar with a contact point of tungsten on one end and a round opening on the other, bushed with fiber, bakelite, or similar nonconductor, on which the arm can swing from a metal pin.

break′er strip (*Auto.*) A strip of canvas in the side wall of a tire casing to increase wearing qualities.

break′ing joints (*Carp.*) The staggering of joints to avoid having them come in a straight line.

break i′ron (wood plane) (*Carp.*) The iron attached to the top of a plane bit which serves to curl and break the shavings.

break line (*Print.*) The last line of a paragraph.

breaks (*Plaster.*) Arrangement of laths with staggered joints; i.e., not all occurring one above another in a vertical line.

breast drill (*Shopwk.*) A small mechanism used in the drilling of holes in metal by hand. Power is transmitted from a hand-turned crank, through bevel gears to the drill chuck. *Breast Drill*

breast of a win′dow (*Masonry*) The masonry forming the back of the recess and the parapet under the window sill.

breast′sum′mer (*Bldg.*) A beam or lintel flush with a wall or partition which it supports, and carried by the side walls or pillars, as a beam over a store window.

bre-vier′ (brê-vēr′) (*Print.*) That type now known as 8 point.

brick. A hardened block of clay, usually of rectangular shape, formed in a mold, dried or burned in a kiln. Used in paving and in building.

brick fac′ing (*Bldg.*) (See BRICK VENEER.)

brick pier (*Arch.*) A plain, detached mass of masonry serving as a support.

brick trow′el (trou′ĕl) (*Masonry*) A flat, triangular-shaped trowel used for picking up mortar and spreading it on the wall. It is larger than the buttering trowel.

brick ve-neer′ (*Arch.*) A facing of brick applied to a frame or other structure.

bridge or **struc′tur-al en′gi-neer′.** One whose activities are concerned chiefly with the design, construction, and erection of bridges and the steel work of large buildings.

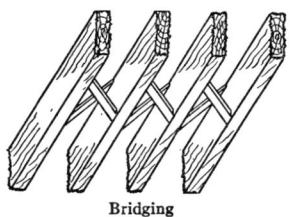

Bridging

bridg′ing (*Arch.*) A method of bracing joists or studding by the use of short strips or braces.

bright an-neal′ing (*Metal.*) A method of annealing by which oxidation and discoloration are prevented by using closed containers with a reducing atmosphere.

bright dip′ping (*Metal.*) The dipping of metal into a chemical solution in order to secure and maintain a bright finish.

bright′ness (*Tel.*) The degree of illumination of a picture on the receiver or picture tube.

bright′ness con-trol′ (*Tel.*) A control on the receiver for regulating the overall brightness of the picture.

brine. Water saturated or strongly impregnated with salt.

Bri-nell′ test (brĭ-nĕll′) (*Engin.*) A hardened steel ball is forced into the metal to be tested under a given pressure. The hardness is determined by measuring the diameter of the impression and referring to a table.

bri-quette′ (brĭ-kĕt′) Compressed fuel, composed of coal dust and a binder.

bris′tle. Coarse stiff hair of swine, used in brushmaking.

Bris′tol board. A good grade of cardboard, coated or uncoated, supplied in white and colors.

Bri-tan′ni-a met′al (*Metal.*) A tin-antimony alloy, silvery white with bluish tinge. Used principally for utensils, works easily, and retains polish.

Britannia Splice

Bri-tan′ni-a splice (*Elec.*) A splice not much used except for heavy wires. It is made by overlapping with the bared ends of two conductors and wrapping with a finer wire.

Brit′ish ther′mal u′nit (*Engin.*) (Abbrev. — B.T.U.) The quantity of heat required to raise the temperature of one pound of pure water 1 deg. Fahrenheit at or near the temperature of maximum density of water 39 deg. Fahrenheit.

brit′tle (*Phys.*) State of being fragile or breakable without deformation.

broach (*Mech.*) A long tool with serrated edges, which is pulled or pushed through a hole in metal to form a required shape or to enlarge the hole.

broach′ing (*Mach.*) The process of cutting or enlarging a hole in metal, of a required shape usually other than round.

broach spire (*Arch.*) An octagonal spire rising without a parapet above a tower with pyramidal forms at the angles of the tower, as in early English churches.

broad′cast (*Noun*) A radio program of any type. (*Verb*) The act of producing a radio program.

broad fold (*Papermkg.*) A term used with reference to paper in which the grain runs the short dimension.

broad′side (*Print.*) A sheet printed on one side only.

bro-chure′ (brô-shür′) A pamphlet; a booklet.

bronze (*Shopwk.*) Alloy of copper and tin. Used in coinage, bells, statuary, musical instruments, etc.

bronze gauze. Fine-mesh wire screening used for straining liquids.

bronz′ing (*Print.*) Applying bronze powder to a printed surface to give the appearance of having been printed in gold.

Brown and Sharpe ta′per (*Mach.*) A very commonly used taper especially on milling-machine spindles. The rate of taper is ½ in. per foot except in No. 10.

Brown & Sharpe wire gauge (*Mach.*) Also known as the American Gauge. Used for gauging sheets and wires of nonferrous metals, such as brass, copper, and aluminum.

brush (*Elec.*) A device for drawing off from the commutator the electric current generated in the armature windings of a generator. Brushes are usually carbon; sometimes copper.

brush hol′ders (*Elec.*) Adjustable arms with springs for holding the commutator brushes of a dynamo against the commutator, feeding them forward to maintain proper contact as they wear, and permitting them to be lifted from contact when necessary.

brush loss (*Elec.*) The loss in watts due to the resistance of the brush contact against the surface of the commutator.

brush rock′er (*Elec.*) A rotary rocker upon which the brush holders of a generator or motor are fixed so that the position of the brushes upon the commutator can be adjusted.

brush spring (*Auto. Elec.*) A flat or coiled compression spring designed to hold a carbon compound brush in contact with a rotating part such as a generator or starting motor armature or a distributor rotor.

brush wire. Usually a tempered high or low carbon steel wire. Finer thicknesses (.0317 in. to .0075 in.) are round and coarser sizes are flat (.150 in. by .018 in. to .038 in. by .013 in.).

B-stage res′ins (rĕz′in) (*Plast.*) Thermosetting resins reacted to a stage where they soften when heated and swell in contact with liquids but do not entirely fuse or dissolve. This is the preferred stage for the resin in molding compositions.

bub′ble (*Plast.*) A spherical void, or a globule of air or other gas, trapped within a transparent or translucent plastic.

bu-bin′ga (*Wood*) *Didelotia africana.* A very large tree native to equatorial Africa. Wood is hard and heavy with evenly spaced dark purple lines on a light violet background. Used for unusual grain effects in furniture and paneling.

buck′et trap (*Steam Heat.*) A type of valve for eliminating condensation and air from radiators and pipes, without permitting steam to pass. A bucket attached to a valve actuates a discharge tube.

buck′eye (*Wood*) *Aesculus glabra.* Commonly known as horse chestnut. Wood is soft, white to pale yellow. Used for pulp, wooden ware, and artificial limbs.

buck′ing bar. A bar held against the head of a rivet while the rivet is being set.

buck′led. That which is crumpled, bent, or warped.

buck′le plate (*Engin.*) A plate with dished or corrugated deformations for the purpose of giving more strength and stiffness than could be had from a flat plate.

buck′ling (*Paint and Lacquer*) Caused by the shrinking of a pyroxylin lacquer film over an oil-base undercoater when the latter has not been given full drying time.

buck′ram (bŭk′răm) (*Bookbndg.*) A very serviceable, stiffened linen or hemp cloth used for book covers.

buck′skin (*Leather.*) A soft, strong, grayish-yellow leather; the skin of a buck, now frequently made from sheepskin.

buff (*Mech.*) An appliance for polishing and finishing metallic surfaces; usually consists of a large number of muslin disks fastened together to form a polishing wheel.

buf-fet′ (bo͞o-fā′) (*Furn.*) A French term, referring to a form of cupboard or sideboard used for dishes.

buf′fet-ing (*Aero.*) The beating of an aircraft's structure or surface by unsteady flow, gusts, etc. Also the irregular shaking or oscillation of an aircraft component owing to turbulent air or separate flow.

buff′ing (*Bookbndg.*) A split cowhide; a term also applied to roughing up with an emery wheel or polishing down with a soft fabric wheel the extending designs on covers; also used on leather to polish the surface or take off the top of the grain on fancy leathers. (*Mech.*) To finish a surface with a buff.

buff′ing leath′er (*Leather.*) A lining leather, thinner but much stronger than skiver. Used for lining large articles.

buff′ing wheels (*Shopwk.*) Polishing wheels made of many disks of cotton or wool cloth which serve to carry abrasive powders, rouge, etc.

buhl′ work′ (bo͞ol) (*Furn.*) Inlay work in which ivory, metal, etc., are used instead of wood.

buhr′stone′ (bûr′stōn′) A circular grindstone revolving flatwise on another stone. Used for grinding grains, etc. Same as millstone.

build′ers′ tape. A long measuring tape of steel or fabric contained in a circular case, usually 50 or 100 ft. in length. See TAPE.

build′ing. The art of putting together materials into a structure.

build′ing line. The line of the outside face of a building wall. Also the line on a lot beyond which the law forbids that a building be erected.

build′ing ma-te′ri-als (*Bldg.*) All materials which enter into building construction.

build′ing pa′per (*Arch.*) Heavy paper used between sheathing and siding, or as an undercovering on roofs as a protection against weather.

build′ing stone (*Arch.*) A general term applied to stone used in building construction including marble, granite, sandstone, limestone, and others.

build′ing up (*Elec.*) The active generation of voltage which a generator undergoes from start to final voltage as a result of self-excitation of field by armature. The first voltage is due to residual magnetism; this, supplied to the fields, causes a strengthening of the fields to give full output voltage.

built'–up' mem'ber (*Engin.*) Any column, beam, or girder built up from standard shapes.

bulb'ous (bŭl'bŭs) (*Furn.*) A protuberant form of turning, introduced by the Dutch.

bulk (*Papermkg.*) A term ordinarily denoting sheet thickness; also applied to paper which is relatively thick in relation to its substance weight.

bulk fac'tor (*Plast.*) The ratio, by volume, of the loose molding powder to the resultant finished article.

bulk'head. A partition of stone or wood to keep back earth as in a mine, or tunnel, or along a water front. Also made of steel or wood to separate compartments in a vessel.

bull block (*Shopwk.*) Block through which wire or rods are drawn to reduce them in size.

bull'doz'er (*Mach.*) A heavy forming machine for bending iron and steel.

bull gear (*Mach.*) The large gear which gives motion to the table on a metal-planing machine. The large driven gear on a crank shaper.

bull'head tee (*Plumb.*) A tee, the branch of which is larger than the run.

bull head'er (*Masonry*) A brick with one rounded corner usually placed with short face exposed. Laid to form the brick sill under and beyond the window frame; also used around doorways.

Bull Header

bul'lion (bŏŏl'yŭn) (*C h e m.*) (1) Gold or silver bars or ingots. (2) A mixture of gold with silver, platinum, or other precious metals obtained by smelting and partial refining. (3) Often applied to gold and silver coins.

bull la'dle (*Fdry.*) A two-man ladle for carrying molten metal.

Bull Ladle

bull pine (*Wood*) *Pinus ponderosa.* Common throughout western United States. The tree grows to a height of 150 to 250 ft. and a diameter of 5 to 10 ft. The wood is of medium strength but very resinous. Used for both interior and exterior work in building construction. Also known as California white pine.

bull's'–eye arch (*Arch.*) An arch which forms a complete circle.

bull's'–nose (*Arch.*) An external obtuse or rounded angle. (*Furn.*) A small plane, used for planing close to projecting parts.  Bull's-nose

bull stretch'er (*Masonry*) A bull brick laid with the long edge exposed.

bull wheel (*Mach.*) (1) The large gear of a metal planing machine (planer) which drives the table. (2) A wheel around which a rope is wound for lifting heavy objects.

bump (*Aero.*) A sudden acceleration of an aircraft caused by a region of unstable atmosphere characterized by marked local vertical components in the air currents.

bump'er (*Auto. Mech.*) A safety device of spring steel or wood placed on front and rear ends of an automobile to provide protection at those points.

bump′er bag (*Aero.*) A cushion secured to the bottom of an airship to prevent damage when in contact with the ground.

bump′er blocks (*Auto. Mech.*) Rubber blocks used between axles and car frame to absorb effect of severe shocks.

bump′ing ham′mer (*Sheet-Met.Wk.*) Used for closing down seams on large work such as waste receptacles, etc.

bun′dling ma-chine′ (*P r i n t.*) A clamping device for compressing signatures, padding, etc.

bun foot (*Furn.*) A foot shaped like a flattened ball.

bung (*Ceram.*) A quantity of filled fire-clay boxes in a kiln.

bun′ga-low (*Arch.*) A one-story house with verandas. Sometimes the attic is finished as a second story.

bunk′er (*Engin.*) A compartment in which fuel, usually coal, is stored.

Bun′sen burn′er. A gas burner, commonly used in the laboratory, in which a mixture of gas and air is burned at the top of a tube, producing an intensely hot flame.

Bunsen Burner

buoy′an-cy (boi′ăn-sĭ) (*Aero.*) The upward force on an aerostat which is derived from aerostatic conditions. It is equal to the weight of air displaced. (*Phys.*) The resultant upward pressure of a fluid on an immersed or floating body. The power or tendency to keep afloat.

bur′ble (*Aero.*) A term designating the breakdown of the streamline flow about a body.

bu-rette′ (bů-rĕt′) (*Chem.*) A finely graduated glass tube by which a small quantity of a solution can be drawn off at a time.

burl (*Wood*) (1) Excrescence sometimes appearing on a tree, caused by abnormal growth, such as large knots. (2) A beautifully marked veneer cut from the stumps of walnut trees.

bur′lap. A coarse-woven material of jute; used for wrappings, hangings, decorations, etc.

burl′ing (*Textile*) A process in cloth finishing. It removes burrs, knots, and similar imperfections from the surface.

burn (*Tel.*) An image which stays on the tube after the camera is off the subject.

burned bear′ing (*Auto. Mech.*) The black rough surface of a bearing usually caused by poor lubrication.

Bur′nett's process (*Wood*) The impregnation of timber with chloride of zinc as a preservative.

burn′ing (*C h e m.*) Oxidation which takes place so rapidly that heat and light are released.

bur′nish (*Mech.*) To polish a metallic surface by the friction of another metallic surface brought in contact with it. (*Furn.*) To polish or smooth wood carving to give the appearance of modeling.

bur′nish-er (*Shopwk.*) Tool of hardened and polished steel for finishing metals by friction. It is held against the revolving work and gives a smooth surface by compressing the outer layer of metal.

burr (*Shopwk.*) The ragged or turned-down edge of a piece of metal resulting from grinding, cutting, or punching. (*Print.*) A piece of dead metal adhering to a linotype slug, causing a blurred impression.

burr'ing ma-chine' (*Sheet-Met. Wk.*) Used for turning edges on cylinders of metal or on disks such as can bottoms.

burr'ing ream'er. A tapered reamer used for countersinking and for removing burrs caused in cutting pipe.

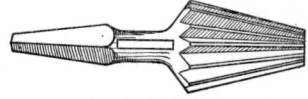

Burring Reamer

burst'ing strength. The resistance of paper to pressure is measured on a Mullen tester in pounds per square inch.

bus bar (*Elec.*) One of the strips of copper run on a switch and panel board from which all circuits are tapped. (Common feeders.)

bush (*Auto. Mech.*) (1) To fit a hollow sleeve into some part in order that it may serve as a bearing. When wear occurs, a new bushing may be applied, avoiding the necessity of replacing an entire part. (2) In general, the insertion of any piece to bring about a reduction of diameter.

bush'eled i'ron (*Metal.*) An iron produced in a puddling furnace from junk scrap.

bush'ing (*Mach.*) A sleeve or liner for a bearing, permits accurate adjustment and inexpensive repair. (*Plumb.*) A plug designed to be threaded into the end of a pipe. One end is bored and tapped to receive a pipe of smaller diameter than that of the pipe into which it is screwed.

butt (*Carp.*) Term usually applied to a hinge other than a strap hinge.

but'ter-fly' ta'ble (*F u r n.*) A small flat-top table with supports for holding up the side wings, which resemble the wings of a butterfly.

but'ter-fly' valve (*Auto. Mech.*) A winged damper supported on a fulcrum or shaft, movement of which controls passage of gas or air through an opening.

but'ter-ing (*Masonry*) The spreading of mortar on the edges of a brick before placing it in position.

but'ter-ing trow'el (trou'ĕl) (*Masonry*) Used for spreading mortar on the brick before it is laid.

but'ter-nut' (*Wood*) *Juglans cinerea.* A medium-sized tree native to eastern United States. Wood is soft and porous. Used for furniture and interior finishing.

butt hinge (*Carp.*) A hinge secured to the edge of a door and the face of the jamb which butts against the edge of the door when it is shut, as distinguished from strap hinge.

Butt Hinge

but'ting, or butt ram'ming (*Fdry.*) Ramming with the flat surface of the round end of the rammer.

butt joint (*Arch. and Woodwk.*) Where the ends of two pieces of timber come together without over lapping.

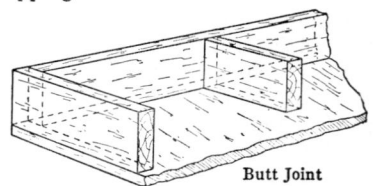

Butt Joint

butt mi'ter (*Sheet-Met. Wk.*) A miter joint in which the pieces to be joined do not overlap.

but'ton ma-chine' (*Uphol.*) A small, hand-operated machine equipped with upper and lower dies. It may be used for attaching buttons or, by changing the attachments, may be used for attaching snap fasteners, eyelets, etc.

but′ton-wood. (See SYCAMORE.)

butt ram′ming (*Fdry.*) Ramming done with the butt or large round end of the rammer.

but′tress, fly′ing (*Arch.*) A detached buttress or pier of masonry at some distance from a wall and connected thereto by an arch or a portion of an arch.

Buttress Thread

but′tress thread (*Mach.*) A screw thread which is triangular in section but which has one face at right angles to the axis of the screw, the second face only being sloped. Used in cases where excessive shock must be absorbed, as in the breech block of a cannon.

butt weld′ing (*Forg. and Shopwk.*) A weld in which the two pieces to be connected do not overlap but are welded directly at their ends; a common method of welding rods by an electric process.

buzz′er (*Elec.*) An electric call signal which makes a buzzing noise caused by the rapid vibrations of the armature. It operates on the same principle as the vibrating bell.

buzz saw (*Woodwk.*) A name often applied to a circular saw.

by′-pass (*Plumb.*) Any method by which water may pass around a fixture, appliance, connection, or length of pipe. Sometimes incorrectly applied to a connection between a drain pipe and a vent pipe which allows sewer air to enter the building.

C

C bat′ter-y (*Elec.*) Used to place the proper grid bias on vacuum tubes thereby insuring the right amount of "B" current in a circuit. It tends to prevent distortion and is economical of B batteries.

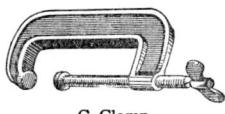
C Clamp

C clamp (*Mech.*) A frequently used form of clamp shaped like the letter "C"; pressure is obtained by means of a thumb screw.

C.O.D. An abbreviation meaning collect on delivery.

C.P. (*Chem.*) Chemically pure.

C scroll (*Furn.*) A C-shaped carved design, introduced by the French.

C-stage res′ins (*Plast.*) Thermosetting resins in the final stage, in which they are infusible and insoluble. The state of the resin in the final molded article.

C wash′er (*Mech.*) A washer with one side open so as to be removed or slipped under the nut to avoid the necessity of taking the nut entirely off. Also known as slotted, slip, or open washer.

ca-bane′ (kȧ-bȧn′) (*Aero.*) A framework for supporting the wings at the fuselage; also applied to the system of trussing used to support overhang in a wing.

cab′bag-ing press (*Mach.*) A press for compressing loose sheet-metal scrap into convenient form for handling and remelting.

cab′i-net (*Furn.*) A cupboard containing shelves, drawers, etc., enclosed by doors and used as a repository for various articles.

cab′i-net bur′nish-er (*Woodwk.*) A piece of hardened steel 4 to 6 in. long, often oval shape in section, inserted in a wooden handle; used to turn the edge of scrapers.

cab′i-net latch (*Furn.*) Name given to a wide variety of catches depending on their use, ranging from the type of latch used on refrigerator doors to the horizontal spring-and-bolt type operated by turning a knob as on kitchen cabinets, etc.

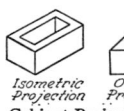
Perspective   Isometric Projection   Oblique Projection   Cabinet Projection
Cabinet Projection

cab′i-net pro-jec′tion (*Draw.*) A system of drawing in which one face of the object is drawn as parallel to the observer and the faces perpendicular thereto are drawn at an angle usually 45 deg., the slant edges being drawn to half scale.

cab′i-net scrap′er (*Woodwk.*) A flat piece of steel having an edge of such shape that when drawn over a wood surface irregularities can be removed and smoothness can be obtained.

cab′i-net-work. The work of one who constructs fine woodwork.

cab′in hook (*Furn.*) A small hook and eye used on doors in cabinetwork.

ca′ble (*Elec.*) An insulated electrical conductor or group of conductors, protected by a waterproof coat.

---

sāle, surfȧce, grăm, humăn, mȧsk, solȧr, bär, bâre; mē, ēdition, lĕnd, momĕnt, bakẽr; kīnd, fĭt; lōde, ȯmit, ŏlive, cŏnsume, sôrt; dūty, ŭtility, nŭt, alŭm, bûrn.

(*Engin.*) A very general term applied to rope or chain used for engineering purposes.

ca′ble box (*Elec.*) A box which houses the splices or connections between cables.

ca′ble-laid rope (*Engin.*) A rope consisting of several ropes or several layers or strands laid together into one rope.

ca′ble length. A marine measure which in the United States is equal to 720 ft. or 120 fathoms.

ca′ble rack (*Elec.*) A framework on which electric cables are supported.

ca′ble turn′ing (*Furn.*) A form of turning resembling coils of rope twisted in solid formation.

ca′bling (*Bldg. and Carp.*) Flutes of columns partly occupied by solid convex masses; or a column having convex projecting parts in place of concaved fluting.

ca′bo′chon′ (kà′bŏ′shôn′) (*Furn.*) A plain, convex or concave, circular surface, surrounded by a carved ornamentation which, when frequently polished, resembles a jewel.

cab′ri-ole (kăb′rĭ-ōl) (*Furn.*) A style of leg which swells in a convex line at the knee and turns in concave form at the ankle, terminated by various feet.

cad′mi-um (kăd′mĭ-ŭm) (*Chem.*) A bluish-white metallic element (Cd) occurring in small quantities in the ores of zinc, from which it is separated by fractional distillation; used in the manufacture of fusible alloys.

cad′mi-um plat′ing (*Metal.*) A coating of cadmium applied electrolytically to hardware and other parts as a protection against corrosion.

cad′mi-um sil′ver (*Auto. Mech.*) An alloy used for bearings. More efficient than babbitt metal in operation under high-load pressure and high temperature.

Ca-du′ce-us (ká-dū′sė-ŭs) The wand of Mercury; the messenger of the gods.

cage-type valve (*Auto. Mech.*) A valve type which was formerly very popular for valve-in-head motors. It consists of a valve of the poppet type operating in a small cylinder or "cage" which is attached to the cylinder block. The valve and cage are removable as a unit. The "cage-type valve" is not necessary on removable-head motors.

Cai′ro (kī′rō) (*P r i n t.*) A face of type available on linotype machines.

cais′son (kā′sŏn) A watertight casing sunk into the bed of a stream to be used in the construction of foundations of bridges under water. The work of excavation is carried on within it.

cake core (*Fdry.*) Core used when it is necessary to remove a portion of a pattern with its core print. When the core print with its attached part of the pattern is withdrawn from the sand, the depression left vacant by the core print is filled with a dry-sand core. Also called "cover core."

cak′ing coal. Coal which fuses and becomes a pasty mass when heated.

cal′a-mine (kăl′à-mīn) (*C h e m.*) $Zn(OH)_2ZnSiO_3$. Silicate of zinc; a common zinc ore.

cal′ci-mine. A wash made of whiting and glue, mixed with water. It is often tinted for use on walls.

cal-cine′ (kăl-sīn′) (*Chem.*) To make friable; i.e., reduce to powder, by heat.

cal-cined′ bone (*Pot.*) Bone changed

to a friable powder through the action of dry heat.

cal-cined' ka'o-lin (*Pot.*) A claylike, mealy, white, grayish or reddish aluminum silicate, used in making porcelain.

cal-cin'ing (kăl-sīn'ĭng) The heating or roasting of metallic ores for the purpose of expelling some of the foreign and injurious ingredients.

cal'cite (kăl'sīt) More commonly known as limestone. Used as a flux in the manufacture of pig iron and steel. Principal U. S. sources are Pennsylvania, Michigan, West Virginia, and Illinois.

cal'ci-um (kăl'sĭ-ŭm) (*Chem.*) Ca. Silvery-white soft light metal, lustrous when freshly produced. Tarnishes quickly in the air due to oxidation. Used for alloying metals and in school laboratories for producing hydrogen gas from water.

cal'ci-um car'bide (*Chem.*) CaC_2. Obtained by heating a mixture of lime and coke in the electric furnace. Used for making acetylene gas by treating with water.

cal'ci-um car'bon-ate (kăl'sĭ-ŭm kär'bŏn-āt) (*Chem.*) Limestone is the most abundant variety, although it is never pure; marble is a pure variety; chalk, shells, and coral are mainly calcium carbonate.

cal'ci-um ox'ide (*Pot.*) Lime is nearly pure calcium oxide.

Cal'cu-la-graph' (kăl'kû-là-grȧf') (*Print.*) A device consisting of clock and time stamp used for stamping exact time of payment on a bill, etc.

cal'cu-lat'ing ma-chine'. Any of the various machines designed to perform mathematical operations mechanically.

cal'cu-lus (*Math.*) A mathematical technique developed by Newton and Leibnitz each working independently. It introduces the concept of limits to the problem of determining the ratio of the change in value of a function to the increment of its variable x, as the increment approaches zero. By this technique an entirely new field of study was opened to mathematical investigation and research.

cal'dron (kôl'drŭn) A large metal kettle or boiler.

cal'en-dered (*Papermkg.*) Refers to polishing of sized and coated papers.

cal'en-der-ing (*Plast.*) The operation of rolling plastic sheet to specified thickness from a doughy mass through two or more sets of counter rotating rolls. The last rolls are cooling rolls. (*Textile*) A smoothness, luster, and other effects imparted to cloth by rolling it under pressure.

cal'i-ber (*Plumb.*) Internal diameter or bore.

cal'i-bra'tion. Ascertaining the amount of variation from absolute accuracy in a scientific instrument.

Cal'i-for'ni-a job case (*Print.*) A commonly used storage case for hand-set type.

ca'lin' (kȧ'lăn') An alloy of lead and tin. Frequently used in thin sheets as a lining of containers.

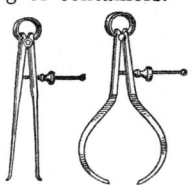

Inside and Outside Adjusting Calipers

cal'i-per (*Shopwk.*) A tool principally for measuring the diameter of circular work. Inside and outside calipers. (*Papermkg. and Print.*) An instrument used for measuring the thickness of paper in thousandths of an inch.

cal′i-per rule. A graduated scale, with fixed head, which slides in a groove in a second piece which carries only a zero graduation. It can be used for both inside and outside calipering.

cal′i-per square (*Mach.*) A measuring instrument similar in shape to the vernier caliper but used where less accuracy is required. It consists of a fixed jaw which is an integral part of the graduated bar. The movable jaw has screw adjustment and can be locked in position.

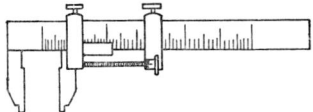

Caliper Square

calk′ing (kôk′ĭng) Making a joint or seam watertight or steam-tight by filling it in with rust cement or by closing the joint by means of a calking tool. Oakum is frequently calked into the seams of wooden vessels.

calk′ing tool. A piece of steel with a blunt end, formed somewhat like a chisel and used for closing up the joints of boiler plates. It is driven against them by sharp blows from a hammer.

cal′o-rie (*Chem., Engin., Mech., Phys.*) A unit of heat. The amount of heat required to raise the temperature of one gram of water one degree centigrade.

cal′o-rim′e-ter (kăl′ô-rĭm′ê-tẽr) (*Elec.*) An instrument for measuring the heat generated by an electrical current in a conductor. (*Phys.*) An apparatus for measuring the quantity of heat generated by friction, combustion, or other chemical change.

cal′o-riz′ing (kăl′ô-rīz′ing) (*Metal.*) A method of coating iron and steel with aluminum or aluminum-iron alloys.

cam (*Mach.*) A device mounted on a revolving shaft used for transposing rotary motion into an alternating, reciprocating or back and forth motion.

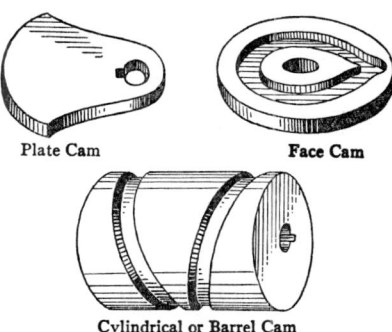

Plate Cam   Face Cam

Cylindrical or Barrel Cam

cam–and–le′ver steer′ing gear (*Auto. Mech.*) Consists of a sort of finger cam attached to the cross shaft, which engages a threaded screw of variable pitch on the lower end of the steering-gear shaft. The pitch of the screw, being slight at the center and increasing toward the ends, permits straight-ahead driving with minimum shock, and makes a rapid turning possible.

cam′ber (kăm′bẽr) (*Aero.*) The rise in the curve of an airfoil section from its chord, usually expressed as the ratio of departure of the curve from the chord to the length of the chord. "Upper camber" relates to the upper surface of an air foil and "lower camber" to the lower surface; mean camber is the mean of these two. (*Arch.*) The amount of upward curve given to an arched bar, beam, or girder. (*Auto. Mech.*) That feature of front-axle design which brings the front wheels closer together at the bottom than at the top, making the car steer easier.

cam'bi-um lay'er (kăm'bĭ-ŭm) (*Wood*) The zone of cells between the wood and the bark. Growth takes place from this layer. It is the source of "bast" taken from basswood.

cam'bric (kām'brĭk) (*Uphol.*) The quality used by upholsterers is a rather stiff cotton fabric with slightly glazed surface. White cambric is used for cushion and pillow casing. Black cambric is used for tacking on the underside of upholstered furniture.

cam drive (*Mach.*) A type of motion obtained by cams through which a certain motion is made to take place in exact time or relation to some other motion, as in the camshaft of an automobile.

cam en'gine (*Aero.*) A type of engine in which the pistons are reciprocated by means of a cam and roller mechanism.

cam'e-o (kăm'ē-ō) A raised carving of delicate workmanship, used on furniture of Sheraton and early Empire styles.

cam'er-a boom (*Tel.*) A device for adding maneuverability to the camera; may be raised or lowered and moved side to side and is used on a wheeled base. Also called a crane.

cam'er-a tube (*Tel.*) The electronic tube used in a television camera to translate a scene from light and shade into electrical impulses.

cam lift'ers or cam fol'low-ers (*Auto. Mech.*) Those fixed or adjustable metal parts fitted between the camshaft and the valve stems. The throw of the cams controls the opening and closing of the valves.

cam'pa-ni'le (käm'pä-nē'lå) (*Arch.*) A bell tower, usually detached from the main building.

cam'phor (*Chem.*) A translucent, volatile, white resin made from an oriental evergreen. Extensively used in the manufacture of explosives, celluloid, and disinfectants.

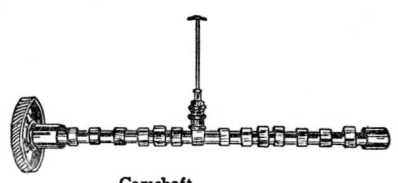

Camshaft

cam'shaft (*Auto. Mech.*) A shaft carrying a series of cams which form integral parts of the shaft and are so spaced as to control the relative operation of the automobile engine valves.

cam vise (*Mach.*) A vise whose opening and closing depend on cam action.

ca-nard' air'plane (*Aero.*) A type of airplane having the horizontal stabilizing and control surfaces in front of the main supporting surfaces.

can'de-la'brum (kăn'dē-lā'brŭm) *pl.* candelabra. A branched ornamental candlestick.

can'dle–foot (*Elec.*) A unit of illumination. The light given by a British standard candle at a distance of one foot.

can′dle pow′er. The illuminating power of a standard sperm candle used as a measure for other illuminants.

cane (*Furn.*) A flexible plant product, used for seats and backs; introduced during the eighteenth century.

can′nel coal (kăn′ĕl kōl). A bituminous coal with decided cleavage. When marketed, it usually is not graded for size as is anthracite coal. This coal, when used in a fireplace, gives off a flame like burning wood.

can′on (*Print.*) Formerly used in referring to 48-point type. (Obsolete.)

can′o-py (*Arch.*) An ornamental rooflike structure projecting from a wall, or supported on pillars. (*Elec.*) A metal cover used to conceal connections where an electric-light fixture enters a wall or ceiling.

can′o-py switch (*Elec.*) A small switch usually located in the canopy of an electric fixture.

cant (*Carp.*) To tilt, to set up on a slant; also a molding formed of plain surfaces and angles rather than curves.

can-teen′ (*Furn.*) A box or case for bottles; also a case in which to deposit cutlery.

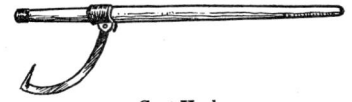
Cant Hook

cant hook. Consists of a stout hickory bar with a sharp pointed steel hook attached near one end. Used for rolling logs, handling telephone poles, etc.

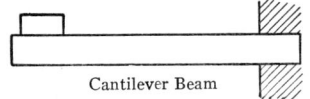
Cantilever Beam

can′ti-le′ver (kăn′tĭ-lē′vẽr) (*Arch.*) A beam fixed at one end and loaded at the other, or loaded uniformly.

can′ti-le′ver spring (*Auto. Mech.*) A spring which has one end fixed at the axle and the other end attached to the frame, as in quarter-elliptic springs.

can′ti-lev′er wing (*Aero.*) A wing with all the bracing on the inside.

cant′ing strip (*Arch.*) In frame buildings same as water table.

cap (*Arch.*) A coping of a wall; a cornice over a door, etc. (*Carp.*) The lintel over a door or window frame; a toppiece. (*Mach.*) The top half of a journal bearing. (*Mech.*) The upper or loose portion of a shaft bearing attached to the lower portion by screws or bolts. (*Print.*) The common name for a capital letter.

ca-pac′i-tance (*Elec.*) Generally, the ability to store up electricity. The capacitance of a condenser is measured by the charge it will hold when the difference of potential across its terminals is one volt.

ca-pac′i-tive re-act′ance (*Elec.*) The measure of resistance to the flow of an a.c. current through a condenser.

ca-pac′i-tor (*Elec.*) An electric condenser.

ca-pac′i-ty (*Elec.*) The quantity of electricity which a condenser is able to store or condense is called its "electrostatic capacity."

ca-pac′i-ty load. The maximum load which can be carried safely.

cape chis′el (*Metalwk.*) A narrow-blade chisel for cutting channels or keyways.

cap′il·lar′y ac′tion (k ă p′ĭ-l ĕ r′ĭ) (*Phys.*) The resultant of adhesion, cohesion, and surface tension which produces the rise and fall of liquids in fine hairlike tubes.

cap′i·tal (*Arch.*) The upper part of a pier, pilaster, or column.

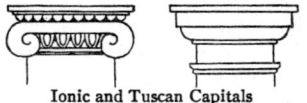

Ionic and Tuscan Capitals

cap′ping (*Carp.*) A topping or placing of a cap at the upper end of a piece of work.

cap screw. A finished machine bolt used either with or without a nut.

cap stone (*Arch.*) Stone used for the top or crowning of a structure.

cap strip (*Aero.*) A continuous member on the outer edge of a wing rib.

cap′tion (*Print.*) A headline or heading placed above a chapter or article.

cap′tive bal·loon′ (*Aero.*) A balloon restrained from free flight by means of a cable attaching it to the earth.

car′at (*Jewelry*) A unit of weight for jewels, about 3.2 grains.

car′bide tools. Metalworking tools consisting of carbide tips brazed on steel shanks to provide support.

car′bo·hy′drate (k ä r′b ō-h ĭ′d r ā t) (*Chem.*) A compound containing carbon, hydrogen, and oxygen with the latter two in the ratio of 2 hydrogen to 1 oxygen; e.g., sugar $C_{12}H_{22}O_{11}$. The most important carbohydrates contain either 6 atoms or a multiple of 6 atoms of carbon.

car·bol′ic ac′id (*C h e m.*) Phenol. C_6H_5OH. A poisonous substance derived from coal tar. Widely used as an antiseptic.

car′bon (*Chem.*) A nonmetallic element (C) found in all organic substances. (*Elec.*) Carbon dust mixed with a binder and baked is used as an electrode in arc lamps. (*Engin.*) Carbon is the solid element of combustion.

car′bon arc (*Elec.*) An arc occuring between carbon points as in an arc lamp.

car′bon arc weld′ing. An arc-welding process wherein a carbon or graphite electrode is used with or without the use of filler metal.

car′bon·ate (*Chem.*) Salts of carbonic acid, e.g., sodium carbonate. (*Mining*) Ore containing a large proportion of lead carbonate.

car′bon black (*Paint.*) An intense black made of the deposit from natural gas flames.

car′bon brush (*Elec.*) See BRUSH.

car′bon but′ton (*E l e c.*) A button made of carbon employed as a resistance medium especially in certain types of telephone transmitters or in some types of rheostats.

car′bon con′tact (*Elec.*) See CONTACTS.

car′bon de·pos′it (*Auto.*) An accumulation of carbon in the combustion chamber and sometimes around valves and piston rings. Poor quality of gasoline and lubricating oil hastens such actions.

car′bon di·ox′ide (*Chem.*) CO_2. Product of complete combustion of carbon fuels. Transported in liquid form in steel cylinders. Used in gaseous form as a fire extinguisher and in solid form as dry ice.

car′bon di·sul′phide (*Chem.*) CS_2. When pure is a colorless volatile liquid with an unpleasant garlicky odor. Used as a solvent for sulphur, phosphorus, iodine, bromide, camphor, gums, resins, waxes, fats, etc. It is also used as an insecticide. Same as carbon bi-sulphide.

car′bon fil′a-ment (*Elec.*) An incandescent lamp filament composed of a thread or fiber which has been reduced to carbon by a carbonizing process.

car′bon hold′er (*Elec.*) A device which holds and feeds the carbons in an arc lamp.

car′bon-i-za′tion. The preparation of low-carbon steel for heat treatment by packing in a container with carbonizing material such as charcoal, or one of the trade articles made for the purpose, then heating to about 2000 deg. F. for several hours, then allowing to cool very slowly.

car′bon-iz′ing (*Elec. and Engin.*) The reduction of a substance to carbon by subjecting it to intense heat in a closed vessel.

car′bon mon-ox′ide (*Chem.*) CO. An odorless, colorless, tasteless, deadly-poisonous gas formed by incomplete combustion of carbon fuels.

car′bon pa′per. A thin paper coated with a combination of wax and carbon, used for duplicating.

car′bon piles (*Elec.*) Plates of carbon which act as resistance units in a high-discharge electrical test set.

car′bon re-mov′er (*Auto.*) A scraper or tool for hand or machine use, or a liquid which usually is added to the gasoline for the removal of carbon deposits.

car′bon rhe′o-stat (rē′ō-stăt) (*Elec.*) A rheostat using carbon plates or grains which act as resistance.

car′bon steel. A broad term applied to tool steels other than high-speed steels or alloy steels. If, under 50-point carbon, it does not harden perceptibly, it is called low carbon, mild, or machine steel. Steel of 75-point carbon will harden, but the best carbon steel contains about 100-point carbon.

car′bon tet′ra-chlo′ride (*Chem.*) A noninflammable liquid used as a solvent for oil and grease for cleansing purposes. It is also the active agent used in many types of fire extinguishers.

Car′bo-run′dum. A trade name covering silicon carbide and other abrasive products. This term is not properly used as a generic name for silicon carbide.

car′boy (*Chem.*) A large glass bottle used as a container for acids. Usually it is protected by a wooden case or box.

car′bu-ret′or (kär′bû-rĕt′ẽr) (*Auto. Mech.*) A device for converting liquid fuel into vapor and mixing it with air in such proportions as to form the most efficient combustible mixture.

car′bu-ret′or bar′rel (*Auto. Mech.*) The metal portion of the carburetor surrounding the suction air chamber forming a wall or barrel for the full length from choke to flange.

car′bu-ret′or bowl (*Auto. Mech.*) The reservoir part of the carburetor which holds liquid gasoline or fuel.

car′bu-ret′or float (*Auto. Mech.*) Usually an airtight metal container which floats on the surface of the fuel in the bowl of the carburetor and controls the flow of gasoline from the main fuel line.

car′bu-riz-ing (kär′bû-rīz-ĭng) Alloys with iron base are combined with carbon through the process of heating the alloys below the melting point while in contact with carbonaceous material.

car′bu-riz-ing flame. A gas welding flame having carbonaceous fuel gas in excess of that required to produce a neutral flame.

car card (*Adv.*) Display advertising as used in street cars and buses.

car′case (kär′kăs) (*Carp.*) Also carcass. The frame, as of a house.

card′board (*Print.*) A general term including a wide variety of heavy, stiff papers, of qualities ranging from low-grade heavy paper to the high-grade ticket cards.

card com′pass (*Aero.*) A magnetic compass in which the magnets are attached to a pivoted card on which the directions are marked.

card–cut (*Furn.*) A Chinese style of latticework.

card′ing (*Textile*) The preparation of animal or vegetable fibers before drawing or spinning.

card–weight pipe (*Plumb.*) A term applied to standard or full-weight pipe, which is the Briggs standard thickness of pipe.

Car-not's′ cy′cle (kär-nōz′) The perfect engine cycle or series of heat changes devised by Carnot, a French scientist.

Car-not's′ prin′ci-ple (*Phys.*) The amount of work done by a heat engine is dependent on its temperature alone, being independent of the nature of the intermediary agent that is employed.

car′pen-try. The art of cutting and assembling timber as in buildings, boats, etc.

car′pet strip (*Arch.*) A strip attached to the floor beneath a door.

car′riage (*Arch.*) The timber or steel joist which supports the steps of a wooden stair. (*Mech.*) That part of a lathe which rides on the ways between the headstock and tailstock, and through which the feed may be controlled, both longitudinal and transverse.

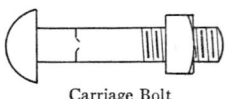

Carriage Bolt

car′riage bolt. An oval or button-head black bolt with square neck which prevents the bolt from turning while the nut is being tightened.

car′ri-er (*Mach.*) Same as lathe dog. The most common form is clamped on the cylindrical piece to be turned and has a projecting tail which is engaged by a slot in the faceplate causing rotation of the piece.

car′ri-er wave (*Tel.*) The radio wave over which television impulses are sent. In television two waves are utilized, one for sight and one for sound.

car′ron oil (kăr′ŭn) (*Chem.*) A mixture of equal volumes of linseed oil and lime water, used for relief of external burns.

car′ry-ing ca-pac′i-ty (*Elec.*) The greatest amount of electrical current that a conductor can safely carry, expressed in amperes. The various size wires, with their carrying capacities, are arranged in a table in the National Electrical Code.

Car′ter proc′ess (*Chem.*) The manufacture of white lead by an atomizing process. Chemically it is the same as when manufactured by the old Dutch process.

car-toon' (*Print.*) An informal type resembling hand lettering.

car-touche' (kär-tōōsh') (*Arch. and Furn.*) An ornamental tablet or scroll bearing an inscription.

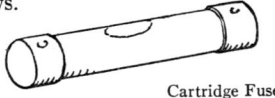
Cartouche

car'tridge fuse (*Elec.*) A fuse enclosed in an insulating tube in order to confine the arc when the fuse blows.

Cartridge Fuse

carv'ing (*Furn.*) A form of ornamentation which is executed by cutting or chiseling designs on a surface.

case (*Bookbndg.*) The cover of a book after being printed, stamped, and made ready to fit a book. (*Ceram.*) A plaster pattern cast in the block or master mold. (*Print.*) A partitioned receptacle for different kinds of type.

case'hard'en-ing. A process by which a thin hard film is formed on the surface of iron base alloys.

ca'se-in (kā'sē-ĭn) (*Chem.*) The principal ingredient in cheese, found especially in milk. Used in calico printing; also as an adhesive in water paints, varnishes, leather finishing, etc.

ca'se-in plas'tics (*Chem.*) The principal source of raw material is the casein of milk, and other proteins. Made in sheets, rods, tubing, and disks. Used for buttons, buckles, novelties, beads, costume jewelry, etc.

case'ment win'dow (*Arch.*) A window hinged on its vertical edge to permit opening inward or outward. More weathertight if opened outward.

case rack (*Print.*) A frame used for the storage of type cases.

cas'ing (*Arch.*) The framework about a window or door.

cas'ket. A small box or case for valuables. A burial case.

Cas'lon (kăz'lŏn) (*Print.*) A widely popular face of type designed by **William Caslon.**

cas-sit'er-ite (*Metal.*) The ore from which tin is obtained.

cast (*Print.*) A duplicate of a type form obtained by stereotyping or electrotyping.

cast brass (*Metal.*) An alloy, usually of 65 per cent copper and 35 per cent zinc. A small percentage of this may be added to increase hardness.

cas'tel-lat'ed (kăs'tĕ-lāt'ĕd) (*Engin.*) Formed like a castle, as a castellated nut which has a portion of its length turned and slotted for the reception of cotter pins.
Castellated Nut

cast'er (*Auto. Mech.*) Name applied to the effect secured when the axle is so set that the top of the axle yoke is slightly back of the lower end, giving an inclination of 2 or 3 degrees to the spindle body. This causes the front wheels to align themselves with the direction in which the car is moving. (*Furn.*) Small wheel attached to the feet, or base, of a piece of furniture to aid in moving without damage to the floor.

cast'er cup (*Furn.*) A cup of glass or wood placed under a caster to distribute weight of an article of furniture over a large area to avoid marring the floor.

cast′ing (*Ceram.*) The process of making pottery in molds from fluid clay. (*Metal.*) Metal part made by pouring the metal, when liquid, into a mold. (*Plast.*) Pouring liquid, catalyzed resin, usually with fillers and pigment, into an open mold, where it hardens.

cast′ing cop′per (*Metal.*) Inferior to electrolytic and lake copper. It is obtained from a variety of copper ores and from by-products of brass foundries.

cast′ing off (*Print.*) Measuring type to see how it will divide into pages.

cast′ing strains (*Metal.*) Phenomena caused by shrinkage in a casting during cooling.

cast′ing up (*Print.*) Consists of measuring the amount of type set to determine the cost of composition.

cast i′ron. Iron of ordinary use, cast in molds; has high carbon content; cannot be rolled, forged, or tempered. Cast-iron nickel alloys have many of the properties of steel castings.

cast-i′ron boil′er. A container, built up of vertical or horizontal sections of cast iron and used for generating low-pressure steam or hot water. Small sizes are frequently round, with a circular grate and horizontal sections joined with tee rods and push nipples. Larger sizes are usually rectangular and made with vertical sections. These sections may be joined internally by push nipples and tee rods, or externally by outside headers through which the steam and water pass.

cast phe-no′lic res′ins (*Chem. Plast.*) This class of resins is prepared from phenol and formaldehyde. Tensile and compressive strength are high and a wide range of color effects is obtainable. They are noninflammable and readily machinable. Used as panels, novelties, laminating varnishes, etc.

cast res′in-oids (*Plast. Art*) Plastic materials shaped by a casting process.

cast steel (*Mach.*) Steel made into the desired shape by the casting process as distinguished from other methods.

cat (*Furn.*) A small piece of tripod furniture with a tripod upper section for resting dishes to warm before the fireplace.

Ca-tal′pa (kå-tăl′på) (*Wood*) *Bignoniaceae*. Also known as Indian bean and cigar tree. Wood is soft and coarse grained but is durable in contact with soil. Used for poles, crossties, etc.

cat′a-lyst (*Chem.*) A substance which aids in bringing about a chemical change without itself being altered or changed. (*Plast.*) A chemical substance added to a liquid resin or a resin compound which initiates chemical action in the plastic, causing its molecules to link and form into chains (polymerize). When the reaction is complete, the resin is "hard."

cat′a-pult (*Aero.*) A device by which an airplane can be launched at flying speed.

catch ba′sin. A cistern, basin, or depression, at the point where a gutter discharges into a sewer, to catch matters which would not readily pass through the sewers. A reservoir to catch and retain surface drainage.

catch line (*Print.*) A line necessary to bind the main lines of a piece of advertising together, but consists of unessential words.

cat′e-na-ry (kăt′ê-nå-rĭ)(*Math.*) The curve formed by a flexible, inextensible, slender cord suspended by its ends.

cat′head (*Mach.*) A collar loosely fitted to a shaft and attached to it by means of headless setscrews. It is used to prevent a steady rest from marking the work.

cath′ode (*Elec.*) The negative electrode in an electrolytic cell.

cath′ode rays (*Elec.*) Streams of electrons emitted from the filament (called the cathode) of a vacuum tube under the influence of high voltage and which, by suitable means, can be brought outside the tube.

cath′ode–ray screen (*Tel.*) The fluorescent material covering the inner surface of the picture end of the kinescope.

cath′ode-ray tube (*Tel.*) An electronic tube in which streams of electrons are shot from a cathode and are formed into a narrow beam directed by means of electrostatic or magnetic fields over a target, usually a photosensitive plate or a fluorescent screen which glows wherever the beam strikes it.

cat′i′on (kăt′ī′ŏn) (*Elec.*) The element or positive ion which appears at the cathode or negative terminal in an electrolytic cell.

cat′walk (*Aero.*) A narrow footway along the keel of a rigid airship.

caul (kôl) (*Shopwk.*) A tool used in forming veneer to the shape of a curved surface.

cau-lic′u-lus (*Arch.*) One of the slender stems springing from beneath the abacus of a Corinthian capital.

caulk′ing. (1) Setting the edges of plates in a riveted joint with hammer and caulking tool to insure a tight joint. (2) In general, making a joint tight or leakproof by forcing some material between parts that are not tightly fitted.

caus′tic so′da (*Chem.*) NaOH (Sodium hydroxide) Lye; much used in textile mills for cleaning, scouring, etc.

ca-vet′to (kä-vĕt′tō) (*Arch.*) A quarter-round, concave molding.

cav′il (kăv′ĭl)(*Masonry*) A type of heavy sledge with one blunt and one pointed end. Used for rough shaping stone at the quarry. *Cavetto*

cav′i-ty (*Plast.*) Depression in a mold made by machining or hobbing or by both methods. Depending on the number of such depressions, molds are designated as "single cavity or multicavity."

cav′i-ty block (*Plast.*) The housing or lower section of a mold in which the depression is sunk.

ce′dar chest (*F u r n.*) A household chest of various sizes, especially used for storing woolens and furs because of its protection against moths.

ce-dil′la (sê-dĭl′å) (*Print.*) A mark used under the letter "c" to indicate that it shall have the sound of "s" as in façade.

ceil′ing (*Aero.*) Height of the lower level of a bank of clouds above the ground.

ceil′ing bal-loon′ (*Aero.*) A small free balloon, whose rate of ascent is known, used to determine the ceiling.

ceil′ing–height in′di-ca′tor (*Aero.*) A device that measures the height from the horizontal to the illuminated spot produced by a ceiling projector as seen from a fixed position.

ceil′ing joist (*Arch.*) One of the timbers to which a ceiling is attached by lath and plaster or by other means.

ceil′ing pro-jec′tor (*Aero.*) A projector that produces an illuminated region on the underside of a cloud for the purpose of determining the height of that part of the cloud above the indicator.

cell (*Elec.*) A single element of an electric battery, either primary or secondary.

cel′lar (*Arch.*) The room or rooms below the main portion of a building, usually containing the heating plant and accessories. The depth of a cellar is, all or in part, below ground level.

cel′lar-et′ (sĕl′ēr-ĕt′) (*Furn.*) A deep drawer or compartment in a sideboard for holding bottles.

cel′lo-phane (*Chem.*) A trade name for a thin, transparent cellulose. Principal use is for wrapping purposes.

cel′lule (or cell) (*Aero.*) In an airplane, the entire structure of the wings and wing trussing of the whole airplane on one side of the fuselage, or between fuselages or nacelles, where there are more than one.

cellulith. Produced by grinding wood pulp to a homogeneous mass and then drying it. It can be worked like wood and is a substitute for ebonite.

cel′lu-loid (*Chem.*) A compound of camphor and guncotton, very inflammable. (*Furn.*) An ivory substitute, used in marquetry.

cel′lu-lose (*Chem.*) An inert substance forming the chief part of the solid framework of plants, wood, linen, paper, etc.

cel′lu-lose ac′e-tate (*Chem. Plast.*) Strength and toughness are outstanding features of this thermosetting plastic. Available in wide color range for steering wheels, decorative novelties, fountain pens, electrical appliances, etc. This material machines in much the same manner as soft metals.

cel′lu-lose ac′e-tate bu′tyr-ate (*Chem. Plast.*) Process of manufacture same as cellulose acetate for the use of a mixture of butyric and acetic acids and anhydrides. Articles made from this plastic have lower moisture absorption and better resistance to weather than if made from cellulose acetate. Used as a molding compound for handles, cases, etc.

cel′lu-lose ni′trate (*Chem. Plast.*) One of the oldest plastics; known by many names such as celluloid, pyralin, amerith, etc. Available as lacquers, emulsions, rods, tubes, and sheets. It has a wide application in a great variety of colors.

cel′lu-lo′sic (*Plast.*) A family of thermoplastics which is based on the chemical treatment of carefully purified cotton linters. Familiar plastics such as Cellulose Nitrate, Cellulose Acetate, and others belong in this catagory. Large volumes of these plastics are used in sheet for thermoforming of products such as signs and packaging items. Much is used in skin-packaging, in craft paper coating, and in blow-molded containers. (See PLASTICS.)

cell vent (*Elec.*) A hole in the cell cap which permits the escape of the gases formed in the battery cell.

Cel′o-tex. A trade name for a fiber board made from sugar-cane waste. It is much used for wall covering, insulating, etc.

ce-ment′ (*Plaster.*) Generally used in reference to Portland cement, stucco, natural cements, etc. Mortar, plaster of Paris, or any substance which causes bodies to adhere to one another.

cem′en-ta′tion steel (*Metal.*) A cutlery steel made in the cementation furnace. Owing to the cost of production the process has been but little used in America.

ce-ment′ed car′bide tools (*Mach.*) Tools made from pulverized carbides fused into hard tips for heavy-duty or high-speed cutting of metals.

ce-ment′ing trow′el. A tool similar to the plasterer's trowel but often of heavier gauge stock.

ce-ment′ite (*Engin.*) Iron combined with carbon as it exists in steel before hardening.

cen′ter. A fixed point about which the radius of a circle or of an arc moves.

cen′ter dis′tance. A commonly used term of wide application. (1) The distance between centers of holes in a machine part. (2) The distance between bearings supporting a shaft. (3) The distance between center lines on a drawing, etc.

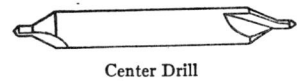

Center Drill

cen′ter drill (*Mach.*) A short drill, used for centering work in order that it may be carried on the lathe centers. Center drills are usually made in combination with a countersink, which permits a double operation with one tool.

cen′tered (*Print.*) The location of a line of type when the space on each side is equal.

Center Gauge

cen′ter gauge. A flat gauge used for setting a tool for the cutting of "V" threads.

cen′ter head (*Mach.*) A device attached to a scale or blade for use in locating the center of some round object; as the center point on the end of a shaft preliminary to centering.

cen′ter-ing (*Arch.*) The false work over which an arch is formed. In concrete work the centering is known as the frames.

cen′ter-ing con-trol′ (*Tel.*) A control on the receiver for centering the picture either vertically or horizontally.

cen′ter-ing work (*Mech.*) The process of locating the exact center of a piece of material for turning on the lathe. A hermaphrodite caliper or a combination square with a center head and a scriber may be used to center cylindrical pieces.

cen′ter-less grind′ing (*Mach.*) Accomplished by a machine with a high-speed grinding wheel opposite which is a regulating wheel moving slowly in reverse direction. A rest forms a support for the work in the throat between the two wheels.

cen′ter line (*Draft.*) A broken line usually dot and dash indicating the center of the object and a very convenient line from which to lay off measurements.

cen'ter of buoy'an-cy (*Aero.*) In a seaplane, the center of gravity of the fluid displaced.

cen'ter of grav'i-ty. That point about which a body will be balanced when placed in any position.

cen'ter-of-pres'sure co'ef-fi'cient (*Aero.*) The ratio of the distance of the center of pressure from the leading edge to the chord length.

cen'ter of pres'sure of an air'foil sec'tion (*Aero.*) The point in the chord of an airfoil section, prolonged if necessary, which is at the intersection of the chord and the line of action of the resultant air force.

cen'ter-piece' (*Arch.*) Ornament placed in the center of a ceiling.

Center Punch

cen'ter punch (*Metalwk.*) A steel punch about 3 or 4 in. long, having one end ground to a conical point, used for laying out work.

cen'ter ream'er (*Shopwk.*) Center reamers, or countersinks, for centering the ends of shafts, etc., are usually made 60 deg. included angle. Combined center drill and reamer are now universally used.

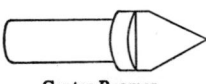

Center Reamer

cen'ter rest (*Mach.*) A support for lathe work which clamps onto the inside ways of the lathe bed. Used when turning long shafts, boring spindles, etc.

cen'ters (*Mach.*) Those pieces carried in the headstock and the tailstock of a lathe having cone-shaped points between which work is supported.

cen'ter sec'tion (*Aero.*) The center panel of a wing; in the case of a continuous wing or any wing having no central panel, the limits of the center section are arbitrarily defined by the location of points of attachments to the cabane struts or fuselage.

cen'ter square (*Metalwk.*) A tool used for finding the center of a circle or of an arc of a circle. Its most frequent use is in locating the center point on the end of a shaft or cylinder to be turned.

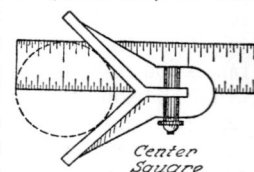

Center Square

cen'ter ta'ble (*Furn.*) Any table, finished or decorated on all sides, suitable for the center of a room.

cen'ti-grade scale. The scale of the centigrade thermometer which rates 0 deg. as freezing point and 100 deg. as boiling point.

cen'ti-me'ter. A measure of length in the metric system equal to the one-hundredth part of a meter; .3937 in.

cen'tral sta'tion (*Elec.*) A power plant from which electric light and power are supplied to consumers.

cen-trif'u-gal (*Shopwk.*) Proceeding from the center.

cen-trif'u-gal flow en'gine (*Aero.*) A gas turbine engine having a centrifugal compressor.

cen-trif'u-gal spark ad-vance' (*Auto. Elec.*) The timer-distributor governor by which the spark is advanced or retarded as the engine speed varies.

cen-trif'u-gal switch (*Elec.*) A switch used on the single-phase, split-phase motor to open the starting winding after the motor has almost reached synchronous speed.

cen-trif′u-gal–type su′per-charg′er (*Aero.*) A high-speed rotary blower equipped with one or more multi-blade impellers which, through centrifugal action, compress the air or mixture in the induction system.

cen′tu-ry (*Print.*) A face of type commonly used in bookwork.

ce-ram′ics (sē-răm′ĭks) The art of producing things out of baked clay.

cer′a-sin (sĕr′a-sĭn) (*Chem.*) A yellow or white wax made by bleaching and purifying ozocerite, used as a substitute for beeswax.

ce′ri-um (sē′rĭ-ŭm) (*Chem.*) A rare metal found in the mineral cerite; specific gravity 6.92; it resembles iron in color and luster, but is soft and both malleable and ductile. Its products are used in dyeing and in the manufacture of gas mantles; also in cigar lighters and gas lighters.

cer-tif′i-cate (sĕr-tĭf′ĭ-kĭt) (*Noun*) A document or written statement certifying as to certain accomplishments. (sĕr-tĭf′ĭ-kāt) (*Verb*) To certify or furnish with certificate.

cer′to-si′no (chĕr′tô-zē′nō) (*Furn.*) An inlay, in which bone or ivory is used on a dark wood, such as ebony.

ce′rus-site (sēr′ŭ-sīt) (*Min.*) $PbCO_3$. An ore of lead. Colorless, white or yellow, transparent crystals.

ce′si-um (sē′zĭ-ŭm) (*Chem.*) A silver white metallic element. One of the active ingredients of photoelectric cells.

cess′pool (*Plumb.*) A pit for the reception or detention of sewage.

ce′tane rat′ing. A measure of the ignition qualities of Diesel-engine fuels. Oils with a rating of 30 to 50 are classed as rough Diesel fuels and those from 50 to 80 as smooth Diesel fuels.

chafe (chāf). To wear away as by friction.

chain drive (*Auto. Mech.*) Power transmitted by chain belting. Silent chain is now largely used for camshaft and timing-gear drive which reduces noise to a minimum; the chief fault is looseness due to stretching caused by wear; easily adjusted if the chain is not too badly worn. Also applies to the rear-wheel drive by chain as in early passenger cars and trucks.

chain hoist (*Engin.*) A block and tackle in which chain is used instead of rope.

Chain Hoist

chain man. One who holds the zero end of the tape or chain.

chain pipe vise (*Steam Fit.*) A portable vise utilizing a heavy chain to fasten the pipe in the jaw.

chain pul′ley (*Mach.*) A sheave wheel or pulley with depressions to engage the links of a chain.

chain riv′et-ing (*Engin.*) Double, or multiple row riveting in which rivets are placed opposite each other as distinguished from staggered or zigzag riveting.

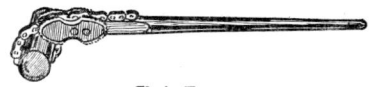

Chain Tongs

chain tongs (*Plumb.*) Used for holding pipe from turning or to turn pipe. It is a heavy bar with sharp teeth at one end, which are held against the pipe by a chain wrapped around the pipe and attached to the bar.

chain trans-mis'sion (*M a c h.*) A means of transmitting power, useful when the distance between driver and driven shafts is too great for gearing and not sufficient for belting.

chair glide (*Uphol.*) Also known as "dome of silence," is a rounded cup-shaped piece of metal used on the bottom of the legs of furniture. It permits easy and noiseless moving of furniture over rugs and floors.

chair rail (*Bldg.*) Usually a wooden band or molded strip attached to a wall at the level of tops of chair backs to prevent marring the plaster.

chaise' longue' (shâz' lông') (*Furn.*) A French style of sofa, made like a chair with a seat long enough to recline upon. During the middle of the eighteenth century, when first in favor, it was made in three parts, a pair of armchairs and a stool.

chal-ced'o-ny (kăl-sĕd'ô-nĭ) (*Mineral.*) A translucent quartz, usually pale blue or gray.

chal'co-cite (kăl'kô-sīt) Cu_2S. Copper ore; a sulphide of copper.

chal'co-py'rite (*Metal.*) ($CuFeS_2$.) A yellow sulphide of copper and iron.

chalk (*Mineral.*) A soft limestone of earthy texture, chiefly composed of the minute shells of Foraminifera, which are very small marine organisms.

chalk'ing (*Plast.*) Dry, chalk-like appearance or deposit on the surface of a plastic.

chalk line. Also called snap line. Used frequently for making a straight line on a floor for placement of shafting, machinery, etc. A piece of string coated with chalk is drawn taut between two points along the floor. When raised at a mid-point and allowed to snap back, a straight chalk line is made on the floor.

chalk o'ver-lay' (*Print.*) A mechanical process for bringing printing plates and type to a smooth, even surface for reproduction. (See MAKE-READY.)

chalk–plate (*Print.*) A kind of plate frequently cast by stereotypers for use in newspaper work.

cham'ber (*Patmkg. and Fdry.*) A pattern or casting which is hollowed or chambered out. (*Shopwk.*) A long recess. (See RECESS.)

cham'fer (*Carp.*) A beveled edge or cut-off corner.

cham'ois leath'er (shăm'ĭ) A soft leather. Chamois skin.

chan-delle' (shän-dĕl') (*A e r o.*) An abrupt climbing turn to approximately a stall in which the momentum of the airplane is used to obtain a higher rate of climb than would be possible in unaccelerated flight. The purpose of this maneuver is to gain altitude at the same time that direction of flight is changed.

change gears (*A u t o. M e c h.*) The transmission device on an automobile. (*Mach.*) The arrangement of lathe gears for cutting screw threads; the train of gears may be combined to give different rates of advance so that the threads of a variety of pitches may be cut.

change-o'ver cues (*Tel.*) A set of marks on frames of motion-picture film which aid projectionist in manual change from one projector to another for continuous action.

chan'nel (*Furn.*) A concave line cut

into a surface; used as a decorative feature in moldings and parts of furniture. (*Tel*) The band or channel in the radio spectrum assigned to a television station or to other forms of communication.

chan′nel i′ron. Rolled bars consisting of a web and two flanges; in section it is like a hollow square with one side omitted.

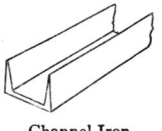
Channel Iron

chap′el (*Print.*) An organized group of workmen in a printing plant.

chap′let (*Fdry.*) A metal support used for holding a core in position.

chap′ter head (*Print.*) The heading at the beginning of a chapter.

chap′trel (chăp′trĕl) (*Arch.*) In Gothic architecture, the capital of a pier or column which receives an arch.

char′ac-ter-is′tic (*Math.*) The index or integral part of a logarithm.

char′ac-ter-is′tic curve of dy′na-mo (*Elec.*) In a generator the relation of the output in volts and amperes to the speed and load. In a motor the relation of its speed to the load placed on it. These values are predictable if the curve has been plotted from the results of a test.

char′coal. Wood which has been charred and carbonized.

char′coal i′ron (*Sheet-Met. Wk.*) A very superior quality of iron which is smelted with wood charcoal as fuel. Its quality lies in its freedom from sulphur.

charge (*Elec.*) The quantity of electricity residing on an electrostatically charged body.

charged cell (*Elec.*) A storage cell which has had direct current passed through it until the positive plate has changed chemically from $PbSO_4$ to $PbSO_2$ and the negative plate has changed from $PbSO_4$ to Pb.

charg′ing (*Elec.*) The process of changing electrochemically the plates and electrolyte of a storage cell or battery.

charg′ing cur′rent (*E l e c.*) Direct current applied to a storage battery to produce chemical action to charge the battery. Its direction is always the reverse of the discharge current.

charg′ing rate (*E l e c.*) The rate of flow, in amperes, of electric current flowing through a storage battery while it is being charged.

Charles′ law (*Phys.*) When the volume is kept constant the pressure coefficient of all gases is the same:
$$\frac{1}{273} = 0.00366 \text{ per degree C.}$$

char′ring (*Shopwk.*) Burning or scorching the surface.

chase (*Mech.*) (1) A lengthwise groove for the reception of a part to make a joint. (2) To cut threads. (*Plast.*) An enclosure of any shape used to: (*a*) shrink-fit parts of a mold cavity in place; (*b*) prevent spreading or distortion in hobbing; (*c*) enclose an assembly of two or more parts of a split cavity block in which the contour of the casting is undercut (with reference to the line of closing of the mold); sometimes called a "yoke." (*Print.*) An iron frame into which pages or columns of type are locked up for the press.

chas′ing (*Furn.*) The ornamenting of metal by indenting, etc.

chas′ing threads (*Mach.*) Cutting threads with a chaser, which usually is a flat tool containing several teeth of the desired pitch.

chas′sis (shà′sê) (*Auto. Mech.*) The unit which includes all parts of the car except the body.

chat′ter (*Metalwk.*) Caused in machine work by lack of rigidity in the cutting tools or in machine parts.

check (*Furn.*) An inlay design composed of squares.

check′er. A checker should be a keen person always on the alert. It is his duty to check drawings for error and to see that specifications have been adhered to. A slip on the part of the checker may prove very expensive to his employer.

check′ing of wood (*Shopwk.*) Cracks in timber caused by uneven seasoning.

check nut (*Mech.*) Commonly called a lock nut. A nut screwed down upon another nut causing a binding on the threads.

check valve (*Plumb.*) A valve which automatically closes to prevent the back flow of water.

cheek (*Fdry.*) The middle section of a three-part flask.

Chel′ten-ham (chĕlt′năm) (*P r i n t.*) The name of a type available in a great variety of faces.

chem′i-cal (*Chem.*) A substance obtained by a chemical process.

chem′i-cal ac′tion. That kind of action, change, or process in which the substance or substances present is or are changed into new or other substances.

chem′i-cal change (*Chem.*) A change by which the identity of a substance is changed; e.g., burning a piece of coal.

chem′i-cal dip braz′ing. A dip-brazing process wherein the filler metal is added to the joint before immersion in a bath of molten chemicals.

chem′i-cal en′gi-neer′. A chemist whose activities include design and erection of chemical plants as well as research and general work in industrial chemistry.

chem′i-cal-ly pure (*Chem.*) Absolutely pure or free of any other chemical. In practice this is almost impossible to attain. The term generally means free from all but the very smallest amounts of chemical impurities.

chem′i-cal pulp (*Papermkg.*) Term applied to wood pulp made by the soda process from the wood of broadleaf trees.

chem′is-try. The science or study of the composition of matter and those changes in matter in which new substances are formed.

chem′ur-ġy. The chemical salvage and conversion of waste materials into new, useful products.

che-nille′ (shê-nēl′) (*Furn.*) A soft fluffy thread or cord used in making a material of that name and fringes for furniture.

cheq′uer (chĕk′ēr) (*Furn.*) A form of decoration made up of squares; much used in inlay.

cher′ry (*Metalwk.*) A form of milling cutter which is more strictly a formed reamer, for finishing out the interior of a die or some similar tool. (*Wood*) *Prunus.* A hard, close-grained, red or brown-colored wood.

chest′nut (*Wood*) *Castanea.* A medium hard, coarse-grained wood, used for building trim and for inexpensive furniture.

chest′nut oak (*Wood*) *Quercus Prinus* and *I. muhlenbergii*. Tree medium size; wood dark brown with lighter sapwood; heavy, strong, and close grained. In many cases serves the same purposes as white oak. The bark is much used in tanning.

chev′ron (*Arch.*) (1) Ornamentation by a zigzag pattern, as used in Romanesque architecture. (2) Rafters in a gable roof that meet at the ridge.

chewed (*Print.*) An expression for the ragged effect of the lines of a plate caused by acid working through an imperfect protection.

chief chem′i-cal en′gi-neer′. An important executive who should be a specialist, both in management and in his specialized line of chemistry

chief drafts′man. The connecting link between drafting room and management. He is responsible for efficient operation of the drafting room. All employees in his department are usually under his direct supervision.

chief en′gi-neer′. In industrial plants the chief engineer is frequently styled "superintendent" or "works manager." He is responsible to the management for the proper carrying out of the plant policies and should be a man of such wide experience that he can ably direct the work of the other engineers.

chief of par′ty. A civil engineer who is in charge of the surveying party in the field. He is responsible to the chief engineer.

chif-fo-nier′ (shĭf-ô-nēr′) (*Furn.*) An ornamental cabinet with shelves and drawers; a high, narrow bureau.

chill. A metallic mold into which specially mixed molten iron is poured to produce a hard casting.

chilled cast′ing (*Mach.*) Casting made in an iron or steel-faced mold. The rapid cooling which takes place in such a mold tends to increase the hardness of the casting.

chi-me′ra (kĭ-mē′rȧ) (*Furn.*) A mythical fire-breathing monster, often used for ornamental purposes.

chim′ney (*Arch. and Engin.*) A vertical flue for drawing off the products of combustion from a stove, a furnace, a fireplace, or some other smoke and gas-producing source.

chim′ney breast (*Arch.*) That surface of a wall which projects into a room at the place where a chimney passes through it. This breast is usually made much wider than the chimney itself, to accommodate a mantel or to improve the appearance of the room.

chim′ney lin′ing (*Arch.*) The tile flues placed within a chimney. Same as chimney flue.

chi′na (*Ceram.*) A term applied to porcelain ware.

chi′na clay (*Pot.*) A very pure, white clay, in the form of a fine powder, used to form the paste of porcelain. A clay used as a filler for paper;

also used in making a coating mixture.

chine (*Aero.*) The intersection of the bottom with the sides or deck of a seaplane float.

chi′noi′se-rie′ (shē′nwȧ′z′-rē′) (*Furn.*) Chinese style of ornamentation.

chip (*Shopwk.*) To remove particles as with a hammer and chisel. A small piece broken or scaled off. Also pieces of metal removed in a machining process, as a lathe chip.

chip board (*Bookbndg.*) Cover board made from wood pulp, chips, and paper; used for folding boxes and similar containers.

chip break′er (*Mach.*) A groove ground on a tool back of the cutting edge which causes chips to curl and break.

chip carv′ing. The making of an ornamental design, usually geometric, by the removal of a number of similar chips, with a small carving tool.

Chip′pen-dale (*Furn.*) Style named after English furniture designer, Thomas Chippendale (1718–1779). Pieces usually of mahogany or walnut; sometimes used softwood, japanned in color, with gilt ornaments, but Chippendale never used inlay or paint. Ornamentation consists of scrolls, shellwork, cupids, flowers, fruits, leaves, and animals. Chair legs are straight and square, cabriole, modified claw and ball, or elaborately carved fantastic designs.

chip′ping (*Shopwk.*) The cutting of metal with cold chisel and hammer.

chip space. In a jig, fixture, or machine, a space provided for the clearance of chips or cuttings so as not to interfere with tooling operations.

chis′el (*Shopwk.*) Tool of great variety whose cutting principle is that of the wedge.

Chisel

chis′el, cape (*Shopwk.*) Chisel with a narrow blade for cutting keyways and similar work in metal.

chis′el, cold (*Shopwk.*) Any chisel for cutting cold metal. Name is usually applied to plain, flat cold chisel.

chis′el, di′a-mond or loz′enge (*Shopwk.*) Similar to a cape chisel, but with a square end and cutting edge at one corner. Used for cutting a sharp-bottomed groove.

chis′el, round (*Shopwk.*) A round-end chisel with the cutting edge ground back at an angle; used for cutting oil grooves and similar work.

chlo′ride (klō′rīd) (*Chem.*) A compound of chlorine with another element or radical; a salt or ester of hydrochloric acid.

chlo′ride of lime (*Chem.*) $CaOCl_2$. "Bleaching powder" or bleaching lime. Obtained by treating lime with chlorine gas. Used as a bleach and as a disinfectant.

chlo′rin-ate (*Plast.*) To treat with chlorine gas.

chlo′rin-at′ed wool (klō′rĭ-nāt′ĕd) (*Textile*) Wool which has been treated with bleaching powder and other material to give luster, increase its affinity for certain dyes, and to destroy its felting property.

chlo′rine (*Chem.*) A greenish-yellow, poisonous, liquefiable gaseous element with an offensive odor (Cl_2). Derived by the electrolysis of sodium chloride in solution. Used for textile bleaching, water purification, poison gas, etc.

chlo′ro-form (*Chem.*) An aromatic liquid; formula $CHCl_3$; used as an anesthetic and solvent.

chocks. Blocks in front or in back of wheels of a stationary vehicle to prevent motion in case brakes should fail to hold.

choke (*Auto.*) A fixed or variable device used to reduce the amount of air and thus increase the richness of the gas mixture in the carburetor.

choke coil (*Elec.*) Turns of wires wound inductively, usually on an iron core, which will tend to retard the rapid change of a varying electric current.

choke′damp (*Chem.*) Name applied to carbon dioxide, especially when present in mines.

chop in′lay′ (*Furn.*) An early form of inlay in which pieces were fitted into a solid surface.

chord (*Aero.*) An arbitrary datum line from which the ordinates and angles of an airfoil are measured. (*Engin.*) The principal member of a truss, either top or bottom. (*Math.*) A straight line connecting the ends of an arc.

chord′al pitch (*Gear.*) The distance from a point on a gear tooth to a corresponding point on the next tooth measured as a chord of the pitch circle.

chord length (*Aero.*) The projected length of an air-foil section.

chro′ma (krō′má) (*Color*) Refers to the brilliancy, strength, or intensity of a color. Neutralization or graying of a color brings about a loss in chroma.

chrom′a-lu′mi-num (krōm′á-lū′mĭ-nŭm) (*Metal.*) A very strong aluminum alloy.

chro′mate (*Chem.*) Salt of chromic acid.

chrome nickel steel (*Metal.*) A rather expensive steel, hard to machine, forge, and heat treat. In most cases chrome vanadium steel or nickel steel will serve the same purpose at lower cost.

chrome tan′nage (*Leather.*) A process of tanning by the use of chromic acid.

chrome–va-na′di-um steel (*Engin.*) A tough steel containing 0.87 per cent chromium and 0.18 per cent vanadium. After heat treatment it has an ultimate strength of 210,000 pounds per square inch and an elastic limit of 191,500 pounds per square inch.

chro′mi-um (*Metal.*) Symbol, Cr. A grayish-white metallic element; specific gravity, 6.50; melting point, 2939° F. Used in alloy steels and in plating.

chro′mi-um–plat′ed tools (*Metalwk.*) Chromium plating of tools and gauges is used to build up worn parts, producing a very hard surface which does not have to be ground and from which chips clear readily.

chro′mi-um plat′ing. Extensively used to provide a durable, bright finish, particularly on such items as automobile parts and hardware exposed to unfavorable weather conditions. It has to a great degree taken the place of nickel plating. Also see CHROMIUM-PLATED TOOLS.

chro′mi-um steel (*Metal.*) Steel containing from 1 to 2 per cent chromium. It is very hard and tough; used as an automotive alloy steel, and for projectiles, armor plate, etc.

chro′mo-diz-ing (*Metal.*) A hot-dip

process of forming a hard-surface film on aluminum alloys; sometimes used in place of anodizing.

chro-nom'e-ter (krô-nŏm'ê-tēr) A precision watch or other accurate, portable time-keeping device.

chrys'o-tile (krĭs'-ô-tĭl) Long-fiber asbestos.

chuck (Shopwk.) In itself a very broad term, meaning a device for holding a rotating tool or work during an operation. There are many different kinds of chucks for various purposes.

Chuck

chuck'ing (Mach.) In lathe turning, the mounting of the work in the chuck.

chuck'ing ream'er (Shopwk.) Spiral fluted chucking reamers with three and four grooves are employed for enlarging cored holes, etc. They are also made with oil passages through them, and in this form are adapted to operating in steel. Another style is used for finishing holes that have been roughed out.

churn'ing (Fdry.) Agitating the fluid metal in a mold by moving a small, heated iron rod up and down in the feeder in order to insure solid castings.

churn mold'ing (Furn.) A zigzag molding often seen in Norman architecture.

chute (shoōt) An inclined trough or tube to guide sliding objects from a higher to a lower level.

cinc'ture (sĭnk'tûr) (Arch.) A ring or fillet at the top and bottom of a column serving to divide the shaft from its capital and its base.

cin'der bed (Fdry.) A layer of cinders beneath a mold to permit the escape of gas.

cin'na-bar (Metal.) The ore of mercury. Also used as a pigment (vermilion) and in the manufacture of costume jewelry.

cinque'foil (sĭnk'foil) (Arch.) A five-leaved rosette or ornament.

Cir-cas'sian wal'nut (sẽr-kăsh'ăn) (Wood) Juglans regia. A fawn-colored walnut with dark-colored streaks. The wood was very extensively used in furniture manufactured from 1900 to the beginning of the World War I.

cir'cle (Math.) A plane figure bounded by a curved line every point of which is equally distant from a fixed point within called the center. The circumference of a circle is divided into 360 equal parts, called degrees. (See CIRCULAR MEASURE.) Area = radius squared x 3.1416 or diameter squared x 0.7854.

cir'cle mark'er (Aero.) A circular band marking the approximate center of the landing area or the intersection of the principal landing strips on an airport or landing field.

cir'cle trow'el (Plaster.) A plasterer's trowel made with either concave or convex blade for working on curved surfaces.

cir'cuit (Elec.) The course followed by an electric current passing from its source through a succession of conductors and back to its starting point.

cir'cuit break'er (Elec.) A switch, usually automatic, which opens to stop the flow of current.

cir′cu-lar and an′gu-lar meas-ure.
60 seconds (″) = 1 minute (′)
60 minutes   = 1 degree (°)
90 degrees   = 1 quadrant
4 quadrants   = 1 circle or circumference

cir′cu-lar loom (*Elec.*) A fire-resisting, flexible, coated, nonmetallic tubing slipped over electric wires for additional insulation.

cir′cu-lar mil (*Elec.*) The area of a circle one mil in diameter; used as a unit in measuring the cross sections of wires.

cir′cu-lar mill′ing ma-chine′ (*Mach.*) A vertical-type, continuous milling machine in which both table and cutter rotate.

cir′cu-lar pitch (*Gear.*) The distance from the center of one tooth to the center of the next, measured on the pitch line.

cir′cu-lar saw. A saw whose teeth are spaced around the edge of a circular disk running upon a central arbor.

Circular Saw

cir-cum′fer-ence. The length of a line which forms a circle. (*Math.*) c. of circle = diameter x 3.1416.

cir′cum-scribe′. To enclose within certain lines or boundaries. To draw around or outside of.

ci′se-leur′ (sē′z′-lûr′) (*Furn.*) An engraver or maker of metal ornaments.

cit′ric ac′id (*Chem.*) A tribasic acid extracted from lemons or other citrus fruits, as a white crystalline substance having a pleasant sour taste. Used in medicines, flavoring extracts, confectionery, etc.

civ′il en′gi-neer′. One whose work includes design, construction, and maintenance of public works, highways, railroads, bridges, steel framework of buildings, etc.

civ′il serv′ice. The appointive employment in a government position of civilian personnel. As a rule civil-service employees are selected from an eligible list prepared from an examination. They hold office so long as they are efficient and comply with all rules.

clamp (*Carp. and Mach.*) A tool for holding portions of work together, both in wood and metal.

clamp cou′pling (*Mech.*) A shaft coupling made in two or more parts, and clamped by means of transverse bolts.

Clamp

clamp dog (*Mach.*) A lathe carrier consisting of two jaws and two bolts which permit a clamping on the work.

clamp′ing bars (*Fdry.*) Those bars either adjustable or solid used for clamping the parts of a mold together to prevent a separation by the expansion of gases.

clamp′ing screw. Any screw by which pieces of work are pinched or held together. A screw which clamps.

clap′board (*Arch.*) A lapping weatherboard used for siding.

clap′per box (*Mach.*) The swinging part of the tool-holding device on a shaper or planer which permits the tool to ride freely over the work on the return stroke.

clap post (*Furn.*) The upright post

of a cupboard on which the door "claps" or closes.

clas′si-cal (*Arch.*) Referring to the architecture of the ancient Greeks and Romans.

clas′sic mold′ing (*Arch.*) Moldings similar to those used in the classic orders of architecture.

clas′si-fi-ca′tion. Arranging in groups by types or characteristics for easy identification.

clav′i-chord (*Furn.*) An early musical instrument, a forerunner of the modern piano.

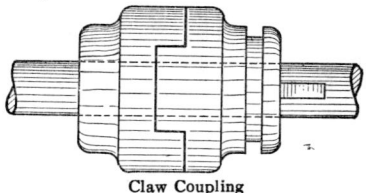

Claw Coupling

claw cou′pling (*Mech.*) A loose coupling used in cases where shafts require instant connection. It is somewhat like a flange coupling, but instead has projections or claws cast on each face which engage in corresponding recesses in the faces opposite.

claw ham′mer (*Carp.*) A hammer used principally by woodworkers. It has a face for driving nails and a claw for use as a nail puller.

clay (*Masonry*) A common earth, compact and brittle when dry, but plastic when wet. Used in the manufacture of bricks.

clay wash (*Fdry.*) Clay thinned with water and used for coating gaggers and flasks.

clean (*Bookbndg.*) A well-printed sheet; work well performed; a well-stamped cover.

clean cut′. A machined surface is said to be "clean cut" when no blemishes or rough edges occur. The term is also often applied to a piece of work well designed and well executed.

clean proof (*Print.*) A proof which needs but few corrections. Opposite of dirty proof.

clean thread (*Mach.*) A screw thread that is sharp, smooth, and free of imperfections.

clear′ance (*Mach.*) (1) In a lathe tool, the angle between the cutting edge and vertical position of the work. The clearance must be not less than 3 deg. and in most cases not more than 10 deg. (2) The amount of space, open or free, between adjacent parts.

cleat (*Carp.*) A strip of wood or metal fastened to other material or nailed against a wall usually for the purpose of fastening something to it.

cleav′age. A split cleft or division. A tendency in a rock to divide in a certain manner.

cleft (*Mech.*) Meaning "split"; stronger than sawed or "cut" stuff, and used for wooden hand screws, etc.

clev′is (*Mech.*) A U-shaped iron such as is used to connect an automobile brake rod to a brake lever.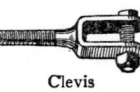

Clevis

climb cut (*Mach.*) The cutting of metal, in a milling machine, in which the table moves in the direction of the rotation of the cutting tool.

clinch (*Shopwk.*) To secure more firmly as by bending down the ends of protruding nails.

clinch′er rim (*Auto.*) A wheel rim

with turned edge or groove on both sides to engage the flange of a tire. Inflating the tire, locks the tire on the rim.

clink′er. A mass of fused or molten ashes.

clip an′gles (*Engin.*) Usually, small pieces of angles used in connecting two members.

clip′per (*Tel.*) Method used to separate synchronization pulses from video picture information.

clip′ping (*Textile*) Finishing certain fabrics by cutting the surface fibers to an even length.

clock′wise. The direction in which the hands of a clock move, with a right-hand motion.

clog. To obstruct, hinder, or choke up; e.g., the stoppage of flow through a pipe by an accumulation of foreign matter, or the filling up of the grooves in a file when operating on soft metal.

clois′ter (*Print.*) Name given to a particular type face.

close (*Arch.*) The precinct of a cathedral or abbey. Sometimes the walls are traceable, but now generally the boundary is known only by tradition.

closed cir′cuit (*Elec.*) A complete path from the source through an external circuit back to the source. Usually accomplished through the closing of a control in the form of a switch.

closed lock joint (*Sheet-Met. Wk.*) A joint made by hooking together the two turned-down edges which are to be fastened, then setting the joint with a grooving tool. Lock joints usually are not soldered.

closed shop. A shop which employs only union members.

close fit (thread, class 4) (*Mach.*) Used on aircraft parts, etc., where accuracy is essential.

close nip′ple (*Plumb.*) Twice as long as standard pipe thread, with no shoulder between the two sets of threads.

Close Nipple

clo′sure (*Arch.*) A portion of a brick used to close the end of a course.

cloth of es·tate′ (*Furn.*) A decorative cloth draped over a throne or chair of state.

clus′ter (*Elec.*) A lighting fixture having more than two lamps on it; usually not widely spaced.

clus′tered (*Arch.*) Grouped together.

clutch (*Auto. Mech.*) A device placed between engine and transmission which permits the engine to run free when the left foot pedal is depressed, or to drive the car when the pedal is released. (*Mech.*) A device making temporary connection between pieces of shafting, etc.

clutch ped′al (*Auto. Mech.*) The left foot pedal which connects and disconnects the clutch.

clutch pres′sure plate (*Auto. Mech.*) Part of the clutch assembly consisting of a metal ring mounted on levers. Helical springs exert a pressure on this clutch plate, which pressure in turn passes to the clutch disk and to the machined face of the flywheel, providing the necessary friction to transmit power from engine to transmission.

coach (*Auto. Mech.*) Has an enclosed two-door-type body with separate seats in front and full width cross seat in rear.

coal. A solid, brown to black, inflammable substance dug from the earth. It is formed from prehistoric vegetable deposits. As shipped from the mines, its principal use is for fuel although many chemical by-products are of great importance.

coal gas. Gas produced by the destructive distillation of bituminous coal. Illuminating gas.

coal siz′es. The sizes by which anthracite coal is marketed are as follows, diameter of opening through which or over which coal will pass:

	Through	Over
Broken	4 1/2 in.	3 1/4 in.
Egg	3 1/4 in.	2 5/16 in.
Stove	2 5/16 in.	1 5/8 in.
Chestnut	1 5/8 in.	7/8 in.
Pea	7/8 in.	9/16 in.
No. 1 Buckwheat	9/16 in.	5/16 in.

coal tar. The black pitch distilled from bituminous coal condensed in the manufacture of coal gas. Widely used in the arts.

coat. An application of paint, plaster. or other material done at one time.

coat′ed pa′per (*P r i n t*.) A highly enameled paper either in glossy or dull finish necessary for high-grade halftone work.

co-ax′i-al (*M a t h*.) Anything with axes that are coincident like an ellipse or a hyperbola.

co-ax′i-al ca′ble (*Tel*.) A specially designed cable which will carry picture signals. It consists of two concentric electrical conductors (a cylindrical conductor with a single wire centered along its length) which are separated by an insulating medium.

co′balt (kō′bôlt) (*Min*.) A tough, pink-white metal of the iron group. Valuable for the blue pigments it forms.

co′balt′crom steel (kō′bôlt′krōm stēl) (*Engin*.) An alloy steel containing 1.5 per cent carbon, 12.5 per cent chromium, and 3.5 per cent cobalt. Suitable for cutting tools.

coch′i-neal′ (kŏch′ĭ-nēl′) (*Chem*.) A red coloring matter extracted from the female of a Mexican insect.

cock (*Plumb*.) A plug type of valve which has an opening to permit passage of liquids or gases. A quarter turn opens or closes the valve.

cock bead′ing (*Furn*.) A small, semicircular, projecting molding, used around drawers.

cock′le (kŏk′′l) (*Bookbndg*.) The condition of papers in books when too much dampness is allowed to permeate through the book; also applied to covers when raising, pulling, waving, warping, or curling exists. (*Finish*) An irregular but intentionally produced finish.

cock′ling (*Papermkg. and Print*.) Wavy edges on paper caused by irregular drying. (*Textile*) An irregular shrinking on the surface of a fabric.

cock′pit (*Aero*.) The open spaces in an airplane provided with seating accommodations for pilot and passengers. When entirely housed in, it is called a "cabin."

cock′pit cowl′ing (*Aero*.) A metal or plywood cowling placed around a cockpit.

co′co-bo′lo (kō′kô-bō′lō) (*W o o d*) *Dalbergia*. A Central American tree of the rosewood family. The wood is reddish in color with bands of black; very hard and oily. Used for bowling balls and knife handles.

co′co-nut oil (*Chem*.) Obtained from the fruit of the coconut palm. Used in the manufacture of hard-water soaps.

code. Any set of rules devised for the purpose of securing uniformity in work and for the maintaining of proper standards is usually called a code; e.g., a building code.

code bea′con (*Aero.*) A flashing beacon light having a recognizable characteristic of dots and / or dashes by which its individual identity can be established.

co′ef-fi′cient (kō′ĕ-fĭsh′ĕnt) (*Math.*) A prefixed number to be used as a multiplier. (*Phys.*) A number indicating the degree of a quality of a substance or material.

co′ef-fi′cient of ex-pan′sion(*Engin.*) The factor which expresses the change per unit length of any material for each degree of temperature.

co′ef-fi′cient of fric′tion. The ratio between the weight of a body and a horizontally applied force required to move it over another surface.

cof′fer (kŏf′ẽr) (*Arch.*) A deeply recessed panel, in a ceiling or dome.

cof′fer-dam′ (kŏf′ẽr-dăm′) A wall of piles between or within which excavating is done for foundations.

cog (*Mech.*) An inserted tooth as in a cogwheel. Gears are often improperly referred to as cogwheels.

cog′ging (*Metal.*) Reduction of ingots to blooms by rolling or forging.

co-he′sion (*Phys.*) The attraction existing between molecules of the same kind.

coil (*Elec.*) Successive turns of insulated wire which create a magnetic field when an electric current passes through them.

coin′age bronze (*Metal.*) An alloy of 95 per cent copper, 2½ per cent tin, and 2½ per cent zinc.

co-in′ci-den′tal start′er (*Auto. Mech.*) A type of starter in which the starting-motor switch and the gasoline feed are both controlled by the foot-accelerator pedal.

coir (koir) The fiber obtained from the outer husk of the coconut, used for brushes, cocoa matting, and rope.

coke. A fuel made by baking bituminous coal in closed ovens to drive off gases and other elements. A ton of coal produces two-thirds ton of coke. Coke is 88 per cent carbon.

Cold Chisel

cold chis′el (*Metalwk.*) An all-steel chisel, i.e., without handle, used for the chipping of metals.

cold drawn (*Metal.*) Production of metal into its final form by drawing through dies while cold.

cold flow (*Plast.*) Change of dimensions or distortion caused by sustained application of a force greater than the elastic limit.

cold mold′ing (*Plast.*) A procedure in which a composition is shaped at ordinary temperatures and hardened by subsequent baking.

cold mold′ing com′pounds (*Plast.*) Those molding powders, consisting of a filler and binder are formed into a mass under pressure in a die at room temperature and later heated in ovens to harden.

cold-rolled steel (*Metal.*) May be either of open-hearth or Bessemer process. The carbon content runs from 0.12 to 0.20 per cent. This steel is marketed with a bright, smooth surface and is made quite accurate to size so that for many purposes no machining is necessary. It may be casehardened but will not temper.

cold roll′ing. Cold rolling of steel produces a high tensile strength but with a sacrifice of ductility and toughness. Cold-rolled steel has a much smoother finish than hot-rolled steel.

cold saws (*Mach.*) Power machines for sawing metal with circular saws.

cold shuts (*Fdry.*) Formed in the mold when two streams of metal become so chilled before meeting that they will not fuse properly when they come together.

cold slug (*Plast.*) The first material to enter an injection mold; so called, because in passing through the sprue orifice it is cooled below effective molding temperature.

cold–slug well (*Plast.*) Space provided directly opposite the sprue opening in an injection mold to trap the cold slug.

cold stretch (*Plast.*) Pulling operation usually on extruded filaments to improve tensile qualities.

col-laps′ing tap (*Mach.*) This type of tap is used in machine tapping. The principle is similar to that of self-opening dies except that the action is reversed. Such taps permit more rapid tapping and do not mar the thread.

col′lar (*Furn.*) A molding extending around a leg. (*Mech.*) A ring formed on a shaft by forging in the solid, or by being made as a separate piece, bored and turned and held in place by a setscrew or pin. It may be shrunk on or allowed to run free.

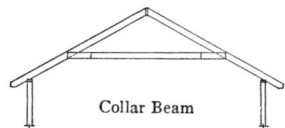

Collar Beam

col′lar beam (*Arch.*) A beam above the lower ends of the rafters and attached to them.

col′lar, oil′ing (*Mach.*) Is used on high-speed installations. A collar which runs in a reservoir of oil in the bearing is either turned on the journal or is attached to it. Wipers are often used in the upper half of the bearing to scrape oil off the collar and spread it on the journal.

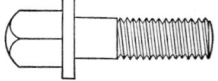

Collar Screw

col′lar screw (*Shopwk.*) Collar or collar-head screws are used for much the same purpose as regular cap screws, and, in fact, are sometimes designated as "collar" or "collar-head" cap screws.

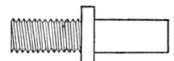

Collar Stud

col′lar stud (*Mach.*) A stud threaded at one end and having a short shaft or spindle at the other, the two separated by a collar which is an integral part of the stud, used for carrying gears, levers, etc.

col-la′tor (kŏ-lā′tẽr) (*Bookbndg.*) One who examines or checks the material to be bound into a book, for verification and correction of arrangement.

col-lec′tor ring (*Elec.*) A circular piece of copper against which a brush contacts in order to carry current from a stationary to a movable part.

col'let (kŏl'ĕt) (*Mach.*) A clamping ring or holding device; in the shops the term is freely applied to sockets for tapered-shank drills, and reducing sleeves and bushings of various types.

col-lo'di-on (kŏ-lō'dĭ-ŭn) (*Chem.*) A solution of the lower nitrate of cellulose in a mixture of alcohol and ether. Used for producing a film over a surface.

Collet

col'loid (kŏl'oid) (*Chem.*) A substance of gelatinous nature, as gelatin, starch, albumin, etc. Also non-gelatinous substances, such as silver and gold, may be obtained in colloidal form. Substances lying between solution and suspension are colloidal dispersions. Any substance when dispersed into particles whose size ranges between 5 and 100 millimicrons. Molecules of many synthetic resins fall within this range.

col'lo-type (*Print.*) A photo-mechanical, nonscreen, halftone process which depends partly on the lithographic principle.

co-lo'ni-al (*Arch.*) Relating to the style of architecture in vogue from early settlements in America up to the establishment of the United States Government; although the term is frequently applied to buildings erected as late as 1840. (*Furn.*) That type of American furniture in vogue prior to the revolution; although often applied to furniture made as late as the first half of the nineteenth century.

col'on-nade' (kŏl'ŏ-nād') (*Arch.*) A row of columns.

col'o-phon (kŏl'ô-fŏn) (*Print.*) (1) A printer's trade-mark usually placed on a title page. (2) Facts regarding the production of a book, or the name of the printer, the place and date when it was published, printed on the last page.

col'or. Any one of the hues of the spectrum, or a tint produced by the blending of these hues.

col'or fil'ter. A colored substance such as glass, dyed gelatin, or colored solution used to absorb certain colors and transmit others.

col'or for tem'per-ing. In the tempering of steel the following colors appear: white, light straw, dark straw, blue, and purple. The tempering is checked at a certain color according to the degree of hardness desired.

col'or form (*Print.*) The second color in a printing job. May be run first: a key form.

col'or-hard'en (*Metal.*) To produce a pleasing color effect by casehardening.

col'or proofs (*Print.*) Proofs of color plates combined and registered.

col'or proofs—pro-gres'sive (*Print.*) Single proofs of each plate of a color set and combined proofs, showing result of each successive color printed and assembled in printing sequence.

col'or scheme. A general arrangement or plan of coloring for a piece of work.

col'or work (*Print.*) General term for color plates to print in two or more colors.

Colt's ar'mo-ry press (*Print.*) A heavy-duty type of platen press.

col'umn (*Arch.*) A vertical shaft or pillar receiving pressure in the direction of its longitudinal axis. (*Print.*)

One of the vertical sections, as on a newspaper page.

com'bi-na'tion (*Chem.*) Union of two or more elements.

com'bi-na'tion chuck (*Mach.*) A universal chuck which may also have independent jaw action.

com'bi-na'tion die (*Mach.*) Die so constructed that it both cuts the blank and draws the piece to required shape. A combination of blanking and drawing dies.

com'bi-na'tion drill and coun'ter-sink' (*Mach.*) Used for centering work to be held between the centers of a lathe. (See CENTER DRILL.)

com'bi-na'tion fix'ture (*Elec.*) A fixture piped for gas and wired for electricity; infrequently used now.

com'bi-na'tion half'tone (*Print.*) An engraving consisting of halftone and line values requiring two negatives.

com'bi-na'tion plate (*Print.*) Halftone and line work combined and etched on one plate.

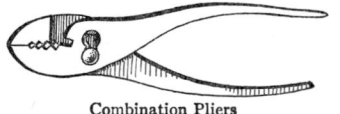

Combination Pliers

com'bi-na'tion pli'ers. Those adjustable for size of opening by means of a slip joint; having the outer grip scored and the inner grip notched for grasping round objects.

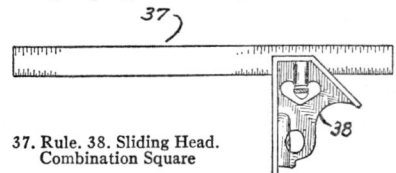

37. Rule. 38. Sliding Head. Combination Square

com'bi-na'tion square (*Shopwk.*) A square containing bevel protractor, level and center head in addition to a movable square head.

com'bi-na'tion switch (*Elec.*) A switch, such as is used on automobiles, for controlling both ignition and lights.

com-bus'tion (*Chem.*) The chemical union of a combustible substance with oxygen, resulting in the production of heat.

com-bus'tion cham'ber (*Auto. Mech.*) That space within the cylinder and in the cylinder head directly above the piston.

com-mer'cial ef-fi'cien-cy of dy'na-mo (*Elec.*) Determined by dividing the output by the input expressed in per cent:

$$\text{Eff.} = \frac{\text{output}}{\text{input}}$$

com-mer'cial ef-fi'cien-cy of mo'tor (*Elec.*) Brake horsepower divided by the electrical horsepower. Or output divided by the input; expressed in per cent.

com-mer'cial flux. A flux sold under a trade name; prepared for use in soldering, brazing, and welding.

com'mi-nute. To reduce solids to minute particles by crushing, grinding, or pulverizing.

com'mon bond (*Masonry*) Similar to a running bond, but with every fifth, sixth, or seventh course a header course, either full or Flemish, the former being all headers, the latter with headers and stretchers alternately.

com'mon brick. Brick such as is used for rough work or for filling in or backing.

com'mon raf'ters (*Arch.*) Rafters,

common to any part of a roof, extending from plate to ridge without a break.

com′mu-tat′ing pole (*Elec.*) An electromagnetic bar inserted between the pole pieces of a dynamo to offset the cross magnetization of the armature currents.

com′mu-ta′tion (*Elec.*) See COMMUTATOR.

com′mu-ta′tor (*Elec.*) A contrivance for reversing the direction of electric current in any circuit.

com′mu-ta′tor bar (*Elec.*) See COMMUTATOR.

com-pact′ car (*Auto.*) An automobile, of any body style, designed especially for easy parking, ease of operation, low maintenance cost and high mileage per gallon of gasoline.

com′pa-ra′tor (kŏm′pȧ-rā′tẽr) (*Shopwk.*) A machine designed by James Hartness to measure screw threads and similar parts by projecting an enlarged shadow on a chart to compare the screw with the desired standard.

com′pass. An instrument with two legs, usually pointed, and joined at the top; used for taking or marking measurements, subdividing distances, describing circles, curves, etc. (*Elec.*) A permanent magnetic needle balanced in center and usually supported above a chart for convenience in reading directions on the surface of the earth.

com′pass plane (*Furn.*) A plane with adjustable sole, used for smoothing concave or convex surfaces.

com′pass saw (*Woodwkg.*) A type of handsaw with small tapering blade,

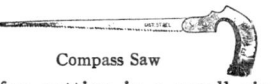
Compass Saw

used for cutting in a small circle or the like.

com-pen′di-um. An abridged edition which summarizes the subjects treated but does not treat them exhaustively.

com′pen-sat′ed watt′me′ter (*Elec.*) A wattmeter which has a compensating coil connected in series with the potential coil for the purpose of correcting the error caused by the absorption of power due to mechanical operation of the potential coil.

com′pen-sat′ing coil (*Elec.*) A coil which serves to compensate for the mechanical friction in the moving coil of a meter.

com′pen-sa′tor (*Elec.*) An auto transformer with a switching mechanism for starting large alternating-current induction motors.

com′ple-men′ta-ry an′gles (*Math.*) Two angles which, added together, equal 90 deg.

com′ple-men′ta-ry col′or. One of two colors, which, when combined, produce white or nearly white light.

com-plet′ed cir′cuit (*Elec.*) Also called closed circuit. One that has been made or closed.

com′plex. Intricate, involved, made up of many parts.

com′plex steel (*Metal.*) Steel which contains more than two alloying elements.

com′pli-cate. To make complex, difficult, or hard to deal with.

com′po board. A trade name for a building board made of narrow strips of wood glued together to make a large sheet, both sides being faced with a heavy paper.

com-po′nent. One of the various forces which combine to make the resultant.

com-pos′ing ma-chines′ (*Print.*) Machines for mechanical typesetting (Monotype, Linotype, Intertype, and Ludlow).

com-pos′ing room (*Print.*) A room where type is set and made up into forms for printing.

com-pos′ing rule (*Print.*) A brass or steel strip, usually two points thick, against which type is composed.

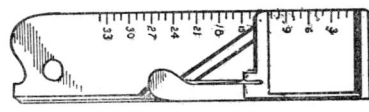

Composing Stick

com-pos′ing stick (*Print.*) A metal device used by compositors for holding type while it is being assembled into lines.

com-pos′ite or′der (*Arch.*) The most ornate of the classic orders of architecture.

com′po-si′tion. A putting together of parts to form a whole. A compound as an alloy. (*Fine Arts*) The general arrangement or style of the work. (*Print.*) That part of printing which pertains to typesetting, making up, etc.

com′po-si′tion of forc′es (*Mech.*) The process of finding a single force which will produce the same effect as the joint action of all the other forces.

com-pos′i-tor (*Print.*) One who sets type by hand.

com′pound (*Chem.*) A union of two or more elements in a very definite proportion. The same compound always contains the same elements in the same proportions.

com′pound arch (*Arch.*) A type of arch made up of a number of concentric archways, successively placed within and behind each other.

com′pound gen′er-a′tor (*Elec.*) See COMPOUND WOUND.

com′pound mo′tor (*Elec.*) See COMPOUND WOUND.

com′pound rest (*Mach.*) A secondary slide, tool rest, and swivel plate superimposed on the cross slide and is capable of hand feed independent of the lathe cross feed. It is of particular advantage in turning to a desired angle.

com′pound slid′ing ta′ble (*Mach.*) The table of a machine tool to which the work is bolted and is provided with at least two movements, one longitudinal and the other transverse.

com′pound wound (*Elec.*) A generator or motor having a part of a series-field winding wound on top of a part of a shunt-field winding on each of the main pole pieces.

com′pound wound con-tin′u-ous cur′rent dy′na-mo (*Elec.*) A direct-current generator employing the use of a cumulative connection between its shunt and series fields, which will bring about an increase in field strength with an increase in load, offsetting the natural tendency for the terminal voltage to fall off.

com-pressed′ air. Practically, air compressed to such a degree that it may be used as a source of power, as for the operation of air tools, etc.

com-press′i-bil′i-ty (*P h y s.*) The

com-press′ing (*Bookbndg.*) After the cover is placed on a book, the book is placed in a large press and allowed to remain until dry. This operation is "compressing."

com-pres′sion. Pressing together. The opposite of tension.

com-pres′sion brak′ing (*Auto. Mech.*) Reducing the amount of gas fed to the engine and depending on engine compression for braking power when descending a hill.

com-pres′sion cou′pling (*Mech.*) A coupling containing tapered parts which grip the shafting when a series of bolts parallel to the shafting are drawn up.

com-pres-sion gauge (*Auto. Mech.*) A meter which registers in pounds per square inch the pressure on gases in the combustion chamber.

com-pres′sion–ig-ni′tion en′gine (*Aero.*) A type of engine in which the fuel is sprayed into the cylinder and ignited by the heat of compression of the air charge.

com-pres′sion mold′ing (*Plast.*) A method of plastic molding which is most generally used to form thermosetting plastic compounds into products. The molding compound, generally preheated, is placed into an open mold, the mold is closed, heat and pressure are applied by a downward moving press, whereupon the material softens and fills the mold cavity, undergoing a chemical change that hardens it. (See INJECTION AND EXTRUSION.)

com-pres′sion ra′ti-o (*Auto. Mech.*) Ratio between the atmospheric pressure when the piston is at the end of the down stroke and the pressure when the piston is in its topmost position of the compression stroke. It is measured in atmospheres.

com-pres′sion ring (*Auto. Mech.*) A type of piston ring used to reduce compression losses and to maintain oil seal. Usually the top or top and second rings on a piston.

com-pres′sion spring (*Mech.*) A helical spring which is designed to operate under pressure, therefore tending to shorten when in action.

Compression Spring

com-pres′sion stroke (*Auto. Mech.*) The second stroke of the piston in a four-cycle engine, occurring when both intake and exhaust valves are closed.

com-pres′sive strength (*Engin.*) Resistance to forces tending to compress, shorten, or crush.

com-put′er (*Math.*) Analog — acts on internally store information to solve complex mathematical problems. Digital — computes information in digital form. It is more accurate than the analog computer.

con′cave. Hollowed out; a curved recess; a bowl-shaped depression.

con-cealed′ wir′ing (*Elec.*) Wiring which has been run in a wall, floor, or ceiling and which does not appear on an exposed surface.

con′cen-trat′ed (*Chem.*) Containing relatively much solute.

con′cen-trat′ed load (*Arch.*) A load localized on a beam, girder, or structure.

con-cen′tric. Having a common center.

con-cen′tric jaw chuck (*Mech.*) A chuck in which all the jaws are moved equally toward or from the center by a common mechanism.

con-cep′tion. A plan or invention of the mind.

con-cise′. Brief but comprehensive.

con-crete′. Cement, sand, and gravel, with proportions varying to suit conditions.

con′crete blocks (*B l d g.*) Molded blocks, usually with hollow spaces, used in construction of walls.

con-cur′rent forc′es (*Mech.*) Forces which either start from a common point or pass through a common point if extended.

con′den-sa′tion (*Phys.*) The change of a substance from a vapor into a liquid state due to cooling.

con′den-sa′tion pump (*Steam Heat.*) A device for removing the liquid condensation from steam returns.

con′den-sa′tion res′ins (*Plast.*) Any of the alkyd, phenol-aldehyde, and urea-formaldehyde resins. The final products are also called "condensation-polymers."

con-densed′ (*Print.*) Cut down, abbreviated. Condensed type is that which is thin in proportion to its height.

con-dens′er (*Elec.*) An accumulator of electrical energy. (*Mech.*) A vessel in which the condensation of gases is effected.

con-dens′er an-ten′na (*Radio*) A small condenser connected in the antenna circuit used to increase the wave length of a short antenna.

con-dens′er ca-pac′i-ty (*Elec.*) See CAPACITY.

con-dens′er di′e-lec′tric (*Elec.*) The material used for insulation between condenser plates.

con-dens′er e-lec′tro-lyte (*Elec.*) The solution used in a liquid-type condenser.

con-dens′er plate (*Elec.*) See PLATE CONDENSER.

con-duct′ance (*Elec.*) The opposite of resistance; i.e., the ease with which a conductor carries an electric current.

con-duc′tion (*Elec.*) The flow of an electric current through a conducting body, such as a copper wire.

con′duc-tiv′i-ty (*Elec.*) The relative ability of materials to carry an electrical current.

con-duc′tor (*Elec.*) A substance which conducts electricity readily.

con-duc′tor or lead′er (*Plumb.*) A pipe to convey rain water.

con-duc′tor stake (*Sheet-Met. Wk.*) A stake having two long cylindrical ends of different diameters. It is used for bending, shaping, and working round objects such as rain conductors, spouts, and sheet-metal tubes.

con′duit (kŏn′dĭt) A conductor, as a large pipe for fluids. (*Elec.*) A metal enclosure used to protect electric wiring. The tubing may be rigid or flexible.

con′duit box (*Elec.*) The steel box to which the ends of a conduit are attached and which may be used as an outlet, junction, or pull box.

con′duit bush′ing (*Elec.*) A threaded cap attached to the end of a line of conduit to make a finished job and to prevent chafing of conductors which pass through it.

con′duit coup′ling (*Elec.*) A short metal sleeve with internal threads to receive the threaded ends of pieces of conduit to be connected.

con′duit wir′ing (*Elec.*) When electric wires are carried inside conduit.

con′du-let′ (*Elec.*) A trade name for conduit fittings.

cone. A solid figure that tapers uniformly from a circular base to a point. (*Mach.*) A piece like the circular segment of a cone. (*Math.*) Convex area = circumference of base x ½ slanting height. Entire area = convex area + area of base. Volume = area of base x 1/3 of the altitude.

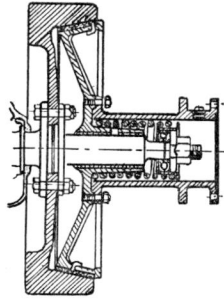

Cone Clutch

cone clutch (*Mech.*) A form of friction clutch in which the power necessary for driving is effected by the friction of smooth, turned conical surfaces. These surfaces are often faced with leather.

co′nel-rad (*Rad.*) A radio alert system for air defense; est. by U. S. government in 1951. (Plan for CONtrol of ELectromagnetic RADiation.)

cone man′drel (*Mach.*) A type of mandrel on which work is centered by the clamping action of two cones against the work. The mandrel has a shoulder to prevent one cone from sliding, and threads to permit a locking of the second cone.

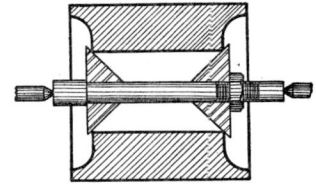

Cone Mandrel

cone pul′ley (*Mach.*) A stepped pulley, one having two or more faces of different diameters; used in pairs, the large end of one being opposite the small end of the other, so that a shifting of the belt will give a change of speed.

cone pul′ley lathe (*Mach.*) A special lathe used for turning cone pulleys.

cone speak′er (*Elec.*) One in which the movable coil is permanently attached to the apex of a stiff paper cone.

con′fi-dente (*Furn.*) A sofa or settee with seats at each end.

con′ic sec′tion (*Math.*) A curve which may be formed by the intersection of a plane with a right circular cone; an ellipse, parabola, or hyperbola. That branch of geometry which treats of these curves.

co-nif′er-ous (kô-nĭf′ẽr-ŭs) Pertaining to plants or trees bearing cones.

con′ing an′gle (*Aero.*) The average angle between the span axis of a blade or wing of a rotary wing system and a plane perpendicular to the axis of rotation.

con′ju-gate ax′is (kŏn′jōō-gāt) The shortest diameter of an oval or ellipse.

con-nect′ing rod (*Auto.*) A rod or arm, with bearings at both ends, which makes the connection between crankshaft and pistons.

con-nect′ing–rod bear′ing (*Auto.*) The bearing at the large end of the connecting rod, where it fits the crankshaft, is halved or split and is usually of Babbitt metal. The bearing at the small end is of the bronze-bushing type.

con-nec′tion (*Elec.*) Electrical conductor joining parts of an electrical circuit.

con-nec′tor (*Elec.*) Any device for holding in electrical contact the ends of conducting wires in such a manner that they may be readily released when it is desired to disconnect them.

co′noid (kō′noid) (*Geom.*) Having the form of a cone.

con′ser-va′tion of en′er-gy. The principle that no energy is ever lost or wasted although it may assume different forms.

con-serv′a-to-ry (*Arch.*) A place of instruction, as a conservatory of music. A glassed-in building, either attached or detached, for the growing of plants.

con-sist′en-cy (*P h y s.*) Degree of density.

con′sole (*Arch.*) A supporting bracket usually ornamented by a reverse scroll.

con′sole mod′el (*Radio*) A radio cabinet, mounted on four legs, containing the chassis, speaker, and all power equipment. The control equipment is mounted on the front face of the cabinet.

con′stant (*Math.*) A number deduced from actual experiment and used as a basis in calculations.

con′stant cur′rent (*Elec.*) A current whose amperage is not variable.

con′stant po-ten′tial (*Elec.*) A constant pressure or voltage in a power and light circuit.

con′stant pres′sure (*Auto. Mech.*) A term used in describing a type of piston, usually alloy, the skirt of which is relieved to enable it to exert a reasonably equal pressure on the cylinder wall at all times.

con′stant speed mo′tor (*Elec.*) A motor which does not show a decrease in speed with an increase in load.

con′stant vac′u-um car′bu-ret′or (*Auto.*) Contains a weighted valve operated by the pull of the intake-manifold vacuum to proportion the amount of fuel to air.

con-stit′u-ent (*Chem.*) One of the elements or compounds present.

con-struc′tion. The act of building; also that which is built; style of building, as of wood, iron, or steel construction.

con-sult′ing en′gi-neer′. An expert engineer usually of experience and standing in his profession who is retained to give advice on engineering matters.

con′tact (*Elec.*) The coming together (touching) of two or more specially arranged ends of electrical conductors to complete an electrical circuit or circuits.

con′tact break′er (*Elec.*) A device for quickly and automatically breaking or making an electric circuit.

con′tac–tors (*Elec.*) Electromagnetically or manually operated contacts.

con′tact–point pres′sure (*A u t o . Elec.*) The spring pressure which holds the contact points in closed positions.

con′tact points (*Auto. Elec.*) Small metal disks or points of iridium, platinum, or alloy steel used to make and break the low-tension circuit.

con′ti-nen′tal code (*Elec.*) A dot-and-dash telegraphic code used in sending radio messages.

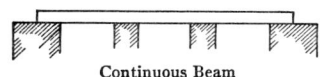
Continuous Beam

con-tin′u-ous beam (*Arch.*) A beam which rests on more than two supports.

con-tin′u-ous du′ty (*Elec.*) That demand on a system which requires operation at a constant load for an indefinite period of time.

con-tin′u-ous ex-tru′sion (*Plast.*) A process by which the plastic takes the shape of the die through which it passes and is forced out in continuous lengths.

con-tin′u-ous hinge (*Furn.*) A long strip hinge such as on the lid which covers the keyboard of a piano.

con-tin′u-ous vent (*Plumb.*) A continuation of a vertical, or approximately vertical, waste pipe above the connection at which liquid wastes enter the waste pipe. The extension may or may not continue in a vertical direction.

con′tour (kŏn′tōor) (*Woodwkg.*) The profile or section of a molding.

con′tour lines (kŏn′tōor) (*S u r v.*) Lines placed on a map to show the topography of the ground and to give a reading of elevations.

con-trac′tion (*F d r y.*) Decrease in volume due to cooling.

con-trac′tor (*Arch.*) One who agrees to supply materials and to perform work for a specified sum.

con′trast (*Tel.*) This refers to the ratio of the dark to the light portions of a television picture. Pictures having high contrast have very deep black and brilliant whites while a pictures with low contrast has an overall gray appearance.

con′trast con-trol′ (*Tel.*) A control on the receiver which regulates the television signal strength, changing the ratio of the dark to the light portions of a picture.

con-trol′ ca′ble (*Aero.*) The line of wire or stranded cable interconnecting or leading from the control levers to the control surfaces.

con-trol′ col′umn (*Aero.*) A lever having a rotatable wheel mounted at its upper end for operating the longitudinal and lateral control surfaces of an airplane. This type of control is called "wheel control."

con-trol′la-bil′i-ty (*Aero.*) The quality in an airplane which makes it possible for the pilot to change its attitude easily and with the exertion of but little force.

con-trol′la-ble pro-pel′ler (*Aero.*) A propeller whose blades are so mounted that the pitch may be changed while the propeller is rotating.

con-trol′ler (*Elec.*) A magnetic device for the automatic regulation and control of an electric current.

con-trol′ stick (*Aero.*) The vertical lever which operates the lateral and longitudinal controls of an airplane. Pitching is controlled by a fore-and-aft movement of the stick, rolling, by a side-to-side movement.

con-trol′ sur′face (*Aero.*) A movable

airfoil, the position of which may be altered by the pilot in order to change the attitude of the airplane.

con-trols' (*Aero.*) Relates to the provision made for the control of power, speed, direction, and attitude of an aircraft.

con-trol' sys'tem (*Auto.*) Consists of steering device, throttle and spark control, brake levers, gear-shift lever, foot pedals, and the brake system.

con-vec'tion (*Elec.*) The flow of electricity by the motion of charged particles of air passing off currents from a pointed electrical conductor. (*Phys.*) Diffusion of heat through a liquid or gas by motion of its parts.

con-vec'tor (*Mech. Engin.*) A type of heating unit, for steam or hot-water heating, fitted with large extended fire surfaces which emit heat principally by convection.

con-ven'ience out'let (*Elec.*) A point on the wiring system at which current is taken to supply portable appliances such as irons, toasters, etc.

con-ven'tion-al (*Fine Arts*) Represented according to artistic convention or rule, rather than to nature or fact. Resulting from, or established by custom; formal.

con-vert'er. Also called transformer. (*Elec.*) A machine employing mechanical rotation in changing electrical energy from one form to another.

con-vert'i-ble (*Auto Mech.*) A passenger-type automobile with top that can be completely removed or top which can be lowered or raised either manually or by an electrically-operated hydraulic system.

con'vex. Curving like the surface of a sphere.

con-vey'. To impart; to communicate; to transport.

con-vey'ors. Such devices as an endless belt, or chain with buckets attached for transferring material.

con'vo-lute. Rolled or wound together, one part upon another.

cool'ant (*Metal Fin.*) A liquid used to dissipate the heat generated by a cutting tool. Coolants most frequently used are soda water, lard oil, kerosene, and turpentine, or combinations of these.

cool'ing fix'ture (*Plast.*) Block of metal or wood, holding the shape of a molded casting, which is used to maintain the proper shape or dimensional accuracy of a casting after it has been removed from the mold, until it is cool enough to retain its shape without further appreciable distortion.

cool'ing sys'tem (*Auto.*) Those devices which prevent the overheating of the engine by rapidly carrying off the heat generated by combustion. Radiators, fans, pump and water jackets are parts of a water-cooling system.

Cooper–Hewitt lamp (*Elec.*) An efficient lamp usually operated on 110-volt direct-current circuits. It consists of a glass tube, several feet long, containing mercury vapor at low vapor tension.

coop'ered joint (*Furn.*) Joint resembling those made in barrels, used in curved parts.

co-or'di-nate (*Math.*) A member of a system of lines by means of which position is determined.

co'pal var'nish. Varnish of which copal is a principal ingredient. Copal is a hard transparent resin obtained from tropical trees; also taken from the earth.

cope. The upper portion of a loam mold, or the top flask used in green-sand molding.

coped joint (*Arch.*) A joint between molded pieces in which a portion of one member is cut out to receive the molded part of the other member.

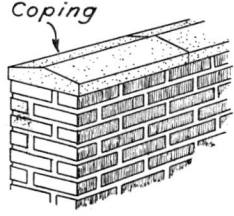
Coping

cop'ing (*Arch.*) The cap or top course of a wall, frequently projecting.

cop'ing ma-chine' (*Shopwk.*) Used for cutting away the flanges and corners of beams and bending the ends

cop'ing out (*Fdry.*) The cutting away of the sand face in the drag half of the mold to bring it to the proper parting line. For any depression thus made, there is a corresponding projection of sand from the face of the cope.

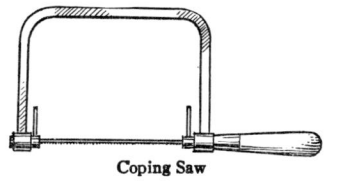
Coping Saw

cop'ing saw (kōp'ĭng) (*Woodwk.*) Consists of a narrow blade, ⅛ in. wide 6½ in. long, carried on pins set in a steel bow frame. Used for cutting curves, coping out molding, etc.

co-pol'y-mer (*Plast.*) Product formed by the simultaneous polymerization of two or more substances; it is not a mixture of separate polymers, but a complex, having properties different from either polymer alone.

co-pol'y-mer-i-za'tion (*Chem. Plast.*) When two or more monomers are involved in a chemical reaction which links their molecules together to form large molecules. (See POLYMERIZATION.)

cop'per. A metal, soft, ductile, and malleable, much used in the arts; tough, but not strong; of great value in the forming of alloys.

cop'per-as (kŏp'ĕr-ăs) (*Chem.*) $FeSO_4 \cdot 7H_2O$. (See GREEN VITRIOL.)

cop'per bit (*Plumb.*) A tool used for soldering. Usually called a "soldering iron."

cop'per gas'ket (*Auto. Elec.*) Any copper or copper and asbestos ring or sheet used to seal two metal faces which are bolted or fastened together.

cop'per lead (*Metal.*) An alloy bearing metal; more effective than babbitt in withstanding high load pressures and high temperatures.

cop'per pipe (*Plumb.*) Size rated by either inside or outside diameters; thickness of wall is measured by Stub's wire gauge. Much used in plumbing and in the industries.

cop'per-plate (*Print.*) An intaglio process of engraving by cutting or biting into copper. The plate is inked, wiped, and then printed with considerable pressure.

cop'per-plate Goth'ic (gŏth'ĭk) (*Print.*) (See GOTHIC.)

cop'per-plat'ing. The depositing of a copper coating on the surface of another metal by any one of several formulas, the principal ingredient of which is cyanide of potassium. The plating is accomplished both by the dipping and the electrolytic method. See ELECTROPLATING.

cop′per steel. Steel of low carbon, containing about 0.25 per cent copper, used for construction work where resistance to corrosion is needed.

cop′per sul′phate (*Chem.*) $CuSO_4 \cdot 5H_2O$. (See BLUESTONE.)

cop′ra-loy (*Metal.*) See COPPER STEEL.

cop′y (*Furn.*) Reproduction of furniture, usually of the historic periods. (*Print.*) All typewritten, handwritten, or printed matter turned over to the printer.

cop′y-hold′er (*Print.*) One who reads aloud from the original copy against which the proofreader checks the printed proof.

co′quil′lage′ (kô′kē′yäzh′) (*Furn.*) An ornamental shell design used on frames and other light pieces of furniture in rococo style.

co-qui′na (kō-kē′nà) (*Chem.*) A rock formed by the adhesion of marine shells. Composition calcium carbonate.

cor′al (*Chem.*) A marine form of calcium carbonate built by the coral polyp.

cor′bel (*Arch.*) A bracket or support; a stepping out of courses in a wall to form a ledge.

cor′bel out (*Arch.*) To build out one or more courses of masonry from the face of a wall to form a support for timbers.   Corbel

cord (*Woodwkg.*) Wood, cut in 4-ft. lengths usually for firewood. A pile of wood, 4 ft. wide, 4 ft. high, and 8 ft. long.

core (*Mold.*) A central portion. In foundry work, a body of sand either dried or green which permits the obtaining of holes, depressions, etc., in a casting. (*Plast.*) In plastics, the central layer in a sandwich panel, the outer faces usually being composed of laminated sheet.

core box (*Fdry.*) A box usually of wood, in which the core is rammed up.   Core Box

core-box plane (*Patmkg.*) A plane for making circular core boxes. When the right-angle sides of the plane rest on the edges of the cut, the point of the plane will cut on the circumference of the circle.

cored car′bon (*Elec.*) A carbon with a longitudinal soft core for use in alternating-current arc to permit efficient operations of the arc.

cored hole (*Fdry.*) A cast hole cored with a dry-sand core instead of delivering as a hole directly from the pattern. In general, the term is applied to any hole in a casting which is not bored or drilled in the shop.

core disks (*Elec.*) Thin circular disks of sheet iron used for building of laminated armature cores.

core dri′er (*Fdry.*) A form which serves to retain the shape of a core while it is being baked.

core drill (*Metalwk.*) A hollow drill which removes metal in a solid piece instead of chips. Such a drill is used for obtaining test specimens from a casting or forging.

core loss (*Elec.*) The electric loss occurring in the core of an armature or transformer due to eddy currents, hysteresis, and like influences.

core ma-chine′ (*Fdry.*) A hand- or power-driven machine having a hopper with a horizontal worm at the bottom. It is used for making round and square stock cores.

core oils (*Fdy.*) Those oils used as binders in making sand cores in foundry work. Linseed oil or linseed oil mixed with less expensive vegetable oil is frequently used.

core ov′en (*Fdry.*) The oven in which cores are baked.

core pin (*Plast.*) A pin for forming a hole or opening in a molded piece.

core print (*Fdry.*) A projection on a pattern which forms an impression in the sand and locates and holds the core in position while the mold is being poured.

core sand (*Fdry.*) Molding sand which is used in the making of cores.

core wash (*Fdry.*) A mixture used for painting cores.

cor′ing out (*Fdry.*) Forming of the interior portions of castings with cores.

cor′ing up (*Fdry.*) The placing of the cores in their position in a foundry mold ready for casting.

Co-rin′thi-an or′der (*Arch.*) One of the five classic orders of architecture in which the conventionalized acanthus leaf is freely used as a decoration of the capital.

Corinthian Capital

cor′ner bead (*Arch.*) A metal bead to be built in-to plastered corners to prevent accidental breaking of the plaster.

cor′ner bit brace (*Woodwk.*) A bit brace designed for use in difficult positions where the regular bit brace could not be operated.

cor′ner-round′ing cut′ter (*Mach.*) Used on milling machines for finishing rounded edges.

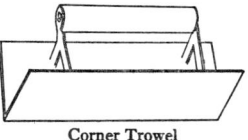
Corner Trowel

cor′ner trow′el (*Plaster.*) A plasterer's trowel with V-shaped blade for working on corners, made in both inside and outside patterns.

cor′nice (kôr′nĭs) (*Arch.*) The projection at the top of a wall.

cor′nice brake (*Sheet Metal*) A floor brake with open throat and jaws. The sheet metal to be formed remains in a fixed position depending upon a binding leaf or folding bar to effect the folding or bending operation.

cor′nu-co′pi-a (k ô r′n ů-k ō′p ĭ-á) (*Furn.*) The horn of plenty, from which issues fruit and flowers, used as a carved ornamentation.

cor′ol-lar′y. A truth made obvious by some preceding demonstration.

co-ro′na (*A r c h.*) The portion of the cornice which projects over the bed molding to throw off the water. (*Auto.*) Any leak of high-tension current from the secondary circuit of the ignition system of an automobile.

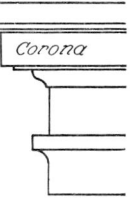

cor′ri-dor (*Arch.*) A passageway in a building, usually having rooms opening upon it.

cor-ro′sion. The rusting or oxidation of metals by contact and chemical union with oxygen in a damp atmosphere.

cor-ro′sion–re-sist′ant a l - l o y s ′ (*Metal.*) Refers to a class of alloys composed of chromium alloyed with iron, nickel, cobalt, copper, and sometimes molybdenum and tungsten. These alloys are supplied under trade names for many specific purposes.

cor′ru-gat′ed board (*Paper*) A board which has a corrugated center of straw paper.

cor′ru-gat′ed i′ron. Sheet iron formed into parallel ridges and depressions, alternately concave and convex.

co-run′dum (*Mach., Min., Shopwk.*) An extremely hard aluminum oxide used as an abrasive.

co′sine (kō′sīn) (*Math.*) The cosine of an angle is the quotient of the adjacent side divided by the hypotenuse.

cos-tum′er (*Furn.*) A stand or frame resembling the hall tree.

co-tan′gent (*Math.*) The cotangent of an angle is the quotient of the adjacent side divided by the opposite side.

cot′ted wool (*Textile*) Matted wool which is hard to work.

cot′ter (*Mech.*) A tapered rod or pin, generally flat in section, used for wedging the ends of rods or of strap ends over their rods.

cot′ter mill (*Mach.*) A milling cutter used for cutting key seats, slots, and grooves.

cot′ter pin (*Mech.*) Usually a form of split pin which is inserted into a hole near the end of a bolt to prevent a nut from working loose.

Cotter Pin

cot′ton gin (*Textile*) A machine for pulling the fibers of cotton from the seeds. It was invented by Eli Whitney in 1793 and was responsible for a tremendous development of the cotton industry.

cot′ton waste. Made of waste cotton threads. Used around engine rooms for "wiping down."

cot′ton-wood′ (*Wood*) *Populous.* Also known as Carolina poplar; a large tree 50 to 75 ft. in height and up to 6 ft. in diameter. The wood is soft, warps easily, is hard to split. Used for paper pulp, boxes, crates, etc.

cou-lomb′ (kōō-lŏm′) (*Elec.*) A unit of electrical quantity. A quantity of electricity delivered by a current of one ampere maintained for one second.

cou′ma-rone in′dene res′in (kōō′mȧ-rōn ĭn′dĕn rĕz′in) (*Chem. Plast.*) Used principally to modify the properties of other resinous bodies or compounds based on them. Its availability ranges from viscous liquids to high melting solids with color range from light yellow to almost black; much used in mastic floor tile, protective coatings, transcription records, etc.

count′er. A device for registering numbers, as the number of persons passing through a turnstile, or the number of parts being turned out by a machine.

coun′ter-bal′ance (*Mech.*) The addition of weight, usually to a wheel or crank, in order to place the same in perfect balance.

coun′ter-bore (*Mech.*) To enlarge a hole through part of its length by boring. (*Mach.*) The cutting tool is sometimes fitted with a pilot or leader to guide and center the cutting edges. For example the enlarging of the beginning of a drilled hole so that the head of a screw will be flush with the metal surface.

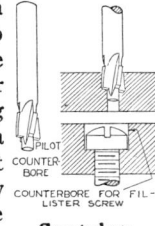
Counterbore for Fillister Screw
Counterbore

coun′ter-brac′ing or cross brac′ing (*Arch.*) Diagonal bracing used in a truss or girder for giving additional support to the beam and relieving it of transverse stress.

coun′ter-clock′wise′ (*Auto.*) A direction opposite to the rotation of the hands of a clock.

coun′ter E.M.F. (*Elec.*) An opposing electromotive force which resists the current in a circuit (C.E.M.F.).

count′ers (*Engin.*) Auxiliary diagonal members in a truss to take a reversal of stress.

coun′ter-shaft′ (*Mach.*) The intermediate shaft between line shaft and machine.

coun′ter-sink′ (*Mech.*) To recess a hole conically for the head of a screw or rivet. The tool with which a hole is countersunk.

Countersink

coun′ter-weight′. A weight attached to give balance; as a weight fastened to the rim of a wheel.

count of cloth (*Textile*) The number of warp and filling threads in a square inch of fabric.

coun′try beam (*Auto. Mech.*) The upper beam of an automobile head lamp designed to give a good driving light on an open highway. This beam is used only in country driving when there are no approaching vehicles.

cou-pé′ (ko͞o-pā′) (*Auto.*) An enclosed single-compartment body with accommodations for two passengers. Usually has a luggage compartment in rear deck.

cou′ple (*Mech.*) Two forces which are equal and act in opposite directions, producing rotation.

cou′pled–in-duct′ance (*Elec.*) Voltages induced in one circuit by current changes in a second circuit.

cou′pling (*Plumb.*) A fitting with inside threads only, used for connecting two pieces of pipe.

course (*Masonry*) To arrange in a row or course. A row of bricks when laid in a wall is called a "course."

course light (*Aero.*) A light projected along the course of an airway so as to be visible chiefly from points on or near the airway.

court (*Arch.*) An open space surrounded partly or entirely by a building.

court cup′board. A short cupboard, originally set on a side table, but later built as one piece.

cove (*Furn.*) A large, hollow cornice; also a niche.

cove ceil′ing (*Arch.*) A ceiling which springs from the walls with a curve.

cove mold′ing (*Arch.*) A concave molding.

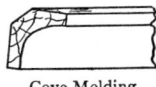
Cove Molding

cov′er mold (*Plast.*) The stationary half of an injection mold; also called "front mold."

cov′er pa′pers (*Print.*) Heavy papers used for covers for booklets; also used where a strong sheet is needed for an individual mailing piece.

cov′er plate (*Engin.*) A plate added to the flange sections of a column or girder to increase resistance to bending.

cowl (*Auto. Mech.*) That part of an automobile body between the hood and the instrument panel, forming a shroud.

cowl′ing (*Aero.*) A removable covering which extends over or around the engine and sometimes also over a portion of the fuselage or nacelle.

crack′ing (*Chem.*) A process of increasing the yield of gasoline from crude oil by the application of heat and pressure to kerosene and fuel oil. (*Paint and Lacquer*) Deep open checks in film occurring in the filler coats, but which later affect color coats, are the outgrowth of improper mixing of materials.

crack′le (*Ceram.*) The fine network of cracks in the finish of a piece of ware, produced for decorative purposes.

craft. Skill in the execution of manual work. An occupation; a trade.

crafts′man. A skilled workman, particularly one who combines originality with workmanlike skill.

cramp i′ron (*Fdry.*) A bent iron used with a wedge to clamp the drag and cope together in foundry practice.

crane. A machine operated by hand, electric, or hydraulic power, used for the lifting of heavy weights by the use of gear wheels, cable drum, cable, and jib.

crane la′dle (*Fdry.*) A ladle for carrying molten metal, so heavy that it must be carried by a crane.

crank (*Mech.*) A lever which rotates about the axis of a shaft.

crank′case (*Auto.*) The lower part of an automobile engine which acts as a reservoir for the supply of lubricating oil.

crank′case ven′ti-la′tor (*A u t o.*) Draft from the fan creates a suction which is used to carry off vapors formed in the crankcase thus avoiding a dilution of the oil which would otherwise result from water and gasoline vapors.

crank′shaft (*Mech. Engin.*) The main shaft of an engine to which the connecting rods are attached, and which controls the throw of the pistons.

Crankshaft

crank shap′er (*Mach.*) A shaper in which the ram is operated by a crank motion.

cra′ter of an arc (*E l e c.*) The hollowed-out tip of the positive carbon in an arc lamp produced by action of the current.

crawl′ing (*Paint and Lacquer*) A defect appearing during application in which the film breaks, separates, or raises, due to application over a slick or glassy surface or to surface tensions caused by heavy coatings, or use of an elastic film over a surface that is hard or brittle.

craz′ing (*Ceram.*) Very fine cracks in the glaze on a piece of ware due to unequal shrinkage between the glaze and the body; often caused by improper firing. (*Paint and Lacquer*)

Fine hairline checks that will sooner or later develop into deep cracks are the result of contraction or expansion of one coat in comparison with another, generally when a heavily pigmented surfacer or enamel is applied over a more elastic coating. (*Plast.*) Fine cracks on the surface or inside a plastic product.

creas'ing (*Print.*) Cover stock or cardboard which is too thick to be folded without breaking must be creased; the process is known as "creasing."

cre'dence (krē'dĕns) (*Furn.*) An antique buffet, or side table, used for carving meat or displaying plates.

creep'er (*Auto. Mech.*) A low platform supported on small casters, on which an auto repairman may lie while working under a car.

cre'o-sote (krē'ô-sōt) (*Chem.*) A light-colored, oily distillate of coal tar. Used as a disinfectant and as a wood preservative.

cre'o-sot'ing (krē'ô-sōt'ĭng) The injecting of creosote into timber which is to be exposed to the weather, in order to increase its durability.

cre'o-sot'ing cyl'in-der. Strong wrought-iron cylinder in which railroad ties, etc., are exhausted of their moisture and filled with creosote pumped in under pressure.

crêpe grain (krāp grān)(*Bookbndg.*) Having a soft crinkled surface.

crest'ing (*Arch.*) An ornamental finish in the wall or ridge of a building.

crest of screw thread (*Mach.*) The top surface joining the two sides of a thread.

cre-tonne' (krê-tŏn') (*Uphol.*) A lightweight cloth of cotton or linen in a plain weave with printed pattern, used extensively for covering fiber or reed furniture and for pillows, draperies, etc.

crew'el-work' (*Furn.*) A form of old embroidery work used for upholstery.

crib (*Engin.*) Usually openwork of horizontally, cross-piled, squared timbers used as a support for the structure above.

crimp'ing (*Shopwk.*) The turning or closing down of an edge.

crimp'ing ma-chine' (*Sheet-Met. Wk.*) A machine for reducing the circumference of the end of one piece (as in stovepipe) in order that it may be fitted to another piece. This is accomplished by passing the material through the grooved rolls of the "crimper."

crip'ple raft'er (*Arch.*) A rafter which extends from a hip to a valley rafter.

cri-te'ri-on (krī-tē'rĭ-ŭn) A standard by which comparison may be made.

crit'i-cal al'ti-tude (*Aero.*) The maximum altitude at which a supercharger can maintain a pressure in the intake manifold of an engine equal to that existing during normal operation at rated power and speed at sea level.

crit'i-cal an'gle (*Aero.*) That angle of attack which is about to produce an abrupt change in lift and drag.

crit'i-cal speed (*Aero.*) The lowest speed of an aircraft at which it is possible to maintain control.

crit'i-cal tem'per-a-ture (*Mach.*) The temperature (varying for different steels) at which certain changes take place in the chemical composition of the steel during heating and cooling.

crock'ing (*Textile*) The rubbing off of loose dye from a dyed material, as from a coat lining.

cro'cus cloth. Cloth to which pulverized oxide of iron is glued; used for polishing.

crop (*Leather.*) An entire hide prepared for sole leather. (*Print.*) To cut a printing plate to desired size for reproduction.

crop'per (*Mach.*) A shearing machine for cutting off rods, etc.

crop'ping (*Textile*) Shearing the surface of cloth.

cross (*Plumb.*) A pipe fitting with four branches arranged in pairs, each pair on one axis and the axes at right angles.

cross'belt' (*Mach.*) A belt changed to run from the top of one pulley to the bottom of another to produce a reversal of direction.

cross'cut saw (*Woodwkg.*) A saw made for cutting wood across the grain. The action of its teeth is similar to that of a knife instead of a chisel as is the case of a ripsaw.

cross'-dye'ing (*Textile*) Dyeing mixed material in a bath which colors only one kind of fibers.

crossed belt (*Mech.*) A driving belt which has a twist between the driving and the driven pulleys causing a reversal of direction.

cross-feed (*Mach.*) A transverse feed. In a lathe, that which usually operates at right angles to the axis of the work. In a planer or shaper. that feed which carries the tool across the work.

cross grain. A section of wood taken at right angles, or at a low angle, with the direction of the longitudinal fiber.

cross'hatch'ing (*Draw.*) The representation of different kinds of material by means of lines, usually drawn obliquely on a part which has been sectioned.

cross'head' (*Engin.*) The connecting unit between connecting rod and piston rod in a steam engine making possible the change from rotary to reciprocal motion. (*Mech.*) That portion of a pump or engine which connects the piston and connecting rod, permitting the reciprocal motion of the piston rod.

cross'ing file (*Mach.*) A taper file with a section like two half rounds with flat faces back to back.

cross'lap' (*Woodwk.*) A crossed joint formed by halving both pieces at the place of joining in order that they will lie on the same plane.

cross mem'ber (*Auto.*) A structural part of an automobile frame connecting the side rails, usually at right angles.

cross'o'ver (*Plumb.*) A fitting shaped like the letter U with the ends turned out. It is used to pass the flow of one pipe past another when the pipes are in the same plane.

cross'-peen' ham'mer (*Shopwk.*) A hammer with a wedge-shaped peening edge at right angles to the direction of the handle.

cross'rail' (*Mach.*) That part of a boring mill or planer which supports and permits movement of tool heads and tool slides.

cross sec'tion. A transverse section at right angles with the longitudinal axis of the work or drawing through which the section is taken.

cross slide (*Mach.*) The horizontal slide or bridge which carries the tool box in a planing machine. The slide which operates on the saddle of a lathe carriage to provide for transverse feed. It also supports the compound rest.

cross′-stitch′ (*Bookbndg.*) A double stitch in the form of a cross.

cross tap (*Elec.*) A joint similar to a cross joint except it is accomplished by tapping two wires off the main conductor instead of using a single cross wire.

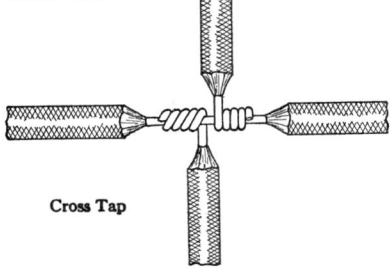

Cross Tap

cross′ty′ing springs (*Uphol.*) This system of tying springs prevents the burlap from sagging into the open spaces between the springs, and adds stability to the upholstering.

cross valve (*Mach.*) A valve fitted on a transverse pipe so as to open communication at will between two parallel lines of piping. Much used in oil- and water-pumping arrangements.

cross′-wind force′ (*Aero.*) The component perpendicular to the lift and to the drag of the total air force on the aircraft or any part thereof.

crotch veneer (*Furn.*) Veneer cut from limb crotch, or from twin trees which have joined together, forming an unusual grain effect.

crow′bar. A heavy pinch bar of round iron or steel flattened to a chisel-like point at one end, used as a lever.

crown. A rise in the contour as the center of the face of a part is approached, as the crown of a road, crown of a pulley, etc. (*Arch.*) The uppermost member of a cornice. (*Plumb.*) That part of a trap in which the direction of flow is changed from an upward to a downward direction.

crown back (*Furn.*) A feature of the Hogarth chair.

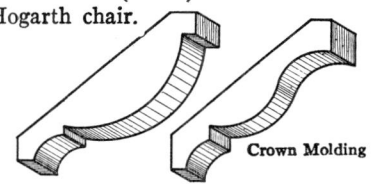

Crown Molding

crown mold′ing (*Arch.*) A molding with a double-curved face. The upper member of a closed cornice placed immediately below the roof proper.

crown pul′ley (*Mach.*) A pulley whose diameter is greater at the middle than at the edges of its face. This crown tends to prevent the belt from running off the pulley provided the belt is not slipping.

crow′s′-foot (*Aero.*) A system of diverging short ropes for distributing the load on a single rope.

cru′ci-ble (krōō′sĭ-b'l) (*Chem.*) A vessel generally of refractory material; used for melting purposes.

cru′ci-ble steel (krōō′sĭ-b'l) A high-grade steel made by melting wrought iron in a crucible and adding charcoal, pig iron, or some other substance rich in carbon, so that the resulting metal will contain from 0.75 to 1.50 per cent carbon; used for cutlery, tools, dies, etc.

crude oil. Petroleum in its natural

state as it comes from the earth.

crush′ing strain. The strain which causes the failure of a material by compression.

cry′o-lite (*Mineral.*) (Na_3AlF_6) A snow-white, sodium-aluminum fluoride found mainly in Greenland. It is used in the making of aluminum, also in the manufacture of glass.

crys′tal (*Chem.*) A natural solid figure bounded by planes, i.e., mineral or chemical, planes not man made.

crys′tal di′ode (*Rad.*) Used as a rectifier, primarily in microwave frequencies.

crys′tal-li-za′tion (*Chem.*) Process of causing a chemical to separate out of either the dissolved or melted state in the form of crystals.

crys′tal-li-za′tion of i′ron. This is effected by the conditions under which a metal is cooled, or from hammering.

C–stage res′ins (rĕz′ĭns) (*Plast.*) Thermosetting resins in final stage of reactions where they are infusible, and insoluble; state of the resin in the final molded article; sometimes called "Resite."

Cu′ban ma-hog′a-ny (*Wood*) *Swietenia mahogoni.* A cabinet wood. The hardest and darkest mahogany of commercial importance. Used for furniture manufacture.

cube (*Geom.*) A solid bounded by six equal squares and having all its angles right angles. (*Math.*) The cube of a number is the product of a number multiplied twice by itself.

cube root (*Math.*) A number which, taken three times as a factor, produces a number called its cube.

cu′bi-cal con′tent. The volume; the amount which a vessel will hold. An expression used in reference to buildings as a basis for estimating cost.

cu′bic meas′ure.

1728 cubic inches(cu.in.)	=	1 cubic foot(cu.ft.)
27 cubic feet	=	1 cubic yard(cu.yd.)
231 cubic inches	=	1 U. S. gal.
128 cubic feet	=	1 cord

culm. Dust, slate, and foreign matter removed from coal at the mine.

cul′vert. An artificially covered channel for the passage of water, as under a road.

cu′mar (koō′mär) A synthetic resin made from coal-tar distillates. It is used as an insulator, also in paint and varnish, rubber compounds, and printing ink.

cu′mu-la′tive (kū′mū-lā′tĭv) Steady increase in quantity or value by repetition or addition.

Cup Center

cup cen′ter (*Mach.*) The center which is used in the tailstock of a wood-turning lathe; also called a "dead center."

cup chuck (*Woodwkg.*) A lathe chuck with a deeply recessed face, used in end-grain turning.

cup grease. A heavy-bodied, semisolid grease used as a lubricant.

cup joint (*Plumb.*) A lead pipe joint in which one end of the pipe is opened enough to receive the tapered end of the adjacent pipe.

cup leath′er (*Mech.*) A leather packing used for the pistons of hydraulic machines.

cu′po-la (*Arch.*) A dome; generally any small structure above the roof of a building. (*Fdry.*) A furnace in which cast iron is melted for foundry use.

cu′prite (cū′prīt) (*Metal.*) Cu_2O. Known as red copper ore. Found in Arizona and in a number of South American countries.

cu′pro-nick′el (cū′prȯ) (*Metal.*) A ductile and malleable alloy of copper and nickel. With varying amounts of nickel, it is adapted to many industrial uses. With a nickel content of 10 per cent or more, it is highly corrosion resistant.

cup shake (*Carp.*) A division or opening between two concentric layers of timber.

cup wheel. A grinding wheel shaped like a cup, designed for cutting on its edge.

curb box (*Plumb.*) A device consisting usually of a long piece of pipe or tubelike casing, placed over a curb cock, through which a key is inserted to permit the turning of the curb cock.

curb cock (*Plumb.*) A valve placed in a service pipe at a point near the curb.

curb roof (*Arch.*) (See MANSARD ROOF.)

cur′dling (*Paint and Lacquer*) Incorporating into lacquer enamel a very fast-drying, weak solvent thinner of very poor quality.

cure (*Plast.*) The change in the physical form and the properties of a resin by means of chemical reaction, following the addition of a catalyst, or heat and pressure, and in some instances without pressure. A product which is cured is at the end of its cycle of changes.

cure time (*Plast.*) In plastic production, the interval between the closing of the mold and the instant at which pressure is released. In laminating plastics, the interval between the addition of the catalyst and hardening.

cur′ing (*Plast.*) The change of a binder from the soluble-fusible condition to the substantially insoluble-infusible form by chemical action. The heat setting of a resinoid. Action is analogous to vulcanization of rubber.

curl (*Furn.*) A feather-form marking in the grain of wood.

curled hair (*Uphol.*) Is obtained from tails and manes of horses, tails of cattle, and from hogs. It must be put through several processes before it is ready for use. The hair from horses' tails is best for upholstery use.

curl′ing die (*Mach.*) A die used for making a curled edge at the top of any cuplike piece drawn from sheet metal.

cur′rent (*Elec.*) The flow of electrical energy along a conductor from the higher to the lower of two points having different potentials.

cur′rent–lim′it ther′mo-stat (*Elec.*) A heat-controlled electrical device used in place of a fuse to prevent damage due to an excess of current.

cur′rent reg′u-la′tor (*Auto. Elec.*) A magnetic-controlled relay by which the field circuit of the generator is made and broken very rapidly to secure unvarying current output from the generator.

cur′rent strength (*Elec.*) The flow of an electric current measured in amperes.

cur′rent trans-form′er (*Elec.*) See TRANSFORMER.

cur′ry-ing (*Leather.*) The dressing of tanned hides for use.

cur′tain wall (*Arch.*) A thin wall supported independently of the wall below, by the structural steel or concrete frame of the building.

curve. A line with continuous change of direction.

curved nee′dle (*Uphol.*) Used for the same purpose as the straight needle but under conditions where it is not possible to handle the straight tool.

curved plate (*Print.*) One that is backed up and curved to suit the cylinder of a rotary press.

cur′vi-lin′e-ar (kûr′vĭ-lĭn′ê-ȧr) Consisting of, or bounded by curved lines.

cush′ioned frieze (frēz) (*Furn.*) A convex, Renaissance frieze.

cush′ion-ing. The use of springs, air cushions, or any type of shock absorber for reducing shock, knock, or excessive wear.

cusp (*Arch. and Furn.*) A lobe or point in the foliation of medieval tracery.

cut (*Print.*) An engraved block or plate. (*Shopwk.*) The removal of a shaving from a piece of work either in wood- or metal-working machines.

cut cards (*Print.*) Cards cut to size.

cut flush (*Print.*) To trim a pamphlet so the edges of the cover and the inside material will be exactly flush, i.e., without overhang.

cut gears (*Mach.*) Gears with machine-cut teeth as distinguished from cast gears.

cut-in note or side note (*Print.*) A note usually in small type, set into the side of a page of printed matter. Frequently used in the composition of textbooks.

cut′ler-y. Cutting instruments although the term is generally applied only to those for household use.

cut nails (*Carp.*) Machine-cut iron nails as distinguished from wire nails which are now in more general use.

cut of file. The manner in which the face of a file is cut, and from which a file takes its name, as smooth cut, rough cut, bastard, etc.

cut′ off′ (*Plast.*) The lines where the two halves of a mold come together; also called a land or flash ridge, or a flash groove.

cut′off rule (*Print.*) Rule used in newspaper or periodical work to separate advertisements.

cut′out (*Elec.*) A device for opening a circuit when the current rise is beyond the safety limit. There are two kinds: electromagnetic, which is usually called a circuit breaker, and thermo which may be one of the various kinds of fuse.

cut′out box (*Elec.*) A box which contains fuse blocks and fuses.

cut′out re-lay′ (*Auto. Elec.*) An automatic magnetic switch attached to the generator to cut out generator circuit to prevent over-charging of battery.

cut′ter (*Mech.*) Any cutting tool fixed in a machine or holder for automatic cutting of wood or metal.

cut′ting an′gle (*Mech.*) The angle measured between the cutting face of the tool and the surface of the material on which the tool operates.

cut′ting com′pound (*Mach.*) Lard oil, soda water, or any of the various coolants used on work being machined. (See COOLANT.)

cut′ting face (*Mech.*) The face of the cutting tool against which the material is moved.

cut′ting gauge (*Furn.*) A gauge with a cutter in place of a marker.

cut′ting nip′pers (*Furn.*) A type of pincers with a cutting bite.

cut′ting oils (*Mach.*) Any of the heavy oils or combination of oils used as a metal lubricant in machining operations. The term does not properly include those watery solutions used merely as coolants.

cut′ting out (*Auto. Mech.*) (1) Descriptive of action of relay in electric circuit in breaking the circuit at predetermined voltage or current. (2) Point at which centrifugal clutch releases pressure or contact.

cut′ting pli′ers. Pliers which, in addition to the flat jaws, have a pair of nippers placed to one side for cutting off wire.

Cutting Pliers

cut′ting rule (*Print.*) Made of steel strips. Used in making up forms for cutting cardboard, etc.

cut′ting tools. A very general term but referring to edged tools used in machines more than to tools held by hand.

cut′ting up (*Mach.*) In milling-machine work, the cutting done when the cutter tool moves up against the work.

cy′a-nide (sī′á-nīd) (*Chem.*) Usually refers to cyanide of potassium; very poisonous; a white powder or in lumps. Used in the extraction of gold and silver from ores, in electroplating heat treatment of steel, etc.

cy′a-nid′ing. The process of surface hardening an alloy with an iron base by heating it at a suitable temperature in contact with cyanide salt, after which it is quenched.

cy′cle (*Elec. and Mech.*) A series of operations forming a closed circle, a new series beginning where another ends, as in a two- or four-cycle motor, so named from the number of piston strokes required to complete the series in each case. (*Plast.*) In plastics, the complete sequence, from one point in a process to the same point in the next round of steps.

cy′clo-gi′ro (sī′klō-jī′rō) (*Aero.*) A type of rotor plane whose support in the air is normally derived from airfoils mechanically rotated about an axis perpendicular to the plane of symmetry of the aircraft, the angle of attack of the airfoils being always less than the angle at which the airfoils stall.

cy′cloid. A curve generated by a point on a circle when that circle rolls on a straight line.

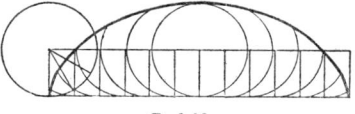

Cycloid

cy-cloid′al tooth (*Gear.*) A type of gear tooth not now in common use. The side of the tooth is machined with a compound curve as distinguished from the involute tooth now in universal use.

cy′clo-tron (*Elec.*) A device for accelerating positively charged particles (e.g. protons, deuterons, etc.) to high energies. The particles in an evacuated tank are guided in spiral paths by a static magnetic field while they are accelerated many times by an electric field of fixed frequency.

cyl'in-der. A circular body of uniform diameter, the extremities of which are equal parallel circles. (*Math.*) Convex area = (circumference x height). Entire area = convex area + area of both ends. Volume = area of base x length of side.

Cylinder

cyl'in-der block (*Auto.*) The main body of the engine which is bored to receive the pistons. The cylinder block and crankcase are frequently cast as one piece.

cyl'in-der bore (*Auto. Mech.*) The internal diameter of an engine cylinder.

cyl'in-der head. Refers to the cylinder covers of an engine.

cyl'in-der oil. Mixture of mineral oil with 5 to 15 per cent of animal or vegetable oils.

cyl'in-der press (*Print.*) A printing press consisting of a cylinder, a flat bed, and an automatic inking device.

cy-lin'dri-cal gauge (*Mech.*) A gauge consisting of two pieces, a plug gauge furnished with a handle, and a collar gauge into which the plug gauge fits. These gauges are used for testing bored and turned parts which are to fit together.

cyl'in-droid (*Geom.*) A solid body like a cylinder but with elliptical right sections.

cy'ma (sī'má) (*Arch.*) A commonly used molding having a reverse curve. There are two types, cyma recta and cyma reversa.

 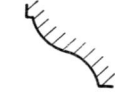

Cyma Recta   Cyma Reversa

cy-ma'ti-um (sĭ-mā'shĭ-йm) (*Arch.*) The portion of a cornice which contains a cyma curve.

cy'press. Grows in southern U. S.; one of the most durable of woods; somewhat like cedar, adapted to both inside and outside work in the building trades.

D

da′do (dā′dō) (*Arch.*) (1) A plain, flat, often ornamented surface at the base of a wall, as of a room. (2) One of the faces of a pedestal. (3) A rebate. (*Carp.*) A groove across a board.

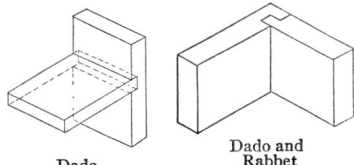

Dado   Dado and Rabbet

da′do and rab′bet (*Woodwk.*) A joint formed by a rabbeted edge or end of one piece fitted into a groove or dado in another piece.

da′is (dā′ĭs) (*Arch.*) A raised platform at the end of a room, or a portion of the floor raised a step above the rest of the floor.

dam′a-scen′ing (dăm′ȧ-sēn′ĭng) (*Furn.*) Imitating ancient damascus work, by an inlay of one metal upon another.

dam′mar (*Paint.*) An oleoresin resembling copal. It is obtained from coniferous trees of Asia, Australia, and South America. Used in varnishes. Soluble in hot alcohol, benzine, chloroform, or ether.

damp′er. A plate, valve, cover, or other contrivance for regulating draught.

damp′ing (*Elec.*) The introduction of a retarding force into or near an electrical recording instrument to reduce the oscillation of the needle and bring it quickly to rest.

damp′ing coil (*Elec.*) A coil mounted near a galvanometer to produce a damping effect; i.e., to bring the needle quickly to a point of rest after deflection.

damp′ing con-trol′ (*Tel.*) A control on the receiver which aids in removing the horizontal distortion or bulge which may appear on the left side of a picture.

damp′proof′ing (*Masonry*) The treating of a wall with some impervious material to prevent moisture from oozing through.

dan′de-li′on met′al (*Metal.*) An alloy used as a heavy-duty bearing metal. One composition consists of 72 per cent lead, 18 per cent antimony, and 10 per cent tin.

dan′dy mark (*Bookbndg.*) A watermark placed in paper by means of a dandy roll.

dan′dy roll (*Papermkg. and Print.*) A cylindrical roll used on a papermaking machine to produce a watermark.

Dan′iell cell (*Elec.*) A closed-circuit type of primary cell.

dar′by. A two-handled, flat tool used by plasterers, especially for working on both walls and ceilings. It is about 7 in. wide and 42 in. long.

Dar′de-let thread (Där′dĕ-lā) (*Mech.*) This screw thread of French design has a 29-deg. angle and a taper contact which makes it self-locking.

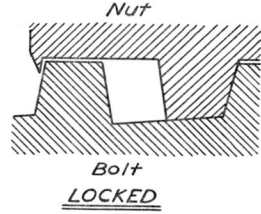

LOCKED

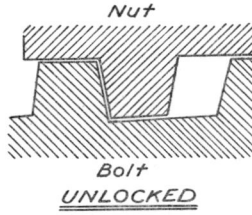

D'Arsonval gal'va-nom'e-ter (găl'-vȧ-nŏm'ē-tẽr) (*Elec.*) A very sensitive periodic or dead-beat galvanometer in which the indicating coil is suspended in the field of a powerful horseshoe magnet.

dash (*Auto.*) The partition which separates the engine compartment from the driver's compartment. (*Print.*) A plain or ornamental line between type matter; also a mark of punctuation.

dash'board in'stru-ments (*A u t o. Mech.*) Ammeter, speedometer, oil gauge, gasoline gauge, thermometer, and sometimes other instruments mounted on the instrument panel of an automobile.

dash'pot (*Mach.*) A small cylinder which, with its piston, absorbs a part of the shock in the quick closing of steam and exhaust valves of a Corliss engine.

da'ta (dā'tȧ) *pl.* of datum. Points of reference. (*Engin.*) Generally refers to tabulated statistical information concerning a piece of work.

da'tum (dā'tŭm) A point of reference.

da'tum line. Any base or fundamental line from which dimensions are taken or graphic calculations made.

daub'ing (*Fdry.*) Filling cracks in cores, or plastering a cupola after heat. (*Plaster.*) Smearing or coating with plaster in an unworkmanlike manner.

Da'vey (*Bookbndg.*) The name of the manufacturer of the best board for book covers, which is sold under the name "Davey Board."

Da'vy safe'ty lamp. A miner's safety lamp, in which the air passages are covered with a fine copper-wire screen, by means of which the products of combustion are cooled to such an extent that gases will not be ignited by them.

d.c. (*Elec.*) The common expression for direct current.

dead (*Print.*) A type form is "dead" when it has been printed and is ready for distribution.

dead'beat (*Elec.*) Instruments where indicators come promptly to a position of rest due to heavy damping.

dead cen'ter (*Mach. and Wood Turn.*) The center which is fitted into the tailstock of a lathe and does not rotate with the work.

dead end (*Plumb.*) The extended portion of a pipe which is closed at one end, and to which no connections are made on the extended portion, thus permitting the stagnation of water or air therein.

dead'en-ing (*Arch.*) The soundproofing of floors and walls by the use of insulating materials made for that purpose.

dead lev'el. An emphatic expression in the sense of absolutely level.

dead line (*Print.*) (1) A line marked on the bed of a cylinder press as a guide for placing the form. (2) The last hour or day when copy will be accepted.

dead load (*Engin.*) A load whose pressure is steady and constant.

dead mat'ter (*Print.*) Type matter not to be used, or type ready to be distributed.

dead rear axle (*Auto.*) A fixed rear axle that cannot turn. Used on double-chain-driven cars and internal-gear-drive trucks.

dead rise (*Aero.*) In a cross section of a float or flying-boat hull, the amount by which the height of the chine differs from that of the keel.

dead–smooth file (*Mech.*) The finest cut file made.

dead spot (*Radio*) Some locality at which a natural phenomenon prevents the reception of radio waves at certain frequencies.

dead weight (*Engin.*) The weight of a vehicle or carrier itself as distinguished from carried or live load.

deal (*Carp.*) A board or plank, or the wood of which the board or plank is made. Scotch fir.

dec'ade re-sist'ance box (*Elec.*) A simple form of resistance box containing two sets of ten coils, one set of one ohm resistance each, and the other of ten ohms' resistance each. Also called a "decimal rheostat."

dé'ca'lage' (dā'kȧ'läzh') (*Aero.*) The acute angle between the wing chords of a biplane or multiplane.

de-cal'co-ma'ni-a (dê-kăl'kô-mā'nĭ-ȧ) (*Paint.*) A process of transferring prints or pictures from paper to some smooth surface, such as glass, porcelain, wood, etc. Such a print before transferring.

Dec'a-lin (dĕk'ȧ-lĭn) (*Chem.*) A turpentine substitute — $C_{10}H_{16}$. Also used as a solvent for fats, resins, and oils. Chemically, it is known as decahydronaphthalene.

de'can-ta'tion (*Chem.*) Pouring off the clear liquid from the top of a suspension after it has settled.

de-car'bu-ri-za'tion. The removal of carbon from combination with metals as in the process of manufacture of malleable iron.

dec'a-style (dĕk'ȧ-stīl) (*Arch.*) A portico having ten columns.

de-cay' (*Wood*) Disintegration of wood substance due to action of wood-destroying fungi. Also known as dote and rot.

de-cel'er-om'e-ter (*Auto.*) A device for recording the rate of deceleration of a moving car and to indicate the stopping ability of the brakes.

dec'i-bel. A unit for measuring sound intensity, named in honor of Alexander Graham Bell. When sound or noise is created it gives off energy which is measured in decibels; e.g., the noise of an airplane engine measures 120 decibels.

de-cid'u-ous. Pertaining to those trees which shed their leaves at specific seasons.

dec'imal. A method of expressing fractional parts by tenths, hundredths, etc.

dec'i-mal e-quiv'a-lent. The value of a fraction expressed as a decimal.

deck'ing (*Arch.*) Material used to protect, from the weather, any flat surface such as the deck of a boat, the flat roof or the floor of a porch. Such decking may be of wood, canvas, or some roofing material.

deck'le (*Papermkg.*) In making paper by hand, the frame which regulates the size of the sheet. In making paper by machine, the straps which regulate the width of the web and prevent the overflow of water-soaked fiber. Also used as a term referring to the width of a web of paper which can be made on a paper-making machine.

deck′le edge (*Papermkg.*) The rough feathery edge of handmade paper. Some machine-made paper also has deckle edges.

de-com′po-si′tion. The act, process, or result of decomposing by natural decay or by chemical action.

dec′o-ra′tion (*Furn.*) The ornamentation of furniture, such as carving, painting, inlaying, applying of moldings, mounts, upholstery, etc.

de-den′dum (*Gear.*) That portion of a gear tooth lying between the pitch and the root lines.

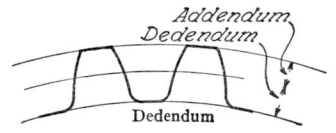

deep′ing (*Cabwk.*) Cutting out to a depth; placing comparatively far below the surrounding surface.

de-face′ment (*Wood Patmkg.*) The scarring, bruising, or marring of a surface or part of a pattern.

de-fect′. A flaw or imperfection.

def′i-ni′tion (*Tel.*) Sharpness of detail in the reconstructed picture.

de-flec′tion. The bending of a beam or structure under an applied load. (*Tel.*) The movement of the electron beam in a picture or camera tube by means of electrostatic or magnetic fields.

de′for-ma′tion. The alteration in form which a structure undergoes when subjected to the action of a load.

de-formed′ bars (*Engin.*) Those reinforcing bars made in irregular shapes to produce better bond between the bars and the concrete.

de′grades (*Wood*) Pieces which on reinspection, prove of lower quality than the grade in which they were shipped.

dé′gras′ (dā′grä′) The grease obtained in scouring wool. It is used to increase the viscosity of lubricants, also in belt dressings.

de-gree′. A 360th part of the circumference of a circle.

de′hu-mid′i-fy′ing. The lessening of the moisture content of the air, as in some industrial plants where dry air is required in certain manufacturing processes.

de–ic′er (*Aero.*) Any of the devices used to free wings, tail, and propellers from ice which sometimes forms in flight.

de-lam′i-nate (*Plast.*) To split a laminated plastic material along the plane of its layers.

de-lete′ (dê-lēt′) A proofreader's mark, meaning to remove or take out.

de-lin′e-ate (dê-lĭn′ê-åt) To portray, to draw out.

del′i-ques′cence (dĕl′ĭ-kwĕs′ĕns) The act or process of becoming liquid by absorption of moisture from the air, as certain salts; e.g., calcium chloride.

del′ta △ δ. The fourth letter of the Greek alphabet.

del′ta con-nec′tion (*Elec.*) The connection of the circuits in a three-phase system in which the terminal connections are triangular like the Greek letter delta.

del′ta met′al (*Metal.*) An alloy of copper and zinc with a small amount of iron.

de luxe′ (dē lüks′) (*Bookbndg.*) A particularly fine or elaborate edition of a book.

de-mag′net-i-za′tion (*E l e c.*) The process of removing magnetism from a magnetized substance.

de-mand′ fac′tor (*Elec.*) The ratio of the maximum demand of an electric supply system or part of a system to the total connected load of the system or of that part of the system being considered.

de′mar-ca′tion line (*Masonry*) A limit or line fixed as a boundary.

de-mount′a-ble rim (*Auto.*) A type of rim that can be removed from the wheel without deflating the tire.

de-mur′rage. The detention of a vessel, railroad car, or other vehicle beyond an allotted time; usually by failure to unload same within a specified number of hours or days.

de-my′ (dê-mī′) (*Paper*) (1) Name given to drawing paper measuring 15 by 20 in. (2) A standard writing paper measuring 16 by 21 in. which is now uncommon in this country.

de-na′tur-ants (*Chem.*) The various substances such as pyridine, benzene, kerosene, etc., added to alcohol to prevent its use as a beverage.

de-na′tured al′co-hol (*Chem. and Wood Patmkg.*) Alcohol changed by the addition of pyridine, methyl alcohol, or other denaturants so as to make it unpalatable; used freely in the industries, in manufacturing, as an antifreeze solution, and in the cutting of shellac.

den′im (*Uphol.*) A strong, twilled, cotton fabric of good wearing qualities, although most denims fade badly on too much exposure to bright sunlight. It is much used for upholstering furniture.

de-nom′i-na′tion. A class or division.

den′si-ty. Compactness. The mass or quantity of matter of a substance per unit of its volume, proportional to its specific gravity since mass is proportional to weight.

den′si-ty al′ti-tude′ (*Aero.*) The altitude corresponding to a given density in a standard atmosphere.

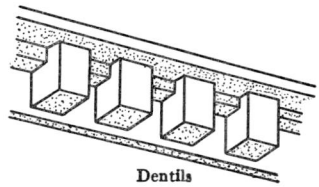

Dentils

den′til (*Arch.*) A rectangular decorative block such as that commonly used in the bed mold of a Corinthian entablature.

de-po′lar-i-za′tion (*Elec.*) The process of preserving the activity of a voltaic cell by preventing polarization.

de-po′lar-iz′er (*Elec.*) An oxidizing substance used for fixing the hydrogen derived from the decomposition of the acid by the zinc in primary cells.

de-pos′it (*Auto.*) (1) The product of combustion which forms on finished surfaces. (2) Solid matter which accumulates on a metal surface, as by any of the various plating processes. Also the accumulation of scale in a boiler, etc.

dep′o-si′tion. The act of depositing or precipitating a coating upon a surface.

de-pre′ci-a′tion. The loss in value which machinery sustains through age and through wear and tear.

depth gauge (*Mech.*) A gauge used by wood- and metal-workers for testing the depth of holes and recessed portions.

Depth Gauge

depth mi-crom′e-ter (*Mach.*) A precision gauge with micrometer adjustment, used to determine the depth of holes, slots, counterbores, or the distance from one surface to a lower level, etc.

der′rick (*Shopwk.*) A structure consisting of a fixed upright and an arm hinged at the bottom, which is raised and lowered, and usually swings around to handle heavy loads.

de-scend′er (*Print.*) That part of a lower-case letter which extends below the body of the letter, such as p, y, j, etc.

de-scribe′. To draw; to trace out; to narrate; to set forth.

de-scrip′tion. An account of anything in words or writing.

des′ic-cate (dĕs′ĭ-kāt) To exhaust or remove the moisture from; to dry thoroughly; to become dry.

de-sign′ (*Arch. and Art*) (*Verb*) To plan, originate, or show by drawings, some figure or object which can be built or reproduced, e.g., an architect's design of a building; a mechanical draftsman's design of a machine; an artist's design of materials used for decoration. (*Mech.*) The working out of mechanical ideas. The drawing out of a machine or structure.

de-sign′er or lay′out man. One qualified through wide experience to prepare designs of the type of product manufactured by his firm.

de-sign′ing en′gi-neer′. One who looks after the engineering and specifications of an assignment. He is responsible for efficient and economical design and approves all layouts before they are detailed.

de-struc′tive dis′til-la′tion (*Chem.*) Heating a substance out of contact with air in order to decompose it and obtain new and often useful products. It differs from ordinary distillation in that it results in chemical change as opposed to physical change resulting from plain distillation.

de-tach′. To disconnect, to remove. In shop practice, frequently, in order to make adjustments or change the setup for other operations.

de-tail′. One of the constituent parts. A separately considered portion of anything. A minor essential part, necessary yet secondary.

de-tail′ draw-ing (*Draft.*) A drawing showing details of a machine or other object with complete tabular data, dimensions, material used, number of pieces, operations to be performed. Not an assembly drawing.

de-tail′er. A draftsman who prepares the detail drawings for shop use.

de-tec′tor (*Elec.*) A device for converting inaudible radiofrequency signals into audible frequency signals.

de-te′ri-o-ra′tion. The state or process of growing worse.

de-ter′mine. To find the value of, mathematically, by exact measurement.

det′o-nate (*Auto.*) To cause gases under compression to expand rapidly through application of heat or flame.

det′o-na′tion. Rapid combustion replacing normal combustion disclosed by loss of power, engine overheating, etc.; also, an explosion.

det′o-na′tor. A cap in which a spark from an electrically heated wire sets off an explosive charge with sufficient violence to explode a greater charge of dynamite.

deu·te′ri·um (dū-tēr′ĭ-ŭm) (*Chem.*) Heavy hydrogen; hydrogen atoms containing two protons and electrons opposed to ordinary atoms of hydrogen which contain only one proton and electron.

de·vel′op. To draw a pattern of. To unfold gradually; make known in detail.

de·vel′op·ment. A drawing representing a pattern or layout.

de·vel′op·ment en′gi·neer′. Primarily an experimental engineer. He must be well versed in all developments in his industry and must be prepared to submit necessary data and information where any change in his firm's product is contemplated.

de′vi·a′tion. Departure from the exact or from a set standard. Variation; error.

de·vice′. A mechanical aid or contrivance which serves to promote the better performance of a job.

dev′il. An apprentice, or one who does odd jobs in connection with the work, as printer's devil.

dex′trin (*Wood Fin.*) An amorphous, colorless compound found in nature as in the sap of plants, soluble in water; is used as a substitute for gum arabic.

di·ag′o·nal. A straight, oblique line, such as would divide a rectangular figure into equal parts. The braces, struts, and ties of a lattice girder are its diagonals.

di·ag′o·nal bond (*Masonry*) Bricks laid obliquely in a wall as often is seen in the end walls of colonial houses.

di·ag′o·nal·ly. Obliquely inclined.

di·ag′o·nal part′ing (*Wood Patmkg.*) The parting of a pattern of rectangular cross section on its diagonal. Such a method of parting facilitates the removal of the pattern from the sand, and the setting of the core.

di′a·gram. An outline drawing, or graphic representation.

di′al. A graduated plate, usually circular or oval, on which a reading is indicated by a needle or pointer.

di′al bridge (*Elec.*) A resistance bridge having its coils arranged in dials, the contacts being made by a movable arm instead of by the insertion of plugs.

di′al gauge. A dial having an index hand actuated by a bent spring, through which the amount of pressure or of vacuum is indicated. All gauges of this kind are made on Bourdon's spring principle.

di·am′e·ter. A straight line passing through the center of a circle, its ends terminating in the circumference. (*Math.*) Diameter = circumference x 0.3183.

di·am′e·tral pitch (*Gear.*) The relation, or ratio, existing between the number of teeth on a gear and its pitch diameter. If a gear has 40 teeth and its pitch diameter is 10, the diametral pitch is 4, etc.

di′a·mond (*Chem.*) A crystalline form of carbon. The hardest known mineral. (*Print.*) Type of four and one half point size.

di′a·mond–point′ chis′el (*Mach.*) Similar to a cape chisel except that its point is shaped for the cutting of sharp-bottomed grooves.

di′a·mond–point′ tool (*Wood Patmkg.*) A tool having two cutting edges inclined to each other and meeting at an acute angle. One face of the tool is flat, the other is beveled from the cutting edges.

di′a-per (*Art*) A form of surface decoration used in art and architecture consisting of geometric designs.

di′a-per work (*Furn.*) A method of decoration, either in squares or lozenges, in which some design or ornament usually is repeated.

di′a-phragm (dī′á-frăm) (*Elec.*) A disk or sheet of metal or other substance flexible enough to permit vibration.

die (*Mech.*) (1) An internal screw used for cutting an outside thread. (2) A formed piece used in stamping out similar parts for quantity production.

Taps and Dies

die cast′ing (*Mech.*) A very smooth and accurate casting made by pouring molten metal or composition, under pressure, into a metal mold or die.

die–cast′ing met′al (*Metal.*) Light-colored alloys of aluminum, lead, zinc, or copper base of widely varying composition depending on the use to which they are to be put. For automobile hardware, an alloy of 90 per cent aluminum, 4 per cent copper, 4 per cent nickel, and 2 per cent silicon is much used.

die chas′er (*Mach.*) A threaded section of a screw-cutting die.

die clear′ance. The space allowed between punch and die to provide for the thickness of metal being worked on.

die forg′ing (*Forg.*) The making of forgings in dies, in quantity work, to secure a better product at reduced cost.

die′head (*Mach.*) The device which carries the threading dies in a screw-cutting machine.

di′e-lec′tric (*Elec.*) Any nonconducting medium which intervenes between two conductors and permits electrostatic attraction and repulsion to take place across it. A nonconductor in general.

di′e-lec′tric con′stant (*Elec.*) The ratio of the conductivity of a dielectric for electrostatic lines of force to that of air.

di′e-lec′tric strength (*Elec.*) Voltage gradient at which a continuous electrical discharge will take place between two electrodes when the material in question is placed between the electrode and a potential difference is applied to them. (*Plast.*) The property in plastics which maintains resistance against the passage of electric current.

Die′sel en′gine. An internal-combustion engine of high efficiency, in which a high temperature is obtained through compression; the oil is ignited by the heat thus developed.

die sink′er. One who makes, or cuts dies.

die stamp′ing (*Metalwk.*) A piece, usually of sheet metal, cut out or formed by a die. (*Print.*) A process of printing raised letters either with or without color.

die stock (*Mach.*) A lever or wrench used in operating threading dies by hand.

di′e-tet′ics. The branch of hygiene which treats of diet and dieting.

dif′fer-en′tial (*Mech. Engin.*) Relating to a construction in which a movement is obtained by a difference in two motions in the same direction,

dif′fer-en′tial block. A chain tackle which depends primarily on a pulley of two diameters fitted with lugs which fit the links of a chain; the larger diameter winds the chain in as the smaller diameter pays it out.

dif′fer-en′tial cal′cu-lus (*Math.*) That part of calculus in which the function is given and it is required to find its differential or derivative. This technique is applied to problems of time, rate, acceleration, maxima and minima, etc.

dif′fer-en′tial gear′ing (*Auto. Mech.*) That system of gearing which permits one rear wheel of an automobile to move independently of the other; thus avoiding excessive tire wear and strain on mechanical parts.

dif′fer-en′tial heat′ing (*Metal.*) Heating an article so that various parts reach different temperatures in order that different properties will be produced on cooling.

dif′fer-en′tial in′dex-ing (*Mach.*) In differential indexing on the milling machine the index plate is connected to the spindle on which the work is mounted, through change gears. Both plate and gears, therefore, revolve to produce the proper indexing.

dif′fer-en′tial mo′tor (*Elec.*) A motor with a compound-wound field, in which the series and shunt coils oppose each other.

dif′fer-en′ti-ate. To constitute a difference between; a mark distinguishing from.

dif-fuse′. To cause to spread out, to permeate or circulate in all directions.

di-gest′ (*Plast.*) To soften a substance by heat and moisture, sometimes under pressure, in order to remove certain substances from vegetable products.

dig′it (*Math.*) Any one of the numbers from one to nine and zero. These digits separately or in combination are used to represent numbers.

di-he′dral an′gle (*Aero.*) The acute angle between the two panels of a wing when rigged so that they slope up from the center section of the tips. Dihedral angle makes for lateral stability when operating in cross winds.

di-late′. To swell; inflate; to spread or increase in all directions.

dil′u-ent (dĭl′û-ĕnt) (*Wood Fin.*) A general term covering the reducers or thinners used for paints, etc., as linseed oil and turpentine for paints, alcohol for shellac, turpentine for varnish.

di-lute′ (*Chem.*) (*Noun*) Relatively weak in concentration. (*Verb*) To lessen the strength of by adding more solvent.

di-men′sion. A definite measurement shown on a drawing, as length, width, or thickness. Dimensions should be given on all working drawings, whether drawn to scale or not, but not on assembly drawings, except "over-all" dimensions.

di-men′sion-al sta-bi′li-ty (*Plast.*) The ability of a plastic part to hold its exact shape over a period of time and under specific conditions.

di-men′sion-ing. Indicating on a drawing the sizes of various parts.

di-men′sion line. A line on a drawing which indicates to what part or line the dimension has reference.

di-men'sion shin'gles (*Arch.*) Shingles of uniform size as distinguished from random shingles.

dim'mer (*Auto.*) A device for reducing the glare of headlights. The usual practice is to raise and lower the headlight beam by means of a foot switch. (*Elec.*) A rheostat placed in series with a lamp to control its brilliancy.

dim'ming re-sis'tor (*Elec.*) Inserted in a lamp circuit to reduce the luminous intensity of the lamp, e.g. head lamps.

dim'pling (*R i v e t.*) A method of forming a depression in thin metal to house the rivet head.

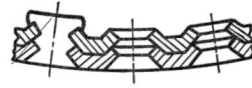

Dimpling

ding'ing ham'mer (*Metal.*) A hand hammer used for removing dents and bends from sheet metal.

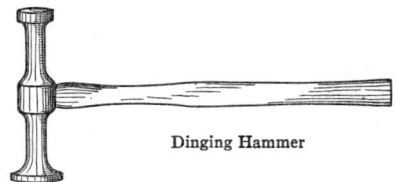

Dinging Hammer

dink'ing die (*Shopwk.*) A small die or punch used for cutting holes in cloth, leather, paper, etc. It may be operated in a machine or as a hand punch aided by blows of a hammer.

di'ode (*Rad.*) A vacuum tube; a two-electrode rectifier.

dip an'gle. The angle which lines of magnetic force at any place make with the horizon.

dip braz'ing (*Weld.*) By this process the work is immersed into the molten spelter until the parts are heated sufficiently to be united by it.

diph'thong (dĭf'thŏng) (*P r i n t.*) A combination of two vowels into one sound as, œ in Phœnix.

di'pole an-ten'na (*Tel.*) An antenna consisting of two conductors of equal length in the same straight line, with a pair of lead wires connected at the inner ends, is known as a doublet or dipole antenna. For short waves the physical dimensions are such that self-supporting metal rods or tubes can be used.

di-rect' ac'tion (*Mach.*) Mechanical movement in which no intermediate is employed.

di-rect' cur'rent (*Elec.*) A current flowing in one direction. In a dynamo the current generated alternates, but it may be converted into direct current by a commutator.

di-rect'–cur'rent arc weld'ing. An arc-welding process wherein the power supply at the arc is direct current.

di-rect' drive (*Elec.*) A compact arrangement of driving a dynamo by direct connection with the prime mover or the load, avoiding the use of shafts and belts.

dir-ect' dyes (*Textile*) Dyes which are effective without the use of a mordant.

di'rect in'dex-ing (*Mach.*) Direct indexing on the milling machine is done in such a manner that the spindle and the work mounted thereon revolve through identical angles with the indexing plate.

di-rec'tion. The position of one point in relation to another.

di-rec′tion-al gy-ro (jī-rô) (*Aero.*) A gyroscopic instrument for indicating direction, containing a free gyroscope which holds its position in azimuth and thus indicates angular deviation from the course.

di-rec′tion-al ra′di-o. Radio transmission in which the radio energy is radiated from the antenna in a certain predetermined direction.

di-rec′tion-al sta-bil′i-ty (*A e r o.*) Stability with reference to rotations about the normal axis; i.e., an airplane possesses directional stability in its simplest form if a restoring moment comes into action when it is given a small angle of yaw. Owing to symmetry, directional stability is closely associated with lateral stability.

di-rec′tion of force (*Phys.*) Is determined by the direction the force moves or tends to move the body upon which it acts.

di-rec′tion of mag-net′ic flux (*Elec.*) The direction is always from the north to the south pole in a magnetic field.

di-rec′tion sig′nal (*Auto.*) An electrical device used on trucks and buses to indicate the direction in which the driver intends to turn.

di-rect′ ra′di-a′tion (*P h y s.*) When the heating of a room is effected by steam or hot-water radiators within the room, the method is called direct radiation.

dir′i-gi-ble (dĭr′ĭ-gĭ-b'l) (*Aero.*) That which can be directed or is steerable, as a dirigible balloon. A noun to indicate an airship.

dirt′y (*Print.*) To "dirty" ink means to make it darker.

dir′ty proof (*Print.*) A proof that contains many errors.

dis-charge′ head′er (*Aero.*) The duct through which the air is conducted from the supercharger to the engine.

dis-charg′ing or re-liev′ing arch (*Masonry*) An arch over the opening of a door or window to relieve the weight from the lintel.

dis-col′or-a′tion (*Plast.*) Any change from an initial color possessed by a plastic. A lack of uniformity in color where color should be uniform over the whole area of a plastic object. In the latter sense, where they can be applied, use the more definite terms "mottle, segregation, or two-tone."

dis′con-nect′. To unfasten, release, or separate from.

dis′en-gage. To disconnect; to remove or separate from so as to free from action.

dis′en-gag′ing clutch (*Mach.*) A clutch for the throwing of a line of shafting or a train of wheels into and out of gear.

dished (*Furn.*) Referring to the pocket-shaped dips in the surface of card tables, used for holding money.

dished wheel (*Auto. Mech.*) A wheel made concave or convex.

dis′in-fec′tant (*Chem.*) A gas, liquid, or solid used to destroy disease germs.

dis′in-fec′tion (*Chem.*) The act of disinfecting or destroying germs of infectious or contagious diseases by the use of gases or liquids.

dis-in′te-gra′tion (*Chem., Masonry*) A crumbling away; gradual decay or wasting as of rocks.

disk (*Shopwk.*) Any thin, circular piece in a shop, not specifically named as a part of some machine or piece of work.

disk clutch (*Auto. Mech.*) Single and multiple. The general action is that in which a disk is held against a plate by springs with such force that there is no slipping during the transmission of power through the clutch. Clutches are engaged and disengaged by means of the clutch pedal.

disk rul'ing ma-chine' (*P r i n t.*) A machine by which lines are ruled with disks instead of steel pens.

disk sand'er (*Wood Patmkg.*) A very efficient machine for the pattern shop. It consists primarily of disks of sandpaper glued to a plate which revolves at high speed.

disk wheel (*A u t o.*) Made as steel stampings. Some have detachable rims, others have the wheel and rim made as a unit. The usual practice is to change the wheel when a tire change is to be made.

dis-man'tle. To tear down, take apart, disassemble

dis-per'sion (*Plast.*) In plastics, the well-distributed suspension of a finely divided material in another substance. As in an emulsion.

dis-play' type (*Print.*) The kind of type used for featuring or giving strength to some portion of the copy.

dis'si-pate. To waste, dispel, or drive off, as to exhaust poisonous gases.

dis'si-pa'tion of en'er-gy (*M e c h.*) The use or application of energy without a commensurate work return; a waste of energy.

dis-so'ci-a'tion (*Chem.*) A reversible chemical action induced by heat; e.g., ammonium chloride on being heated breaks down into hydrogen chloride and ammonia, and these compounds tend to unite to form ammonium chloride.

dis-solve'. To liquefy, melt, or change from a solid to a fluid state by the addition of some other substance. (*Tel.*) To bring one sound or picture into and through another sound or picture. Sometimes called a cross fade or lap dissolve.

dis-tem'per. Term applied to painting with colors mixed with size or other glutinous substance.

dis-tend'. To expand, lengthen, or spread out.

dis'til-la'tion (*Chem.*) The separation of the more volatile parts of a substance from those less volatile by vaporizing and subsequently condensing.

dis-tilled' wa'ter. Water from which impurities have been removed through distillation.

dis-tor'tion (*Tel.*) Any change in the original frequency, amplitude, or phase of a radio signal, consequently distorting the picture at the receiver. (*Wood Patmkg.*) That deviation from accuracy or correctness in a casting which may be caused by poor design of a pattern, by the manner in which the mold is rammed up, or by unequal cooling of the different parts of the casting.

dis-trib'ute (*Print.*) To break up a form and return type to proper cases.

dis-trib'ut-ed load. A load spread evenly over the whole extent of a surface. A girder will carry a load twice the total weight which it would carry if concentrated.

dis'tri-bu'tion (*Print.*) Placing type, leads, rules, and other materials in their proper places.

dis'tri-bu'tion box (*Elec.*) A large

metal box used in conduit installation as a center of distribution.

dis'tri-bu'tion line (*Elec.*) An exterior supply line from which individual installations are supplied.

dis'tri-bu'tion pan'el (*Elec.*) An electrical switchboard used as a connecting and distributing link between main supply wires and lights or motors to be supplied.

dis-trib'u-tor (*Auto.*) The device, operating in fixed time with the engine, which distributes the high-tension current to the spark plugs.

dis-trib'u-tor gear (*Auto.*) A gear at the lower end of a distributor shaft, in mesh with a gear cut or mounted on the camshaft, which drives the distributor shaft.

dive (*Aero.*) A steep descent, with or without power, in which the air speed is greater than the maximum speed in horizontal flight.

di-ver'gence (dī-vûr'jĕns) (*Aero.*) A motion in which, after a disturbance from equilibrium, the body departs continuously, without oscillations, from its original state of motion.

di-vide'. To cut or part into two or more pieces.

di-vid'ed light (*Arch.*) A window having several small panes of glass.

div'i-dend (*Math.*) A number or quantity divided or to be divided into equal parts.

Wing Dividers

di-vid'ers. Compasses for measuring or setting off distances.

di-vid'ing head (*Mach.*) A mechanical device which provides for the dividing of the circumference or perimeter of a piece of work into equal parts or spaces, as in the spacing of gear teeth.

di-vi'sor (*Math.*) That by which a number or quantity is divided.

doc'tor (*Shopwk.*) Local term for adjuster or adapter so that chucks from one lathe can be used on another. Sometimes used in the same way as the term *dutchman*. A common shop expression meaning to repair, remedy, or patch up. To doctor up.

dodg'er (*Print.*) A small printed circular or handbill such as is distributed from door to door.

doe'skin (*L e a t h e r.*) The dressed skin of a doe.

dog (*Mach.*) The carrier of a lathe. One of the jaws of a chuck. (*Woodwkg.*) A small piece of metal with two or more points for binding pieces of wood together while being worked.

Lathe Dog

Woodworker's Dog

dog'tooth (*Arch.*) A type of early English decoration in the form of a four-leaved flower, probably so named from its resemblance to the dogtooth violet.

dol'ly (*M e c h.*) A tool held against heads of rivets while riveting.

Dolly Block

dol'ly blocks (*Sheet-Met. Wk.*) Odd-shaped steel blocks used as seaming irons for irregular shapes and for reshaping and straightening fenders.

dol'o-mite (dŏl'ô-mīt) (*Mineral.*) A limestone containing a high percentage of magnesia. (*Min.*) Used as a refractory in the steel industry principally for the bottom and sides of open-hearth furnaces. Found in many sections of the United States.

dome (*Arch.*) The vaulted roof of a rotunda; a cupola.

domed (*Plast.*) Showing a symmetrical distortion which makes a flat section of a plastic object appear convex, and a curved section more convex.

don'go-la (*Leather.*) Calfskin, goatskin, or sheepskin tanned by the use of mineral and vegetable substances, and finished to resemble French kid.

don'key (*Furn.*) A machine used for cutting marquetry.

don'key en'gine (*Engin.*) An auxiliary engine used for special purposes on shipboard, in shipyards, for logging operations, etc.

door check (*Arch.*) A device which insures the closing of a door, the movement of the door being retarded to guard against a too rapid closing.

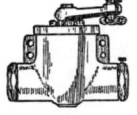

Door Check

door'frame' (*Arch.*) The surrounding case into and out of which a door opens and shuts.

door'head' (*Arch.*) The upper portion of a door frame.

door'stop' (*Arch.*) (1) A device, which may or may not be attached to a door, to hold it open in a desired position; usually attached near the bottom of the door and operated by pressure from the foot. (2) The strip on the inside face of a door frame against which a door closes.

dope (*Aero.*) Liquid material for application to the cloth surfaces of an airplane, to act as a filler, to increase strength, and to give tautness to the covering, resulting in an opaque finish.

Dor'ic frieze (*Arch.*) That part of a Doric entablature between the architrave and the cornice.

Dor'ic or'der (*Arch.*) The oldest of the Grecian orders of architecture.

Dormer Windows

dor'mer win'dow (*Arch.*) A small window projecting from the slope of a roof.

dor'mi-to-ry (*Arch.*) A large sleeping room capable of accommodating many people. Also a separate building used for sleeping.

do-sim'e-ter (dose meter) (*Phys.*) An instrument which determines the radiation dose a person has received.

dote (*Wood*) See DECAY.

dou'ble-act'ing hinge (*Cabwk., Carp., and Furn.*) A hinge designed to permit motion in either direction as on folding draught screens, swinging doors, etc.

dou'ble-ac'tion press (*Mach.*) A press for handling two operations for each revolution of the press. It carries two rams, one inside the other, so actuated that one motion immediately follows the other.

dou'ble belt'ing. Belting formed of extra thick or double thickness of leather.

dou'ble bond (*Chem.*) Ethylene. $H_2C=CH_2$. In organic chemistry, a double linkage between two atoms of the same element, one link frequently stronger than the other.

dou′ble–break switch (*Elec.*) A switch which opens or closes the circuit in two wires at the same time.

dou′ble–con′tact lamp (*Elec.*) A lamp whose base has two bottom terminals which make contact when the lamp is inserted in the socket.

dou′ble–cut (*Shopwk.*) Refers to double-cut file; i.e., one which has two rows of teeth crossing each other at an angle of 45 to 50 deg. The double-cut gives a broken tooth, the surface of the file having a large number of small teeth shaped like the end of a diamond-point cold chisel.

dou′ble de-my′ (dê-mī′) (*Paper*) Name given to drawing paper measuring 20 by 30 in.

dou′ble–end bolt (*Mech.*) A bolt having no solid head, being threaded at each end for the reception of nuts; often called a "stud" bolt.

Double-End Bolt

dou′ble–end trimmed. Lumber sawed square at both ends.

dou′ble–fil′a-ment lamp (*Elec.*) A lamp having two filaments, only one of which is lighted at a time. The filaments may be of the same or of different resistances, giving the same or different candle power.

dou′ble–geared (*Mech.*) A lathe or drill press equipped with an ordinary "back gear" is said to be double-geared.

dou′ble–hung win′dow (*Arch.*) A window consisting of upper and lower sash, both carried by sash cord and weights.

dou′ble ig-ni′tion (*Auto.*) See dual ignition.

dou′ble–pitch sky′light. A skylight sloping in two directions.

dou′ble–point push but′ton (*Elec.*) A push button capable of controlling two independent circuits at one operation, having one top and two bottom contacts.

dou′ble roll (*Print.*) When the ink rollers cover the form twice to each printing impression.

dou′ble riv′et-ing. Two lines of riveting in a lap joint, or four in a butt joint. (*Engin.*) A riveted joint made by two parallel rows of rivets.

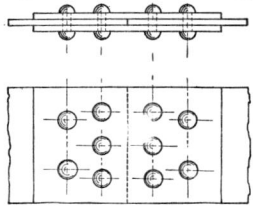

Double Riveting

dou′ble–row ra′di-al en′gine (*Aero.*) An engine having two rows of cylinders arranged radially around a common crankshaft. The corresponding front and rear cylinders may or may not be in line.

dou′ble–seam′ing ma-chine′ (*Sheet-Met. Wk.*) A machine for turning up against the body of a vessel that flange which is left after the seam has been set by the setting-down machine.

dou′ble–thread′ed screw (*Mech.*) A screw consisting of two distinct helices winding parallel with each other around the body; used to give an increase in the rate of travel; seldom used in V or National threads.

double-throw switch (*Elec.*) A switch that can be thrown into two different positions, connecting one circuit to two different circuits but not at the same time.

Doug'las fir. (See OREGON PINE.)

douse. To plunge into a liquid, as in quenching a piece of hot metal during a hardening process.

dou'zième' (doo'zyĕm') A unit of measure used by watchmakers. It equals .0074 inch.

dove'tail (*Woodwkg.*) An interlocking joint.

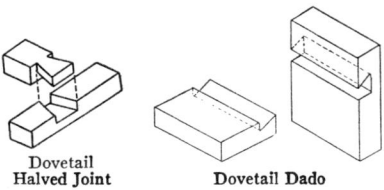
Dovetail Joint

dove'tail cut'ter (*Shopwk.*) Inner and outer dovetails are milled with this tool, and edges of work are conveniently beveled.

dove'tail' da'do (*Woodwk.*) A groove across a board cut so that the base is wider than the face of the opening. This shape resists pull perpendicular to the face of the board.

Dovetail Halved Joint   Dovetail Dado

dove'tail-halved joint (*Woodwk.*) A halved joint in which both cuts are narrowed at the heel as in a dovetail.

dove'tail'ing (*Furn.*) Fastening together by means of dovetailed joints. (*Print.*) When doubling up leads, the arrangement of them so that they overlap or break joints.

dove'tail lap joint (*Woodwk.*) Same as dovetail-halved joint.

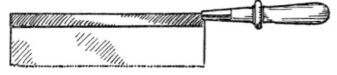
Dovetail Saw

dove'tail saw (*Woodwk.*) A saw similar to a backsaw but somewhat smaller, with finer teeth and usually with different shape handle.

dove'tail tongue (*Wood Patmkg.*) It is sometimes necessary to permit a part of a pattern to remain in the sand until after the withdrawal of the body of the pattern. This is often accomplished by means of a dovetail tongue, which is a piece held in place by its beveled edges. The principle is similar to that of the steel slide which covers the shuttle in a sewing machine.

dow'el. A pin of wood or metal used by patternmakers to keep portions of patterns in position during the process of molding. Also used in making permanent joints.

dow'el-ing (*Furn.*) The making of joints by the aid of dowels. Frequently butt joints are made secure by glue and dowel pins.

dow'el pin (*Wood Patmkg.*) Wood or metal pin used for keeping two parts of a core box in proper relation, or for keeping the parts of a pattern in position during the ramming up.

dow'el screw (dou'ĕl) (*F u r n.*) A wood screw threaded at both ends.

down'draft' car'bu-ret'or (*Auto.*) A carburetor in which the air enters at the top and travels downward past the spray nozzle.

down'spout' (*Arch.*) A pipe or conductor for carrying rain water from a roof to the ground or to a sewer connection.

down'wash (*Aero.*) The air deflected perpendicular to the direction of motion of an airfoil.

down'wash an'gle (*Aero.*) The angle through which the lifting surfaces of an airplane deflect the airstream.

drachm (dram) Same as dram. (See APOTHECARIES FLUID MEASURE.)

draft (*Fdry. and Wood Patmkg.*) The taper on a pattern that makes possible its easy removal from the sand.

draft'ing. The art of drawing.

drafts'man. One who prepares drawings, or portrays graphically; usually applied to one who uses mechanical aid or instruments in his work.

drafts'man's scale (*Draw.*) The triangular or flat measuring scale used by the draftsman. Usually made of boxwood with one edge graduated in 16ths, ⅛, ¼, ½, etc., as on a standard scale. Other edges are divided into fractional parts thereof to facilitate drawing at a reduced scale.

draft stop or fire stop (*Bldg.*) Obstructions placed in air passages to prevent the passage of flames up or across a building.

drag (*Aero.*) A retarding force acting upon a body in motion through a fluid, parallel to the direction of motion of the body. It is a component of the total fluid forces acting on the body. (*Fdry.*) The bottom section of a founder's molding box or flask.

drag link (*Auto.*) The rod which connects the left steering-knuckle arm with the steering-gear arm. There are two cups and a spring at each end to engage the ball ends of these arms.

drag'on's blood (*Paint.*) A resinous substance obtained from a species of palm growing in Siam, odorless, tasteless, insoluble in water, but soluble in alcohol and ether; forms a red solution; used in the coloring of varnish and other substances, and in photoengraving.

drag rope (*Aero.*) A long rope which can be hung overboard from a balloon so as to act as a brake and a variable ballast when making a landing.

drag strut (*Aero.*) A fore-and-aft compression member of the internal bracing system of a wing.

drag wire (*Aero.*) A wire intended primarily to resist the forces acting backward in the chord direction. It is generally enclosed in the wing.

drain. A pipe, channel, or trench through which waste water or other liquid is carried off as to a sewer.

drain'age (*Plumb.*) A system of drains; the act or means of draining. That which is drained off, as waste water.

drain cock (*Plumb.*) A small valve placed at a low point in a line of piping to permit draining.

drain'tile. Hollow tile, such as sewer tile, used for draining wet places.

draw (*v.*) (1) To portray by a system of lines. (2) To bring the temper of steel from extreme hardness to the desired hardness or temper. (3) To form by a stretching or distorting process; as to draw out wire.

draw'bar (*Auto.*) A bar with an eye at each end used as a tow bar. The name also is applied to other devices used for the same purpose.

draw bolt. The ordinary bolt, such as is used for fastening doors.

draw chis′el (*Mach.*) A pointed cold chisel used for shifting the center for a hole to be drilled, in cases where the drilling has been started but the drill has run, i.e., not drilling in the exact position desired.

draw chuck (*Mach.*) Used on small accurate work. It operates by a longitudinal motion in a taper bearing.

draw-cut shap′er (*Mach.*) A shaper which cuts with a pull stroke rather than the usual push stroke.

draw′er pull. The handle or other attachment on the front of a drawer so that it may be readily opened.

draw′er slip (*Cabwk.*) One of the guides or strips on which a drawer moves.

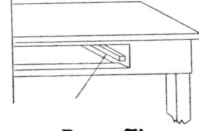

Drawer Slip

draw fil′ing (*Metalwk.*) A metal polishing operation, with a single cut file, for the purpose of removing finish marks, scratches, and nicks from the face or edges of a metal object.

draw′ing (*Arch.*) The representation on a plain surface by means of lines, and shades, of some figure or object, either freehand or by the use of instruments. (*Ceram.*) Removing ware from the kiln after it has been fired. (*Engin.*) As applied to the heat treatment of steel — heating to some temperature below the lower limit of the critical range, followed by cooling as desired. (*Mach.*) The delineation of machinery and machine parts in plans, elevations, and sections, to proportional scales. (*Metal.*) (1) A process in the manufacture of wire. (2) The shaping of thin metal by use of dies.

draw′ing back (*Metal.*) Reheating to a temperature below the critical after hardening for the purpose of changing the hardness of steel.

draw′ing board (*Draft.*) The board to which a draftsman attaches his paper preparatory to making a drawing. Drawing boards are made of white pine, basswood, or soft poplar, and with either end or back battens.

draw′ing die (*Metalwk.*) Die used in power presses for pressing sheet metal into cuplike shapes.

draw′ing in (*Textile*) The threading of the warp threads through the loom harness.

draw′ing of pat′tern (*Fdry.*) The lifting of a pattern from the molding sand.

draw′ing of tem′per. The heating of steel to red heat and allowing it to cool slowly. The reverse of hardening or tempering.

draw′ing out (*Forg.*) A heating and hammering process by which a piece is lengthened, accompanied by a proportional reduction in section area.

draw′ing pa′per (*Paper*) A paper made for pencil, crayon, and pen-and-ink drawing purposes.

draw′ing pen (*Draw.*) The ruling pen used by draftsmen.

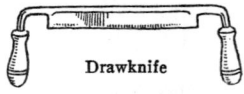

Drawknife

draw′knife. A two-handled wood-cutting tool having a long, narrow blade, the handles being at right angles to the blade.

draw′plate′ (*Fdry.*) A plate with a

threaded hole placed in a pattern. A draw screw inserted in this hole facilitates the removal of the pattern from the sand.

draw screw (*Fdry.*) A small rod with threads at one end for insertion in the threaded holes of the draw plate on a pattern.

draw'sheet (*Print.*) The top sheet of a tympan on a platen press to which the guides and fenders are attached.

draw spike (*Wood Patmkg.*) The pointed metal rod with which a pattern is removed from the molding sand.

draw ta'ble (*Furn.*) A table which can be increased in size by drawing extension leaves from beneath the top.

dredge. A machine for removing mud or sand from the bed of a stream by scoops or by suction.

dress (*Mach.*) To dress a tool means to restore a tool to its original shape and sharpness by forging or grinding.

dress'er (*Plumb.*) A tool used for straightening lead pipe and sheet lead.

dress'ing (*Textile*) Substances used in cloth finishing to give stiffness and body.

dri'er (*Paint.*) A number of different driers are used for paints, such as (1) salts or oxides of lead and manganese boiled in oil; (2) sugar of lead; (3) litharge; (4) cobalt driers. (*Print.*) Material added to ink to hasten its drying.

Drift

drift (*Aero.*) The side speed or departure laterally from a normal course due to air currents. (*Mech.*) A strip of steel, rectangular in section, wedge-shaped in its length, used for driving drill sockets from their spindles, etc.

drift angle (*Aero.*) The horizontal angle between the longitudinal axis of an aircraft and its path over the ground.

drift bar (*Aero.*) A part of a drift meter or other instrument for indicating the apparent direction of motion of the ground relative to the fore-and-aft axis of the aircraft. It usually consists of a wire or arm which can be set along this direction of motion.

drift me'ter (*Aero.*) An instrument which measures the angle between the longitudinal axis of an aircraft and its path over the ground.

drift pin (*Mach.*) A round tapered pin driven into rivet holes when they are not in perfect alignment. In some cases the holes may be distorted sufficiently to permit the setting of the rivet.

drift plug (*Plumb.*) A wooden plug driven through a lead pipe for the purpose of straightening out a kink.

drift punch (*Mach.*) A tool used to align rivet or bolt holes in adjacent parts so that they will coincide, or to drive out pins or rivets. (See DRIFT PIN.)

Drill

drill (*Mech.*) A tool for boring holes in metal or wood. Drills may be flat toward the point and simply beveled, or they may be of the twist type. (*Mech. Drg.*) Indicates that hole is to be made by drilling.

drill brace (*Mech.*) The name sometimes given to an ordinary bit brace and breast drill.

drill bush'ings (*Mach.*) Hardened steel bushings inserted in the face of jigs and fixtures to serve as drill guides in locating holes in proper position, thus making possible rapid and accurate production of interchangeable parts.

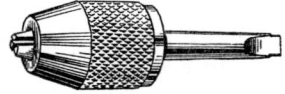

Drill Chuck

drill chuck (*Mech.*) A chuck made especially for holding drills.

drilled hole. Hole finished with drill.

drill gauge (*Mach.*) A flat steel plate drilled with holes of different sizes and properly marked so that the size of a drill may be easily determined by fitting it to the plate.

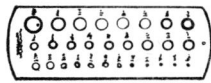

Drill Gauge

drill grind′ing gauge (*Mach.*) Used for checking the length and angle of the cutting lips of the drill.

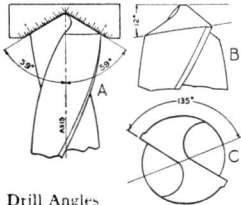

Drill Angles

drill′ing jig (*Mech.*) A device very accurately made of cast or wrought iron which becomes a guide for the drilling of holes. The work is fastened in the jig, and the drill is guided through holes drilled in the face of the jig itself. The use of a jig makes interchangeable work easily obtainable.

drill press (*Mach.*) A geared, automatic-feeding machine tool used for drilling holes in metal.

drill–press vise (*Mach.*) A special vise used on the table of a drill press to hold parts being drilled.

drill rod (*Mach.*) A 90- to 100-point carbon, ground and polished tool steel finished to a limit of .0005 in.

Drill Socket

drill sock′et (*M a c h.*) The socket which receives the tapered shank of a drill.

drill spin′dle (*Mach.*) The vertical spindle of a drilling machine which carries the drill and revolves, and through whose vertical movement the feed is operated.

drill vise (*Mach.*) A vise used on the table of a drill press for holding work to be drilled.

drip line (*Mech. Engin.*) In a heating system the return pipes through which the condensation from a radiator flows back to the boiler.

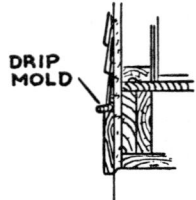

Drip Mold

drip mold (*Arch.*) A molding designed to prevent rain water from running down the face of a wall.

drip′stone (*Arch.*) A label molding used over a window for throwing off rain; also called "weather molding."

drive chain (*Auto.*) A form of heavy roller chain used to deliver power

driv'en (*Mech.*) The wheel, wheels, or pulleys actuated by a driver.

drive pin'ion (*Auto.*) Drives the large bevel gear which is connected to the differential.

drive punch (*Leather.*) A steel punch operated by blows from a hammer. Used for punching holes for eyelets, etc.

driv'er (*Mech.*) The wheel or pulleys from which power is transmitted to the driven.

drive screw or screw nail. A type of screw intended to be set by blows of a hammer but which can be removed with a screw driver.

Drive Screw

drive shaft (*Auto.*) The shaft which connects the transmission to the rear axle by the use of universal joints, and which carries the power of the motor to the rear axle. (*Mech.*) Also used for a similar purpose on other machinery.

driv'ing fit (*Mech.*) One which requires the blows of a hammer to accomplish the desired result, as in fitting a bushing to a hole.

driv'ing home (*Shopwk.*) The setting of a part into its final position by the action of blows as from a hammer.

driv'ing mech'a-nism (*Shopwk.*) A general term signifying the arrangement of wheels, pulleys, belts, levers, etc., by which motion is communicated.

drop (*Furn.*) A pendant ornament.

drop el'bow (*Plumb.*) A small ell that is frequently used where gas is put into a building. These fittings have wings cast on each side to permit fastening to wall, ceiling, or framing timbers.

drop ell (*Plumb.*) An ell with lugs in the sides by means of which it can be attached to a support.

drop-feed oil'er (*Mech.*) Sight feed oil cup equipped with a needle valve which can be adjusted to control the flow of oil.

drop forg'ing (*Mech.*) One formed in dies under a drop hammer.

drop front (*Furn.*) The front of a desk which is dropped forward for use.

drop ham'mer (*Engin.*) A heavy weight carried by a supporting frame which guides its travel. The weight is raised by power, then allowed to drop on the metal being forged.

drop han'dle (*Furn.*) Variously shaped handles which hang pendantlike.

drop hang'er (*Mach.*) A shafting support attached to a ceiling or underside of a beam.

drop or'na-ment (*Furn.*) An ornament used like the apron but which does not run the full width of the frame.

drop'out' (*Fdry.*) The loosening of the sand in the cope when the mold is closed.

drop sid'ing (*Arch.*) A type of weatherboard used on the exterior surface of frame buildings.

drop tee (*Plumb.*) A small tee having wings as a drop elbow.

Drop Siding

drop win'dow (*Bldg.*) A window that

can be lowered into a pocket below the sill, as on trolley cars.

dross (*Fdry*.) The scurf, oxide, and other impurities which are skimmed off the top of molten metals, or which accumulate in the head or in the riser.

drum (*Shopwk*.) Usually a hollow cylinder mounted on a shaft. Frequently used for transmitting power to other parts by means of belts or cables.

drum ar'ma-ture (*Elec*.) A dynamo or motor armature having its coils wound longitudinally or parallel to its axis.

drum trap (*Plumb*.) A trap, now practically obsolete, made from a piece of 4-in. lead pipe closed at the bottom, and fitted with a screw cap at the top.

dry bat'ter-y (*Elec*.) An electric battery made up of a number of dry voltaic cells. The term is often wrongly applied to a single dry cell.

dry cell (*Elec*.) A primary cell which does away with the liquid electrolyte so that it may be used in any position.

dry disk clutch (*Auto*.) The driving disks are covered on both sides with a friction material and are driven by keys in the clutch ring which is bolted to the engine flywheel. Called "dry" because no oil or grease must contact the clutch facings.

dry grind'ing. Grinding dry, without the use of water or other liquid coolant.

dry kiln (drī kĭl) (*Wood*) A chamber in which the seasoning of wood is hastened artificially.

dry meas'ure.
  2 pints(pt.) = 1 quart (qt.)
  8 quarts = 1 peck (pk.)
  4 pecks = 1 bushel (bu.)
  105 quarts = 1 barrel (bbl.) (for fruits, vegetables, etc.)

dry re-hears'al (*Tel*.) A run without cameras or other equipment.

dry rot. A rapid decay of timber which causes its substance to be reduced to a fine powder.

dry rub'ble (*Masonry*) Rough stone laid into a wall without mortar.

dry sand (*Fdry*.) Mixtures of sand which, after being dried in an oven or otherwise, become hard and better resist the strain put upon them from molten metal.

dry–sand core (*Fdry. and Wood Patmkg*.) One which has been baked or thoroughly dried in an oven. Dry-sand cores are made in core boxes independent of the mold, as distinguished from green-sand cores which are delivered directly in the mold by holes or depressions in the patterns.

dry spot (*Plast*.) Area in laminated plastics, e.g., laminated glass, where the interlayer and the glass have not become bonded.

dry steam. Saturated steam which contains no entrained moisture.

dry weight of an en'gine (*Aero*.) The weight of the engine, including carburetor and ignition systems complete, propeller hub assembly, reduction gears, if any, but excluding exhaust manifolds, oil, and water. If the starter is built into the engine as an integral part of the structure its weight shall be included.

dry well (*Plumb*.) A hole in the ground lined with stone in such a manner that liquid effluent or other sanitary wastes will leach into the surrounding soil.

dry wood. Timber from which the sap has been removed by seasoning.

dry'er (*Furn*.) Mechanical or other type of drying machine used for taking moisture from veneer.

dry'ing (*Fdry.*) The process of evaporating moisture from a mold by means of hot air injected, or of a charcoal fire basket, or by baking in an oven.

dry'ing oil (*Plast.*) A special type of oil, such as tung or perilla, which hardens readily when exposed to the air; used as an ingredient in varnishes.

dry'ing rack (*Print.*) A rack or frame to dry printed matter.

du'al ig·ni'tion. An ignition system having two sources of current (such as battery and magneto) and using the same set of spark plugs; also an ignition system having two spark plugs which fire simultaneously for each cylinder.

dub (*Print.*) A poor workman; an inexperienced printer.

duc·til'i·ty. That property of metals by virtue of which they can be drawn out into wires. (*Phys.*) The property of materials which permits permanent deformation without failure after the elastic limit has passed. Drawing metal into a wire is a common example of ductility.

dull–coated pa'per (*Papermkg. and Print.*) A smooth, unglossed enamel paper.

dull–fin'ish pa'per (*Print.*) Coated stock without glossy finish.

dull i'ron (*Fdry.*) Iron not as hot as it should be for best pouring.

dumb'–wait'er (*Arch.*) A type of small elevator, usually operated by hand, for moving food or small supplies between floors.

dum'my (*Print.*) A general layout of a book or piece of work, used to give an idea of how the work will look when finished, and to show size and arrangement; usually made up of blank pages.

dump'y lev'el (*Surv.*) Has its vertical axis, the horizontal bar, and the supports of the telescope all in one piece to which the spirit level is attached. The dumpy level will stand rougher usage than the wye level, and permits just as accurate work.

Dun'can Phyfe (dŭn'kăn fīf) (*Furn.*) An American furniture designer, prominent in the early part of the nineteenth century. His style, which carries his name, is based on the empire type, but is more delicate.

du'o·dec'i·mo (dū'ô-děs'ĭ-mō) A book page or leaf about 5 by 7½ in.

du'o·graph (*Print.*) Two halftone plates made from one copy, usually printed in black and one tint; the two plates being made with different screen angles.

du'o·tone (*Print.*) An ink which, on drying, gives the work the appearance of having been printed in two different colors.

du'o·type (*Print.*) Two halftone plates made from one copy and etched differently.

du'plex car'bu·ret'or (*Auto.*) A carburetor which has a double venturi for mixture distribution.

du'plex print'ing (*Textile*) The printing of a pattern on both sides of a fabric.

du'plex steel (*Metal.*) A cheap low carbon steel produced by the acid Bessemer process with further refining in the basic open hearth. If the second refining is done in an electric furnace the product should be of better quality.

du′pli-cate (dū′plĭ-kāt) To reproduce exactly.

du′pli-cate part (dū′plĭ-kåt) A part which is identical with and which would serve the same purpose as some other part.

du′ra-bil′i-ty (*Masonry*) The capacity to stand long and hard use.

du′ra-lu′min (*Aero.*) An alloy much used in aeronautics on account of its strength and lightness. It is composed of copper, 3.5 to 4.5 per cent; manganese 0.4 to 1 per cent; magnesium 0.2 to 0.75 per cent, and aluminum 92 per cent minimum. Its ultimate tensile strength is 55,000 lb. per sq. in., elastic limit at 30,000 lb. per sq. in., and specific gravity not more than 2.85.

dur′ir-on (*Metal.*) A trade name for an iron rich in silicon. Used for drainpipes in laboratories, etc., on account of its acid-resisting qualities.

dust bot′tom (*Furn.*) A thin surface of wood placed between drawers.

Dutch arch. A bonded arch, flat both top and bottom, with bricks sloping from a common center.

Dutch bond, or Eng′lish cross bond. A bond in which the courses are alternately made up of headers and stretchers.

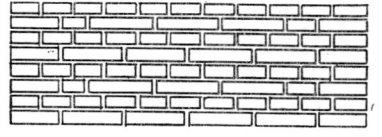

Dutch Bond

dutch′man (*Mech.*) A piece fitted in to cover a defect.

Dutch met′al. A very malleable alloy consisting of eleven parts copper to two parts of zinc.

dwell (*Auto.*) The period of time during which the contact points are separated. This is controlled by the cam shape.

dwell′ing (*Arch.*) A term of broad use, meaning a house or residence.

dye (1) To fix a color by soaking; (2) to stain or tint; (3) a coloring matter used for dyeing.

dye′wood. Wood that yields coloring matter for dyeing.

dy′na-flow transmission (*Auto. Mech.*) Consists of a hydraulic converter which, plus a planetary-gear set, gives the driver a choice of direct drive, emergency low, reverse, and neutral.

dy-nam′ic bal′ance (*Auto.*) That type of balance which permits parts to rotate without vibration at any speed for which they have been balanced.

dy-nam′ic fac′tor (*Aero.*) The ratio between the load carried by any part of an aircraft when accelerating and the corresponding basic load.

dy-nam′ic lift (*Aero.*) One of the four forces acting on an airplane in flight. Lift tends to hold an airplane up.

dy-nam′ic load (*Aero.*) Any load due to the acceleration of an aircraft. The dynamic load is proportional to the mass of the aircraft.

dy-nam′ic pres′sure (*Aero.*) The product of $\frac{1}{2}pV^2$ where p is the density of the air and V is the relative speed of the air.

dy-nam′ics. That branch of mechanics which treats of the laws of forces that produce motion in bodies.

dy-nam′ic speak′er (*Radio*) An apparatus for converting audiofrequency currents into sound waves. It consists of an electromagnetic field in which is placed a movable voice coil attached to a diaphragm.

dy-nam′ic sta-bil′i-ty (*Aero.*) A stability which tends to steady an airplane after it has been disturbed in its steady motion during flight.

dy′na-mite. An explosive composed of an absorbent saturated with nitroglycerin.

dy′na-mit′ing (*Textile*) Overweighting of silk with mineral salts.

dy′na-mo (*Elec.*) An electrical machine for converting mechanical energy into electrical energy.

dy′na-mom′e-ter (*Elec.*) A name given an instrument or machine for measuring the amount of energy expended in work.

E

e.m.f. (e-lec′tro-mo′tive force)(*Elec.*) The force which starts and maintains a current of electricity through a conductor; it is commonly measured in terms of volts.

ear (*Furn.*) An upholstery term referring to the frame which forms the wings of a wing chair. Also a term used to refer to the projecting top-rail ends of a fan back.

ear′mark′ To place an identifying mark on a piece to indicate that it is to be set aside or used for some particular purpose.

ear′piece (*Elec.*) That part of a telephone receiver which rests against the ear of the listener.

earth in-duc′tor com′pass (*Aero.*) A compass, the indications of which depend on the current generated in a coil revolving in the earth's magnetic field.

ea′sel (*Furn.*) A framework made to stand on the floor and support a picture.

ease′ment (*Arch.*) The curved part of a handrail or baseboard. (*Bldg.*) In stair construction, an ease-off or triangular piece to match the inside string and the wall base where these join at the bottom of the stair. (*Law*) The right one person has to make use of land belonging to another for some particular purpose.

eaves (*Arch.*) The projecting edges of a roof.

eaves trough (*Arch.*) A channel or trough at the eaves of a roof for carrying off rain water.

eb′on-ite. Black vulcanite, or hard rubber.

eb′on-ize (*Cabwk. and Furn.*) To stain or finish in imitation of ebony.

eb′on-y. A hard, heavy, very dark wood used in cabinetwork.

eb′ul-li′tion. The bubbling of a liquid; boiling.

ec-cen′tric (*Engin.*) A device used on engines for changing the rotary motion of the crankshaft into a reciprocating motion on the slide valve.

ec-cen′tric ad-just′ment (*Auto.*) The bringing of related parts into proper adjustment by turning an eccentrically bored bushing.

ec-cen′tric clamp (*Metalwk.*) A quick-acting clamping device which works on the principle of the eccentric.

ec-cen′tric fit′ting (*Plumb.*) A fitting in which the center line is offset in the fitting.

ec-cen′tric fluted reamer (*Mach.*) A reamer so milled that the concave channels are unevenly spaced to obviate chattering, but placed exactly opposite to permit diameter measurement with a micrometer.

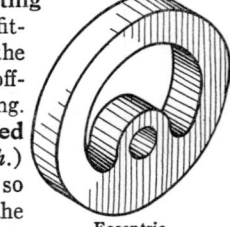
Eccentric

Eaves

ec′cen-tric′i-ty. The deviation of the

centers of two circles from one another.

ec-cen'tric rod (*Engin.*) The rod which connects the eccentric with the valve mechanism.

ec-cen'tric strap (*Engin.*) The metal ring or container which encircles the eccentric sheave and transmits its motion to the rods and valve gearing in a steam engine.

ec-cen'tric turn'ing (*Mech.*) Lathe turning work which is not concentric with the axis. (*Woodwkg. and Mach.*) Turned work not concentric with the axis of the main turned shaft. A mandrel is used with two sets of centers that offset the amount required for the eccentricity needed.

Echinus

e-chi-nus (ê-kī'nŭs) (*Arch.*) An ornamental molding, sometimes spoken of as egg-and-dart molding.

e'co-nom'ic. Pertaining to money matters or wealth, or to the means and methods of living well and wisely.

e'co-nom'ic speed (*Aero.*) The speed at which fuel consumption is at a minimum for a given distance covered in still air.

e-con'o-miz'er (*Engin.*) An arrangement of pipes or reservoirs in which the feed water for steam boilers is heated up to or higher than the boiling point. Feed-water heaters, therefore, are economizers.

e-con'o-my coil (*Elec.*) A combination of choking coil and transformer, used with alternating-current arc lamps when the supply voltage is greater than that needed by the lamps.

e-con'o-my wall (*Masonry*) A brick wall four inches thick blanketed with back mortaring, strengthened at intervals with vertical pilasters, having brick corbelling for the support of floors and roof, providing a four-inch outside reveal for doors and windows, and with every window and door frame bricked in.

ed'dy cur'rents (*Elec.*) Induced electric currents occurring when a solid metallic mass is rotated in a magnetic field. They consume a large amount of energy and often cause a harmful rise in temperature.

edge cross lap (*Carp.*) A cross-lap joint in which the pieces approach each other edgewise. See CROSS LAP. **Edge Lap**

edged tools. Cutting tools used in the handicrafts especially in woodworking.

edge roll (*Furn.*) A molding detail of Gothic origin.

edge flare (*Tel.*) A rim of illumination around the edge of the picture on the receiver tube.

edg'ing (*Cabwk. and Furn.*) The small, solid squares set in on the edge of a top when the face is veneered, as a protection to the veneer.

edg'ing board (*Lumber*) Usually the first board cut from a log after the slab cut, the edges not being filled out.

edg'ing ma-chine' (*Sheet Metal*) Also known as "adjustable bar folder"; used for folding edges on pieces of sheet metal.

edg′ing trow′el. A rectangular shaped trowel with turned down edge on one side; used for edging pavements, curbing, etc.

ed′i-fice (*Arch.*) A building. A term usually applied to architecture distinguished for its size or grandeur.

Ed′i-son stor′age bat′ter-y (*Elec.*) A bimetallic cell developed by Edison with special reference to the need of automobiles. The active material of the positive plate is peroxide of nickel and that of the negative plate is finely divided iron.

ef-face′. To rub out, erase, remove, or obliterate.

ef-fec′tive a′re-a (*Aero.*) The effective area of a screw blade is that obtained by the projection of the blade on a plane at right angles with its axis. It is less than the superficial area.

ef-fec′tive con-duct′ance (*Elec.*) The ratio of the energy component of a current to the total e.m.f. in an alternating-current circuit.

ef-fec′tive cur′rent (*Elec.*) The strength of a current as indicated by a constant reading ammeter.

ef-fec′tive he′lix an′gle (*Aero.*) The angle of the helix described by a particular point on a propeller blade as the airplane moves forward through air otherwise undisturbed.

ef-fec′tive horse′-pow′er (*Engin.*) The amount of useful energy that can be delivered by an engine.

ef-fec′tive land′ing a′re-a (*Aero.*) That portion of the landing area, with approaches clear within the allowable safe climbing and gliding angle available for the take-off and landing of aircraft.

ef-fec′tive pro-pel′ler pitch (*Aero.*) The distance traveled for one revolution of the propeller.

ef-fec′tive pro-pel′ler thrust (*Aero.*) The net driving force developed by a propeller when mounted on an aircraft.

ef-fec′tive thrust (*Aero.*) The net driving force of a propeller in action.

ef-fec′tive val′ue (*Elec.*) The value of an alternating current or voltage which is indicated on a volt or ammeter connected in the circuit. It is a value which is .707 times the maximum (peak) value of that voltage or current.

ef′fer-ves′cence. The escape of bubbles of gas from a liquid otherwise than by boiling.

ef-fi′cien-cy. The efficiency of a joint, structure, machine, or part, is the ratio which it bears to some standard of reference.

ef′flo-res′cence (*Bldg.*) The formation of a whitish powder on the face of a brick or stone wall.

ef′flu-ent (*Plumb.*) The liquid discharged from a septic tank or sewage disposal plant.

egg′shell fin′ish (*Papermkg.*) A finish given to uncoated papers either woven or laid.

e-jec′tor (*Shopwk.*) On punch-press work it is a ring, collar, or disk actuated by spring pressure or by pressure of a rubber disk, to remove blanks from the interior of compound and other dies. It is often called a "shedder."

e-jec′tor pin (*Plast.*) A device that knocks a finished piece out of the mold.

e-las′tic (*Engin.*) That condition which permits of a deformation when force is applied and a return to original shape on the removal of such force.

e-las'tic ax'is (*Aero.*) (Stress analysis.) The locus of all points through which a force may be applied to a structure without causing torsional deflection.

e-las'tic de'for-ma'tion (*Plast.*) A change in a substance whereby it reverts to its original dimensions on release of an applied stress.

e'las-tic'i-ty (*Engin.*) Has reference to the extent to which a bar or structure may be elongated by tensile stress, without causing permanent set.

e-las'tic lim'it(*Engin.*) That point beyond which permanent set takes place.

e-las'tic strength (*Engin.*) The greatest stress a bar or structure is capable of sustaining within the elastic limit.

e-lat'er-ite. A bitumin obtained from Colorado and Utah. It contains considerable sulphur but is valuable for roofing.

el'bow (*Plumb.*) A fitting joining two pipes at an angle.

e-lec'tri-cal–ca-pac'i-ty al-tim'e-ter (*Aero.*) An altimeter, the indications of which depend on the variation of an electrical capacity with distance from the earth's surface.

e-lec'tri-cal con'duc-tiv'i-ty. The relative power of carrying the electric current possessed by different substances; the conducting power of pure copper being taken as a standard.

e-lec'tri-cal en'gi-neer'. One well versed in the theory and practice of the development and utilization of electrical energy.

e-lec'tric braz'ing. A group of brazing processes wherein the heat is obtained from an electric current.

e-lec'tric drill. Usually refers to the electrically operated, self-contained hand drill.

e-lec'tric horse'pow'er. 746 watts.

e-lec-tri'cian. A person familiar with the theory and practical application of electricity.

e-lec-tric'i-ty (*Elec.*) Current electricity is electrons in motion. Static electricity is electrons at rest.

e-lec'tric mo'tor (*Elec.*) A machine for transforming electrical energy into mechanical power.

e-lec'tric po-ten'tial. See ELECTROMOTIVE.

e-lec'tric pow'er (*Mech. Engin.*) The rate of doing work by electricity; measured in watts or kilowatts.

e-lec'tric py-rom'e-ter. A sensitive pyrometer for exact temperature measurements. It utilizes the changes in electrical resistance of platinum when heated.

e-lec'tric steel (*Metal.*) High quality steel produced in an electric furnace by a method which eliminates most of the sulphur and phosphorus. A cleaner steel with fewer defects is produced by this system than by most other methods.

e-lec'tri-fi-ca'tion (*Elec.*) Charging a body with electrostatic charges.

e-lec'tro-chem'i-cal. Chemical action employing a current of electricity to cause or sustain the action.

e-lec'trode (*Elec.*) A pole of a battery or magnet, either positive or negative. (*Weld.*) The part or parts of a resistance welding machine through which the welding current and pressure are applied directly to the work.

e-lec'tro-form'ing (*Plast.*) Process of forming a mold cavity by electroplating with iron, a master hob of metal, wood, glass, or plaster.

e-lec′tro-lier′ (*Elec.*) An electric fixture designed to hang from a ceiling.

e-lec-trol′y-sis (ē-lĕk-trŏl′ĭ-sĭs) (*Elec. and Engin.*) Decomposition of a material by passing an electric current through it.

e-lec′tro-lyte (*Elec.*) The common term applied to the mixture of sulphuric acid and water used in a lead storage cell or battery. All acids, bases, and salts are electrolytes.

e-lec′tro-lyte lev′el (*Auto.*) The proper amount of electrolyte coverage of the plates in a storage-battery cell.

e-lec′tro-lyt′ic con-dens′er (*Elec.*) See CONDENSER ELECTROLYTE.

e-lec′tro-ly′tic cop′per (*Metal.*) Copper produced mainly from the sulphide ores of the western United States by electrolytic processes. After passing through several processes, it is cast into cakes, slabs, wire bars, ingots, and billets.

e-lec′tro-lyt′ic cor-ro′sion (*Elec.*) Corrosion by electrolysis, of metal bodies in contact with dampness when in the vicinity of electric currents.

e-lec′tro-lyt′ic i′ron (*Metal.*) A very pure iron produced by an electrolytic process. It has excellent magnetic properties and is often used in magnet cores.

e-lec′tro-lyt′ic rec′ti-fi′er (*Elec.*) A rectifier employing the principle of electro-chemistry to change A.C. to D.C.

e-lec′tro-ly′tic re-fin′ing. The refining of metals by electrolysis.

e-lec′tro-mag′net. A magnet produced by passing an electric current through the insulated wire conductor coiled around a core of soft iron.

e-lec′tro-mag-net′ic field (*Elec.*) The area between the poles of an electromagnet through which the magnetic lines of force travel; or the area of magnetic effect.

e-lec′tro-mag-net′ic in-duc′tion (*Elec.*) A wire cutting lines of force of a magnetic field has induced in it an e.m.f.

e-lec′tro-mag′net-ism (*Elec.*) Magnetic lines of force set up by current flowing through turns of wire wound on an iron core.

e-lec′tro-mo′tive. The force which starts and maintains a current of electricity through a conductor, measured in terms of volts.

e-lec′tro-mo′tive force of self–in-duc′tion (*Elec.*) E.M.F., set up in a single coil due to the inductive effect between its windings.

e-lec′tron (*Elec.*) A very small atomic particle; it possesses the smallest amount of negative electric charge found in nature.

e-lec′tron beam (*Tel.*) A stream of electrons constrained and focused into the shape of a beam by external electrostatic magnetic fields; also called cathode-ray beam.

e-lec′tron gun (*Tel.*) A system of metallic cylinders arranged in the narrow ends of both the camera and receiver tubes in which the electron beam, used for scanning the image before the television camera, and for reproducing it in the television receiver, is formed.

e-lec′tron-ic ap-pa-ra′tus. (1) One which accomplishes its purpose through the intermediary of electrons, relatively free from the grosser matter to which they are ordinarily bound; (2) Arc for safety interruptions of power circuits, spark gaps in lightning arrestors, spark plugs, electric arc welders, electric arc furnaces, precipitrons for cleaning air of dust.

e-lec′tron-ics (*Elec.*) The science which deals with free electrons, the means of setting them free, their motions when free, and the effects they can produce by being acted upon while free. These electrons are free in the sense that they are at greater distances than the radii of the outermost stable orbits of the normal atom. These free electrons are more than 10–8 c.m. away from nuclei. The science of the practical application of the theory of electrons in such devices as radio tubes, photoelectric cells, etc.

e-lec′tron tube (*Elec.*) An electron device in which conduction by electrons takes place through a vacuum or gaseous medium within a gastight envelope.

e-lec′tron met′al (*Metal.*) An alloy of magnesium with 5 per cent zinc and .5 per cent copper. Used for automobile pistons.

e-lec′tro-plat′ing. The act or process of depositing metal by electric means.

e-lec′tro-scope (*Elec.*) A device for detecting the presence of electrostatic charges.

e-lec′tro-stat′ic co-ro′na (*E l e c.*) Ionic discharge which surrounds the electrodes when a static charge builds up sufficient frequency and potential.

e-lec′tro-stat′ic dis-charge′ (*Elec.*) Arc formed by a difference of potential between electrostatic bodies.

e-lec′tro-stat′ic field (*Elec.*) The area about an electrostatically charged body.

e-lec′tro-stat′ics (*Elec.*) That branch of electrical science which treats of the phenomena of electricity at rest, or of frictional electricity.

e-lec′tro-type (*Print.*) A copper-covered printing plate; a duplicate of a cut or of type matter, made type high, usually with a wooden or metallic base.

e-lec′trum (*Chem.*) A natural alloy of gold and silver containing approximately 40 per cent of silver.

el′e-ment(*Chem.*)That form of matter which cannot be decomposed by any means known to science. One of a limited number of distinct varieties of matter which, singly or in combination, compose every material substance.

el′e-men′ta-ry. Treating of the first principles of anything. Of or pertaining to an element or elements.

el′e-ments of a stor′age bat′ter-y (*Elec.*) The positive and negative metal plates of a storage battery in which chemical changes take place during charge and discharge.

el′e-va′tion (*Draw.*) A geometrical projection on a vertical plane, as a view in mechanical drawing.

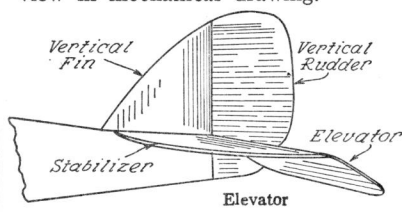

Elevator

el′e-va′tor (*Aero.*) A movable auxiliary airfoil, the function of which is to impress a pitching moment on the aircraft. The elevator is usually hinged to the stabilizer.

el′e‑va′tor an′gle (*Aero.*) The angular displacement of the elevator from its neutral position. It is positive when the trailing edge of the elevator is below its neutral position.

el′e‑va′tor rope (*Engin.*) Wire rope composed of hemp core around which are located 6 strands of 19 wires each.

e‑lim′i‑nat′ing. Act of getting rid of; casting out. Setting aside as unimportant or inapplicable.

e‑lix′ir of life (*Chem.*) A mythical substance sought by the alchemists and believed by them to be capable of prolonging life.

E‑liz′a‑be′than (*Arch. and Furn.*) Relating to the time of Elizabeth, Queen of England.

elk hide (*Leather.*) A heavy, soft leather suitable for moccasins and shoes.

ell (*Arch.*) A wing or addition to a building forming an angle with the main structure.

el‑lipse′ (*Geom.*) A plane curve, such that the sum of the distances from any point of the curve to two fixed points is a constant. (*Math.*) Area = long diameter x short diameter x 0.7854

el‑lip′soid (*Geom.*) A solid, every plane section of which is an ellipse or a circle.

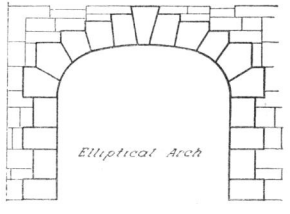
Elliptical Arch

el‑lip′ti‑cal arch (*Arch.*) An arch, elliptical in form, being described from three centers.

el‑lip′ti‑cal or ec‑cen′tric gears (*Shopwk.*) Gears, in which the shaft is not in the center; of almost any shape, oval, heart-shaped, etc. Printing presses usually have good examples of these.

elm. A coarse, open-grained wood much given to warping; is very sparingly used in engineering work.

e′lon‑ga′tion (*Mech. Engin.*) Malleable iron and steel, when subjected to tensile stress, elongates up to the breaking strain with a consequent reduction of area. The amount of elongation and reduction of area it undergoes is considered a test of its quality. (*Plast.*) The increase in length of a stressed material.

em (*Print.*) The square of a type body. The cost of setting reading matter is generally based on a price per thousand ems.

em‑bel′lish. To ornament or decorate. To beautify by adding ornamental features.

em‑bla′zon. To adorn with figures of heraldry.

em′blem (*Furn.*) A symbolic ornament often used as a carved decoration.

em‑bossed′ (*Shopwk.*) Decorated or richly ornamented with raised figures.

em‑bossed′ split–grain cow′hide′ (*Leather.*) Less expensive but similar in appearance and used for the same purpose as grained cowhide.

em‑boss′ing (*Art Met. and Ceram.*) The process of decorating with raised ornamentation. (*Print.*) Printing by the use of dies so as to leave the design in relief.

em-boss'ing ham'mer (*Art Met.*) Used for working on the inside surface of hollow objects.

em-boss'ing plate (*Print.*) A plate cut or etched below its surface into which the paper is forced for the purpose of raising the image of the printed surface.

e-mer'gen-cy brake (*Auto.*) A hand-operated brake commonly known as a parking brake. Rarely used in actual driving except when the car is stopped on a grade. Its principal use is to prevent motion of a car when parked.

e-mer'gen-cy flo-ta'tion gear (*Aero.*) A device attached to a landplane to provide buoyancy in case of an emergency landing on the water.

e-mer'gen-cy switch (*Elec.*) A switch connected ahead of the power company's meter for the purpose of disconnecting current from all parts of a building in case of an emergency or fire.

em'er-y. A species of corundum composed of oxide of alumina, iron, silica, and a small portion of lime. It is used as an abrasive.

em'er-y cloth. Powdered emery glued on thin cloth, used for removing file marks and for polishing metallic surfaces.

em'er-y wheel (*Mech.*) A wheel made of emery. It is revolved at a high speed and is used for grinding.

em'pen'nage' (äN'pē'nàzh') (*Aero.*) The tail surfaces of an airplane.

em-pir'i-cal rule (*Engin.*) Any rule or equation which is not deducted from purely mathematical or physical considerations, but which is based upon experience or custom.

e-mul'si-fy (*Plast.*) To suspend a material in a finely divided (emulsified) state in a liquid.

e-mul'sion (*Chem.*) A liquid preparation of a color and consistency resembling milk, or in which minute particles, especially of a liquid, remain in suspension as the fat globules do in milk.

en (*Print.*) One half of an em.

en-am'el (*Cabwk., Color, and Furn.*) A material applied as a paint which dries with a hard, glossy finish.

en-am'eled (*Papermkg.*) Term applied to paper that has been coated and the surface calendered to a high polish.

en-am'eled brick (*Bldg.*) Brick with a glazed or enamel-like surface.

en-am'eled wire (*Elec.*) Wire coated with insulating enamel and usually covered with cotton or silk for protection.

en-ar'gite (ĕn-är'jīt) (*Metal.*) Cu_3AsS_4. A copper ore (copper arsenic sulphide).

en-cased' knot (*Wood*) A knot whose growth rings are not intergrown and homogeneous with the growth rings of the piece it is in.

en-caus'tic tile (ĕn-kôs'tĭk tīl) (*Masonry*) A painted tile in which the hues have been fixed by heat.

en-cir'cle. To circumscribe, to surround, to draw a line around.

en-closed'-arc lamp (*Elec.*) An arc lamp in which the arc is enclosed in a globe so shaped that only a small amount of air can enter, thus retarding consumption of the carbons.

en-closed' fuse (*Elec.*) A fuse contained in an airtight insulating holder to prevent ignition of gas or dust.

end'-grain' (*Woodwk.*) That face of

a piece of timber exposed by the cutting of its fibers transversely.

en′dive scroll (*Furn.*) A carved leaf design.

end′–lap joint (*Woodwkg.*) A corner joint formed by halving both pieces for a distance equal to their widths.

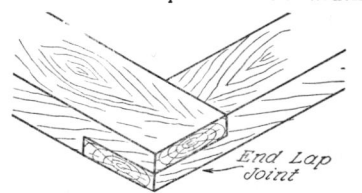

end′less saw (*Woodwkg.*) A band saw.

end meas′ur-ing rod (*Shopwk.*) Arranged for internal measurements similar to internal cylindrical gauges.

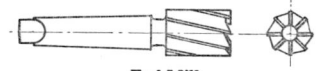
End Mill

end mill (*Mach.*) Milling cutter usually having tapered shank, for direct fitting to spindles or sockets. The cutting portion is cylindrical in shape, so made that it can cut both on sides and end.

en-dog′e-nous (ĕn-dŏj′ê-nŭs) (*Bot.*) A plant that grows from within, i.e., one that increases by the growth of new tissue among that already formed.

end pa′per (*Bookbndg.*) Sheet of paper in the front and back of bound books.

end play (*Mech.*) The play at the ends of a revolving part, i.e., play in a longitudinal direction.

end thrust (*Engin.*) The end or longitudinal pressure exerted by a rotating vertical or horizontal shaft. Usually cared for by a thrust bearing.

en-dur′ance (*Aero.*) The maximum length of time an aircraft can remain in the air at a given speed and altitude.

en-dur′ance lim′it (*Metal.*) The maximum stress to which material may be subjected without causing failure by fatigue.

en′er-gy (*Phys.*) A body is said to possess energy when it is capable of doing work or of overcoming resistance. Energy may be either kinetic or potential.

en-gage′ (*Mach.*) To bring parts together or in contact in order to transmit motion or power, e.g., the operation of the gearshift lever engages and disengages the change-speed gears of an automobile.

en′gine (*Phys.*) A machine or mechanism by which generated power is applied to doing work, as the steam, gas, or gasoline engine.

en′gine al-tim′e-ter (*Aero.*) An altimeter for indicating the altitude corresponding to the pressure produced in the intake manifold of a supercharged engine.

en′gine con-trols′ (*Aero.*) The means employed to control the power output of the engine. Control of speed may be affected by the air controls or engine controls independently, or by either in conjunction with the other.

en′gine cowl′ing (*Aero.*) A cowling placed around an aircraft engine for directing and regulating a flow of cooling air for streamlining or for protection.

en′gine dis-place′ment (*Aero.*) The total volume swept by the pistons of all the cylinders during one complete stroke of each piston.

en′gi·neer′. An expert in design, construction, and development in the fields of electricity, mining, mechanics, building, etc.

en′gi·neer′ing. The art and science relating to expert planning and constructing in various fields of industry.

en′gi·neer′s′ chain (*Surv.*) Has 100 links, each one foot long. Gunter's chain, formerly much used in land surveys, is 66 feet in length and has 100 links each 7.92 inches long.

en′gine lathe (*Mach.*) A lathe having cross slide, compound rest, lead screw and power feed; equipped with change gears and back gearing.

en′gine sized (*Papermakg.*) A term applied to paper pulp sized with resin size while in the beater.

en′gine weight per horse′pow′er. The dry weight of an engine divided by the rated horsepower.

Eng′lish bond (*Bldg.*) (See ENGLISH CROSS, or DUTCH BOND.)

Eng′lish cross bond (*Bldg.*) Same as Dutch bond. A bond in which the courses are alternately headers and stretchers.

Eng′lish fin′ish (*Papermkg.*) Abbreviation E.F. A finish which is intermediate between super calender and machine finish.

en-gobe′ (*Ceram.*) The thin layer of fluid clay applied to the body of a defective piece of ware to cover blemishes.

en-grailed′ (*Furn.*) Indented with small concave scallops or curves.

en-grav′ing (*Cabwk., Furn., Print.*) (1) The act or art of cutting designs on a plate; (2) an engraved design; (3) a picture printed from an engraved plate.

en-rich′ment. Embellishment. The addition of ornament to plain work.

en′sem′ble (än′sän′bl′) The work considered as a whole, not in part.

en-tab′la-ture (*Arch.*) The uppermost member of a classical order sometimes considered as all that portion above the column.

en′ta-sis of a col′umn (ĕn′tȧ-sĭs) The slight bulge in the middle of a column, to avoid the hollow appearance which would result if it were made straight.

en′trance switch (*Elec.*) The switch to which the wires entering a building are connected.

en′tro·py (ĕn′trô-pĭ) (*Phys.*) The thermodynamic function; an index of the relative amount of unavailable energy in a physiochemical system.

e-nu′mer-at′ed. Named one by one; specified singly.

en′ve-lope cor′ner card (*Print.*) The address printed in the upper left-hand corner of envelopes.

e′o-sin (*Chem.*) A reddish coloring matter derived from coal tar; used in dyeing cotton, silk, and wool; for making red ink and pink lakes.

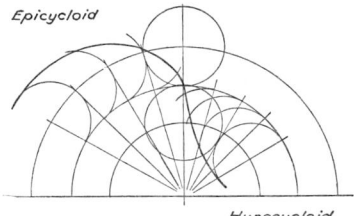

ep′i-cy′cloid (ĕp′ĭ-sī′kloid) (*Geom.*) A curve formed by a generating circle rolling upon and outside a fundamental circle.

e-pox′y res′ins (*Plast.*) An indispensible plastic, made by the reaction of bisphenol and epichlorohydrin, a family which includes a number of modified types, and all of which are tough, flexible, adhesive, and chemically resistant; a combination of properties rarely found in a single resin. These, together with exceptionally low shrinkage and excellent electrical properties have been responsible for the wide acceptance of the resin in almost all industries, especially for protective coatings, laminations, casting, and electrical coverings, for aircraft and automotive tooling, and for high performance adhesives. (See PLASTICS.)

ep′som salt (*C h e m.*) Chemically known as magnesium sulphate. It is a colorless, crystalline salt, used medicinally and in the finishing of cotton fabrics; also for weighting paper, silk, and leather.

e′qual forc′es (*Phys.*) Forces which act in opposite directions and balance each other.

e′qual-i′zer (*Elec.*) Low resistance wires or bars connecting the points where the armature, series field, and shunt field are joined on all compound generators which are to run in parallel.

e′qual-iz′er brake (*Auto. Mech.*) An arrangement of levers and rods, so designed that pressure applied to the brake pedal or brake lever will be transmitted through one rod to two or more rods in such a manner as to give equal braking pressure on the wheels.

e′qual-iz′er wire (*Elec.*) Connection between two compound generators connected in parallel through which the equalizing current flows.

e′qual-iz′ing cur′rent (*Elec.*) Current circulating between two compound generators connected in parallel to equalize output.

e-qua′tion (*Math.*) In mathematics, a proposition expressing the equality of two quantities. A representation of a chemical reaction expressed by symbols.

e′qui-li′bra-tor (ē′kwĭ-li′brȧ-tēr) A device for establishing equilibrium.

e′qui-lib′ri-um (*P h y s.*) A perfect balance.

e-quiv′a-lent. Numbers or quantities numerically equal to each other but expressed in different terms.

e-quiv′a-lent e-vap′o-ra′tion (*Engin.*) The amount of water a boiler will evaporate, in pounds per hour, if it received feed water at 212 deg. F. and vaporized it at the same temperature and at atmospheric pressure.

e-quiv′a-lent mon′o-plane (*Aero.*) A monoplane wing equivalent as to its lift and drag properties to any combination of two or more wings.

e-quiv′a-lent weights of pa′per (*Papermkg. and Print.*) Used with reference to different papers which have the same basic weight but because they differ in size have different ream weights.

e-rect′ing. The final building up, or putting together in position, of machine parts or structural parts.

e-ro′sion (*Geol.*) A wearing away as of material, particularly rocks or soil, as by water. A physical action distinguished from corrosion; a chemical action, which is a rusting or oxidizing. (See CORROSION.)

er-ra′ta (ĕ-rā′tȧ) (*Print.*) A list of

errors or corrections in a book or other printed matter.

er'ror. Fault, mistake, omission, inaccuracy. Deviation from that which is correct or desired.

es'ca-la'tor (ĕs'ká-lā'tēr) A moving stairway such as is used in stores, railroad stations, etc.

es-cal'op shell (ĕs-kŏl'ŭp) (*Furn.*) The cockleshell ornament.

es-cape'ment. A mechanical contrivance used in timepieces to secure uniformity of movement.

es'cri-toire' (ĕs'krĭ-twär') (*Furn.*) A small writing desk. The term is now but little used.

es-cutch'eon (ĕs-kŭch'ŭn) (*Arch. and Furn.*) The plate about a keyhole or the one to which a door knocker is attached.

Escutcheon

es-cutch'eon pins (ĕ s-k ŭ c h'ŭ n) (*Furn.*) Small roundhead nails, usually brass, used for attaching escutcheon plates.

es-par'to pa'per (*Paper*) A paper made from esparto grass pulp chiefly in Europe and England. It has high-grade bulking and finishing qualities.

es-pog-no-lette' (*Furn.*) An ornament placed at the corners of furniture representing the head of a woman surrounded by a ruff, especially used on Louis XIV furniture.

es'sex board meas'ure (*Shopwk.*) Means for the rapid calculation of board feet.

es'ter (*Chem.*) An organic salt; a compound theoretically obtained by the reaction of an organic base and acid. E.g., $CH_3C_7H_5O_3$ is methyl salicylate. (*Plast.*) In plastics, the reaction product of an acid and an alcohol. Also the reaction product of fatty acids and alkalis.

es'ter gum (*Chem.*) Used in the manufacture of spar varnish. Made from rosin and glycerin.

es'ti-mat'ing (*Masonry and Bldg.*) Calculating the amount of material required for a piece of work; also the labor required and determining the value of the finished product.

etch'ing. A process of engraving or marking, in which lines are scratched with a needle on a plate or other surface covered with wax, and the parts exposed are subjected to the action of an acid.

eth'ane (ĕth'ān) (*Chem.*) A colorless gaseous compound (C_2H_6) contained in the gases given off by petroleum, and in illuminating gas.

eth'a-nol (*Chem.*) (C_2H_5OH.) Ethyl alcohol.

e'ther (*Chem.*) $(C_2H_5)_2O$. This compound is made by treating alcohol with sulphuric acid. Ether is a colorless liquid chiefly used as an anesthetic; also in the manufacture of smokeless powder, in medicines, and as a solvent for gums, fats, and waxes.

eth'yl (*Chem.*) The C_2H_5 radical. The radical left by the replacement of one atom of hydrogen from ethane.

eth'yl cel'lu-lose (*Chem. Plast.*) Prepared from wood pulp or cotton linters. Properties are toughness thermoplasticity and low order of flammability. Used for injection molding, protection coatings, adhesives, and for wire insulation.

eth'yl-ene (ĕth'ĭ-lēn) (*Chem.*) A colorless, inflammable, unsaturated, gaseous compound (C_2H_4) contained in illuminating gas.

eu-col-loids (*Chem. Plast.*) Linear polymers of a degree of polymerization over 1000; e.g., each molecule is made up of over 1000 units of a simple substance. They show pronounced swelling and their solutions are highly viscous. The solid eucolloids are very tough and hard.

eu-tec′tic (û-těk′tĭk) (*Phys., Metal., and Chem.*) To melt readily or at a low temperature.

eu-tec′tic al-loys (*Metal.*) Such alloys as aluminum and silicon, cadmium and bismuth, cadmium and zinc, silver and lead. They are made up of two metals entirely soluble in each other when liquid but on "setting or freezing" the crystals of the individual metals form.

e-vap′o-rate (*Chem.*) To convert into a vapor.

e-vap′o-ra′tion. A rising or passing off in a vapor. The act of drying or concentrating.

ev′o-lute (*Furn.*) A wave scroll used on frieze moldings.

ex′ca-va′tion (*Bldg.*) A digging out of earth to make room for engineering improvements. A cavity so formed.

ex-cel′si-or (*Furn.*) Long, fine, wood shavings used as a stuffing in the upholstering of a cheap grade of furniture; mostly used to pack furniture for shipment.

ex-cess′ chalk′ing (*Paint and Lacquer*) Excess or premature chalking is the result of applying too many coats, lack of proper percentage of binder to pigment, or a heavy porous undercoating.

ex-change′. The process of rendering service for service, or selling goods for money, and money for goods, or of trading goods for goods.

ex′ci-ta′tion of field (*Elec.*) Sending of electric current through the turns of wires on the fields of a motor or generator to set up magnetic lines of force.

ex-cite′ (*Elec.*) See excitation of field.

ex-cit′er (ĕk-sīt′ēr) (*Elec.*) A small d.c. generator used to supply electricity for the field of the alternator.

ex-cit′er cur′rent (*Elec.*) The output of a smaller a.c. generator used to supply field current to a larger alternator or generator.

ex-cit′er gen′er-a′tor (*Elec.*) A d.c. generator used to supply field current to an a.c. generator or alternator.

ex′er-cise. To exert; employ actively; a problem.

ex-haust′ (ĕg-zôst′) (*Mech.*) The passage through which the spent steam on an engine cylinder is carried to the outer air or to a condenser.

ex-haust′–col-lec′tor ring (*Aero.*) A circular duct into which the exhaust gases from the cylinders of a radial engine are discharged.

ex-haust′ fan (*Elec.*) A rotary fan used to draw off dust, fumes, etc., as distinguished from a blower fan.

ex-haust′ man′i-fold (*Auto.*) The hollow casting through which the gases from the various cylinders are conducted on their way through the exhaust pipe and through the muffler.

ex-haust′ pipe (*Auto.*) The pipe which extends from exhaust manifold to muffler to carry off exhaust gases. (*Mech.*) The pipe which carries away the exhaust steam from the exhaust port from an engine cylinder.

ex-haust′ valve. The valve of an engine which provides an outlet for the gas or steam which has contributed its power to the operation of the engine.

ex li′bris (ĕks lī′brĭs) (*P r i n t.*) An expression commonly used on book plates. From the Latin, meaning, from the books of.

ex-og′e-nous (ĕk-sŏj′ê-nŭs) (*B o t.*) Applied to those plants which increase in size by successive concentric rings beneath the bark and outside the previous growth.

ex-pand′ed. That which is increased in size without increasing the substance. (*Print.*) Name given to a type face whose width is slightly greater than a normal one.

ex-pand′ed met′al. Sheet metal, so stamped or cut that it may be stretched to form. A sort of network for concrete reinforcement or to retain plaster.

ex-pand′ing man′drel (*Mach.*) A form of lathe mandrel or arbor which is made to expand within the work.

ex-pan′sion (*Phys.*) Spreading out, enlarging, increasing in size.

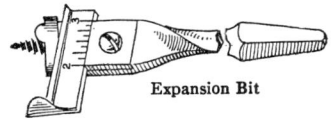
Expansion Bit

ex-pan′sion bit (*Woodwk.*) A boring bit having a cutter or cutters arranged to permit radial adjustment, to enable one tool to bore holes of different diameters.

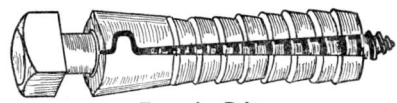
Expansion Bolt

ex-pan′sion bolt. A bolt equipped with a split casing which acts as a wedge; used for attaching to brick or concrete.

ex-pan′sion fit (*Metalwk.*) For a tight fit of metal parts one within another, the inner part is contracted by dry ice or freezing and placed in position. Opposite of shrink fit.

ex-pan′sion joint (*Engin.*) A device for overcoming the motion of expansion and contraction in pipes due to heat or cold. In steam and hot-water heating systems, the expansion joints in risers are of the (*a*) sliding sleeve type or (*b*) "sylphon" bellows type. The latter are preferable on low-pressure systems up to 15 pounds pressure.

ex-pan′sion ream′er (*Mach.*) A reamer which admits of a limited amount of adjustment for size. Such adjustment is usually through wedge action controlled by a screw.

ex-per′i-ment. A test or trial for the purpose of determining the results, obtainable under certain known conditions.

ex-per′i-ment (or test) cham′ber (*Aero.*) The central portion of a wind tunnel, where aircraft models or other objects are tested.

ex-plo′sion (*Auto.*) The igniting and expanding of the gases in the combustion chambers of an engine.

ex-plo′sive. That which is liable to explode or to violently burst forth from within by force.

ex-po′nent (*Math.*) A small number or symbol placed above and to the right of a mathematical quantity, to indicate the number of times the quantity is to be taken as a factor. Thus a^4 means a·a·a·a.

ex-tend′ed type (*Print.*) Type of extra width, even wider than expanded type. A general term used to describe any extra-wide type.

ex-tend'ing. Carrying out farther than the original point or limit.

ex-ten'sion bit (*Elec., Wood.*) A bit with an extra long shank to permit the drilling of deep holes or where obstructions would make impossible the use of a regular bit.

ex-ten'sion cord (*Elec.*) A length of cable or lamp cord fitted with a plug and socket for the purpose of bringing light or power closer to the point where it is needed.

ex-ten'sion tap (*Mach.*) A tap with an extra long shank to permit tapping in places difficult to reach as for set screws in the hub of a pulley.

ex'ten-som'e-ter (ĕks'tĕn-sŏm'ê-tēr) A micrometer by which is measured the expansion of a body. (*Engin.*) A device used in the testing of metals.

ex-te'ri-or (*Bldg. and Masonry*) The outside of, as a whole or in part, as the exterior of a building; an exterior wall.

ex-te'ri-or fin'ish, paint, etc. A type of finish suited to outside work.

ex-ter'nal ai'ler-on (ā'lēr-ŏn) (*Aero.*) A separate airfoil mounted clear of the wing surfaces of an airplane but usually attached to them and deflected for lateral control.

ex-ter'nal cir'cuit (*Elec.*) That part of an electric circuit which is outside the source of current.

ex-ter'nal drag wire (*Aero.*) A drag wire run from a wing to the fuselage or other part of the airplane.

ex-ter'nal thread (*M a c h.*) The thread on the outside of a screw, or bolt.

ex'tra con-densed' (*Print.*) Relates to a type face much thinner than average; i.e., the letter is narrow with regard to its height.

ex-tra'dos (*Arch.*) The outside curve of an arch.

ex'tra heav'y (*Plumb.*) When applied to pipe, indicates pipe thicker than standard pipe.

ex-tra'ne-ous (ĕks-trā'nê-ŭs) Not essential; foreign.

ex-tru'sion (*Plast.*) The more or less continuous forcing of plastic, reduced from the granulated resin compound by heat and pressure to a fluid, through a shaped orifice into a finished product such as tube, sheet, rods, and packaging stock.

ex-tru'sion mold'ing (*Plast.*) A molding p r o c e d u r e for extended shapes of uniform cross section, whereby a heat-softened substance is forced through a die having an orifice shaped like the cross section of the article.

ex-tru'sion of met'al (*Metalwk.*) This is a process by which hot or cold metal is forced under high pressure through an opening to produce a desired shape.

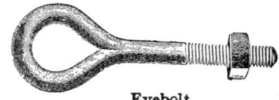

Eyebolt

eye'bolt' (*Mech.*) A bolt provided with a hole or eye at one end, instead of the usual head. The eye receives a pin, stud, or hook, which takes the pull of the bolt.

F

fab′ri-ca′te (*Plast.*) Working plastics into products by any or a combination of manufacturing methods.

fab′ri-ca′tion (*E n g i n.*) The act of building or putting together. Forming into a whole by uniting or assembling of parts; e.g., the fabrication of a ship or a bridge.

fab′ric u′ni-ver′sal joint (*Auto.*) Made of heavy fabric. This type of joint is best adapted to short shafts and close quarters, as accessory shafts about the engine, although it is sometimes used between transmission and rear axle.

fa-çade′ (fa-säd′) (*Arch.*) The front elevation or exterior face of a building.

face (*n.*) (*Mech.*) The face of a casting is that surface which is turned or polished. The face of a gear wheel indicates the breadth of the teeth; of a belt pulley, the breadth of the rim. (*Print.*) That part of type which makes the printed impression. (*v.*) (*Mach.*) To true up the end of a piece carried between lathe centers, or to machine the flat surface of a piece carried on an arbor, a faceplate, or in a chuck.

facebrick (*Arch., Masonry*) Brick of the better quality, such as is used on walls prominently exposed.

face ham′mer (*Masonry*) Used for rough dressing stones. It has one blunt end and one cutting end.

face lathe (*Mach.*) A short-bed, deep-gap lathe designed for the machining of large, flat surfaces.

face mark (*Woodwkg.*) A mark placed on one surface of a piece of wood which is being worked, in order that it may be identified as the face from which other surfaces are trued.

face mold (*Arch. and Bldg.*) The full size or scale drawing or diagram of the curved portions of a sloping handrail. The drawing gives the true dimension and shape of the top of the handrail.

face′plate or face chuck. A circular plate for attachment to the spindle in the headstock of a lathe. Work may be clamped or bolted to it. The slots engage the tail of the lathe dog.

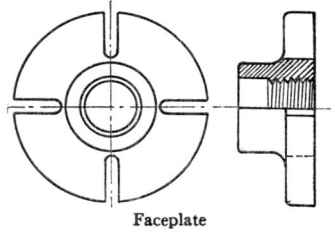

Faceplate

fac′et (făs′ĕt) One of the flat surfaces cut on gems or precious stones.

fa-cil′i-tate. To promote easier operation or completion.

fac′ing (*Fdry.*) To produce smooth small castings a facing material such as plumbago or talc is dusted over the mold after the pattern has been removed. For large castings a mixture of sea coal and sand is placed over and around the pattern prior to ramming up the mold.

fac-sim′i-le (făk-sĭm′ĭ-lē) An exact copy or reproduction.

fac′tor of safe′ty. The number which results by dividing the ultimate strength of a material by the actual unit stress on a sectional area.

---

sāle, surfâce, grăm, humăn, màsk, solar, bär, bâre; mē, ĕdition, lĕnd, **momĕnt**, bakēr; kīnd, fīt; lōde, ômit, ŏlive, cŏnsume, sôrt; dūty, ûtility, nŭt, al*ŭ*m, **bûrn.**

fade in (*Tel.*) To bring up the television image electronically so that it appears gradually.

fade out (*Tel.*) (Reverse process.) To black out a television image electronically so that it disappears gradually.

fad'ing (*Elec.*) In radio reception: the temporary varying of signal strength generally due to atmospheric conditions.

fag'ot (*Forg.*) A bundle made up of a number of iron bars to be heated, hammered, and welded into a unit for rolling to form another bar.

fah'lum met'al (*Metal.*) A white alloy used in the manufacture of cheap jewelry. It contains 40 per cent tin and 60 per cent lead.

Fah'ren-heit. Gabriel Fahrenheit, a German physicist (1686–1736). His name is given to the commonly used thermometer scale in which the freezing point is 32 deg., and the boiling point 212 deg.

fa'ience' (fá'yäns') (*Pot.*) A variety of majolica ware, usually highly decorated.

fail'ure. The inability of materials and structures to endure or accomplish the work for which they were selected and designed.

fair'ing (*Aero.*) An auxiliary member or structure whose primary function is to reduce head resistance or drag of the part to which it is fitted (without, in general, contributing strength).

fald'stool (*Furn.*) A desk at which the litany is read, as in the Church of England; also a type of folding stool or chair.

false key. A round pin driven into a hole drilled one half

False Key

in the end of a spindle and the other half into a boss.

false raf'ter (*Arch.*) A short extension added to a main rafter over a cornice; especially where there is a change of roof line.

false wing rib (*Aero.*) An incomplete rib, frequently consisting only of a strip of wood extending from the leading edge to the front spar, which is used to assist in maintaining the form of the wing where the curvature of the airfoil section is sharpest.

false'work' (*Engin.*) Usually temporary framework, bracing, or support used as an aid in construction and removed when construction is completed.

fam'i-ly (*Print.*) A classification of related type faces in different sizes.

fan belt (*Auto.*) A belt which drives the cooling fan, generator, and water pump.

fan blow'er. A rotating fan for producing a current of air. It may be used for carrying off fumes as of chemicals, for ventilating, and for forced draft in furnaces.

fan'cy rule (*Print.*) Brass rule obtainable in various designs.

fan-dan'go (*Bookbndg.*) A trade name for genuine binder's board.

fang bolt (*Engin.*) Used for attaching ironwork to timber. The nut is a plate with teeth which bite into the wood. To tighten, the bolt is turned while the nut remains stationary.

fan light (*Arch.*) A fanshaped or semicircular window frequently seen over colonial doorways.

fan out (*Print.*) A method of separating sheets for easier feeding to the press.

fan pul′ley (*Auto.*) A pulley attached to the fan to engage the belt which drives it and on many cars also the circulating pump and the generator.

F.A.O. (*Draft.*) An expression frequently used in machine drawing, indicating that a piece is to be finished or machined all over.

far′ad (făr′ăd) (*Elec.*) A unit for measuring electrical capacity. A condenser of one farad will be charged to a potential of one volt by a quantity of one coulomb. It is too large a unit for practical work. Its common use is in terms of "microfarad."

Far′a-day, Mi′chael (1791–1867). English scientist; early investigator and experimenter who invented the transformer.

Far′a-day′s laws of e-lec′trol′y-sis (*Elec.*) (1) The weight of the products of electrolysis is proportional to the quantity of electricity which has passed through the electrolyte. (2) For a given quantity of electricity the weight of the products of electrolysis is proportional to their electrochemical equivalents.

farm′ers′ drill (*Metalwk.*) A straight-fluted twist drill, used on soft metals.

farm out (*Print.*) To sublet.

fas′ces (făs′ēz) (*Furn.*) A decorative ornament in the form of a bundle of rods bound with a projecting axe; a Roman badge of authority.

fas′ci-a (făsh′ĭ-à) (*Arch.*) A flat, broad member in the entablature.

fast charg′er (*Auto.*) Electrical device for recharging any capacity lead plate storage battery in 30 min. or less.

fast pul′ley. A pulley employed to transmit motion, being attached to its shaft by a setscrew or a key.

fas′ten-ing (*Mech.*) Such holding devices as bolts, screws, keys, etc.

fat (*Ceram.*) A term applied to very sticky clays. (*Chem.*) An ester of glycerin and a higher fatty acid. The acid is generally oleic, stearic, or palmitic, although other acids form esters which are regarded as fats. (*Print.*) Printed matter that is full of illustrations, blank lines, or open spaces.

fath′om. A unit of measurement equaling 6 ft. or 1.828 meters.

fa-tigue′ of ma-te′ri-al (fà-tēg′) Material which has been long subjected to severe or moderate straining actions often repeated, deteriorates in strength, and will break under loads previously sustained with safety.

fat spark (*Auto.*) An ignition spark that is short and thick.

fau′cet (*Plumb.*) A fixture attached to the end of a pipe having a spout and valve to permit the drawing off and control of flow of liquids.

fault (*Mach.*) Flaw or imperfection.

faun (fôn) (*Arch.*) A legendary demigod, represented by a half goat and half man, used as decorative detail in work of the Adam period.

fau′teuil′ (fō′tû′y′) (*Furn.*) An armchair of French design open under the arms, in contradistinction to the bergere, an eighteenth-century upholstered armchair.

fa′vus (fā′vŭs) (*Arch.*) Diaper detail, resembling the cells in a honeycomb.

feath′er (*Aero.*) In rotary wing systems, to periodically increase and decrease the incidence of a blade or wing by oscillating the blade or wing about its span axis.

feath′er or sunk key (*Mach.*) A parallel key which is partly sunk into a recess in its shaft, so as to form an integral part of the shaft. The keyway in the wheel or clutch carried on the shaft is made large enough to permit these parts to slide longitudinally on the shaft.

feath′er-edge′. A keen edge, tapering off to nothing.

feed (*Print.*) To supply paper to be printed to a press. (*Mach.*) In machine-tool operations, refers to the rate of tool travel across a surface from which material is being removed.

feed–back coil (*Radio*) A coil connected in the plate circuit of a vacuum tube; used to reintroduce or feed back energy from the circuit to the grid circuit of the same tube.

feed edge (*Print.*) The front edge of the sheet which feeds to the grippers and is carried around the cylinder of a press.

feed′er (*Elec.*) The line which carries the supply of current to the branch circuits. (*Print.*) (1) One who feeds work to a press. (2) A device which automatically regulates the feeding of sheets on a press.

feed gears (*Mach.*) Gears used to drive the feed rod and control the rate of feed.

feed guides (*Print.*) Printing-press accessories which bring the sheet into position for printing.

feed′ing (*Print.*) Supplying a press with sheets.

feed mech′a-nism (*Mach.*) Consists of an arrangement of gears, screws, or other devices for controlling the feed of the tool to the work or the work to the tool.

feed pipe (*Plumb.*) A main line pipe; one which carries a supply directly to the point of use, or to secondary lines.

feed screw. The screw by means of whose rotation a measurable amount of feed is imparted to the cutting tool of a machine.

feed–wa′ter heat′er. A boiler in which the supply water for a steam boiler is heated, preliminary to being taken up by the pump or injector.

feel′er (*Mach.*) Gauge for determining the size of a piece of work, the accuracy of the test depending on the sense of touch.

feet (*Print.*) The two parts, at the bottom of the body, which support the type.

feld′spar (*Chem., Bldg. and Pot.*) Any one of a group of rock-forming minerals which consist of silicates of aluminum with potassium, sodium, or calcium.

fel′loe or fel′ly (fĕl′ō) (fĕl′ĭ) The rim of a wheel to which the outer ends of the spokes are attached; not applied to a removable rim, or the metal tire on a wooden wheel.

felt pa′pers (*Bldg.*) Used as sheathing papers on roofs and side walls for protection against dampness, heat, and cold. Those used for roofing are often impregnated with tar, asphalt, or chemical compounds.

felt side of pa′per. The finish given to paper for the purpose of partly eliminating the wire or screen mark on one side of it.

fe′male. The recessed portion of any piece of work into which another part fits is called the female portion.

fe′male thread. A thread which is cut in a hole or on a hollow surface.

fence (*Woodwk.*) An adjustable metal

bar or strip mounted on the table of a circular saw to act as a guide and to insure a parallel cut.

fend'er (*Furn.*) A metal guard, often quite decorative, placed before the open fire to protect the floor. (*Mech.*) Guard, usually over wheels to prevent the throwing of water or dirt, as the fenders of an automobile. (*Print.*) Pieces of cardboard glued to the tympan to prevent a sheet from slipping over the guides.

fe-nes'tral (*Arch.*) In early times a frame on which oiled paper or thin cloth was fastened to keep out wind and rain, before or when windows were not glazed.

fen'es-tra'tion (*Arch.*) The design or arrangement of the windows of a building.

fer'e-to-ry (*A r c h.*) A shrine, either portable or fixed, in which the relics of saints are kept.

fer'men-ta'tion (*Chem.*) A chemical decomposition of an organic compound induced by living organisms or by chemical agents.

fer'ro-chro'mi-um (*Metal.*) A chromium-iron alloy used in the manufacture of chromium-alloy steels. With a carbon content of 5 per cent it is used in making tool, cutlery, and automobile steels. With a low-carbon content it is used in making stainless steels.

fer'ro-man'ga-nese (fĕr'ô-măn'gà-nēs) (*Metal.*) An alloy of 20 to 80 per cent of manganese and 5 to 7 per cent of carbon in powder form is added to the molten metal in the ladle. Acts as a deoxidizing agent and counteracts the influence of an excess of sulphur. Used especially when the mix contains a large proportion of steel scrap.

fer'ro-nick'el (*Metal.*) A nickel-steel alloy used for rheostats and coils.

fer'ro-phos'pho-rus (fŏs'fô-rŭs) (*Metal.*) An iron of high phosphorous content used in making steel for tin plate.

fer'ro-sil'i-con (*Metal.*) A hard steel containing 97.6 per cent iron, 2 per cent silicon, and 0.4 per cent carbon.

fer'rous (*Chem.*) Pertaining to iron compounds in which the metal is bivalent, or to iron with that valence.

fer'rule (*Mech.*) Ring of metal enclosing and confining the wood around the tang of an edged tool to prevent splitting. (*Plumb.*) A metallic sleeve, calked or otherwise joined to an opening in a pipe, into which a plug is screwed which can be removed for the purpose of cleaning or examining the interior of the pipe.

fer'ti-liz'er (*Chem.*) A combination of chemicals usually in powdered form used for improving the quality of the soil.

fes-toon' (*Arch. and Furn.*) An ornament of carved work, representing a garland or wreath of flowers or leaves, or both.

fet'tle (*Ceram.*) To remove lines left on cast or pressed ware by the joints of the mold.

F–head en'gine (*Auto.*) A combination of the L-head and I-head types. Intake valves are overhead and the exhaust valves are in the cylinder block. This style engine is not much used.

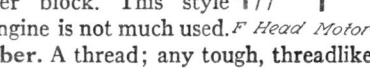
F Head Motor

fi'ber. A thread; any tough, threadlike

substance capable of being spun and woven.

fi′ber-glas (*Plast.*) See GLASS CLOTH.

fi′ber-lic (*Bldg.*) A trade name for a particular type of building board.

fi′brous. As applied to the structure of metals; the opposite of granular.

fid′dle-back′ (*Furn.*) Name given to a chair in which the back panel is somewhat similar to a fiddle in shape.

field (*Elec.*) The space occupied by electric or magnetic lines of force. (*Tel.*) One set of scanning lines making up a part of the final picture. In present standards, pictures are transmitted in two fields of alternating lines which are interlaced to form a 525-line picture at the rate of 30 complete pictures or frames per second.

field book (*Elec.*) A blank book used by engineers and others for making notes "on the job."

field coil (*Elec.*) The coil or winding around the field magnets or pole pieces of a motor or generator.

field core (*Elec.*) The iron projection usually salient, upon which is wound the field winding of a generator or motor.

field den′si-ty (*Elec.*) The density of the magnetic field or the magnetic flux, measured in the number of lines of force per unit area, is dependent upon the strength of the field element, the number of turns of wire, and the size and characteristics of the pole piece.

field dis-tor′tion (*Elec.*) The distortion of the normal field existing between the north and south poles of a generator due to the counter-electromotive force generated in the armature windings.

field′ed. Applied to a panel which is molded, sunk, or raised, or broken up into smaller panels.

field ex′ci-ta′tion (*Elec.*) The magnetic effect produced in an electromagnet when current is passed through a winding, usually with an iron core.

field fre′quen-cy (*Tel.*) The repetition rate of the field which, in present television systems, is 60 fields per second.

field mag′net. The electromagnet by which the magnetic field of force is produced in a dynamo.

field re-sist′ance (*Elec.*) A resistance connected in series with field coils to limit the amount of current flowing through the field windings.

field rhe′o-stat (*E l e c.*) A variable high resistance of low-current capacity inserted in the field circuit to regulate within limits the output of a generator.

field volt′age con-trol′ (*Auto. Elec.*) A method of controlling the voltage applied to the field winding of a generator, usually by a vibrating armature and resistance so that the output of the generator is definitely within certain limits.

field wind′ing (*Elec.*) The electromagnets used in motors, generators, etc., to provide an electromagnetic field.

fifth wheel. The horizontal flat bearing on a wagon or similar vehicle which permits a change of position of the axle with regard to the body as in turning corners.

fig′ure (*Carp.*) In wood, the mottled, streaked, or wavy grain.

fil′a-ment. A thin wire or fiber. (*Plast.*) In the plastic industry, a fiber of resin or of glass, which, when used in multiple, serves as unspun yarn in the production of woven glass cloth and roving.

fil′a-ment trans-form′er. A transformer used in radio to reduce the supply voltage to the proper voltage for the filaments or heaters of radio tubes.

File

file. (*n*) A hard steel instrument, made in various shapes and sizes, for smoothing wood or metal. (*v.*) To cut, trim, or finish with a file.

file card. A kind of brush fitted with short, fine wires; used for cleaning files.

file hard (*Metal.*) When a metal is so hard that it cannot be filed it is said to be "file hard."

files, kinds of (*Metal Fin.*) Many kinds of files are made for special purposes and known by the name of the purpose for which they are intended. In general, however, files are named for the manner in which they are cut, as bastard, rough cut, second cut, smooth, etc.

fil′i-gree. Delicate ornamental work, used chiefly in decorating gold and silver.

fil′ing (*Metalwk.*) The removal of material, finishing, and/or fitting by use of a file.

fill (*Engin.*) In engineering, the material used to bring a low spot up to desired grade.

fill′er (*Papermkg.*) Clay or other mineral matter used in paper manufacture to give weight and body to the paper and to improve the printing surface. (*Plast.*) As used in plastics, an inert, small-particle material such as china clay, wood flour, asbestos, etc., mixed into the compound or into the liquid resin, to extend it or to impart such physical benefits as hardness, impact strength, and stiffness. (*Wood Fin.*) A composition for filling holes or pores in wood before painting or varnishing.

fill′ers (*Engin.*) Spacers used to fill in when riveting two members where a gusset plate is not used.

fill′er specks (*Plast.*) Visible specks of wood flour, asbestos, or other filler, which stand out in contrasting color against a plastic binder.

fil′let. A concave curve connecting two surfaces which meet at an angle. By avoiding sharp angles, it adds to the strength and beauty of a design.

fill′ing (*Textile*) Substance such as clay or starch used in cloth finishing to give body and weight.

fill′ing in (*Masonry*) The process of building in the center of the wall between the face and back.

fil′lis-ter (*Furn.*) A plane for making grooves. (*Mach.*) A cylindrical head of a cap screw slotted for a screw driver.

film (*Plast.*) A term for thin plastic sheeting.

fil′ter (*Elec.*) A device consisting of choke coils and condensers used for smoothing out a varying current, eliminating, or permitting to pass, certain alternating-current frequencies.

fil′ter el′e-ment (*Auto.*) The active part of an oil filter consisting of cloth or other material. Its purpose is to remove grit, dirt, and other foreign matter from the motor oil.

fil′ter pa′per (*Paper*) An unsized rag paper made entirely from fibers, and is used for filtering purposes.

fil-tra′tion of wa′ter. The act or process of filtering, as the removal of foreign matter by passing water through sand beds.

fin. Any thin, waferlike expansion of metal occurring on the side or edge of a large portion. (*Aero.*) A fixed or adjustable airfoil, attached to an aircraft approximately parallel to the plane of symmetry, to afford directional stability; for example, tail fin, skid fin, etc. (*Fdry.*) A thin projecting bit of metal on a casting which occurs at the joint of a mold.

fine arts. The arts consisting of architecture, drawing, painting, and sculpture.

fine feed (*Mach.*) Opposite of coarse feed. A feed minute in quantity.

fine′ness ra′ti-o (rā′shĭ-ō) (*Aero.*) The ratio of the length to the maximum diameter of a streamline body, as an airship hull.

fine pitch. A relative term. A gear with small teeth, or a screw with a comparatively high number of threads per inch is said to be of fine pitch.

fines (*Plast.*) Pulverized particles of material accompanying larger grains or fibers.

fin′ger. A narrow, projecting piece used as a guide or index in various kinds of work.

fin′ger joint (*Furn.*) Composed of five tongues or fingers interlocking, used on table brackets.

fin′i-al (*Arch.*) An ornament at the top of a spire or steeple. A terminating or crowning detail.

fin′ing (fīn′ing) The act of making clear or pure; as the fining of a precious metal.

fin′ish (*Bookbndg.*) Degree of brilliance, pliability, and working qualities of cloth, paper, leather, and other binding materials.

fin′ish all o′ver (*Mach.*) A notation on a working drawing indicating that all surfaces are to be finished. Frequently represented as F.A.O.

fin′ish al-low′ance (*Patmkg.*) The amount added to a pattern to allow for machining the casting to "finish size."

fin′ished string (*Arch. and Bldg.*) The end string of a stair, secured to the rough carriage; cut, mitered, dressed, and often finished with a bead or molding.

fin′ish-ing. Completing or bringing to an end. Perfecting finally. (*Plast.*) In the plastic industry, this term means tumbling, sanding, removing flash, printing, decorating, spraying, metalizing, embossing, flocking, etc.

fin′ish-ing cut (*Mach.*) A cut usually of small depth and fine feed for imparting a smooth surface and bringing the work to desired size.

fin′ish-ing tool. Commonly applied to the cutting tool, used by metalworkers, whose cutting edges are broad and straight, for removal of the ridges left upon work by the roughing tools.

Fink Truss

Fink truss. A type of roof truss commonly used for short spans. It is very economical due to the shortness of its struts.

fin–neck bolt. Similar to carriage bolt. Used through wood or through wood and metal. Two fins under the head prevent turning while the nut is being tightened or loosened.

Fin-Neck Bolt

fire'brick'. Brick made especially to withstand the effects of great heat.

fire clay (*Masonry*) Clay capable of withstanding high temperature; its quality is due to the large amount of silica and small amount of fluxing agents. It is usually light in color and is used for firebrick, retorts, furnace linings, etc.

fire'damp'. A combustible gas which enters mines from coal seams; also the explosive mixture formed by this gas and air.

fire i'rons (*Furn.*) Metal utensils for a fireplace, usually matching the fender.

fire'proof. To cover or to treat with an incombustible material to reduce danger of fire. (*Bldg.*) To build with a minimum amount of combustible material.

fire screen (*Furn.*) A framelike piece of furniture, used for protection against the heat of the fireplace and flying sparks.

fire stops (*Bldg.*) Filling in air passages, or passages through which flames might travel, with some incombustible material.

fire up (*Tel.*) A cue to start arc in projector preparatory to actual projector start.

fire wall (*A e r o.*) A fire-resistance, transverse bulkhead, isolating the engine compartment from other parts of the structure, reducing the fire risk in the engine compartment.

fir'ing or'der (*Auto.*) Sequence of explosions in multiple-cylinder gas engines.

Firmer Chisel

firm'er tools (*Woodwkg.*) The ordinary short chisels and gouges of woodworkers, used in benchwork.

firm joint cal'i-per (*Mach.*) Ordinary calipers, the two legs of which are attached by a large firm joint instead of a rivet.

First-Class Lever

first'–class le'ver (*Mech.*) A lever with fulcrum between power and weight.

first gear (*Auto.*) The gear connection which is used for lowest speed, often spoken of as low gear.

fished joint (*Woodwk.*) When a stud or other piece is to be lengthened, an extra piece may be butted against it longitudinally and the joint covered by two pieces which are nailed or bolted to opposite sides.

fish' eye (*Plast.*) Term for any small globular mass in a transparent or translucent plastic, due to incomplete blending with surrounding material.

fish glue. Glue made from the bladderlike "sounds" of fish; principally hake.

fish'ing (*Elec.*) The means by which a single wire, rope, etc., is gotten from one outlet to another so that electrical conductors can be pulled in.

fish oils. Non-drying oils of disagreeable odor obtained from menhaden, cod, herring, etc., used in heat treating and as lubricants.

fish'plate (*Mech.*) A plate of metal covering the butt joints of boilers, rails, and other work. Any plate covering a riveted joint.

fish'tail (*Aero.*) A colloquial term describing the motion made when the tail of an airplane is swung from side to side to reduce speed in approaching the ground for a landing.

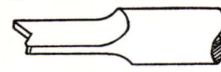
Fishtail Cutter

fish'tail' cut'ter (*Mach.*) A tool for cutting grooves or seats in shafts; suitable for light cut and feed.

fish wire (*Elec.*) Usually a flat steel wire used for pulling electrical wires in a wall, ceiling, or through a conduit.

fis'sion (*Phys.*) The splitting of an atomic nucleus into two parts accompanied by the release of radioactivity and heat.

fis'sure (fĭsh'ẽr) A narrow crack or opening; a crevice.

fit (thread) (*Mach.*) Loose fit (class 1), standard for tapped holes in numbered sizes only; free fit (class 2), generally used on work of average quality — also called "medium fit, regular"; medium fit (class 3), used on the better grade of screw-thread work (automobiles, etc.); close fit (class 4), used on screw-thread work where close fit is necessary — on aircraft parts, etc. Shrink fit, force fit, drive fit, are common designations of fits used in the non-thread assembly of non-threaded parts.

fit'ment (*Carp. and Furn.*) Any article made and fixed to a wall or room, including paneling, chimney pieces, and fitted furniture.

fit'ting (*Aero.*) A general term applied to any small part used in airplane construction. (*Mach.*) The bringing together and adjusting of the different portions of engines, machines, etc., after they have left the hands of the machine workers.

fix'a-tive (*Man. Arts*) A liquid commonly used as a spray to form a protective coating on some surface which is likely to rub or smear, as on a charcoal drawing.

fixed land'ing gear (*Aero.*) A landing gear that remains fixed in position at all times. Sometimes called a nonretractable landing gear.

fixed light (*Aero.*) A light which is constant in luminous intensity with respect to both time and directions.

fixed pitch pro-pel'ler (*Aero.*) A propeller whose blade angle cannot be changed.

fix'ture (*Elec.*) A lamp bracket or electrolier, or fittings used in construction of same. (*Mach.*) A general term referring to devices used in manufacturing interchangeable parts and intended to do away with individual fitting of work in process. (*Plumb.*) A tub, basin, toilet, etc.

Fixture Splice

fix'ture splice (*Elec.*) The fixture wire is wound in close turns around the main conductor after which the end of the main conductor is bent tightly back over the coils of fixture wire.

fix′ture wire (*Elec.*) Usually 16 or 18 gauge, solid or stranded and insulated. It is used for wiring electric fixtures.

flag′ging. A pavement of flagstones.

flag′stones (*Masonry*) Flat slabs of stone used for sidewalks.

flam-boy′ant (*Arch.*) A name applied to the ornamentation of a certain period of French architecture. Characterized by elements of tracing that flow upward in long, wavy divisions.

flam′ing arc (*Elec.*) An arc lamp using mineral cored carbons, giving a greater arc flame and greater light.

flam′ing of arc (*Elec.*) A flaring or flaming of an arc between two carbons, caused by the carbons being set too far apart.

flange (flănj) (*Mach.*) A rib or offset on a casting. The circular faces of couplings or of pipe fittings. The turned edge of a metal shape or plate, which resists bending strain.

flanged pul′ley (*Mach.*) A pulley, having a flange or increase in diameter on one edge of its face, is a single flanged pulley; on both edges, it is a double flanged pulley. It prevents the belt from slipping off.

flange nut (*Mach.*) A nut having a broad flange as a part of it, turned flush with its bottom face. It is used instead of a separate washer.

flange pipe (*Plumb.*) A steam or water pipe, provided with flanges at the ends to attach to other pipes or connections. In cast-iron pipes, the flanges are a part of the casting.

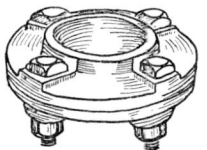

Flange Union

flange un′ion (*Plumb.*) A pair of flanges to be threaded onto the ends of pipes to be joined. Flanges are bolted together when pipes are joined.

flange wheel (*Mech.*) A truck or trolley wheel having a flange or flanges at the edge to keep it from leaving the rail.

flank (*Arch.*) The side of an arch. (*Mach.*) The side of gear teeth lying below the pitch line.

flap (*Aero.*) A hinged or pivoted airfoil forming the rear portion of an airfoil, to vary the effective camber.

flap′ping an′gle (*Aero.*) The difference between the coning angle and the instantaneous angle of the span axis of a blade of a rotary wing system relative to the plane perpendicular to the axis of rotation.

flare (*Tel.*) A white signal generated in an iconoscope at the edges of scanning when illumination at these points is low; also halation at points where extremes of light and dark subject matter are adjacent.

flash (*Plast.*) Excess of molding material which runs out of the cutoff when the mold is closed. (*Weld.*) Metal and oxide expelled from a joint made by resistance welding.

flash butt weld′ing. A resistance butt-welding process, wherein the potential is applied before the parts are brought in contact and where the heat is derived principally from a series of arcs between the parts being welded.

flash–dry ink (*Print.*) Manufactured from synthetic varnishes and gums. The ink on a printed sheet is set instantly by intense heat as the sheet comes from the rollers.

flash'er (*Elec.*) A device for flashing on and off a lamp or group of lamps as in some electric signs.

flash'ing (*Arch.*) Pieces of tin or copper worked in the shingles or slates of a roof or around chimneys and windows to prevent leaking.

flash'ing light (*Aero.*) A light which is intermittent as viewed from a single direction.

flash'ing ov'er (*Elec.*) Term applied to current passing from one commutator segment to another when the machine is in operation. This is in the form of a ring of fire or a series of sparks jumping from one bar to another, caused usually by faulty insulation of the commutator.

flash'light' (*Elec.*) A portable electric hand lamp operated by dry cells.

flash'light' pow'der (*C h e m.*) Two parts of powdered magnesium with one part of potassium chlorate.

flash lines (*Plast.*) Marks formed where the excess material flowed out of a mold.

flash mold (*Plast.*) A mold designed to permit excess molding material to escape during final closing.

flash point. The degree of temperature at which an oil gives off vapor in sufficient quantity to burn on the approach of a flame or spark.

flashpots (*Tel.*) Receptacles filled with flashlight powder and set off electrically by short circuiting.

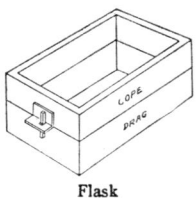

Flask

flask (*Fdry.*) The wooden or metal frame in which a foundry mold is "rammed up."

flat (*Print.*) Unfolded sheet. Usually sheets up to 17 x 28 in. are delivered flat; hence the name.

flat arch, or jack arch (*Masonry*) A construction in which both the soffits and extrados are flat.

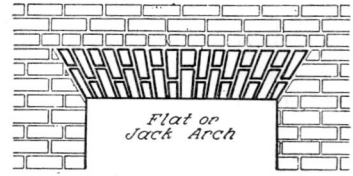

flat'–bed' (*Print.*) On a press, the flat form from which printing is done.

flat carv'ing (*Furn.*) Carving in which only the background is cut out, leaving the design itself flat.

flat chis'el (*Metalwk.*) An all-metal chisel used for obtaining a flat surface on metal by chipping.

flat drill (*Mach.*) A type of drill now but little used. Its cutting blade has two parallel, beveled edges. It was formerly much used for drilling out cored holes.

flat mold'ing. Thin, flat strips used for finishing woodwork.

flat plate (*Print.*) An etched plate with poor contrast.

flat pull (*Print.*) The proof taken with under- or overlay.

flat roof (*Arch.*) A roof with just enough pitch for drainage.

flat sky'light (*Arch.*) A skylight, the entire surface of which is flat, having only sufficient pitch to carry off water.

flat spin (*Aero.*) A spin in which the longitudinal axis is less than 45 deg. from the horizontal.

flat spots (*Paint and Lacquer*) Lack of gloss in spots on a finished surface indicates porous undercoat, or improper surfacing.

flat'ter. A kind of hammer used by blacksmiths.

flat'ting (*Furn.*) A veneering process used on buckled veneers. (*Paint.*) Painting finished so as not to leave a gloss.

flat-tube ra'di-a'tor (*Auto.*) Made from flat tubes which, instead of running direct from tank to tank, are bent in such manner that they will be two or three times as long as a straight tube used for the same purpose. This bending retards the flow of water and presents greater cooling surface. It is frequently spoken of as a Honeycomb Radiator, but it is not the true honeycomb type.

flaw. A crack or fracture in a casting or forging. In general, any defect which may eventually cause failure.

flax (*Uphol.*) A plant which grows from 1 to 4 ft. in height, in many countries. The seeds produce linseed oil. The fiber from the straw produces linen thread and yarn. The straw called "tow" is used for stuffing upholstered furniture.

flax'en weave (*Bookbndg.*) Trade name for a pattern like B A and L W (from linen effect) used on book cloth.

flax'seed. The seed of flax from which linseed oil is made.

flax twine (*Uphol.*) Used for stitching edges, sewing springs to webbing and burlap, sewing mattresses, etc. It is sold in half-pound balls.

fleam (*Woodwkg.*) The angle of bevel of the edge of a saw tooth with respect to the plane of the blade.

Flem'ing's rule (*Elec.*) Right-hand rule: If the forefinger points along the lines of flux, and the thumb in the direction of the motion of the conductor, the middle finger will point in the direction of the induced e.m.f. Left-hand rule: Point the forefinger in the direction of the flux, the middle finger in the direction of the current in the conductor, then the thumb will point in the direction in which the conductor tends to move. Fleming's rules determine the direction in which a motor will rotate, or the polarity of a generated current from a generator.

Flem'ish bond (*Masonry*) Consists of alternate headers and stretchers in every course, each header centering on the stretchers in the courses above and below.

Flem'ish bond, dou'ble (*Masonry*) When both the inner and outer surfaces of an exposed wall are laid in Flemish bond, all headers being true or full headers, the bond is termed "double Flemish bond."

Flem'ish gar'den bond (*Masonry*) Consists of three stretchers followed by a header in each course. The headers in each course center between the stretchers in the course above and below.

fleur′-de-lis′ (flûr′-dē-lē′) The royal insignia of France. It is widely used as a decorative unit.

Fleur-de-lis

flex′i-ble con′duit (*Elec.*) Flexible metallic tubing in which electrical conductors are placed or pulled.

flex′i-ble cou′pling. A flexible ball coupling consists of two disks attached to the shaft ends, hollowed on their faces to encircle a ball placed between them.

flex′i-ble mold (*Plast.*) A latex or elastic resin mold for the casting of liquid plastics.

flex′i-ble shaft (*Mech.*) A shaft made of jointed links encased in flexible tubing; used to transmit power in places where a straight shaft could not be used.

flex′ure for′mu-la (flĕk′shĕr) (*Engin.*) The formula which treats of the horizontal, tensile, and compressive stresses in beams.

$$M = \frac{SI}{c} \text{ or } S = \frac{Mc}{I}.$$

When S equals the unit stress at any extreme fiber of the beam due to the bending moment, c is the distance from that fiber to the neutral surface, M, the resisting moment, and I is the moment of inertia of the section.

fli′er (*Bldg.*) A stair tread that is of uniform width throughout its length.

fli′ers (*Print.*) Preliminary advertising matter, usually in small attractive form, announcing a coming event.

flight in′di-ca′tor (*Aero.*) An instrument in which a lateral inclinometer, a fore-and-aft inclinometer, and a turn indicator are combined to form a compact unit.

flight of stairs (*Bldg.*) The series of steps between floors or landings. Two flights of stairs may be broken by a landing.

flight path (*Aero.*) The path traced by the center of gravity of an aircraft in flight.

flight′-path an′gle (*Aero.*) The angle between the flight path of the aircraft and the horizontal.

flight re-cord′er (*Aero.*) An instrument for recording certain elements of the performance of an aircraft.

flint (*Mineral.*) A subvitreous dull-colored variety of quartz.

flip ti′tles (*Tel.*) Cards fastened to ring binder and allowed to drop in place in front of camera singly or in sequence.

flitch beam. A combination beam in which outer timbers enclose a central beam of iron, bolts passing through the whole to fasten the members together.

float (*Aero.*) A watertight attachment on an

Plasterers' Float

aircraft which permits the latter to float on water. (*Mach.*) An instrument resembling a file. The cutting action is caused by a series of saw-like serrations. (*Plaster.*) A piece of board with handle attached used for spreading plaster or stucco on the surface of walls. (*Textile*) The long thread of either the warp or the filling yarn brought to the surface in weaving to form the pattern.

float car′bu-ret′or (*Auto.*) A carburetor in which a float of cork or hollow metal controls the height of gasoline.

float′ing. The equal spreading of plaster, stucco, or cement work by means of a board called a "float."

float′ing ax′le. An axle on which the shaft is relieved of all loads or stresses except turning the wheel.

float′ing pow′er (*Auto.*) A method of mounting the engine in the chassis frame so that its vibration is absorbed by rubber cushions.

float′ing tool (*Mach.*) A tool so secured in its holder that it may be guided in its operation by the piece on which it works.

float switch (*Elec.*) A switch which is opened and closed by a float which rises and falls with the level of the liquid in a tank.

float sys′tem (*Aero.*) The complete system of permanent floats, used to give buoyancy and stability to a seaplane or a flying boat while it is at rest on the water, and to provide hydrodynamic lift while taking off.

float trap (*Steam Heat.*) A valve actuated by a hollow metal float so arranged that condensation and air may pass but steam will be held.

float valve (*Plumb.*) A valve such as used in a toilet tank. A hollow ball floating on the surface shuts off the supply of water at the intake.

flock (*Textile*) The soft, fluffy fibers which are thrown off in the processes of woolen and worsted manufacture.

flong (flŏng) (*Print.*) In stereotyping, a flong is made from several sheets of paper, wetted and pasted together. This flong forms the matrix which receives the molten metal, which, after cooling, is a duplicate of the type page.

flood′ing (*Auto.*) An excessive amount of rich fuel mixture being fed to the engine resulting in difficult starting.

flood′light′ (*Elec.*) A lamp or battery of lamps of high power equipped with reflectors to supply brilliant light. Both arc and incandescent lamps are used.

floor (*Arch.*) (1) That portion of a structure or building on which one walks. (2) A story of a building is often referred to as a floor, as ground floor, first floor, etc.

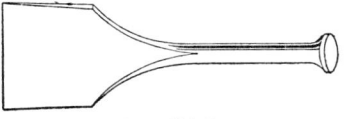

Floor Chisel

floor chis′el (*Woodwk.*) An all-steel chisel having an edge from 2 to 3 in. wide. Used to remove floorboards, etc.

floor drain (*Arch. and Plumb.*) A fixture used to drain water from floors into the plumbing system. In homes, floor drains are usually located in the laundry and near the heating boiler, and are fitted with a deep seal trap.

floor mold′ing (*Fdry.*) The process of making molds on the floor as distinguished from bench molding. Used on large work.

floor plan (*Arch.*) A drawing which shows the length and breadth of a building and of the rooms which it contains. A separate plan is made for each floor.

flo′re-at-ed (*Furn.*) Carved or decorated with floral designs.

flo-ta'tion gear (*Aero.*) An emergency gear attached to a land plane to permit alighting on the water and to provide buoyancy when resting on the surface of the water.

flow'er-ing dog'wood (*Wood*) *Cynoxylon floridum.* Also known as "boxwood." A small, ornamental tree bearing white flowers. Wood is very hard and tough; valuable for golf-stick heads, tool handles, and scales.

fluc'tu-a'tion. A variation, an irregular change of movement.

flue. A pipe, chimney, or passageway to carry off smoke, hot air, etc.

flu'id. A substance that yields to any force tending to change its form without changing its volume; consisting of particles which move and change in shape but do not separate.

flu'id drive (*Auto.*) A type of constant-torque drive mechanism built in the flywheel of an automobile. It consists of two rotors having vanes, these rotors operating in oil. Motion of the driving plate causes oil to impinge upon the driven plate. Slippage between the plates varies inversely as the speed, permitting a smooth starting of the car in any gearshift position.

flu'id fric'tion (*Mech.*) When the particles of a fluid are in motion and the outer surfaces of the fluid are in contact with solid surfaces the fluid body is divided into numerous layers within itself. The friction produced by the slipping of these layers over one another and by rubbing effect between the molecules of the fluid is called fluid friction.

flu-id'i-ty (*Plast.*) A synonym of viscosity.

flu'id meas'ure. (See APOTHECARIES' FLUID MEASURE.)

flu'id pres'sure. Pressure is transmitted by fluids in all directions alike. The transmitted pressure is equal in all directions, and is directly proportional to the area of the surface.

flu'o-res'cent lamp (*Elec.*) A tubular lamp operating on the principle of the mercury arc. The ultra-violet rays given off by the mercury arc activate the fluorescent material with which the inside of the tube is coated.

flu'or-ine (*Chem.*) A colorless, corrosive, poisonous gas which is derived by electrical decomposition of anhydrous hydrofluoric acid.

flu'o-rite or flour spar. A calcium fluoride occurring in crystalline or granular form. Used as a binder in making abrasive wheels, and as a flux in the manufacture of steel. Found in considerable quantity in Kentucky and Illinois.

flu-or'o-car'bons (*Plast.*) A plastic family with a molecular structure consisting of carbon and fluorine atoms. It is unsurpassed in chemical and physical properties such as extreme resistance to chemical attack, high heat stability and dielectric strength, but especially for its non-adhesion and low frictional properties. It is used for gaskets, bearings, rings, electric components and tape, and for nonadhesion applications. (See PLASTICS.)

flush (*Shopwk.*) Parts are said to be flush when their surfaces are on the same level.

flush bolt. A bolt whose head is let into a counterbored hole so that the top of its head rests level with the face of the plate into which it is sunk.

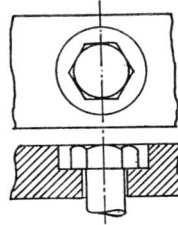

Flush Bolt

flush head riv′et. A rivet, the head of which does not extend above the surface of the plate, etc., into which it is driven.

flush re-cep′ta-cle (*Elec.*) That type of pin or screw shell receptacle which is recessed in the wall, only the plate extending beyond the surface line.

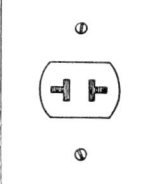

Flush Receptacle

flush switch (*Elec.*) A wall switch of the key, button, or toggle type in which the entire device is recessed into the wall with only the operating mechanism protruding beyond the face of the plate.

flush valve (*Plumb.*) A valve used for flushing a fixture by using water directly from the water-supply pipes or in connection with a special flush tank.

flute (*Arch. and Furn.*) A concave channel as in a column, baluster, leg, frieze, etc. (*Mech.*) The concave channel in a reamer, tap, or drill.

flut′ed ream′er. A reamer fluted longitudinally, to cut at its sides.

flut′ing cut′ter (*Mach.*) Used on a milling machine for fluting taps, reamers, etc.

flut′ter (*Aero.*) An oscillation of definite period but unstable character set up in any part of an aircraft by a momentary disturbance and maintained by a combination of the aerodynamic, inertial, and elastic characteristics of the member itself.

flux (*Chem.*) Any substance or mixture used to promote the fusion of metals or minerals, as alkalies, borax, lime, fluorite, etc.

flux den′si-ty (*Elec.*) The number of lines of force or induction per unit area taken perpendicular to the induction. In free space, flux density and field intensity are the same numerically, but within magnetic material, the two are quite different.

fly (*Aero.*) (1) To operate an aircraft in flight; (2) to ride as a passenger in an aircraft. (*Print.*) The apparatus which delivers the sheets from a cylinder press.

fly cut′ters (*Mach.*) Cutters set in a cutter block or chuck held in a lathe or other machine, and used for shaping the ends of metal rods or for other formed work.

fly′ing boat (*Aero.*) A form of seaplane supported, when resting on the surface of the water, by a hull or hulls providing flotation in addition to serving as fuselages. For the central-hull type, lateral stability is usually provided by wing-tip floats.

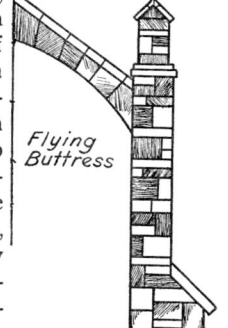

Flying Buttress

fly′ing but′tress (*Arch.*) Consists of

a detached pier or buttress connected with a wall some distance from it by a portion of an arch, thus distributing the roof thrust. Has frequent application in church architecture.

fly′ing disk (*Furn.*) An Egyptian decoration in the form of a disk with wings.

fly′leaf (*Print.*) The blank leaf at the front or back of bound books.

fly′wheel (*Mach.*) A heavy wheel used in machinery where reciprocal motion is converted into circular motion. It aids in maintaining uniformity of motion.

fly′wheel mark′ing (*Auto.*) Marks on the face of a flywheel which serve as a guide for the proper timing of valve action in an engine.

foamed plas′tics (*Plast.*) Resins, cast rigid or flexible, into sponge, in either closed or connected structure, and either dense or open. Foams are made of a variety of plastic types, the rigid forms being widely used for insulation and floatation while the flexible kind is common in upholstery. Urethane Foam is an example of plastic foam. (See ISOCYANATE.)

f. o. b. Free on board; an engagement to deliver goods on board ship or other carrier without extra charge.

fo′ci (fō′sī) The centers from which the end curves of an elliptical figure are struck.

foil (*Arch.*) A leaflike division in architectural ornamentation, used in groups of three, a trefoil, of four, a quatrefoil, etc.

fol′ders (*Print.*) Usually sheets of printed matter having only one fold, making four pages.

fold′ing ma-chine′ (*Print.*) A machine for folding large printed sheets of books, newspapers, etc.

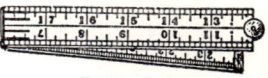

Folding Rule

fold′ing rule. A collapsible instrument used for measuring.

fo′li-at′ed (*Furn.*) Decorated with a leaf design.

fo′li-o (*Print.*) A page number.

fol′low board (*Fdry.*) A molding board recessed, or cut away in such a manner that the pattern with which it is to be used will lie in it to the parting line. When using a follow board, no sand parting need be cut.

fol′low cop′y (*Print.*) Instruction to the compositor indicating that he is to consider the copy correct and to make no changes.

fol′low dies (*Metalwk.*) Two or more punches and dies in one punch holder and die body arranged so the work is fed from one punch to another until a series of required operations has been completed.

fol′low-er (*Mach.*) (1) A wheel which is driven by another wheel. (2) The roller which operates against a cam face, or the roller and the arm to which it is attached.

fol′low-er rest (*Mach.*) A support for lathe work, attached to the carriage. It follows or is opposite the cutting tool, thus preventing the work from springing away from the tool.

font. The vessel used in the right of baptism. (*Print.*) A complete assortment of any one size of type.

fools′cap′ (*Papermkg.*) A term used

with references to a size of writing paper measuring 13 by 16 in.

foot (*Furn.*) The lowest supporting member of a piece of furniture; the termination of the leg. Variant in form and decoration.

foot brake (*Auto.*) Brake operated by foot action as distinguished from the hand or parking brake.

foot-can′dle (*Elec.*) The amount of illumination produced by a standard candle at a distance of one foot.

foot′ing (*Arch.*) A foundation, as for a column.

foot le′ver. A lever worked by the pressure of the foot alone.

foot′note (*Print.*) An explanatory note at the foot of a page.

foot pound. A unit of work used in calculation, meaning one pound lifted one foot high.

foot se-lec′tor switch (*Auto.*) The foot switch which controls the high and low headlight beams. See FOOT SWITCH.

foot′step or **foot′step bear′ing** (*Mach.*) A bearing used at the lower end of a vertical shaft or spindle to carry the end thrust.

foot switch (*Auto. Elec.*) An electric switch operated by foot pressure; e.g., the switch attached to the floor boards of an automobile, by which the headlight beams are controlled. See FOOT SELECTOR SWITCH.

force (*Mech. and Phys.*) That which changes, or tends to change the station of rest or motion of the body acted upon. It is measured in pounds. Force has three characteristics: direction, place of application, and magnitude.

force feed lu′bri-ca′tors (*Auto. Mech. and Mach.*) A plunger system similar in action to a tire pump. The plungers are actuated by a camshaft and as they move up and down, a metered charge of oil is delivered to the parts to be lubricated.

force feed of oil (*Auto. Mech.*) Force feed is a lubrication system in which a pump forces oil to main bearings, rod bearings, and piston-pin bearings. When supplied to all three it is called a *full* force-feed system.

force fit (*Mach.*) A fit accomplished by force with the result that the parts so joined become a unit.

force plate (*Plast.*) The plate that carries the plunger or force plug of a mold and the guide pins or bushings. As it is usually drilled for steam or water lines, it is sometimes called the steam plate.

force plug (*Plast.*) The portion of a mold that enters the cavity block and exerts pressure on the molding compound, designated as the top force or bottom force by position in the assembly; also called plunger or piston.

force pump (*Mach.*) A pump in which the water is lifted by the force due to atmospheric pressure acting against a vacuum.

for′eign mat′ter (*Plast.*) Particles of substance incorporated in a plastic material which seem different from its average composition.

fore′man. A man in charge of a group of workmen. He is usually responsible to a superintendent or manager.

fore plane (*Woodwkg.*) A plane intermediate in size between a jack- and a jointer plane.

fore-short′ened (*Fine Arts*) Shortened or represented as shortened, as the effect of perspective.

forge. (1) To form a piece of metal by hammering while it is hot. (2) The structure wholly of iron or of iron and brick upon which a smith's fire is built. Forges may be either fixed or portable.

forge weld'ing. A group of pressure welding processes wherein the parts to be welded are brought to suitable temperature in a furnace and the weld is consummated by pressure or blows.

forg'ing brass (*Metal.*) An alloy of copper and zinc with small amounts of tin and lead. It is much used in die forging.

forg'ing press (*Mach.*) A machine used to exert the pressure needed in die forging.

forg'ings. Pieces or masses of metal shaped by hammering.

forked cen'ter (*Mach.*) A center with taper or straight shank and V head for holding cylindrical objects in position during drilling and other operations

Forked Center

form (*Ceram.*) Any container in which plaster is poured over a pattern to make a mold. (*Concrete*) The retainer which gives required shape to the poured concrete and is removed after the concrete has set. (*Print.*) A page or pages of type, plates, etc., locked in a chase ready for printing.

form-al'de-hyde (*Chem.*) (HCHO) A colorless, poisonous gas obtained by passing the vapors of methyl alcohol through a heated copper tube. It is very soluble in water. In the liquid form it is known as formalin. One of the best disinfecting agents known. Used also in dyestuffs, rubber goods, inks, tanning, etc.

for-mat' (*Bookbndg.*) The form, size, type face, margins, and general style of a book when printed and bound.

formed plate (*Elec.*) The plate in a special type of storage cell which is formed by a process of charging and discharging.

form'ing proc'ess (*Elec.*) As applied to plates of storage batteries; the process of developing a storage battery or cell from plates of lead immersed in sulphuric acid and water through charging and discharging until the plates are chemically PbO_2 and Pb.

form'ing rolls (*Sheet-Met. Wk.*) A series of three rolls adjustable for various gauges of sheet metal. Used for turning or forming cylinders of desired diameter.

form'ing tools. Tools with their working or cutting edges shaped like the form to be produced on the work. Often applied to any tool or device used to facilitate a mechanical operation.

form truck (*Print.*) A two-wheeled truck used for rolling heavy forms from place to place.

for'mu-la (*Math.*) An arithmetical or algebraical statement of figures, letters, signs, and symbols, arranged to indicate the mathematical operations necessary for the solution of a problem.

for'mu-la'tions (*Plast.*) This term refers to variations within a plastic type, one formulation being rigid, another flexible, and still another fire-resistant.

form–wound coil (*Elec.*) An armature coil or winding which is formed or shaped over a wooden fixture. The coil is then placed on the armature as a whole.

for′ward-ing (*P r i n t.*) The binding process after the sheets of a book are fastened together.

foul′ing. The incrustation of steam boilers, and steam and water pipes with scale. The interference of machines and structural parts generally with each other, hindering their action.

foun-da′tion (*Arch.*) That part of a building or wall which is below the surface of the ground, or that part on which the superstructure is erected.

foun-da′tion bolts. Bolts used for holding down or anchoring machinery or structural parts to the foundation on which they rest.

foun-da′tion plate (*Engin.*) A plate to which a pump, an engine, or a motor, is bolted. A sole plate. (*Fdry.*) A plate of cast iron placed in the bottom of a mold to receive the spindle to maintain a sweep.

found′ry. A building or place in which metal castings are made.

found′ry sand. The sand into which molten metal is run in order to impart the shape required in castings.

Four-drin′i-er (fōōr-drĭn′ĭ-ēr) (*Papermkg.*) Relating to, or designating a papermaking machine; the first to make a continuous web. Original machine invented by Louis Robert, but improved by Henry and Sealy Fourdrinier, assisted by Bryan Donkin, at the beginning of the nineteenth century.

Four′nier′ (fōōr′nyā′) (*Print.*) Pierre Simon Fournier, a Frenchman, inventor of the point system.

four–pole de-sign′ (*Auto.*) Any generator or starting motor having four field poles.

four–stroke cy′cle (*Auto.*) A power cycle concluded in four strokes of the engine. In the auto engine, the first downstroke is the intake; the next upstroke allows compression; ignition and expansion on the third stroke, and exhaust on the fourth.

four–way switch (*Elec.*) Used when control is desired from three or more places, in which case two three-way switches are required, all others four-way.

four–wheel drive (*Auto.*) The type of automobile which has live axles both front and rear, driving power being delivered to all four wheels.

foxed (*Papermkg.*) A term applied to stained or spotted leaves of paper caused by mildew and the like.

fox lathe (*Mach.*) A brass worker's lathe which has a chasing bar or "fox" for thread cutting.

frac′tion. A part of anything.

frac′tion-al dis′til-la′tion (*Chem.*) The act of separating a mixture, as a liquid, into fractions having more or less fixed properties but not necessarily definite compounds.

frac′ture (*Metal., Mach., Masonry*) To break apart; to separate the continuous parts of an object by sudden shock or by excessive strain.

frame (*Arch.*) The woodwork of windows, doors, etc. (*Carp.*) The timber work supporting floors, roofs, etc. (*Furn.*) The case or border which surrounds or encloses a glass, picture, etc., often richly carved or ornamented; also the skeleton structure of furniture. (*Print.*) The stand or framework on which type cases are placed. (*Tel.*) One of a series of complete television pictures. In present standards, pictures are transmitted at the rate of 30 frames per second, giving the effect of a moving picture. In relation to film, frame means one complete picture on a 35mm. or 16mm. film. 35mm. motion pictures are projected at the rate of 24 frames per second.

frame high (*Masonry*) The height of the top of the window or door frames; the level at which the lintel or arch is to be laid.

frame of a house (*Arch.*) The skeleton of a house, including joists, studs, plates, sills, partitions, roofing, etc.

frame'work. A skeleton structure or frame about which something is to be built.

fram'ing (*Carp.*) The skeleton work of a structure. The act of erecting the same.

fram'ing con-trol' (*Tel.*) This control on the receiver allows the repetition rate of the picture to be adjusted to that of the transmitter. It also may be called the vertical hold control.

fray'ing (*Bookbndg.*) Spreading out cords or bands preparatory to "tipping down" to a book.

free (*Papermkg.*) A term applied to paper stuff which is separated readily from the water.

free bal-loon' (*Aero.*) A balloon, usually spherical, whose ascent and descent may be controlled by releasing ballast or gas, and whose direction of flight is determined by the wind.

free–burn'ing coal. Coal which burns freely but which does not fuse together and become a pasty mass when heated.

free–burn'ing mix'ture (*Auto.*) Twelve to sixteen times as much air as gasoline, if figured by weight, or nine thousand times as much air as gasoline by volume, produces a mixture which will instantaneously ignite throughout its mass when the ignition spark occurs.

free end. In a cantilever, the end which is not fixed is always called the "free end."

free fit (class 2) (*Mach.*) Gives a liberal allowance for running fits of machine parts.

free'hand. Executed with the hand without the aid of drawing instruments.

free sheet (*Papermkg.*) Paper free from ground wood pulp.

free'stone (*Arch.*) Stone suitable for molding, etc., which may be cut or carved with a chisel without a tendency to split.

free-wheel'ing (*Auto.*) An overrunning clutch placed in second and high-gear assembly, permitting easy engagement and full coasting effect irrespective of engine speed.

French curve (*Draw.*) Also called universal curve or irregular curve. A tool used by draftsmen in drawing curved lines which are not arcs.

French fold (*Print.*) Fold made both vertically and horizontally.

French fo'li-o (*Paper* and *Print.*) A thin writing paper used for proofing and other work requiring a lightweight paper.

French seam (*Uphol.*) A seam standing upright.

French win'dow (*Bldg.*) A double-sash casement window extending down to the floor and serving as a door to a porch or terrace.

Fre′on (frē′ŏn) (*Chem.*) Dichlorodifluoromethane. F_{12}. Used as a refrigerant.

fre′quen-cy (*Elec.*) The number of double alternations per second made by an alternating current. (*Tel.*) The number of vibrations or cycles in a unit of time. Radio waves fall into low frequencies, high frequencies, and ultra-high frequencies and micro waves.

fre′quen-cy me′ter (*Elec.*) An a.c. meter which indicates directly the frequency of the circuit to which it is attached.

fre′quen-cy mod′u-la′tion (**FM**) (*Tel.*) A method of radio-wave transmission by which the carrier wave varies in frequency in accordance with the sound waves impressed on it while its amplitude (loudness or power) remains constant.

fres′co (*Arch.*) The method of painting on wet plaster. The term is often incorrectly applied to painting on a dry wall.

fresh–air in′let (*Plumb.*) A connection made to a house drain above the house or drain trap, leading to the outside atmosphere.

fret. Ornamental work done in relief characterized by angular interlocked or interlacing lines.

fret saw. A saw with a very narrow blade; used as a jig or scroll saw.

fri′a-ble. Easily crumbled or reduced to a powder.

fric′tion. The resistance to motion which is set up when two moving surfaces come in contact with each other.

fric′tion cal′en-der (*Papermkg.*) A calender having rollers of different sizes which glazes paper by the action of the smaller rollers.

fric′tion catch (*Furn.*) A device used on small doors of articles of furniture to keep them tightly closed but not locked. It consists essentially of a spring and plunger contained in a casing.

fric′tion cou′pling (*Mech.*) Any one of a variety of couplings which operate through frictional contact.

fric′tion disk. The disk of a friction drive.

fric′tion drive (*Mach.*) Transmission of power by frictional contact.

fric′tion of mo′tion (*Mech.*) That friction which must be overcome by force in order to keep any solid, spherical, or cylindrical body moving over a plane surface after it is once set in motion.

fric′tion of rest (*Mech.*) That friction which must be overcome by force in order to start any solid, spherical or cylindrical body sliding or rolling over a plane surface.

fric′tion tape (*Elec.*) An impregnated cotton insulating tape used to cover the rubber tape required to protect a splice in electrical conductors.

fric′tion wheel. Any wheel which drives or is driven by friction, as when contact takes place only between smooth or grooved surfaces.

Friesland de-sign′ (*Furn.*) Angular and circular design executed in flat carving.

frieze (*Arch.*) The middle division of an entablature.

frilled (*Furn.*) A term used to refer to a scroll which has added decorative carving along its projecting edges, such as a frilled C scroll.

fringe. An ornamental edging used as a finish to dresses, upholstery, etc., in European countries, from the beginning of the Renaissance, consisting of a band with depending tassels or twisted threads of silk or other material.

Frise ai′ler-on (ā′lê-rŏn) (*Aero.*) An aileron having the nose portion projecting ahead of the hinge axis, the lower surface being in line with the lower surface of the wing. When the trailing edge of the aileron is raised, the nose portion protrudes below the lower surface of the wing, increasing the drag.

fris′ket (*Print.*) A heavy sheet of paper stretched across the grippers of a job press, when certain parts of a form mark and spoil a sheet.

frith′stool (*Furn.*) A round stool used in Anglo-Saxon times.

frit′ted (*Ceram.*) Refers to a glaze which contains some pulverized material which has been made insoluble by melting and suddenly cooling in water.

fron′tis-piece (*Bookbndg.*) An illustration in the front of a book, facing the title page.

front–wheel drive (*Auto.*) A construction in which the live propelling axle is at the front end. The rear axle is dead.

frost′ing (*Plast.*) An apparently crystalline pattern on the surface of a plastic.

fro-zen bat′ter-ies (*Auto.*) When a battery is completely discharged, it will freeze at a temperature considerably above zero. In winter, water should not be added to the battery unless the car is to be operated at once, otherwise the water will stay at the top and freeze.

fro′zen i′ron (*Fdry.*) Solidified iron, too cool to pour.

frus′tum (*Geom.*) That which remains of a solid, as a cone or pyramid, after cutting off the upper part by a plane parallel to the base. (*Math.*) Of a cone or pyramid; Convex area = (the sum of the periferies or the circumferences of the upper and lower bases) x ½ the slant height. Entire area = convex area + the area of the upper base + the area of the lower base. Volume = (the sum of the area of the upper + the area of the lower base + the square root of the product of the areas of the upper and lower bases) x 1/3 of the vertical height of the frustrum.

fu′el. Combustion matter, such as wood, coal, gas, or oil, which may be used to feed a fire or operate an engine.

fu′el by′–pass′ reg′u-la′tor (*Aero.*) A device placed in the fuel line of a supercharged engine to regulate the fuel pressure in the carburetor float chamber so that it will be a fixed amount above the carburetor air pressure.

fu′el con-sump′tion (*Aero.*) The weight of fuel (or oil) consumed per brake horsepower hour.

fu′el dope (*Aero.*) Any material added to the fuel in small quantities for the purpose of slowing up detonation.

fu′el-lev′el in′di-ca′tor (*Auto.*) An instrument for indicating the amount of fuel in a tank. On older cars the reading was taken directly at the tank. This has been replaced by a system which permits a reading from a gauge on the panel board.

fu′el lock (*Auto.*) See VAPOR LOCK.

fu′el pump (*Auto.*) A device operated by a piston or diaphragm to create vacuum which insures supply of fuel to carburetor or mixing chamber.

fu′el-tank vent (*Aero.*) A small tube used to conduct surplus fuel from a fuel tank, overboard clear of the airplane, and to equalize pressure.

fu′gi-tive col′ors (*Papermkg.*) Colors which are not fast to light.

ful′crum (*Mech.*) The point on which a lever turns.

full an·neal′ing. Alloys with iron base are heated above the critical temperature range, are held above that range for a certain length of time, and then slowly cooled through the range.

full′er. To form grooves, as in blacksmith's work.

Full′er fau′cet (*Plumb.*) A faucet in which the flow of water is stopped by means of a rubber ball which is forced into the opening.

full-float′ing ax′le (*Auto.*) In this type of axle the full weight of the car is carried on the housing. When assembled, the axle drive shaft is usually held in place by the hub cap. To remove the shaft, the hub cap is removed and the shaft pulled out. Some cars have a snap ring which fits into a slot of the wheel hub and dog of the shaft, to prevent the axle from working out against the hub cap.

full′ing or mill′ing (*Textile*) The felting or shrinking of woolens to secure close, firm material.

full load (*Aero.*) Weight empty plus useful load; also called "gross weight."

full point (*Print.*) A punctuation mark, such as a period.

full size. Drawings are full size when made to the actual size of the work which they represent. The term "full size" is usually written on the drawing.

full thread (*Mach.*) A screw thread which is cut clean and sharply to its proper depth.

fum′ing (*Wood Fin.*) Aging wood by the use of chemicals.

fum′ing sul·phu′ric ac′id (*Chem.*) An oily-looking viscous liquid used in refining petroleum, in the manufacture of explosives, dyes, shoe blacking, etc.

fun·da·men′tal. Of or pertaining to the foundation or basis; essential. A principle, rule, or law.

fun′nel (*Engin.*) (1) A hollow cone-shaped vessel with spout at the end to permit free pouring from one container to another. (2) A vent for ventilation as used on steamships.

fur′long. A measure of length equal to $\frac{1}{8}$ of a mile, 660 ft.

fur′nace (*Engin.*) The compartment in which fuel is burned for heating water, melting metals or other materials, and for heating, drying, or baking various kinds of substances.

fur′nace braz′ing. A brazing process wherein the heat is obtained from a furnace in which the atmosphere may or may not be controlled.

fur′ni·ture. Useful and decorative movable articles, such as tables, chairs, etc., placed in a building. (*Print.*) Pieces of wood or metal used in making up forms. It can be had in various widths which are multiples of picas, and in different lengths. (*Shopwk.*) Tool racks, lathe pans, tote boxes, etc.

fur'ni-ture fend'ers (*Furn.*) Small half-round rubber bumpers with nail or screw point projecting to permit attachment to articles of furniture.

fur'ni-ture glides (*Furn.*) Small bowl-shaped pieces of pressed metal attached to table legs, chair feet, etc., with convex side resting on the floor to permit easy moving of furniture, also to reduce noise when stools or chairs are frequently shifted, as in a classroom.

furred (*Arch.*) Provided with wood strips so as to form an air space between the walls and the plastering.

fur'ring (*Arch.*) The leveling up or building out of a part of a wall or ceiling by wood strips, etc.

fur'ring strips (*Arch.*) Pieces of wood attached to a surface, as for lathing.

fuse (*Elec.*) An electrical safety device; the weakest thermo link in the circuit, which "blows out" when the rise of the current is greater than that for which the circuit was designed.

Fuse

fuse block (*Elec.*) A porcelain or slate base to which are fastened fuse clips or other contacts for holding fuses.

fuse clips (*Elec.*) The spring part of a cutout or switch which holds the ferrules of a cartridge fuse.

fu'se-lage (*Aero.*) The body of an airplane, to which are attached the wings and tail unit.

fuse link (*Elec.*) The fusible part of a cartridge fuse.

fuse plug (*Elec.*) See PLUG FUSE.

fuse wire (*Elec.*) Wire made of an alloy which melts at a low temperature.

fu-si-bil'i-ty. The readiness with which a metal fuses or passes from the solid into the liquid form.

fu'si-ble al-loys (*Chem.*) Alloys which will melt at definite low temperatures.

fu'si-ble plug. A plug, composed of soft and easily melted metal or alloy, inserted into a brass casting, which is screwed into the furnace crown of a steam boiler, and which melts when the level falls as low as that of the crown; this allows the escaping water and steam to extinguish the fire.

fus'ing point. The temperature at which metals or metallic alloys melt and become liquid.

fu'sion (*Phys.*) The joining of atomic nuclei to form a heavier nucleus, using extreme heat.

fus'tic (fŭs'tĭk) (*Wood Fin.*) The wood of a tropical tree used as a yellow dyestuff.

fuzz (*Paper*) A hairy appearance found especially on the "wire" side of paper which is caused by the projection of individual fibers.

G

ga′ble (*Arch.*) The triangular end of an exterior wall above the eaves.

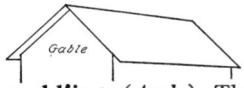

ga′ble mold′ing (*Arch.*) The molding used to finish a gable.

ga′ble roof (*Arch.*) A ridge roof terminating in a gable.

gadg′et (*Engin.*) A slang word applied to any small, handy appliance or device.

gag′gers (*Fdry.*) Metal supports used to reinforce the sand in the cope; commonly used to support hanging bodies of sand when making molds on the floor.

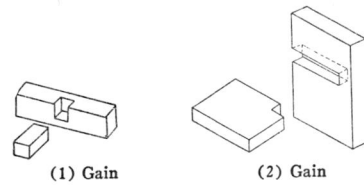

(1) Gain   (2) Gain

gain (*Woodwkg.*) The mortise or notch cut out of a timber to receive the end of a beam.

ga-le′na (*Mineral.*) The most important ore of lead. It is a sulphide, that is, a compound of lead and sulphur (PbS) containing 86.5 per cent lead.

gal′ler-y (*Arch.*) (1) An elevated floor in a large audience room, usually projecting from the walls, supported by columns from below, or hung from above, or both; generally equipped with seats. (2) A room in which works of art are displayed.

gal′ley (*Print.*) A wooden or metal oblong tray for holding type after it has been set. It consists of a flat base and three raised sides, the fourth being left open so that composed matter may be pushed off without lifting it.

gal′ley lock (*Print.*) A device for holding type in position on the galley while proofs are being pulled.

gal′ley press (*Print.*) A press used for proofing galleys of type. It consists, essentially, of a base and a heavy roller running on tracks.

gal′ley proof (*Print.*) A rough proof taken from a galley of type matter.

gal′ley rack (*Print.*) A rack divided into sections for holding galleys of type.

gal′lic ac′id (*Chem.*) Colorless or slightly yellow, crystalline needles or prisms $(C_6H_2(OH)_3COOH)$. Specific gravity 1.694; melting point 222 to 240 deg. C. Used for photography, ink, dyeing, medicine, etc.

gall′ing (*Metal.*) A characteristic of metals which causes them to seize when brought into intimate contact with each other. A material which is subject to galling is one which will seize or "freeze" when brought into close contact with like material under pressure and no lubricant.

gal′li-pot. A small earthen jar such as is used for ointments.

gal′lon. A unit of liquid measure containing 4 quarts, 8 pints, 231 cubic inches.

gal-loon′ (*Uphol.*) A narrow binding of tapelike material.

gal-van′ic ac′tion (*Chem.*) The action upon one another of electropositive and electronegative metals,

---

sāle, surfâce, grăm, humȧn, màsk, solȧr, bär, bâre; mē, ėdition, lĕnd, momĕnt, bakēr; kīnd, fĭt; lōde, ômit, ŏlive, cŏnsume, sôrt; dūty, ûtility, nŭt, alŭm, bûrn.

wasting away the positive metal; particularly noticeable where iron and copper, or zinc and copper, or brass and iron, are in contact in the presence of acidulated water.

gal·van'ic cor·ro'sion (*Metal.*) The accelerated corrosion of one metal when it is connected with a more noble metal, e.g., if steel and copper are connected together in sea water, the steel will suffer accelerated corrosion and the copper will be protected.

gal'va·nize. To coat iron with zinc. It is not usually an electrical process, but consists simply of dipping the iron in molten zinc.

gal'va·nized i'ron. Iron, which, after having undergone a cleansing process, has been dipped in a bath of molten zinc. The most common process has nothing to do with galvanic action.

gal'va·nized sheets. Sheets of galvanized iron 20 to 30 in. wide and 96 in. long.

gal'va·niz'ing. The depositing of a zinc coating on iron.

Galvanometer

gal'va·nom'e·ter (*Elec.*) An instrument for detecting small currents or difference of potential.

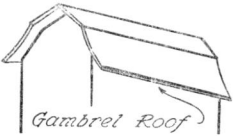

gam'brel roof (*Arch.*) A roof having its slope broken by an obtuse angle.

gam'ma rays (gamma radiation) (*Phys.*) High energy, deep penetrating X rays.

gang dies (*Metalwk.*) Two or more punches and dies in one holder for making an equivalent number of openings in a blank with one stroke of the press.

gang drill'ing ma·chine'. A drill press equipped with several spindles so that a number of holes can be drilled at one time. It is particularly useful in quantity production work.

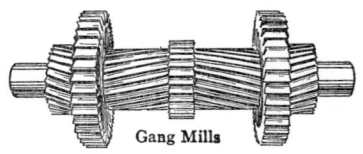
Gang Mills

gang mills. A series of milling cutters arranged on the same mandrel to increase production; may be used to machine two or more surfaces at one time.

gang print'ing. A combination of several jobs locked up in one form for printing at one time.

gang switch (*Elec.*) A unit of two or more switches to give control of two or more circuits from one point. The entire mechanism is mounted in one box under one cover.

gang tool (*Metalwk.*) A tool holder with several cutting tools arranged so each tool cuts a little deeper than the one in advance of it. Gang tools are used on lathes and planers.

gangue (găng) (*Mineral.*) The nonmetalliferous minerals found in a vein of ore.

gang'way. A passageway to or out of any enclosure. The term is mostly used in its nautical sense, meaning the opening in the bulwark of a vessel, also the gangplank leading from wharf to deck.

gap (*Aero.*) The distance separating two adjacent wings of a multiplane. (*Auto.*) (1) The space between the electrodes of a spark plug. (2) The distance between contact points when open. (3) The air gap in an electrical circuit.

gap bed (*Mach.*) A lathe bed having a portion recessed out in front of and below the headstock, to receive work larger in diameter than the lathe would otherwise accommodate. The bed is strengthened below the gap. The gap when not in use is filled up with a gap bridge.

gap shears (*Sheet-Met. Wk.*) A shearing machine similar in purpose to the squaring shears. The gap in the housings permits the insertion of the sheet of metal either lengthwise or crosswise. It takes the place of long-length shears where floor space is limited.

ga-rage′ (gȧ-räzh′) (*Auto.*) A building for storing automobiles, as a small, private garage or a large public garage where servicing also may be had.

Garden Bond

gar′den bond (*Masonry*) Consists of three stretchers in each course followed by a header, although this bond may have from two to five stretchers between headers.

garde′robe (gärd′rōb) (*Woodwkg.*) A wardrobe. A private room, as a bed chamber.

gar′goyle (gär′goil) (*Arch.*) A stone spout, grotesquely carved, projecting at the upper part of a building.

gar′net. An inexpensive gem stone found in rock formations in many countries. It is used as an abrasive and for watch bearings.

gar′net pa′per. Paper coated with a reddish abrasive, used in the same manner as sandpaper.

gar′ni-er-ite (gär′nĭ-ēr-īt) (*Metal.*) An important ore of nickel containing about 5 per cent nickel, found in New Caledonia.

gas braz′ing. A brazing process wherein the heat is obtained from a gas flame.

gas en′gine. An internal combustion engine designed to operate on a mixture of gas and air as a fuel.

gas′e-ous fu′el, or "pro-duc′er gas." This is gas prepared in a gas producer, from bituminous coal. Mixed with heated air it forms an economical and effective fuel for maintaining an even heat, e.g., for the heating of the tanks in which glass is melted in a glass factory.

gas–filled lamp (*Elec.*) A lamp which is exhausted of air and then filled to about atmospheric pressure by a mixture of inert gases usually nitrogen and argon.

gash′ing (*Mach.*) The rough cutting of machine parts, particularly the teeth in bevel gears.

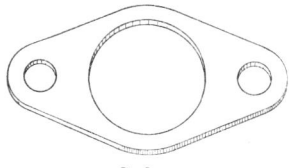

Gasket

gas′ket (*Mach.*) Paper, metal, rubber, or especially prepared material used between cylinder head and cylin-

gas′o-line der, or under similar conditions, to prevent leaking.

gas′o-line. A volatile distillate from crude petroleum, used principally as a fuel in internal-combustion engines.

gas′o-line en′gine (*Auto.*) An internal-combustion engine designed to operate on a mixture of gasoline and air as a fuel.

gas pli′ers (*Plumb.*) Pliers used for gripping small pipe or round objects.

gas pro-du′cer. A gas-making furnace in which coal gas is obtained by the distillation of fuel.

gas′sing (*Elec.*) The giving off of gas bubbles from a storage battery under charge. Due to electrochemical action. (*Textile*) Burning off fuzzy ends from cloth to secure a smooth surface.

gas tur′bine (*Aero.*) A turbine rotated by expanding gases as in a turbojet engine or in a turbosupercharger.

gas weld′ing. A nonpressure (fusion) welding process wherein the heat is obtained from a gas flame.

gate (*Fdry.*) Any opening in a mold through which metal is poured to form a casting.

gat′ed pat′tern (*Fdry.*) A gang pattern consisting of several metal patterns fastened together so that it may be possible to produce a number of duplicate castings at one time. Very essential in production work on small parts.

gate′–leg-ged′ ta′ble (*Furn.*) A drop-leaf table whose leaves, when raised, are supported by swinging or gate legs.

gate valve (*Engin.*) A valve whose action depends on the motion of a wedge-shaped gate between the inlet and outlet openings.

gath′er-ing (*Print.*) Collecting signatures of a book or pamphlet preparatory to binding.

gauge (gāj) (*Metal.*) An instrument or device for determining the size of parts. Gauges for different purposes are known by specific names. (*Plaster.*) To mix plaster of Paris with common plaster to cause quick setting. (*Woodwkg.*) A tool used by woodworkers to make a line parallel to the edge of a board.

gauge pins (*Print.*) Pieces of sheet metal used as guides on the tympan of a job press.

gauge stick. A graduated stick may be inserted in a tank or reservoir for determining the depth or quantity of the contents.

gaug′ing. To determine, by measurement or other test, the size of an object, the capacity of a vessel, or the amount of its contents. (*Masonry*) To cut bricks or stones to make them uniform in size. (*Plaster.*) To mix plaster of Paris with mortar to bring about quick setting.

gav′el. A type of mallet used by a presiding officer for calling a meeting to order.

Gay′–Lus′sac's′ law (l ü′s à k s′) (*Phys.*) When the pressure is kept constant, the volume coefficient of all gases is the same;
$$\frac{1}{273} = 0.00366 \text{ per degree C.}$$

gear (*Mech.*) A very general term applied to toothed wheels, valve motions, pump work, lifting tackle, ropes, etc. The point or portion of the tooth of a gear wheel lying outside the pitch circle is the addendum; that portion between the pitch and the root lines is the dedendum.

gear case (*Mach.*) A housing or metal box within which gears operate. Usually the gear case is filled with lubricant.

gear cut′ters. Circular cutter of hardened steel whose section is that of the tooth spaces which they are intended to cut.

gear driv′en su′per-charg′er (*Aero.*) A supercharger driven by gears from the engine.

geared chuck. A form of universal chuck.

geared head. A headstock equipped with back gear.

geared pro-pel′ler (*Aero.*) A propeller driven through gearing, generally at some speed other than the engine speed.

geared pump. A pump which is driven by an engine through the use of gearing.

geared shap′er (*Mach.*) A rack and pinion operates the ram with a slow cutting stroke and a quick return, by open and crossed belts as on a planer.

gear′ing. The term has the same general meaning as gear, but is applied more specifically to gear wheels.

gear′ing down. The reduction of speed from the driver to the driven by the use of gear wheels, with an accompanying gain in power.

gear ra′ti-o (*Auto.*) The relation between number of teeth on driving and driven gears.

gear shift′ing (*Auto.*) Throwing into mesh different sets of the change-speed gears in order to vary the speed ratio and power between engine and rear axle.

gear-shift le′ver (*Auto.*) A lever by means of which the change-speed gears are shifted.

gear stock′ing cut′ter (*Gear.*) A cutter used to rough out gear teeth, to speed production, and to permit a light and accurate finish cut.

gear–tooth cal′i-per (*Mach.*) A vernier-type caliper used for measuring the depth and thickness of gear teeth on the pitch line.

gear train (*Mach.*) An arrangement of two or more gears connecting driving and driven parts.

gei′ger count′er (*Phys.*) A gas-filled electric device which detects the presence of radioactivity by counting the formation of ions.

gel (jĕl) (*Chem. Plast.*) A somewhat rigid, generally transparent, two-phase liquid-solid system in which the solid is precipitated as aggregates in and around which the liquid is held.

gel′a-tin (*Chem.*) Made from certain kinds of bones and parts of skin, selected, washed, and treated with special care. Glue is an impure gelatin. High-tested, sweet gelatin made from clean stock, under sanitary conditions, is sold for food purposes.

ge-la′tion (*Plast.*) A state in the hardening cycle of liquid plastic in which the linkage of molecules has progressed to a point where the resin turns from a fluid state to that of a jellylike form, just preceding hardening. The thickening stage.

gel time (*Plast.*) The interval elapsed between catalyzation of the resin and its initial thickening.

genelite (*Metal.*) A bronze, bearing metal, which contains about 40 per

per cent, by volume, of graphite, which permits a considerable absorption of oil.

gen'er-al draw-ing (*Draft.*) A scale drawing showing an entire machine or other article, with all the parts located in their proper relations to one another. More commonly known as an assembly drawing.

gen'er-a'tor (*Elec.*) A general term applied to machines which are used for the transformation of mechanical energy into electrical energy.

gen'er-a'tor bus bars (*Elec.*) The bars of copper placed in back of a switchboard carrying the output of the generator. The distributing circuits are fed from these buses.

Geneva Motion

Ge-ne'va mo'tion (*Shopwk.*) A device which gives a positive but intermittent motion to the driven wheel, but prevents its moving in either direction without the driver. The driver may have one tooth or a number of teeth if desired. Also made so as to prevent a complete revolution of the driven wheel.

ge'o-det'ic sur-vey'ing (jē'ō-dĕt'ĭk) That very accurate method of surveying which takes into consideration the spheroidal form of the earth's surface. Used in topographic and hydrographic work.

ge-ol'o-gy (jē-ŏl'ō-jĭ) The science of the history of the earth as shown in its rocks.

ge'o-met'ri-cal. Of or pertaining to geometry; according to the rules of geometry; forming or consisting of regular lines, curves, and angles.

ge'o-met'ri-cal mean. The geometrical mean of two numbers is obtained by multiplying the two together and extracting the square root of the product.

ge'o-met'ri-cal pitch of a pro-pel'ler (*Aero.*) The distance an element of a propeller would advance in one revolution if it were moving along a helix having an angle equal to its blade angle.

ge'o-met'ri-cal pro-gres'sion (*Math.*) Each term of a series is equal to that which precedes it, multiplied by some factor which is constant for all the terms, e.g., 2, 4, 8, 16, 32 are in geometrical progression, the multiplier in this case being 2.

ge'o-met'ri-cal stair (*Arch. and Bldg.*) A stair which returns on itself with winders or with winders and a landing built around a comparatively narrow well. The balustrade follows the curve without newel posts at the turns. Often called a spiral stair.

ge-om'e-try. A mathematical science which treats of the properties of lines, surfaces, and solids.

Geor'gi-a pine (*Wood*) *Pinus palustris.* Dark in color, with well-marked grain. It is often used as a finishing material. The wood is hard, heavy, and strong, but decays rapidly in damp places. It is of resinous nature and does not take paint well.

ger-ma'ni-um (jĕr-mā'nĭ-ŭm) (*Chem.*) A grayish-white rare metal with fine metallic luster. Its melting point is 1562 degrees F.

Ger'man sid'ing (*Bldg.*) A type of weatherboard on which the upper portion of the exposed face is finished with a concave curve, and the lower part of the back face is rebated.

Ger'man sil'ver. An alloy of copper, zinc, and nickel.

ges'so (jĕs'ō) A plasterlike or pasty material spread upon a surface to fit it for painting or gilding.

get-a-way speed (*Aero.*) The air speed at which a seaplane becomes entirely air-borne.

ghost (*Tel.*) A secondary image or picture formed on a television receiver screen by a signal from the transmitter which reaches the antenna by more than one path. Ghosts usually are caused by the reflection of the signal by large buildings, hills, etc., near the receiving antenna.

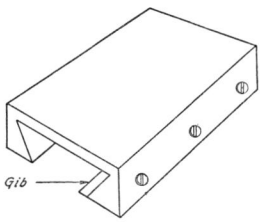

gib (gĭb) (*Mach.*) (1) A thin piece of steel used as an adjusting strip to bring about a perfect sliding fit in machine parts, e.g., in the cross slide of a lathe. Adjustment is usually secured by the pressure of setscrews against the gib. (2) That portion of a gib and cotter arrangement used in the strap end of a connecting rod to keep it from spreading. It is a flat piece of steel with hook ends.

gib-head'ed key. A key having a prong or offset standing at right angles with the thicker end to facilitate drawing it back.

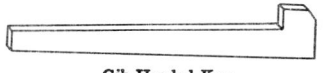
Gib-Headed Key

gild'ing. Depositing a layer of gold by electroplating, or coating with gold leaf or powder by hand. The term is often applied to coating with bronze powder or liquid.

gim'bals. The device which permits a supported article to remain level regardless of the motion of adjacent parts; e.g., the support for a ship's compass.

gim'let (gĭm'lĕt) A small wood-boring tool with handle attached at right angles to the bit.

Gimlet

gimp (*Uphol.*) A form of braid or tape used to cover the upholstery tacks where the covering material is fastened to exposed woodwork. It is sold by the yard or by the piece of 36 yards. Heavy gimp with raised surface is called a "galloon."

gimp'ing (*Uphol.*) Trimming furniture by tacking on gimp to cover seams and joints in covering material.

gimp tack (*Uphol.*) A tack having a small, round head, used for tacking cloth gimp to furniture.

gin. To remove seeds from cotton.

gin'ger-bread' work (*Arch.*) Gaudy or overornamented work as in the trim of a house.

gin pole (jĭn) (*Engin.*) A vertical, wooden or steel mast rigged with block and tackle, together with rope or steel cable, by which mechanical power is employed to raise heavy weights to a desired position. Used in place of a crane.

gir'an·dole (jĭr'ăn-dōl) (*Furn.*) A branching chandelier, electrolier, or bracket light used originally on walls of late 17th and 18th century French salons, usually in pairs. (*Jewelry*) A pendant used as an earring.

gir'der (*Bldg.*) A beam, either timber or steel, used for supporting a superstructure.

girt. (1) The circumference of round timber. (2) (*Engin.*) Light framing such as small angles or channels on structures to fasten siding in position.

girt strip (*Arch.*) (See RIBBON STRIP or LEDGER BOARD.)

gland (*Mach.*) The small bearing which closes the mouth of a stuffing box and takes the wear of the piston. Gland

glare (*Paper*) The reflection from a glossy paper.

glass. A hard, brittle substance made by melting together sand or silica with lime, potash, soda, or lead oxide.

glass cloth (*Plast.*) Cloth woven of fibrous glass. Fiberglas. This material is the chief component in resin laminations, and gives the product its strength, and to be as strong as steel, weight for weight. Resin is its binder. A variety of resins are employed as binders. A common resin in laminating is Polyester. Glass cloth comes in a selection of weights and weaves, depending on use.

glass cut'ter. Any device used for cutting glass to size; usually a diamond or a small rotary wheel set in a handle.

Glass Cutter

glass'-hard' (*Metal.*) Term applied to material hard enough to scratch glass.

glass·ine' (*Papermkg.*) A paper, almost as transparent as cellophane used commonly for sanitary wrapping purposes. It is made from sulphite pulps by long beating and heavy supercalendering.

glass in'su·la'tor (*Elec.*) Most common types are used on pole-line construction. They are supported on the crossarms by pins. The line wires are tied to the insulators.

glazed. Prepared with a smooth, shiny surface. (*Bldg.*) Equipped with window panes.

glazed brick (*Bldg.*) Brick having a glassy surface made by fusing on a glazing material.

glazed doors (*Furn.*) Doors fitted with glass, usually having a pattern or lattice of woodwork between the panes.

glazed tile (*Masonry*) A tile with a glassy or glossy surface.

glaz'ing (1) Fitting window panes. (2) The filling up of the interstices of the surface of a grindstone or emery wheel with minute abraded particles detached in grinding.

glide (*Aero.*) A descent at a normal angle without sufficient power for level flight.

glide land'ing (*Aero.*) A landing in which a steady glide is maintained to the landing surface without the usual leveling-off before contact.

glid'er (*Aero.*) An aircraft somewhat

similar in appearance to an airplane but does not have a power plant.

glid′ing an′gle (*Aero.*) The angle between the flight path during a glide and a horizontal axis fixed relative to the air.

globe valve (*Plumb.*) A type of valve in which a disk operated by a screw and hand wheel seats on a circular opening. It should be so installed that the pressure impinges on the underside of the seat.

gloss (*C e r a m.*) A glazed surface which has a shiny, lustrous finish.

glost (*Ceram.*) Glazed ware in the process of firing.

glu′cose (*Chem.*) A practically flavorless sweet syrup chiefly made from starch by the action of heat and acids. It is valuable in the manufacture of candies, preserves, jellies, etc.

glue. Obtained by boiling properly prepared animal matter, such as skin, bones, etc. Sold in many forms, such as sheets, strips, flakes, and ground or granulated. Occurs in all shades of white, yellow, and brown. Such glues are prepared for use by boiling; others may be bought in liquid form.

glyc′er-in (*Chem.*) A colorless, heavy liquid obtained as a by-product in the manufacture of soap and candles. Largely used in the manufacture of munitions, as an antifreeze liquid, in medicines, confectionery, printing-press rollers, etc.

glyph (glĭf) (*Arch.*) A short, vertical groove.

gneiss (nīs) (*Mineral.*) A metamorphic rock consisting, like granite, of quartz, feldspar, and mica, but in which the mica so occurs that it breaks readily into coarse slabs.

gō bō (*Tel.*) A shield used to mask light from spilling into unwanted areas.

go-droon′ (gô-drōōn′) (*Furn. and Woodwkg.*) An ornament of oval or almond shape, used on moldings.

go gauge (*Mach.*) Any gauge, internal or external, which closely fits, without forcing, the part for which it is intended.

gog′gles. Shrouded dark glasses worn by welders and grinders as a protection against eye injury.

Goncalo Alves (*Wood*) *Astronium fraxinifolium.* A tall slender tree found in Brazil. It is a hardwood with general color and grain similar to mahogany but marked with light and dark longitudinal streaks. Used for small table tops, borders, and panel sections.

go′ni-o-pho-tom′e-ter (gō′nĭ-ô-fô-tŏm′ĕ-tẽr) A device for measuring paint glare.

go or no–go gauge (*Mach.*) Often a double-end gauge with certain allowable tolerance between the ends. One end fits nicely the part being gauged; the other end is too small for an outside diameter or too large for an inside diameter.

goose′neck. (1) A mechanical contrivance bent or shaped like a goose's neck. (2) A bent pipe or tube having a swivel joint so that its outer end may be revolved. (*Bldg.*) The curved or bent section of the handrail on a stair.

Gor′don press (*Print.*) An early-type platen press.

Goth′ic (*Arch.*) A particular style of classic architecture or ornament. (*Print.*) A name applied to a type face square in outline and without serifs.

Goth′ic arch (*Arch.*) A pointed arch. One usually high and narrow, coming to a point at the center.

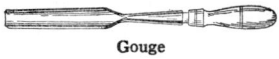
Gouge

gouge. Cutting chisel which has either a concave or convex cutting surface
gov′er-nor (*Mech.*) A device for regulating the speed of engines and machines.
grab (*Mech.*) A device used for hauling or hoisting.
grab hook (*Fdry.*) Hooks connected by short chains or rods for the purpose of attaching loads to the crane hook.
grade (*Arch., Draw., and Bldg.*) The level of the ground around a building.
grad′ing. (1) The leveling of a plot of ground, or sloping it to a desired angle. (2) The sloping of a sidewalk to secure proper drainage.
grad′u-al load. A load gradually applied to a structure and which furnishes the most favorable conditions of stress.
grad′u-ate. To divide into regular steps or grades, as a scale.
grad′u-a′tion. The method or system of dividing a graduated scale; also one of the equal divisions or one of the dividing lines of such a scale.

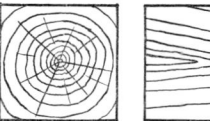 
End and Long Grain

grain (*Leather.*) (1) To scrape off the hair from a hide. (2) The knife used by tanners for scraping off hair. (*Papermkg.*) Term having reference to the alignment of fibers lengthwise in paper corresponding to the direction of their movement on the paper machine. (*Woodwkg.*) Relating to the direction or arrangement of wood fibers; working a piece of wood longitudinally may be with or against the grain; transversely is spoken of as cross grain.
grained cow′hide (*Leather.*) An embossed, nontoolable cowhide, supplied in different grains and colors. Used for making bags, cases, etc.
grain′ing (*Furn.*) A painting process applied to cheap woods to imitate oak, walnut, and other better woods.
grain′ing comb (*Wood Fin.*) A comblike tool made of steel or leather. Used by wood finishers for obtaining grain effects.
Gramme ring wind′ing (*Elec.*) An armature winding which is now practically obsolete except for very special applications.
gram mo-lec′u-lar weight (*Chem.*) The molecular weight of a substance expressed in grams. A gram molecular weight of a gas measures 22.4 liters under standard conditions.
gran′ite (*Bldg.*) A rock composed of quartz, feldspar, and mica. It is very

hard and takes a high polish. Used extensively in building work and for monuments.

gran′u‑lar. Composed of granules; not fibrous in composition.

gran′u‑lar car′bon (*Elec.*) Small granulated particles of carbon, used in telephone transmitters or in variable resistances.

gran′u‑lar struc′ture (*Plast.*) Non‑uniform appearance of finished plastic material due to retention of, or incomplete fusion of, particles of composition, either within mass or on surface.

grape sug′ar (*Chem.*) Appears in the market as a hard, waxy solid; when fresh, it is white, but darkens with age. It is a crude dextrose, or glucose, used in the manufacture of wine and confectionery, preparing tobacco, and chrome tanning liquors.

graph′ic. Illustrating ideas by pictures or diagrams.

graph′ic arts (*Art*) A broad term which embraces every branch of pictorial representation. (*Print.*) Embracing every form of printing represented by text and illustrations.

graph′ic meth′ods. The methods used for ascertaining strains upon structures, velocity, ratios, etc., by means of drawing.

graph′ite (*Fdry. and Engin.*) Is either artificial or natural, and seldom contains more than 90 per cent carbon. It has a peculiar silvery luster, and is used in the manufacture of lead pencils, as a lubricant, and in foundry work as a mold coating.

graph′ite paint (*Paint and Lacquer*) A mixture of graphite, boiled linseed oil, and a small amount of drier. A very good paint for ironwork.

graph′i‑tiz′ing (*Metal.*) The method by which most of the carbon in gray cast iron is transformed to a graphitic condition by an annealing process.

grate a′rea or grate sur′face. The area in square feet covered by the fire bars of a boiler, i.e., equivalent to the area over which full combustion can take place.

grat′ing. A gratelike arrangement of bars used to cover an opening. (*Engin.*) Also used for forming platforms in engine rooms, stair landings, on fire escapes, etc.

grav′el. A natural mixture of sand and pebbles.

grav′er. A tool used by engravers.

grav′i‑ty. That force which draws all bodies toward the center of the earth or to its surface.

grav′i‑ty cell (*Elec.*) A modified form of Daniell cell in which the two electrolytes are separated by gravity.

grav′i‑ty–drop an‑nun′ci‑a′tor (*Elec.*) A signal device operated by electromagnets which release a catch permitting a hinged part to fall, revealing a number, name, etc.

grav′i‑ty lu′bri‑ca′tion sys′tem (*Auto. Mech.*) Feeding oil to parts to be lubricated by gravity from an elevated tank or reservoir. Such systems are frequently equipped with a pump to return oil to its original container.

grav′i‑ty wa′ter sys′tem. Any water system in which pressure is obtained by gravity.

gray i′ron. Pig or cast iron which, on being fractured, shows a gray crystalline structure.

grease gun (*Auto.*) A device for forcing lubricant into a bearing.

Α α ALPHA *a*	Β β BETA *b*	Γ γ GAMMA *g*
Δ δ DELTA *d*	Ε ε EPSILON *ĕ*	Ζ ζ ZETA *dz*
Η η ETA *ē*	Θ θ THETA *th*	Ι ι IOTA *i*
Κ κ KAPPA *k*	Λ λ LAMBDA *l*	Μ μ MU *m*
Ν ν NU *n*	Ξ ξ XI *x*	Ο ο OMICRON *ŏ*
Π π PI *p*	Ρ ρ RHO *r*	Σ σ SIGMA *s*
Τ τ TAU *t*	Υ υ UPSILON *ü*	Φ φ PHI *ph*
Χ χ CHI *ch(k)*	Ψ ψ PSI *ps*	Ω ω OMEGA *ō*

Greek Alphabet

grease lu′bri-cants. Gillet divides grease into six classes: (1) the tallow type, a mixture of tallow and palm oil with some mineral oil; (2) the soap-thickened mineral-oil type; (3) types 1 or 2 mixed with graphite, talc, or mica; (4) the rosin-oil type; (5) nonfluid oils; (6) special greases with special fillers.

grease trap (*Plumb.*) A device for solidifying and separating grease from domestic wastes and retaining the same so that they may be removed. Its purpose is to prevent the stoppage of waste pipes.

green (*Papermkg.* and *Print.*) Term applied to paper and printing rollers indicating incomplete seasoning.

green core (*Fdry.*) A core that has not been baked.

Green′field (*Elec.*) The original trade name for flexible conduit.

green gold (*Chem.*) An alloy of 25 per cent silver and 75 per cent gold.

green sand (*Fdry.*) Ordinary foundry sand moistened with water and not dried.

green sand core (*Fdry.*) A core made of green sand; that is, moistened sand.

green vit′ri-ol or cop′per-as (*Chem.*) A by-product from the pickling of steel; also known as "ferrous sulphate." It is important as a disinfectant, and in the manufacture of ink, Prussian blue, and red oxide.

green wood. Timber from which the sap has not been removed by seasoning and drying.

grid (*Elec.*) An electrode having one or more openings for the passage of electrons or ions. (1) Heavy resistances used in connection with the fields of generators. (2) The foundation on which the plates are formed in storage bateries. (*Plast.*) A parallel, channel-shaped, cast-iron support, a number of which hold the steam plates away from the press platens during knockout operation and also provide air spaces between plates and platens to reduce loss of heat. (*Radio*) Part of a radio tube, usually between the filament or heater and the plate.

grid con-dens'er (*Radio*) A condenser which is a part of the grid circuit.

grid leak (*Radio*) A resistance used in the grid circuit of an electronic tube.

grid re-sist'ance (*Elec.*) Starting resistances for very large d.c. motors are made of cast iron in the form of grids.

grid re-sis'tor (*Radio*) A high resistance used in the grid circuit of a radio tube.

grille (*Arch.*) An openwork of metal or wood, plain or ornamental, used to cover an opening, or as a protection over the glass in a door or window.

grind. To sharpen, to reduce to size, or to remove material by contact with a rotating abrasive wheel.

grind'er (*Shopwk.*) Any appliance or device on which work is done by grinding.

grind fin'ish (*Mach.*) A finish imparted by an abrasive wheel. A great deal of the work is now finished by grinding that was formerly tool finished.

grind'ing al-low'ance. The amount of material left on a piece of work to allow for a finish by grinding. On fine work .003 to .007 in. is sufficient, while on heavy work it may be 1/64 or 1/32 in.

grind'ing com'pound (*Auto.*) A grease and abrasive or water-carried abrasive used in valve-grinding operations.

grind'ing in (*Mach.*) Bringing to a perfect fit of parts, which are to operate together, by means of an abrasive. This may be accomplished either by a hand or machine process.

grind'stone. A revolving stone against which tools and materials are abraded by grinding. Grindstones are natural sandstone.

grip (*Mech.*) A device for grasping or holding.

gripe (g r ĭ p) (*M a c h.*) A name occasionally applied to "machine clamp."

grip'pers (*Print.*) Small metal fingers that press against the sheet on a press, and hold it firmly in position while an impression is being taken.

gri-saille' (grĭ-zāl') (*Furn.*) A style of painting done in shades of gray.

grit. The particles which are used to make up grinding wheels. The size of these particles is referred to by a grit number.

groin (*Arch.*) The line of intersection of two vaults where they cross each other.

groined vault'ing (*Arch.*) The system of covering a building or passageways with stone vaults which cross and intersect.

grom'met. A metallic eyelet, used principally in awnings and flags. Also, a ring of candle wicking used as a water tight

Grommet

gasket or washer around bolts and studs.

groove (*Arch., Bookbndg., Patmkg.*) A depressed or sunken channel, usually small; so designated, whether some other part does or does not fit into it.

groov′ing (*Mach.*) The cutting of a groove or channel. (*Sheet-Met. Wk.*) The finishing or grooving of a lock joint with a grooving tool.

groov′ing ma-chine′ (*Sheet-Met Wk.*) A machine used in place of a hand grooving tool for setting lock seams.

groov′ing stake (*Sheet-Met. Wk.*) A bar in which are milled four grooves of different sizes. It is used for closing lock seams with a mallet, without the use of a hand-grooving tool. The bar is rigidly held in a type of vise called a "holder."

gross. Twelve dozen; 144.

gro-tesque′ (grô-tĕsk′) A fantastic style of ornament.

ground (*Arch.*) Nailing strip set in or attached to a brick or stone wall. (*Auto. Elec.*) (1) A direct connection to frame, generator, motor, lights, or body by means of which the circuit is completed. (2) A leakage of current into the ground without performing the work intended. (*Elec.*) Point of contact between electric circuit and earth by means of water and gas pipes, etc.

ground cir′cuit (*Elec.*) A circuit which makes use of the ground for one wire of a two- or three-wire circuit.

ground clamp (*Elec.*) A clamp used for attaching a wire or other conductor to a pipe to make a good electrical connection.

ground de-tec′tor (*Elec.*) A lamp mounted on a switchboard, used to indicate a ground when it occurs on a circuit wire.

ground′ed cir′cuit (*Elec.*) The grounding of a circuit through faulty insulation, in an electrical connection between a wire, carrying current, and the ground.

ground floor (*Arch. and Masonry*) The first floor above the ground level; usually the main floor.

ground gear (*Aero.*) The gear or equipment necessary for the landing and handling of an airship on the ground.

ground′ing (*Elec.*) Intentional connection made between a circuit wire and the ground, as in the neutral wire of a three-wire system, or the bonding together electrically of electrical conduits and water pipes.

ground′ing con-duc′tor (*Elec.*) A conductor used to connect the equipment or wiring system with a grounded electrode or electrodes.

ground′ing out (*Furn.*) The removing of the background of a design in carved work.

ground joint (*Mach.*) A fitting of parts by grinding them together with abrasive paste, or by loose abrasive with oil or water, e.g., the grinding of automobile valves.

ground joist (*Arch.*) A joist that is blocked up from the ground.

ground loop (*Aero.*) An uncontrollable, violent turn of an airplane while taxying, or during the landing or take-off run.

ground re-turn′ (*Auto. Elec.*) The chassis and those parts of the automobile to which all electrical devices are commonly attached to provide a complete circuit.

ground speed (*Aero.*) The velocity of an aircraft, relative to the earth, measured horizontally.

ground-speed me′ter (*Aero.*) An instrument for measuring the speed of an aircraft with relation to the ground.

ground strap (*Auto.*) A stranded copper cable or woven copper band used to connect the battery to the frame of the car, or the engine to the frame when the engine is mounted on rubber.

ground wa′ter (*Plumb.*) Water that is standing in or passing through the ground.

ground wire (*Elec.*) A wire connected between the ground and any piece of electrical apparatus. (See GROUND.)

groundwood (*Papermkg.*) Also called mechanical wood, it is made by grinding logs.

grout. A fluid cement mixture for filling crevices.

growl′er (*Elec.*) A small transformer used for detecting shorts, opens, or grounds in armatures.

guard (*Mach.*) Any protective device attached to or used in connection with a machine to reduce liability of injury to the operator.

gud′geon pin (gŭj′ŭn) (*Auto.*) Same as wrist pin or piston pin.

gud′geons (*P r i n t.*) Metal wheels keyed to the ends of the roller stock on job presses. They roll on the tracks and cause the rollers to rotate.

gue′ri′don′ (gā′rē′dôn′) (*Furn.*) A stand for lamp or vase with flowers, adapted from the antique and usually carved and gilded.

guide bear′ings (*Mach.*) Bearings which consist of a channel or groove in which parts slide; e.g., crosshead bearings.

guide pins (*Plast.*) Devices that maintain proper alignment of force plug and cavity as the mold closes.

guide rail. A rail placed on the inside of the main rail of a railroad track to guide the wheel flanges; used principally on curves and bridges.

guides (*Print.*) Used to place the sheets against so that the printing may be in exactly the same place on each sheet. Guides are adjustable, and may be set and locked in any required position.

guil-loche′ (gĭ-lōsh′) (*Arch.*) An ornament in the form of bands or strings characterized by a wavy interlacement of the main motifs, leaving circular openings filled with round ornaments.

Guilloche

guil′lo-tine cut (gĭl′ô-tēn kŭt) (*Bookbndg.*) Paper cut or trimmed by a machine known as the "guillotine."

gum bloom (*Paint and Lacquer*) A transparent haze or lack of normal gloss, due to use of incorrect reducer.

gum′ming test for oils. This test may be used to measure the extent to which oils will carbonize in gas-engine cylinders. It is made by treating oil with acid, which brings about the changes that take place in an oil when used.

gums (*Chem. Plast.*) Viscous vegetable secretions which harden but, unlike resins, are water soluble. The name is often applied in the varnish industry to natural resins such as copal.

gum'wood. A medium hard, dark-colored wood with grain effect similar to Circassian walnut; used extensively in the manufacture of furniture and for interior trim in buildings.

gun'cot'ton (*Chem.*) A highly explosive mixture obtained by treating cotton with nitric and sulphuric acids.

gun lathe (*Mach.*) A large lathe used for turning and boring cannons.

gun met'al. An alloy of copper and tin.

gun'ning (*Aero.*) To race an airplane engine. A rapid, jerky application of the throttle.

gun'pow'der (*Chem.*) An explosive mixture of saltpeter, charcoal, and sulphur; it may be either black or brown in color.

Gun'ters chain. A surveyor's measure 66 ft. in length. It consists of 100 links each being 7.92 in. long.

gus'set (*Engin.*) An angle bracket or brace used to stiffen a corner or angular portion of a piece of work.

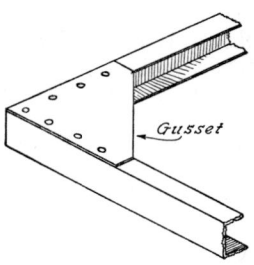

gut'ta-per'cha. The gum is obtained from the milk juice of several trees found native in the East Indies. Gutta-percha has many uses, the most important being for insulating.

gut'tae (gŭt'ē) (*Arch.*) Small cylindrical or cone-shaped pendants used to ornament the Doric entablature.

gut'ter (*Arch.*) A channel along the eaves of a house to carry off rain. (*Masonry*) A bricked or paved surface in the street adjoining the curb.

gut'ter brack'et (*Arch.*) Small metal brackets used to support hanging gutters.

guy (*Engin.*) Wire, rope, or chain used to steady, support, or hold in place a boom, mast, pole, chimney, or other similar piece of construction.

guy rope (*Engin.*) Galvanized rope consisting of 6 strands, 7 wires each, and a hemp core.

gyp'sum (jĭp'sŭm) (*Bldg., Paint., Plaster., and Pot.*) Hydrous sulphate of calcium ($CaSO_4.2H_2O$), colorless when pure. When it is heated slowly, part of the water is driven off, the resulting product being known as "plaster of Paris."

gy'rate (jī'rāt) To turn on an axis of rotation.

gy'ro ho-ri'zon (jī'rō) (*Aero.*) A gyroscopic instrument that indicates the lateral and longitudinal attitude of the airplane by simulating the natural horizon.

gy'ro-pi'lot (jī'rô-pī'lŭt) (*Aero.*) A gyroscopic and mechanical device which automatically flies an airplane. Used to relieve pilots of the fatigue of routine cross-country pilotage.

gy'ro-plane (*Aero.*) A type of rotor plane whose support in the air is chiefly derived from airfoils rotated about an approximately vertical axis by aerodynamic forces, and in which the lift on the opposite sides of the plane of symmetry is equalized by rotation of the blades about the blades' axis.

gy′ro-scope (jī′rô-skōp) (*Aero.*) A device consisting of a wheel mounted in a ring, with its axis free to turn in any direction as if independent of gravity, sometimes used as a steering apparatus and balancing device in flying machines.

gy′ro-scop′ic turn in′di-ca′tor (jī′-rō-skŏp′ĭk) (*Aero.*) A turn indicator dependent on gyroscopic action.

H

H beam (*Bldg.*) A steel beam whose section is like the letter H. (*Engin.*) A structural shape made with a variety of flange widths for any given depth, the inner side of the flange being practically parallel with the outside. Shapes in which the flange width is nearly the same as the depth of the section are used principally for columns. For use as beams the sections usually have a depth considerably greater than the flange width.

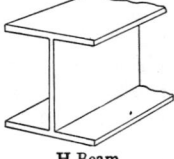
H Beam

hack. To cut roughly in an unworkmanlike manner.

hack′ling (*Textile*) A process for separating woody particles and tow from long flax fibers.

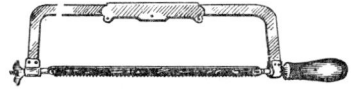
Hack Saw

hack saw. A light-framed saw used for cutting metal, operated by power or by hand.

haft (hȧft) A handle as of a dagger, a knife, or an awl.

hair (*Plaster.*) Hair for use by plasterers is obtained from hides of cattle. It is washed, dried, and put up for sale in bushel bags, weighing 7 or 8 pounds to the bag. Asbestos and manila fiber are both used in place of hair.

hair hook (*Plaster.*) A tool consisting of two or three prongs, fixed at right angles to a long handle; used to incorporate hair with mortar.

hair line (*Print.*) The thin line of a type face connecting or prolonging its parts.

half-back bench saw (*Woodwk.*) Gives both the advantage of a stiff cutting edge and the ability to cut entirely through the work. Usually made in 14 to 20-in. lengths. The stiffening bar extends over only a portion of the blade length thus combining the action of both the handsaw and the backsaw.

half bear′ings (*Mach.*) Bearings such as are used on railway cars where the load is constantly in one direction and sufficiently heavy to hold the journal against the bearing.

half bind′ing (*Bookbndg.*) A book with leather back and corners, and stiff sides covered with cloth or paper.

half′-di′a-mond in-den′tion (*Print.*) When successive lines of a piece of printing are shortened at both ends.

half-lap joint (*Woodwkg.*) A joint made by cutting away half of the thickness of the pieces to be joined. (See HALVING.)

half′-moon′ stake (*Art Met.*) A stake with the top curved and beveled to an edge. Its principal use is in circular flanging operations.

half nut (*Shopwk.*) A nut which is split lengthwise. Sometimes half is used and rides on a screw; in others,

---

sāle, surfȧce, grăm, humȧn, mȧsk, solȧr, bär, bâre; mē, êdition, lĕnd, momĕnt, bakẽr; kīnd, fĭt; lōde, ômit, ŏlive, cȯnsume, sôrt; dūty, ûtility, nŭt, alŭm, bûrn.

both halves clamp around a screw as in the half nut of a lathe carriage.

half pat′tern. One of the halves of a pattern which is parted through the center for convenience of molding.

half–round file. A file which is flat on one side and curved on the other. The amount of convexity never equals a semicircle.

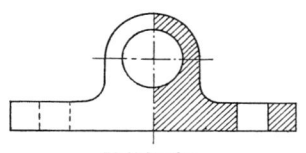

Half Section

half sec′tion (*Draft.*) In mechanical drawing, a sectional view which terminates at the center line, showing an external view on one side of the center line, and on the other side an interior view.

half story (*Arch.*) That part of a pitched roof structure directly under the roof, having a finished ceiling and floor and some side wall.

half ti′tle (*Print.*) A short title heading; a one-line title on a full page, or the title of a book placed on the first page of the book preceding the full title.

half tone (*Print.*) A kind of photoengraving, in which relief lines are produced by etching a plate that has received the photographic picture through a fine-ruled glass screen having 55 to 200 lines to the inch.

half′-tone pa′per (*Paper* and *Print.*) A smooth printing paper used for reproducing half tones.

hal′o-gen (hăl′ô-jĕn) (*Chem.*) "Salt former." Applied to the family of elements consisting of fluorine, chlorine, bromine, and iodine.

halved pat′tern (*Patmkg.*) A foundry pattern made in two parts to permit withdrawal from the sand when molding.

halv′ing. The making of a joint by cutting away half of the thickness from the face of one piece and the other half from the back of the piece to be fitted to it, so that when the two are put together the outer surfaces will be flush.

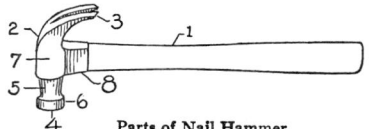

Parts of Nail Hammer
1, Handle; 2, head; 3, claw; 4, face; 5, neck; 6, poll; 7, cheek; 8, eye

ham′mer. An instrument or tool used for striking blows in metalworking, driving nails, etc. Hammers are of various kinds, each bearing a name according to the purpose it is to serve. The name is applied to machines, such as are used in forging, as well as to hand "hammers."

hand′bill (*Print.*) A small printed advertisement for distribution by hand. (See DODGER.)

hand block′ing (*Furn.*) A process of dyeing a design in upholstery material.

hand′book. A book of reference to be carried in the hand. A manual or guide, usually containing a compilation of data and formulas, as an engineering handbook.

hand brake (*Auto.*) A brake operated by hand, used principally as a parking brake. When applied, it remains set until released by hand.

hand doll′y (*Sheet-Met. Wk.*) A steel block, rectangular in section, and fitted with a handle on the underside.

The usual size is about 5 by 6 in., with a thickness of 1 in. The working face is curved to fit the inside of fenders, tanks, etc. Particularly useful as a support inside of tanks when seaming by hand, or for use as a stake. (See DOLLY BLOCKS.)

hand drill (*Shopwk.*) A drilling machine operated by hand.

h a n d - e d (*Mech.*) When two similar pieces are to be used one to the right and the other to the left, or are so attached to some other part, they are said to be right-handed or left-handed. Workmen's tools are also so designated, depending on whether they are to be used with the left or the right hand.

Hand Drill

hand feed. The feeding by hand of the cutting tools of machines of various kinds.

hand file (*Shopwk.*) This file has parallel sides but is tapered in thickness. It is double cut with various degrees of fineness. Its principal use is in finishing flat surfaces.

hand hook or hook wrench (*Mech.*) A long bar with a hook end to be used in straightening bent pieces, such as axles.

hand'i-work'. Work done by hand. Usually refers to work which requires some skill.

hand-made fin'ish (*Papermkg.*) A term descriptive of the handmade appearance of certain papers. It does not mark them as being, in reality, handmade.

hand mill′er (*Mach.*) A small milling machine with the feed operated by hand. It is adapted only to light work.

hand′rail (*Arch.*) A rail, as on a stair or at the edge of a gallery, placed for convenient grasping by the hand.

hand′rail wreath (*Arch. and Bldg.*) Curved section of a stair rail.

hand rule (*Elec.*) If a conductor, carrying current, is grasped in the right hand with the extended thumb pointing in the direction of the flow of current, the fingers will indicate the direction of the resulting lines of force.

Handsaw

hand′saw (*Shopwk.*) An ordinary one-handled saw, either rip or cross-cut, used by woodworkers.

hand screw. A woodworkers' clamp consisting of two parallel jaws and two screws. Clamping action is obtained by means of the screws, one operating through each jaw.

hand tools (*Shopwk.*) Tools that are guided and operated by hand.

hand turn′ing (*Shopwk.*) Turning accomplished by tools held in the hand.

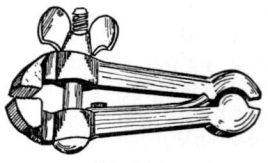

Hand Vise

hand vise (*Shopwk.*) A small vise held

in the hand, used for clamping small, light work.

hand'wheel (*Mach.*) Any wheel operated by hand; usually to secure an adjustment.

han'gar' (hăn'gär') A building or structure for housing airplanes.

hang'er (hăng'ẽr) (*Arch.*) A strap of iron or steel used as a drop support, attached to one beam or joist and used to support the end of another. (*Mech.*) A frame and bearing used in series to support shafting from the floor, side wall, or overhead.

hang'er bear'ing (*Mach.*) A shaft bearing supported by a hanger.

Hanger Bolt

hang'er bolt (*Mach.*) Consists of a lag screw at one end and a machine-bolt thread and nut at the other. It is used for attaching hangers to woodwork.

hang'ing core (*Fdry.*) Core supported by a wire hanger that is imbedded in the core. Hanging cores are used to avoid a deep lift for the cope.

hang'ing in-den'tion (*Print.*) When the first line of a paragraph hangs over the rest of the type matter. A good example appears in this book. Principally employed in dictionaries, catalogues, etc.

hang'ing stile (*Bldg.*) That vertical part of a door or of a casement window to which the hinges are fastened.

hard (*Ceram.*) Material which cannot be fused or melted.

hard brass. Brass which has not been annealed after drawing or rolling; used for springs, etc.

hard–drawn cop'per wire (*Elec.*) Copper, when drawn through several dies to size, becomes hard. This hard wire is used on telephone- and telegraph-pole lines where its greater tensile strength is desired.

hard'en-er (*Plast.*) See CATALYST.

hard'en-ing. Hardening of steel is brought about by heating it to a high temperature and then suddenly cooling it in oils, water, or other suitable solutions. Special steels may require different methods of hardening.

hard i'ron. Cast iron which is dense and close-grained. It is lighter in color than soft iron.

hard'ness (*Phys.*) The resistance a body offers to being scratched or worn by another substance.

hard'pan'. A layer of rock under soft soil.

hard–sized (*Papermkg.*) A paper sized to the point at which it will resist penetration of moisture and ink.

hard sol'der (sŏd'ẽr) (*Shopwk.*) A solder composed principally of copper and zinc. Also known as "spelter." The terms *hard soldering* and *brazing* are often used interchangeably.

hard top (*Auto. Mech.*) A passenger automobile, either two door or four door, with a metal top and no side-center post supports.

hard wa'ter. Water containing a large quality of compounds of calcium and magnesium in solution.

hard'wood. Wood which is close-grained, dense, and heavy, as oak, hickory, ash, and beech.

har′dy (*F o r g.*) A square-shanked chisel or fuller for insertion in the hardy hole of a smith's anvil or block.

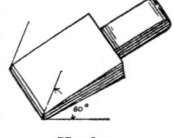
Hardy

har′dy hole (*Forg.*) The square hole in an anvil which receives the shank of the hardy.

hare′wood (*W o o d*) *Acer pseudoplatanus.* Originally from West Indies; owing to limited supply a substitute was developed by a dyeing process of the English sycamore. Color: silver gray with satinlike cross streaks. Used for furniture and panels.

har′mo-nize. To make a pleasant, harmonious arrangement of parts.

Hasp

hasp. A fastening as for a door, usually passing over a staple, and secured by a peg or padlock.

hatch′et cop′per (*Sheet-Met. Wk.*) A soldering copper with the head set at right angles to the handle. Shaped like a hatchet.

hatch′et i′ron (*Plumb.*) A special form of soldering iron.

hatch′et stake. A tool used by tinsmiths for bending sheets of tin.

hatch′ings (*Draft.*) Parallel or crossed lines, usually at an angle of 45 deg., giving the effect of shading; used to indicate a section in drawing.

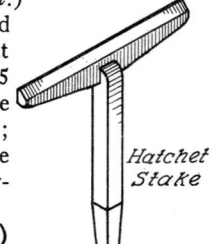
Hatchet Stake

hatch′way (*Arch.*) An opening covered by a trap door, as in a roof, to permit easy access for repairs; or in a ceiling to give entrance to an attic.

haunch. The shoulder of an arch.

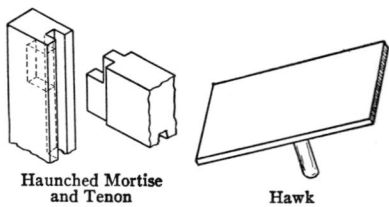
Haunched Mortise and Tenon   Hawk

haunched mor′tise and ten′on (*Woodwk.*) A joint in which the tenon is reduced in width for a portion of its length, the mortise being cut to fit.

hawk (*Plaster.*) A small, square board with handle underneath, used to hold plaster or mortar.

haw′ser-laid rope. Made of three small right-handed ropes laid up into one.

hay rope (*Fdry.*) A rope made of hay, used in the making of foundry cores. The rope is wrapped around a core bar, then covered with loam, the hay forming a porous mass through which the gases may be carried off.

haze (*Plast.*) Indefinite cloudy appearance in a transparent plastic; described as "internal" or "surface."

head (*Print.*) The title of a news article; also the top of a page or book.

head′band′ (*Print.*) A decorative band placed at the head of a page or chapter in a printed book.

head′er. A brick or stone placed with its end toward the face of a wall.

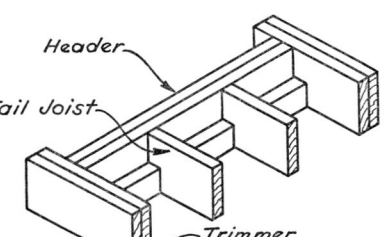

head′er joist (*Arch.*) The joist into which the common joists are framed around openings for stairs, chimneys, etc.

Heading Tool

head′ing tool (*Forg.*) A tool used for shaping the heads of bolts. The body of the bolt is passed through a hole in a plate and the end of the bolt flattened against it while hot to form the head.

head′less set′screw (*Mech.*) A setscrew which, instead of having a head, has a slot to permit adjustment by a screw driver.

head of water (*Phys.*) The vertical distance between the highest level and the point from which the waterhead is being measured; e.g., the vertical distance between level of water in a standpipe and the faucet from which water is drawn.

head′piece (*Print.*) Any ornamentation placed at the top of a page in a book or pamphlet.

head room (*Bldg.*) The vertical space between a stair and the ceiling or stair above. (*Tel.*) Leeway between subject's top and top of set or picture in which it appears.

head set (*Elec.*) Also called earphones. Two flat receivers connected by a spring which holds them in position over the ears.

head′stock (*Mach.*) The fixed head of a lathe which carries the faceplate or chuck.

heart cam (*Mach.*) A cam, heart-shaped in form, used for the conversion of rotary into reciprocal motion.

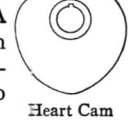

Heart Cam

hearth (*Bldg.*) The floor of a fireplace including that portion in front of it.

heart′wood. The wood in and just around the center of a tree.

heat (*Fdry.*) The reduction of a cupola charge to a fluid state.

heat dis-tor′tion point (*Plast.*) Temperature at which a standard bar of plastic material will be deflected .010 in.

heat en′gine (*Elec.*) An engine that converts the energy of heat into mechanical or kinetic energy, such as steam and internal combustion, reciprocating and turbine engines, rocket engines, ramjet engines.

heat′er tube (*Elec.*) A large, tubular, carbon, filament lamp or tube of resistance wire or other material.

heat′ing (*Forg.*) Placing a piece in a forge or fire until it is of a temperature to be properly worked.

heat′ing ef-fect′ of cur′rent (*Elec.*) The heating effect of a current is in direct proportion to the current flow.

heat′ing of bear′ings. Rise in temperature of bearings, commonly due to faulty lubrication; may cause the axle and bearing to stick or to wear rapidly.

heat′ing of dy′na-mos (*Elec.*) Three factors contribute to the heating of dynamos: mechanical friction in the bearings, core losses due to eddy currents and hysterisis, and losses in the windings.

heat′ing sur′face. All surfaces of a boiler which have hot gases on one side and steam or water on the other.

heat′ing u′nit (*Elec.*) That part of any electrical heating device in which the heat is generated.

heat mark (*Plast.*) An extremely shallow, regular, or irregular depression or groove in the surface of a plastic, visible only because of a sharply defined rim or roughened surface.

heat seal (*Plast.*) To bond or weld a material to itself or to another material by heat alone.

heat time (*Weld.*) The time of duration of each current impulse in pulsation welding.

heat treat′ment (*Metal.*) The carefully controlled heating and cooling of steel to bring it to its highest efficiency. The treatment prescribed by the manufacturer for any particular kind of steel must be rigidly followed as different steels require different treatment.

heav′y joist (*Woodwkg.*) Timber over four inches and less than six inches in thickness and eight inches or over in width.

hec′to-graph. A gelatine pad for making multiple copies of drawing or writing.

heel (*Arch.*) The end of a rafter or beam which rests on the wall plate.

height (*Arch.*) Of an arch, the distance from the middle line of the chord to the intrados.

hel′i-cal an′gle (hĕl′ĭ-kăl) (*Mach.*) The angle which any portion of a helix or screw makes with a line drawn at right angles to its axis.

hel′i-cal gear (*M a c h.*) A tooth gear in which the wheel teeth, instead of being at right angles with their faces, are set at some other angle therewith. Often incorrectly called spiral gear. It may be used to transmit power between (1) parallel shafts, (2) shafts at right angles and not intersecting, (3) shafts inclined at any angle and not intersecting. It gives greater strength and smoother operation, but develops considerable end thrust.

hel′i-cal groove (*Shopwk.*) A groove of uniform advance. The amount of advance in one revolution in a single helical groove is called the "pitch"; in the case of a multiple helical groove, as double or triple, the amount of advance in one revolution is spoken of as the "lead."

hel′i-cal spring (*Mach.*) A compression-type spring shaped like the frustum of a cone.

hel′i-coid (hĕl′ĭ-koid) Coiled in such a manner as to resemble a helix.

hel′i-cop′ter (*Aero.*) A type of airplane which can rise or descend vertically; fly in any direction, forward, backward, or sidewise, or stop suddenly and hover motionless in the air. Its ability to land or take off from a very small area adds greatly to its value in both military and commercial operations. Perfected by Igor Sikorsky.

he′li-um. One of the rarest elements. It exists in certain uranium minerals and to a small extent in the air. Its chief source is in the natural gas of southwestern United States.

he′lix (*Draft.*) A curve, as would be obtained by winding a thread around a cylinder in such a manner that there would be a uniform amount of advance with each revolution.

he′lix an′gle (*Mach.*) The angle made by the helix of the thread at the pitch diameter with a plane perpendicular to the axis.

hell′box′ (*Print.*) A box into which is thrown all kinds of broken and battered type and all useless printing material.

help′er. One who serves as an assistant, working with and under the direction of someone more skillful.

helve. The handle of a hatchet or ax.

hem′a-tite. An important iron ore.

hem-i-col-loids (*Chem. Plast.*) Polymers of molecular weight up to 10,000 corresponding to an order of polymerization equal to 20 to 100 monomeric units. They dissolve without swelling and give solutions of low viscosity. Precipitation from solution yields powdery masses.

hem′is-phere. A half sphere.

hem′lock. An inexpensive wood somewhat like spruce in appearance; used extensively for framing.

hemp′seed oil (*Paint.*) Obtained from the hemp plant. The oil, when fresh, is light green, but becomes brownish yellow on standing. It is used in paints, varnishes, and in soft soaps.

henry (*Elec.*) An electrical unit of inductance. A circuit has an inductance of one henry when a current changing at the rate of one ampere per second induces an e.m.f. of one volt in the circuit.

Hep′ple-white (*Furn.*) This style, named after George Hepplewhite of London (died 1786), was much influenced by Chippendale, the Brothers Adam, and the French. The classic motif runs through all his designs, yet severity and coldness are missing. Inlay on mahogany was freely used. Shield, heart-shaped, and oval chair backs were designs commonly used by Hepplewhite.

hep′ta-gon. A plane figure having seven sides and seven angles.

her-maph′ro-dite cal′i-per (hẽr-măf′rō-dīt) (*Mach.*) A caliper in which one leg is pointed as in a pair of dividers, the other being slightly hooked as in the ordinary outside caliper.

Hermaphrodite Caliper

her′ring-bone′ (*Masonry*) The name given to masonry or brickwork when laid up in a zigzag pattern.

her′ring-bone′ bond (*Masonry*) A zigzag arrangement of bricks or tile, in which the end of one brick is laid at right angles against the side of a second brick.

her′ring-bone′ gear. A gear in which the teeth slope both ways from the center line of the gear face, as would be the case if two spiral gears, one left hand and one right hand were fastened together; used for heavy work on mining machinery, etc.

her′ring-bon′ing (*Furn.*) A veneered detail of Queen Anne work, consisting of two narrow bands of striped veneer, cut obliquely and placed together, resembling herringbone patterns in half-timbered work.

het′er-o-dyne′ (*Radio*) The "beating"

together of two different frequencies to produce a different or intermediate frequency such as produced in the superheterodyne receiver.

hew′ing. The dressing of timber by chopping or by blows from an edged tool.

hex′a-gon. A plane figure having six sides and six angles. All sides of a regular hexagon are equal. All angles are equal; their sum totals 720 deg.

hex-ag′o-nal sock′et set′-screws′. See ALLEN SET-SCREWS.

hex′a-gon nut. The ordinary six-sided form of nut. Hexagon Nut

hex head (*Mach.*) A common shop expression referring to screws and bolts with hexagonal heads.

hick′ey (*Elec.*) Fixture hickey — A small threaded fitting of brass or iron placed in a fixture assembly between the stem and the support to provide an outlet for the wires coming out of the fixture stem. Conduit hickey — A pipe-bending device used for bending conduit or other pipe to the desired shape.

hick′o-ry. A very hard and tough wood, hard to work; used extensively in work which requires bending.

hid′den sur′face line (*Mech. Drg.*) A line consisting of short dashes. It is used to indicate the surface of a hidden part.

high′boy (*Furn.*) A tall chest of drawers mounted on legs.

high brass (*Metal.*) Commercial sheet and strip brass containing about 65 per cent copper and 35 per cent zinc. Used for spinning; also for drawing and forming.

high bulk (*Papermkg. and Print.*) A term descriptive of book paper whose thickness is relatively great compared to substance weight.

high car′bon steel (*Metal.*) A rather general term applied to steels of more than 0.50 per cent carbon, of good tempering qualities, and suitable for cutting tools.

high com′mu-ta′tor bars (*Elec.*) Due to mechanical faults segments or bars of commutators often rise above adjacent bars through the centrifugal force set up by the revolving armature.

high com-pres′sion (*Auto. Mech.*) A state of compressibility of gases, usually in a combustion chamber, brought about by a small amount of compression space in the upper part of the chamber.

high dis-charge′ (*Elec.*) A heavy flow of current from the storage battery.

high fi-del′i-ty ra′di-o (*Rad.*) A radio designed to provide the most faithful sound reproduction possible by a balanced combination of tuner, amplifier, and speaker systems. The high frequency response, low frequency response and the distortion present measure the degree of fidelity achieved.

high flash′ing point. When oil will ignite only at a very high temperature, it is said to have a high flashing point.

high fre′quen-cy (*Elec.*) An alternating current having many thousands of alternations or cycles per second.

high gloss (*Paint.*) Paint which dries with a lustrous, enamel-like finish.

high lead bronze (lĕd) (*Metal.*) An alloy containing about 75 per cent copper and varying percentages of tin and lead. Its principal use is for bearings operating under high speeds.

high light (*Furn.*) A term used in the finishing of furniture, when finishes are blended from a darker to a lighter shade, or vice versa.

high mi'ca (*Elec.*) Mica which is higher than the copper commutator bars of the armature due to slower wear.

high po-ten'tial (*Elec.*) A high voltage of six hundred or more volts.

high–po-ten'tial test'ing trans-form'er (*Elec.*) A specially constructed transformer designed to supply several desirable high voltages to be used for testing insulations, etc.

high–pres'sure cyl'in-der. The smallest cylinder of a compound engine which receives the steam directly from the boiler. In this cylinder the steam is first expanded, and then it is exhausted into the adjacent low-pressure cylinders.

high re-lief' (*Furn.*) Carving in which the design stands out, at least in part, farther from the background than in low relief.

high re-sist'ance (*Elec.*) Rust, corrosion, or any other influence which interferes with or blocks the full flow of electrical current under normal voltage.

high speed (*Auto.*) Relates to position of speed-change gears for normal open-road driving which gives a one-to-one ratio from crankshaft to drive shaft.

high–speed steel. Steel containing tungsten or molybdenum, which has been added to increase its efficiency for cutting tools. Such tools can be operated at much higher speeds without injury than can the ordinary carbon-steel tools.

high spots (*Mach.*) (1) Spots to be taken down by scraping or grinding in order to secure an absolutely plane surface. (2) Area of a plane extending above a true plane.

high ten'sion (*Elec.*) A high voltage or e.m.f. (See HIGH POTENTIAL.)

high'–test' fu-el (*Auto.*) Gasoline of 75 octane rating or better.

high volt'age (*Auto. Elec.*) (1) Refers to the voltage in auto circuit which rises higher than the normal 6 volts, due to faulty generator cut-out (relay) or points of high resistance in circuit. (2) Voltage induced in secondary winding of ignition coil which is passed to spark plugs through distributor.

high'way en'gi-neer'. One who plans the engineering work, design, and construction of modern highways.

high–wing mon'o-plane (*Aero.*) A monoplane whose wing is mounted directly at the top of the fuselage or above the fuselage.

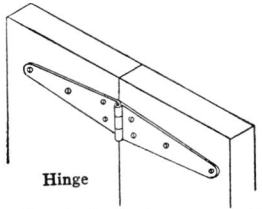
Hinge

hinge. A mechanical device, consisting primarily of a pin and two plates, which may be attached to the door and door frame to permit opening and closing of the door, or for use under any similar condition.

hip (*Arch.*) The external joint usually from eaves to ridge between two parts of a sloping roof which approach each other at an angle, e.g., a joining or front and side roofs. The term is not applied to "ridge." Hip is the opposite of "valley" which is an interior angle.

hip raft′ers. The rafters which form the hip of a roof; distinguished from ridge.

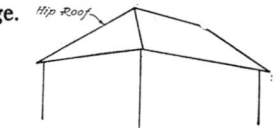

hip roof. A roof which rises with equal angles from all four sides of a building.

hob (*Mach.*) A master cutter for cutting worm wheels and spur gears; also a master tap. (*Plast.*) A master model in hardened steel used to sink the shape of mold into a soft-steel block.

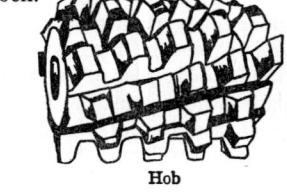

Hob

hob′bing. Cutting the teeth of worm wheels, threads of dies, or chasers, with a hob or master tap.

hock leg (*Furn.*) A style of cabriole leg with a curve and angle on the underpart of the knee.

hod. A long-handled receptacle for carrying bricks and mortar.

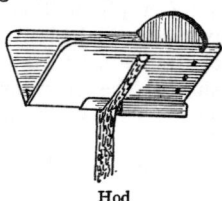

Hod

Hoff′man ap′pa·ra′tus (*Chem.*) An apparatus for the electrolysis of water.

hog′ging (*Mach.*) A term frequently used in machine-shop practice referring to very heavy cuts taken on machine tools.

Hoke blocks. Gauge blocks used for checking shop gauges, designed by Major Hoke.

hold time (*Weld.*) The time that pressure is maintained at the electrodes after the cessation of the welding current.

hol′low plane. A plane with face and cutting iron hollowed out, for planing rounded surfaces, as for beads and moldings.

hol′low punch (*Metal.*) A hardened steel punch with a hollow head. It is used with a hand hammer for cutting holes in metal, cardboard, fabric, etc., especially for the placing of grommets. Punches to be used on metal are more blunt than those for softer materials.

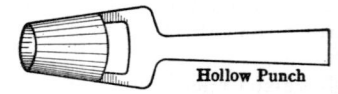

Hollow Punch

hol′low tile. A building material used extensively for both exterior walls and partitions. It is made in a variety of forms and sizes. When used for an outside wall, it is usually covered with stucco.

hol′ly (*Wood*) *Ilex*. Usually a small, slow-growing tree. Wood is white, hard, and close grained. Used for piano keys, inlay work, and interior finish.

ho′mo·ge′ne·ous. Made up of similar parts. Of the same quality throughout.

hone or oil′stone. A stone used for whetting edged tools, to give the clean, fine edge necessary for clean cutting.

hon′ey-comb (*Plast.*) Thin metal or resin-impregnated paper core material, used with resin-Fiberglas laminated facing, which, together with the core, produces an extremely light, strong panel for some aeronautical body structure. Some fabrications are said to carry a load two million times their weight. The honeycomb is formed into vertical hexagonal cells, about the size of natural honeycomb.

hon′ey-comb ra′di-a′tor (*A u t o.*) Made from a number of small cells extending from front to back, laid one upon another, and soldered together. Water flows in a thin film around the cells or tubes and is cooled by the air flowing through them.

hon′ey lo′cust (*W o o d*) *Gleditsia triacanthos.* Tree of medium size. It is a flower and pod-bearing tree. Wood is hard and strong, very durable in contact with soil. Used for fence posts, rails, and wheel hubs.

hon′ing (*Auto.*) The reshaping and polishing of engine cylinders by means of hones or abrasive stones using either the wet or dry method.

hood. (1) That part of an automobile which covers the motor and extends from the radiator to the dash. (2) A projecting cover as to a hearth, a forge, etc.

hook bolt (*Mech.*) A bolt which, instead of having a head, has the unthreaded end bent U shaped, or

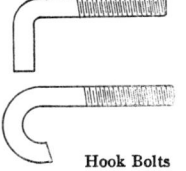

Hook Bolts

straight at right angles to the body of the bolt.

Hooke's law (*Engin.*) This law states that within the elastic limit the deformation produced is proportional to the stress.

hook joint. A dustproof joint for doors of showcases.

hook rule (*Shopwk.*) A rule with a projecting piece attached to one end at right angles to the blade.

hook span′ner (*Mach.*) For use on round nuts notched on the periphery.

hoop i′ron. The iron used for securing the corners of packing cases.

hop′per. A box or receiver used for the purpose of feeding supplies of materials to machines or furnaces of various kinds.

hor′i-zon′tal. In the direction of or parallel to the horizon; on a level.

hor′i-zon′tal boil′er. A boiler, the longitudinal axis of which is horizontal.

hor′i-zon′tal bor′ing ma-chine′. A machine tool having a horizontal spindle adjustable both vertically and longitudinally. The worktable is also adjustable and may be rotated, making the machine adaptable to a wide range of work.

hor′i-zon′tal cen′ter-ing (*Tel.*) The position of a picture with respect to the axis of the cathode ray tube. This is accomplished by a control on the receiver.

hor′i-zon′tal drill press (*Mech.*) A drill press which operates horizontally instead of vertically.

hor′i-zon′tal hold con-trol′ (*Tel.*) A control on the receiver used to adjust the horizontal sweep oscillator so that it will synchronize with the synchronizing signals in the received picture signal.

hor′i-zon′tal mill′ing ma-chine′. A milling machine with horizontal spindle and cutter arbor. The table which can be raised and lowered to suit work conditions is capable of horizontal feed.

hor′i-zon′tal re-turn′ tu′bu-lar boil′er (*Engin.*) A type of steel boiler consisting of a cylindrical shell with fire tubes, enclosed in brickwork to form the furnace and combustion chamber.

horn (*Aero.*) A short lever attached to a control surface of an aircraft, to which the operating wire or rod is connected.

horn′blende. A common, greenish-black or black mineral containing iron and silicate of magnesium, calcium, and aluminum.

horn cen′ter. A small, transparent disk of horn used by draftsmen to place the points of their compasses upon when describing circles, to avoid piercing the paper itself. Not in very general use.

horn′ing press (*Mach.*) Used for closing down side seams on sheet-metal receptacles, such as buckets, etc.

horn re-lay′ (*Auto. Elec.*) A magnetic control introduced in a horn circuit. Pressure on horn button moves an armature into position to close contact points so that full effect current passes directly to horn or horns.

ho-rol′o-gy. The construction and repair of clocks, watches, etc. The science of time measurement.

horse (*Bldg. and Woodwkg.*) (1) A trestle. (2) One of the slanting supports of a set of steps to which are attached the treads and risers.

horse′hair (*Furn.*) A material woven from the coarse hair of horses, used for upholstering.

horse′pow′er. In mechanics, the standard unit by which power is measured. One horsepower is equivalent to 33,000 pounds lifted one foot in one minute. Abbreviated as h.p.

horse′pow′er rat′ing, S.A.E. (Soc. of Auto. Engs.) (*Auto.*) Horsepower

$$= \frac{\text{bore in inches}^2 \times \text{no. of cylinders}}{2.5}$$

expressed thus $\dfrac{D^2 \times N}{2.5}$

horse′shoe′ mag′net (*Elec.*) A magnet shaped like a horseshoe or letter U. See MAGNET.

hose clamp (*Auto.*) A clamp for making a tight joint between a hose and some less flexible object over which the end of the hose fits.

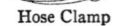
Hose Clamp

hose cou′pling. A device, generally a union, for joining together the ends of hose lengths.

hot (*Tel.*) Any area having or reflecting too much light.

hot′box′ (*Mach.*) A bearing, which from a poor fit or lack of lubrication, has become overheated.

hot-die steel. Steel employed for forging dies used in contact with red-hot metal.

hot dip′ping. Any cleaning or coating process accomplished by dipping in a hot solution.

hot em-boss′ing (*Print.*) Embossing by the use of heated dies.

hot met′al (*Fdry.*) A term applied to molten iron or brass when the temperature is too high for the class of work for which it is intended.

hot plug (*Auto.*) A spark plug with long porcelain runs warmer than one with short porcelain; therefore, it is often referred to as a hot plug.

hot rolled (*Metal.*) Applied to the rolling of steel into commercial shapes while hot.

hot short. A condition of wrought iron in which it becomes brittle at a welding heat, so that it either welds with difficulty or does not weld at all. It is due to the presence of sulphur.

hot-wire am′me′ter (ă m′m ē′t ē r) (*Elec.*) An ammeter which makes use of the heating effect of current which causes a wire to elongate and move a pointer over a scale. This type of meter required frequent adjustment and is now obsolete.

hot work′ing steels (*Metal.*) Steels containing anywhere from 5 to 15 per cent tungsten, some chromium, and a moderate carbon content. They are used as hot working tools.

hour′glass′ worm (*Auto.*) A steering gear, worm shaped like an hourglass, of larger diameter at the ends than at the middle, said to increase efficiency on extreme right or left turns.

housed joint (*Carp.*) A joint formed by a recess that receives the entire end of a board or timber. Differs from a dado by fitting four sides instead of two, and from a mortise and tenon in that there is no reduction in size to form the tenon.

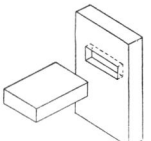
Housed Joint

house drain (*Plumb.*) That part of the lowest horizontal piping of a plumbing system which receives the discharge from soil, waste, and other drainage pipes inside of any building and conveys the same to the house sewer.

housed string (*Bldg.*) A stair string with vertical and horizontal grooves cut on the inside to receive the ends of the risers and treads. Wedges covered with glue are generally used to hold the risers and treads in place in the grooves.

house or′gan (*Print.*) A publication made up partly of general reading matter and partly of advertising of the products of the business concern issuing it. Published periodically and distributed to customers and those interested.

house slant (*Plumb.*) A T or Y connection in a sewer to receive the connection of a house sewer.

hous′ing (*Mech.*) A term of very general application usually referring to a body casting, a main part, a container, a cover, or support for other parts.

Howe Truss

Howe truss. A form of truss used both in roof and bridge construction; especially adapted to wood and steel construction.

hub (*Patmkg.*) The central portion of a wheel through which the axle passes; usually cylindrical in shape.

hub′bing (*Shopwk.*) The forcing of a hardened die or "hub" into cold, soft steel to produce a die or mold. A depth of ½ in. is common. Pressure averages 100 tons to the square inch.

hub dy′na-mom′e-ter(*Aero.*)A device built into a propeller hub for measuring engine thrust and for torque.

hue (*Color*) The particular shade of a color.

hull (**sea'plane**) (*Aero.*) That portion of a flying boat which furnishes buoyancy when in the water. It contains accommodations for the crew and passengers, usually incorporating the functions of a float and fuselage in one unit.

hunt'ing link (*Auto.*) The link at which a timing chain can be opened to permit length adjustment by adding or removing a link.

hu-mid'i-ty. Relating to moisture, or dampness. The amount of moisture in the air. To humidify means to pass air for ventilating purposes through a film of water to cleanse and properly moisten.

hutch. (1) A small or dark room; a chest; a measure. (2) A place for storing.

hy'drant. A fire plug; a plug or pipe with a valve connected to a water main for service in extinguishing fires.

hy'drate (*Chem.*) (1) A compound formed by the union of molecules of water with other molecules or atoms. (2) To combine with water or its elements to form a hydrate.

hy'drat-ed (*Papermkg.*) A gelatinized pulp which is made into a water-resistant paper.

hy'drat-ed lime (*Bldg.*) Powdered lime for structural use, usually furnished in 50-lb. bags. Mix with water to the consistency desirable for the purpose needed.

hy-drau'lic brake (*Auto.*) A system of operating mechanical brakes by power supplied by hydraulic pressure. When pressure is applied to the pedal a piston is forced into a master cylinder, and the fluid contained in it (a mixture of denatured alcohol and castor oil) is distributed through copper tubes or flexible tubing to various parts of the system.

hy-drau'lic bronze (*Metal.*) Name applied to casting bronze or brass used for valves, pump parts, etc.

hy-drau'lic drive (*Auto.*) See FLUID DRIVE.

hy-drau'lic en'gi-neer'. One who handles the engineering work of design, erection, and construction of sewage-disposal plants, water works, dams, water-operated power plants, etc.

hy-drau'lic glue. Glue which has the property of partially resisting the action of moisture.

hy-drau'lic jack. A lifting jack, actuated by a small force pump enclosed within it, and operated by a lever from the outside.

hy-drau'lic lime (*Bldg.*) Manufactured in the same manner as natural cement from rock having sufficient lime to permit it to slake like quick lime. It sets and hardens as a hydraulic cement.

hy-drau'lic press (*Mach.*) A press operated by water power.

hy-drau'lic ram. A commonly used automatic device, by means of which the fall of a volume of water furnishes power to raise a part of it to a point much higher than its source.

hy-drau'lics. The science of liquids, especially of water in motion.

hy-drau'lic valve. A valve for regulating the distribution of water in the cylinders of hydraulic elevators, cranes, etc.

hy'dro-ba-rom'e-ter. An instrument for determining the depth of sea water by its pressure.

hy'dro-car'bons (*Chem.*) Those compounds that contain hydrogen and carbon only; paraffins, olefines, acetylenes, benzines, etc.

hy′dro-chlo′ric ac′id (HCl) Occurs in nature as a constituent of volcanic gases. Commercially it is the principal product of the action of sulphuric acid and salt. Used as a flux for soldering; also has wide use in industry.

hy′dro-cy-an′ic (hī′drȯ-sī-ăn′ĭk), or **prus′sic ac′id.** An intensely poisonous, colorless gas or liquid. Obtained by distilling a concentrated solution of potassium cyanide with dilute sulphuric acid and absorption of the vapors in water.

hy′dro-dy-nam′ics. That branch of mechanics which treats of the laws of motion and action of water and other liquids.

hy′dro-e-lec′tric (*Elec.*) Relating to the production of electricity by water power.

hy′dro-flu-or′ic ac′id. A volatile, colorless, corrosive liquid compound (HF) formed by decomposing metallic fluorides and sulphuric acid. It is used for etching on glass, in ceramics, in brewing, and in yeast.

hy′dro-foil′ or **hy′dro-vane** (*Aero.*) Any surface designed to obtain reaction from the water through which it moves.

hy′dro-gen (*Chem.*) Found free in nature in very small quantities. In combination it is one of the most abundant of the elements. When pure, it is a colorless, tasteless, odorless gas.

hy′dro-gen-a′tion (*Plast.*) Chemical process whereby hydrogen gas is introduced into a compound.

hy-drol′y-sis (*Plast.*) Chemical decomposition of a substance involving the addition of water.

hy′dro-mat′ic weld′ing. A resistance welding process wherein each one of two or more electrodes in sequence goes through a complete welding cycle under the control of a hydraulic-sequencing device synchronized with a welding-current control device.

hy′dro-me-chan′ics (*Phys.*) A branch of mechanics which considers the equilibrium and motion of fluids and of bodies in or surrounding them. Hydrostatics and hydrodynamics are divisions of hydromechanics.

hy-drom′e-ter. An instrument for determining the specific gravity of liquids.

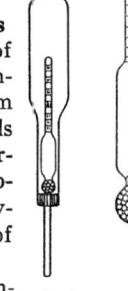
Hydrometer

hy′dro-stat′ic brakes (*Auto.*) A brake system, containing fluid, which is hermetically sealed. Pressure on the foot pedal distorts the fluid reservoir and pressure is distributed equally to all four wheels. At each wheel a brake fluid chamber expands outward, forcing six brake shoes against the brake drum.

hy′dro-stat′ic joint (*Plumb.*) Used in large water mains, in which sheet lead is forced tightly into the bell of a pipe by means of the hydrostatic pressure of a liquid.

hy′dro-stat′ics. Treats of the equilibrium and pressure of fluids at rest. (*Phys.*) The science of pressure and equilibrium of fluids.

hy-drox′yl (*Chem.*) (OH) A characteristic part of bases consisting of one atom of hydrogen and one of oxygen.

hy-grom'e-ter (hī-grŏm'ê-tēr) An instrument for measuring the amount of moisture in the atmosphere.

hy'gro-scop'ic (*Plast.*) Property of absorbing moisture.

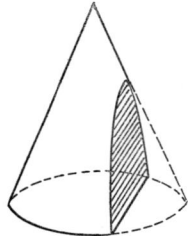

Hyperbola

hy-per'bo-la (hī-pûr'bō-là) A conic section. The curve obtained by passing a plane through a cone parallel to its vertical axis.

hy'per-bol'ic (*Math.*) Of, pertaining to, or having the shape of a hyperbola.

hy'per-eu-tec'toid (*M e t a l.*) Steel containing less than the eutectoid percentage of carbon.

hy'po-cy'cloid. A curve formed by the path of a point on a circle which rolls on the interior of a base or fundamental circle. The curves of the flanks of cycloidal gear teeth are hypocycloids.

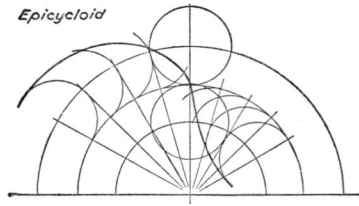

hy'poid (*Mach.*) An abbreviation of hyperboloidal. The term is applied to a special type of spiral-bevel gear tooth.

hy'poid gears (*Auto. Mech.*) A type of spiral bevel gears which permit the location of the pinion above or below the center of the gear with which it meshes. Hypoid gears are now largely used for the rear axle drive in all passenger automobiles.

hy-pot'e-nuse. The diagonal which joins the sides of a right-angled triangle.

hy-pot'e-nuse ob'long (*Print.*) Refers to the ratio of page depth to width, approximately 1½ to 1.

hy-poth'e-sis. An assumption as a basis for investigation or reasoning.

hys'ter-e'sis (hĭs'tēr-ē'sĭs) (*Elec.*) A lagging of magnetic density behind the magnetizing force, causing a loss resulting in heat.

I

I beam (*Engin.*) A steel beam shaped like the letter I. Used in structural work.

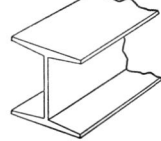
I Beam

i-con′o-scope (*Tel.*) A tube used in the television camera to convert the light and shadow of a scene into electrical impulses.

i-den′ti-fi-ca′tion light (*Aero.*) A group of lights, clear and colored, carried on the rear part of an airplane for identification at night.

i-den′ti-ty (*Math.*) The state of being identical or absolutely the same.

i′dle wheel or i′dler (*Mech.*) A gear transmitting motion between two active gears, or a pulley used against a belt to take up slack.

i′dling (*Auto.*) Refers to the slow running of the engine when the car is not in motion.

i′dling jet (*Auto.*) The jet which controls the amount of gasoline needed for operating the engine at idling speed. Always taken off above the butterfly valve.

ig′ne-ous rock. Rocks formed under the action of heat, as basalt, quartz, granite, etc.

ig-ni′tion (*Elec.*) The lighting of the charge in gas engines, effected generally by an electric spark.

ig-ni′tion bat′ter-y (*Auto.*) A storage battery or a combination of dry cells used to supply current for the ignition system of a gasoline engine.

ig-ni′tion coil (*Elec.*) Used on automobiles to produce a high-voltage current to jump the spark-plug gaps.

ig-ni′tion dis-trib′u-tor (*Auto. Elec.*) That part of the timer-distributor mechanism by which high-tension spark is distributed from the coil to the spark plugs.

ig-ni′tion spark (*Auto.*) The high-tension spark or arc induced in the secondary winding of the ignition coil and passed to the spark plugs where it explodes the gas in the engine cylinders.

ig-ni′tion switch (*Auto.*) An electrical control which completes or breaks the circuit to ignition coil either by wiping contacts or push-pull, or toggle fingers.

ig-ni′tion tem′per-a-ture. The temperature to which a combustible must be raised to cause a rapid chemical union with oxygen.

ig-ni′tion tim′er (*Auto. Elec.*) A mechanical device, usually a cam by which time of sparking is set to provide effective combustion.

ig-ni′tion–tim′er–dis-trib′u-tor (*Auto.*) The complete assembly including rotor, breaker arm, and point, shaft, cam, and worm and gear driven from the camshaft of the engine. Attached to the top of the timer body is the distributor cap by means of which high-tension electricity is distributed to respective cylinders.

I–head en′gine (*Auto.*) The type of motor commonly known as the "valve-in-head" or "overhead-valve motor."

il-lu′mi-nat′ing (*Print.*) Embellishing

a page or a book by decorative color work; e.g., an elaborately colored initial letter at the beginning of a chapter.

il-lum'in-at'ing gas (*Chem.*) (1) Coal and carbureted water gases and their various mixtures. (2) The different classes of oil gas. (3) Acetylene, gasoline gas, and producer gas. The first is the most important for illuminating purposes. Producer gas is the most important for fuel and power gas.

il-lu'mi-nat'ing oil (*Chem.*) Certain oils obtained by special distillation of crude petroleum.

il-lu'mi-na'tion. The state of being lighted up.

il-lus'trate. To explain by means of figures, examples, comparisons, and the like; to make clear.

il'men-ite (ĭl'mĕn-īt) A dark-colored ore of titanium found in southeastern U. S. Its principal use is for making a white pigment which forms a very durable paint.

im'age (*Tel.*) A picture or scene focused on the mosaic of the camera tube, or the picture reproduced electronically on the face of the picture tube.

im'age-orth (*Tel.*) (Abbreviation of image-orthicon) A supersensitive camera tube developed by RCA capable of picking up scenes in semi-darkness.

im-ag'i-na-ry num'ber (*Math.*) Quantity or value that involves the square root of a negative quantity and is unreal.

im'i-ta'tion em-boss'ing (*Print.*) A method of securing a raised printed surface. Powder is dusted over a freshly printed sheet; application of heat causes the powder to fuse and adhere to the inked portions.

Immelman turn (normal) (*Aero.*) A maneuver made by completing the first half of a normal loop; from the inverted position at the top of the loop, half-rolling the airplane to the level position, thus obtaining a 180-deg. change in direction simultaneously with a gain in altitude.

im-merse'. To submerge, plunge, sink, or dip entirely, as under water.

im-mo'bile. Immovable; fixed in position.

im'pact. Collision.

im'pact strength (*Plast.*) Ability of plastics or other material to resist fracture when a sudden load at a test point strikes it.

im-pact' test (*Engin.*) The testing of materials for resistance to shock.

im-pair'. To lessen in quantity or quality; to deteriorate.

im-ped'ance (*Elec.*) The total opposition in an electric circuit to the flow of an alternating current. The combined results of the resistance and inductive and capacitive reactances in a circuit. It is measured in ohms.

im-pel'ler (*Auto.*) The rotating member in a pump, usually consisting of a number of vanes, which puts in motion the medium through which it travels.

im-pe'rial. A drawing paper of ordinary quality sold in sheets 30 by 22 in., made either rough or smooth.

im-per'vi-ous-ness (*Masonry*) Is obtained by laying up a wall with paving brick; using cement or cement-lime mortar. These bricks should always be dry when laid.

im'pe-tus. Momentum; the force with which any body is driven or impelled.

im-pinge'. To come into physical contact with an object after motion. To strike.

im-pos'ing stone (*Print.*) The stone or metal-topped table on which forms are imposed and locked up.

im'po-si'tion (*Print.*) The operation of arranging pages of type preparatory to printing.

im'post (*Arch.*) The top member of a pillar on which the arch rests.

im-preg'nat-ed. Timber for outdoor use is impregnated with various fluids to enable it the better to resist the decomposing influences of the atmosphere.

im-pres'sion (*Print.*) The imprint of type or illustrations on a page or sheet.

im-pres'sion screws (ĭm-prĕsh'ŭn) (*Print.*) Screws by which the position of the platen on a platen press is regulated.

im'print (*Print.*) The name of the printer placed on a piece of printing to show by whom the printing was done.

im'pulse (*Auto. Mech.*) As applied to impulse starter or impulse fuel pump, it refers to momentary acceleration given to speed of engine, shaft, or armature to produce starting, increase of vacuum, or advance of timing position. Applied to auto engine and aviation engine.

in'board sta'bi-liz'ing float (*Aero.*) A stabilizing float placed relatively close to the main float or hull.

in'can-des'cence. Glowing due to heat.

in'can-des'cent. That which gives light or glows at a white heat.

in'can-des'cent lamp (*Elec.*) Electric bulb containing a thin wire or filament of infusible conducting material.

in-car'na-dine. Shades of color from red to flesh.

in-cin'er-a'tor (*Arch.*) A container in which rubbish is burned.

in-cise' (ĭn-sīz') (*Arch.*) To carve; cut in; engrave.

in-cised' work (*Furn.*) Carved work.

in'cli-na'tion. The slope or slant with regard to the horizontal or vertical.

in-clined' plane. A plane which is inclined to the plane of the horizon, the angle which it makes being its inclination.

in'cli-nom'e-ter (ĭn'klĭ-nŏm'ê-tẽr) (*Aero.*) An instrument for indicating the attitude of an aircraft. Inclinometers are termed fore-and-aft, lateral, or universal, according as they indicate inclination on the vertical plane through the fore-and-aft axis, or in the vertical plane through the lateral axis, or in both planes respectively.

in-creas'er (*Mech.*) Any device that increases the size, strength, etc., of something else. (*Plumb.*) A coupling with one end larger than the other.

in'cre-ment. The amount which a varying quantity increases between two of its stages.

in-crust' (*Furn.*) To lay a hard surface of ornamental material over a main surface; a sort of veneering process.

in'crus-ta'tion (*Engin.*) The forming of scale on the interior portions of steam boilers.

in-def′i-nite. Not precise; unsettled; uncertain.

in-dent′ (*Print.*) To space in front of a line to give it a "set in."

in′den-ta′tion (*F u r n.*) A zigzag molding.

in-den′tion (*Print.*) The amount of "setback" of a line of printing beyond the other lines which follow, as the first line of a paragraph. If the first line projects beyond the other lines, it is called "hanging indention."

in-den′ture. (1) A legal instrument for binding an apprentice to an employer. (2) A deed, mortgage, or lease. The name *indenture* comes from the fact that such documents were formerly made in duplicate on one piece of parchment which was cut in half in an irregular or indented manner for the purpose of identification.

in′de-pend′ent jaw chuck. A jaw chuck whose jaws move independently of one another.

in′de-pend′ent wheel sus-pen′sion (*Auto.*) Front-wheel suspension by means of which the wheels react to road shocks or motion of travel independently of each other.

in′de-struct′i-bil′i-ty (*P h y s.*) The property due to which matter cannot be destroyed.

in′dex (*Print.*) An alphabetically arranged list of items or contents printed in a book for the purpose of quick reference. (*Shopwk.*) To space work off in equal divisions by means of an index head or similar device.

in′dex die (*Shopwk.*) For certain classes of work, such as notching the edges of large disks or armature punchings, an index die is sometimes used. It consists of a rotary index adapted to carry the work, step by step, past the punches which cut out one notch or a series of notches at each stroke of the press.

in′dex head or di-vid′ing head (*Mach.*) A mechanical device, usually attached to a machine, used for the purpose of spacing circular work into equal divisions.

Index Head

in′dex-ing (*Mach.*) Dividing the circle into regular spaces, for purposes of milling, fluting, and gear cutting.

In′di-a ink. An opaque but free-flowing ink used by draftsmen.

In′di-a rub′ber. The product made from the milky juice of many tropical plants, which, after manufacturing processes, is widely used in the industries.

in′di-cate. Point out; show; to point out very briefly.

in′di-cat′ed horse-pow′er (*Engin.*) The horsepower as determined from an indicator diagram.

in′di-cat′ing switch (*Elec.*) A switch which shows whether current is on or off.

in′di-ca′tor (*Engin.*) An instrument used to show the pressure and action of the steam in an engine cylinder.

in′di-ca′tor card (*E n g i n.*) Paper which is wound upon the drum or cylinder of an indicator and upon which the diagram of the indicator is traced.

in'di-ca'tor di'a-gram (*Engin.*) A diagram of work traced by the pencil of the indicator upon an indicator card.

in'di-rect' light'ing (*Elec.*) Lighting effect secured by throwing the light against the ceiling or some other surface from which it is diffused in the room.

in'di-rect ra'di-a'tion (*Phys.*) Warm-air heating system relying on a central heating plant to heat air to a desired temperature and then distribute heated air to the space to be warmed, by means of duct distribution system.

in'di-um (*Metal.*) A very rare metal. It is lustrous white, soft, and ductile. Its cost makes its use prohibitive except for experimental purposes.

in'di-vid'u-al drive (*Mach.*) Refers to a direct motor drive for each unit as opposed to drive through countershaft from a line shaft.

in'draft' (*Aero.*) The flow of air into the blades from in front of the propeller.

in-duced' an'gle of at-tack' (*Aero.*) The difference between the actual angle of attack and the angle of attack for infinite aspect ratio of an airfoil for the same lift coefficient.

in-duced' cur'rent (*Elec.*) See INDUCTION.

in-duced' draft (*Engin.*) An artificial draught produced by suction; as opposed to forced draught.

in-duced' drag (*Aero.*) That part of the drag induced by the lift.

in-duced' mag'net-ism (*Elec.*) See INDUCTION.

in-duced' volt'age (*Elec.*) A voltage set up by a varying magnetic field linked with a wire, coil, or circuit.

in-duc'tance (*Elec.*) The ratio between the total induction through a circuit and the current producing it. The ability to oppose change in current flowing through a circuit.

in-duc'tion (*Elec.*) The production of magnetization or electrification in a body by the mere proximity of magnetized or electrified bodies, or of an electric current in a conductor by the variation of the magnetic field in its vicinity.

in-duc'tion braz'ing. An electric brazing process wherein the heat is obtained from an inducted current.

in-duc'tion coil (*Elec.*) Essentially a transformer with open magnetic circuit, in which an alternating current of high voltage is induced in the secondary by means of a pulsating direct current in the primary.

in-duc'tion com'pass (*Aero.*) A compass, the indications of which depend on the current generated in a coil revolving in the earth's magnetic field.

in-duc'tion mo'tor (*Elec.*) An alternating-current motor which does not run exactly in step with the alternations. Currents supplied are led through the stator coils only; the rotor is rotated by currents induced by the varying field set up by the stator coils.

in-duc'tive re-act'ance (*Elec.*) The opposition to the flow of an electrical current in a circuit which consists of turns of wire. The opposition is greater if the turns are wound on an iron core. The measure of resistance to the flow of an a.c. current through a coil.

in′duc-tiv′i-ty (*Elec.*) The capacity or power for induction.

in-duc′tor (*Elec.*) An electrical conductor in which an induced e.m.f. is produced.

in-duc′tor–type mag-ne′to (măg-nē′tō) (*Auto. Elec.*) A magneto in which the permanent magnet rotates with the armature, the coil windings remaining stationary.

in-dus′tri-al life. That sphere of human activity which concerns itself with industry.

in-dus′tri-al sys′tem. The system of factory organization and management; factory production, employment of labor, etc.

in-dus′tri-al waste (*P l u m b.*) The liquid waste resulting from the processes employed in industrial establishments.

in-ert′. Will not readily combine with anything.

in-er′tia (*Phys.*) The tendency of a body at rest to remain at rest, or of a body in motion to remain in motion.

in-fe′ri-or fig′ures and let′ters (*Print.*) Small-type figures and letters set at the bottom of a line, e.g., C_6H_5OH.

in-fla′tion. (1) The act of expanding by filling with air or gas. (2) Establishing of false standard of value.

in′flow (*Aero.*) The flow of air into a propeller.

in′fra-red′ (*Plast.*) Zone of invisible radiations below the red end of the spectrum of visible radiations. Waves are longer and more penetrating than those of light; zone is characterized by heat.

in-fringe′ment of pat′ent. The unlicensed manufacture, sale, or use of a thing patented.

in′fu-so′ri-al earth. An earthy deposit or sediment in water.

in gear (*Mach.*) A mechanism or device is said to be in gear, when it is so connected that it performs its work in unison with other parts but is capable of quick release so that it may remain idle while other parts continue in motion.

in′gle-nook′ (*Arch.*) A fireside corner.

in′got. A mass of metal, which after being purified, is cast from such metals as gold, copper, tin, etc. Ingots are usually rectangular in section, and bear the imprint of the manufacturer.

in′got i′ron. Mild steel, low in carbon, prepared by open-hearth or the Bessemer process.

in-gre′di-ent. One of the parts which enter into the make-up of a mixture.

in-her′ent sta-bil′i-ty (*Aero.*) Stability of an aircraft due solely to the disposition and arrangement of its fixed parts.

in-hib′i-tor (*C h e m.*) A chemical agent which either arrests or slows chemical action. A substance used to prevent or retard rust.

in-i′tial (*Print.*) Large letter used at beginning of chapters or on main sections of other printed matter.

in-i′tial ve-loc′i-ty (*Phys.*) The motion possessed by a body at the instant from which its rate of motion is being considered.

in-jec′tion mold′ing (*Plast.*) Heat softened plastic molding material of a themosetting type, forced by a ram through the heating area and into a highly finished metal mold. On withdrawal of the ram, the mold opens and ejects the finished product, closing again for the next cycle. (See COMPRESSION MOLDING AND EXTRUSION.)

in-jec′tor (*Engin.*) A device used for affording a continuous supply of feed water to a steam boiler.

ink (*Print.*) A combination of pigment, varnish, and drier made in many forms, colors, and consistencies.

ink ball (*Print.*) Made of leather stuffed with cotton and used for the inking of forms. Their use was discontinued after the invention and common use of roller presses.

ink disk (*Print.*) The circular plate, or disk, upon which the ink is fed and distributed on a platen press.

ink foun′tain (*Print.*) A device for the automatic feeding of ink to the disk and rollers of a press while it is in operation.

ink′ing in. The process of applying ink to a drawing.

ink knife (*Print.*) A palette knife used for mixing inks.

ink mill (*Print.*) A massive machine, composed of hollow steel rolls, used by ink manufacturers for grinding and mixing ink.

in-laid′ work (*Man.Arts*) Work which has been ornamented by inlaying or "setting in" small pieces of another material.

in-lay′ (*Furn.*) (1) To decorate with ornamental design by setting pieces of ivory, wood, or metal into a ground of some other material. (2) The design itself.

in′let port (*Auto.*) The passageway through which the fuel charge is fed to the cylinder.

in′-line′ en′gine (*Auto.*) An engine in which all the cylinders are arranged one behind the other.

in-or-gan′ic (*Chem.*) Chemicals which ordinarily do not contain carbon.

in′put (*Phys.*) The total amount of energy expended in doing work.

in-scribe′. To write or imprint in any way, especially in a form that will endure. In drawing, to draw within another figure.

Inscribed Figures

in′se-cure. Not well fastened or attached so as to interfere with safe performance of a job.

in′sert, same as in′set (*Print.*) An extra piece of printed matter produced separately and inserted in proper position in a book before binding. (*Shopwk.*) Any small piece set in as a patch.

in-sert′ed blade cut′ters (*Mach.*) Large-size milling-machine cutters in which the cutting is done by inserted blades of high-speed steel, fastened in position.

in-sert′ed-tooth cut′ter (*Mach.*) A milling cutter having inserted teeth which are held in position by various methods. Inserted teeth are commonly used when the cutter is six inches or more in diameter.

in′side cal′i-pers (*Shopwk.*) A calipers with the points at the end of the legs turned outward instead of inward, so that it may be used for gauging inside diameters.

in′side thread (*Mach.*) An internal thread; a thread cut on an inside diameter as to receive a bolt.

in-spec′tion (*Mech.*) The process of examining the parts and materials of manufactured articles to insure that the specifications of manufacture have been met.

in-spec′tion bench (*Shopwk.*) A bench with smooth, level top, frequently metal, on which work can be checked with surface gauges, etc.

in-spec′tion gaug′es (*Mach.*) A term applied to those gauges used by a buyer to test the accuracy of work purchased.

in-spec′tor. One whose duty is to check a product with regard to requirements or to pass judgment on quality and quantity of work performed.

in′stal-la′tion. The placing in position or "setting up" of machinery, factory or power-plant equipment, etc.

in-stall′ment. (1) A delivery in part. (2) A partial payment.

in′stan-ta′ne-ous. Acting instantly without noticeable lapse of time.

in′stru-ment fly′ing (*Aero.*) The art of controlling an aircraft solely by the use of instruments; sometimes called "blind flying."

in′stru-ment pan′el (*Auto., Aero.*) The panel on which various instruments and indicators are mounted in such position as to be readily observed by the driver.

in′stru-ment trans-form′er (*Elec.*) A device which makes it possible to read high voltages with a low-registering meter, or vice versa.

in′su-lat′ed (*A r c h.*) A building or column is said to be insulated when it is detached from other buildings or when different parts are separated by incombustible materials. (*Elec.*) Covered with, or separated by nonconductors to prevent the transfer of electricity or heat.

in′su-lat′ing tape (*Elec.*) Adhesive tape made nonconducting by being saturated with an insulating compound; used for covering wire joints and exposed parts.

in′su-lat′ing trans-form′er (*Elec.*) A transformer which has the primary carefully insulated from the secondary. There is no electrical metallic connection between the primary and secondary.

in′su-lat′ing var′nish (*Elec.*) A special varnish having excellent insulating qualities, for use on coils, windings, etc.

in′su-la′tion (*Arch.*) Any of those fireproofing materials (many known by trade names) used in building construction for the reduction of fire hazard or for protection against heat and cold.

in′su-la′tion re-sist′ance (*Elec.*) The resistance between the electrical conductors of a circuit or the electrical winding of a machine and the ground, earth, or frame.

in′su-la′tor (*Elec.*) A nonconductor, usually of glass or porcelain.

in-tact′. Left as completed, without change.

in-tagl′io (ĭn-tăl′yō) Engraving cut into the surface of wood or metal, in distinction from engraving in relief. Such plates are known as "intaglio-type plates."

in-tagl′io print′ing. The process of printing from intaglio-type plates, or from incised engraving or copper plates.

in-take′ (*Auto. Mech.*) The flow or fuel mixture in the intake manifold of a gas or gasoline engine.

in′take belt course (*Bldg.*) A belt course in which the molded face is so cut that it serves as an intake between the varying thicknesses of two walls.

in′take head′er (*Aero.*) A short duct extending from outside the engine cowling to the supercharger intake.

in′take man′i-fold (*Auto.*) The branch pipe, usually Y shaped, through which the combustible mixture of gas and air pass from the carburetor to the motor.

in-tar′si-a (*Furn.*) A kind of inlay work in wood much used by the Italians during the fifteenth century.

in′te-ger (ĭn′tĕ-jẽr) (*Math.*) A number that is not a fraction.

in′te-gral (ĭn′tĕ-grăl) All of a unit, usually applied to nonseparable parts considered as a whole; e.g., the cams of a camshaft are integral parts of the shaft.

in′te-gral cal′cu-lus (*Math.*) The inverse of differential calculus. The object is to find a function of a single variable when its differential is known. It has application to problems of areas of curves, length of curves, volumes and surfaces of solids, moments of inertia, mean value, and probability.

in′te-gra′tion. The act of bringing together of parts into a whole.

in-ten′si-fi′er (*Mech.*) A device often used in place of a hydraulic accumulator for converting a low pressure into a higher pressure.

in-ten′si-ty of light (*Elec.*) The degree of illuminating power of any source of light.

in-ten′si-ty of pres′sure (*Phys.*) The force, energy, or quantity of action of a fluid estimated by its ratio to the space within which it acts.

in′ter-cep′tor (*Aero.*) A lateral-control device consisting of a small plate placed just back of a wing slot to spoil the effect of the slot at high angles of attack.

in′ter-change′able. Refers to similar parts so accurate in manufacture that they can be substituted one for another.

in′ter-change′able gear. Gear with teeth so designed that it will mesh properly with any other gear of the same pitch.

in′ter-fere′ (*Shopwk.*) Parts are said to interfere when one part is in such a position that it prevents the proper placing or locating of some piece which is to be fitted to it.

in′ter-fer′ence (*Aero.*) The aerodynamic influence of two or more bodies on one another. (*Radio*) Any electrical or magnetic disturbance which will change or modulate the received signal. (*Tel.*) Spurious electrical signals which cause noise in the sound reproduced by a receiver and which disrupt or tear the received picture.

Intergrain (*Bookbndg.*) A trade name for buckram book cloth, corresponding to Caxton buckram, often with an embossed crepe grain.

in-te′ri-or fin′ish (*Bldg.*) (1) The general effect of the inside finishing of a building. (2) The kind of material and the manner in which it is finished as trim and general decorations.

in′ter-lac′ing (*Tel.*) The picture-scanning system in television whereby the odd-numbered lines are sent as a separate field and the even-numbered lines are then filled in or superimposed to create one frame or complete picture.

Interlaken (*Bookbndg.*) Trade name for a varied line of book cloth; the second oldest book cloth manufactured in America.

in′ter-lock′ing (*Mech.*) Fastening together as by a dovetail joint.

in′ter-med′iate fre′quen-cy (*Radio*) The best frequency obtained from the mixer or first detector in a superheterodyne receiver.

in′ter-me′di-ate gear. An idler; a gear, loose on its stud, for transmitting power between two active gears.

in′ter-mit′tent gear (*Shopwk.*) Gear where the teeth are not continuous, but have plain surfaces between. On the driven gear, these plain surfaces are concave to fit the plain surface of the driver, and the driven wheel is stationary while the plain surfaces are in contact.

in-ter′nal cir′cuit (*Elec.*) That part of an electrical circuit included between external terminals. The resistance of the internal circuit causes losses which reduce the effective output of the battery or generator.

in-ter′nal com-bus′tion (*Mach.*) Refers to any engine which develops power through the expansive force of a fuel which is fired or discharged within a closed chamber or cylinder.

in-ter′nal forces (*Phys.*) Forces within a body due to the motion of its molecules.

in-ter′nal gear. Where spur wheels or pinions engage with teeth set on the internal circumference of a ring, the gear is called "internal." The reverse of spur gear.

in-ter′nal gear drive (*Auto.*) Any drive in which an internal (annular) gear meshes with a spur pinion in order to increase or decrease speed ratio, e.g., rear-axle drive and transmission overdrive.

in-ter′nal grind′er (*Mach.*) A grinding machine designed for the accurate grinding to size of cylinders, holes, and the better grade of internal work.

in-ter′nal thread (*Mach.*) A thread cut inside a piece of material as, for example, in a nut.

in-ter′po-la′tion (*Math.*) The act of computing intermediate values of a quantity between a series of given values.

in′ter-pole′ (*Elec.*) A small field pole placed between the main field poles and electrically connected in series with the armature.

in′ter-rupt′ed arch (*Furn.*) An arch-shaped pediment, the central part of which is cut away.

in′ter-rupt′er (*Elec.*) A device which opens and closes a circuit at very frequent intervals.

in′ter-sect′. To pass across, cut through or into, so as to divide.

in′ter-sec′tion (*Geom.*) The line of joining of two bodies which intersect.

in-ter′stice. A small crack or crevice.

In′ter-type (*Print.*) A line type-casting composing machine similar to the linotype.

in′ter-val (*Shopwk.*) A space of time

occurring between similar mechanical operations.

in-tra′dos or sof′fit (ĭn-trā′dŏs or sŏf′ĭt) The interior curve or under-surface of an arch.

in′tro-duce′. To bring into notice, use, or practice. To insert, as in writing, by way of change. To bring into existence; to produce.

in-var′strut (*Auto.*) A steel strut cast in aluminum pistons to equalize the expansion between skirt and head of pistons.

in-ven′tion. An idea, method, or device embodying some new and original scheme.

in-verse′. Opposite in order: inverted.

in′vert (*Plumb.*) The lowest portion of the inside of any pipe or conduit which is not vertical.

in-vert′ed arch (*Masonry*) Arch in which the keystone is at the lowest point of the arch.

in-vert′ed en′gine (*Aero.*) An engine having its cylinders below the crankshaft.

in-vert′ed nor′mal loop (*Aero.*) A loop starting from inverted flight and passing successively through a dive, normal flight; climb, and back to inverted flight.

in-vert′ed out′side loop (*Aero.*) An outside loop starting from inverted flight and passing successively through a climb, normal flight, dive, and back to inverted flight.

in-vert′ed spin (*Aero.*) A maneuver having the characteristics of a normal spin except that the airplane is in an inverted attitude.

in′voice. An itemized list of articles purchased, and their charges, sent to a buyer.

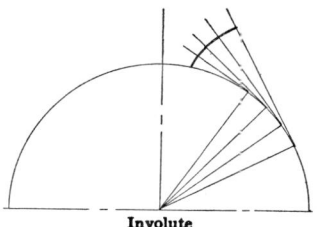
Involute

in′vo-lute. If a piece of string wound about a cylinder at a certain point should be unwound and kept taut during the unwinding, the end of the string would describe the curve known as an involute.

in′vo-lute gear (*Mech.*) Gear, the teeth of which are developed after the involute system as distinguished from those of the cycloidal system. The involute gears are now much more used than the cycloidal.

in′vo-lute teeth. Most commonly used form of gear teeth, development being based on involute curve.

in′vo-lu′tion (*Math.*) The multiplication of a quantity by itself any number of times; the raising of a quantity to any power.

i′o-dide (*Chem.*) A salt or compound in which iodine is the acid radical; a salt of hydriodic acid, as potassium iodide.

i′o-dine (ī′ô-dīn)(*Chem.*) Made from Chilean nitrate of soda and from the ashes of seaweeds. Used medicinally, both internally and externally, and in dyestuffs.

i′on (ī′ŏn) (Abbreviation of ionic) (*Chem.*) Pertaining to the theory of electrolytic dissociation; i.e., the molecules of all acids, bases, and salts dissociate in varying degrees when dissolved in water or certain other solvents. (*Phys.*) An atom which has lost one or more of its electrons, and left with a positive electrical charge.

i'on burn (*Tel.*) A discoloration of the center of the fluorescent screen of a cathode-ray tube caused by heavy negative ions striking it.

I-on'ic (*Arch.*) Pertaining to that order of Greek architecture characterized by scroll-like ornaments of the capital. (*Print.*) Name given to a particular type face

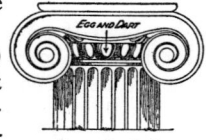
Ionic Capital

I-on'ic or'der. The style of architecture developed by the Ionians. Its columns are fluted and surmounted by a capital in which scrolls form an important feature of decoration.

i'on-i-za'tion (*Chem.*) The breaking up of a compound, as an electrolyte, into positive and negative ions.

i'on trap (*Tel.*) A device used in eliminating the ion burn on the end of the picture tube.

ir'i-des'cence (ĭr'ĭ-dĕs'ĕns) (*Phys.*) A multicolored appearance.

i-rid'i-um. A silver-white metallic element of the platinum group.

i'ris (*Tel.*) Diaphragm of controllable aperture used to control light emission.

I'rish moss. Derived from a form of seaweed, which, on boiling with water, forms a jelly much used in the textile and leather industries.

i'ron. (1) That metallic element which plays the most important part in the industrial world. It is obtained from ores in combination with other substances. Iron is marketed as cast, wrought, malleable, and steel. (2) A measure of thickness for leather equal to 1/48 of an inch.

i'ron core trans-form'er (*Elec.*) A transformer in which the coils are wound around an iron core for greater magnetic coupling of the coils.

i'ron–ox'ide paint. Made from an iron-oxide earth and prepared for use by mixing with linseed oil. It is much used as a protective coating for metals.

i'ron-work' (*Arch.*) The term relates to the use of iron for ornamental purposes. In the architecture of the Middle Ages very elaborately designed ornamentation in ironwork was used for hinges, knockers, escutcheons, etc.

ir-reg'u-lar. Departing from or being out of the usual or proper form, or order.

ir-reg'u-lar curve (*Draft.*) A draftsmen's tool used as an aid in drawing curves which are not arcs of circles. Also called French curve or universal curve.

ir-reg'u-lar pol'y-gon. Polygon in which the sides are of unequal length, hence the angles are unequal.

i'so-cy'a-nate resin (*Plast.*) The readiness of isocyanates to combine with active hydrogen atoms has opened the way for a new field of technology in the plastic industry known as urethane chemistry, the field of flexible and rigid foams. Not only have the properties and techniques improved, but urethane is now foamed-in-place, and made in molds to any need and shape. (See FORMED PLASTIC.)

i′so-gon′ic lines (*Surv.*) Those lines drawn on a map connecting all places where the declination of the needle is the same at a given time.

i′so-lat′ing switch (*Elec.*) A switch used for isolating a circuit from its source of power; to be operated only when the circuit has been opened by some other means.

i′so-met′ric. A form of perspective drawing accomplished without reference to vanishing points. Lines which are parallel on the object appear parallel on the drawing.

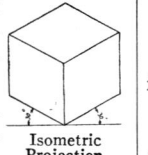
Isometric Projection

i′so-pro′pyl al′co-hol (*Chem.*) Rubbing alcohol.

i-sos′ce-les (*Math.*) Having two sides of equal length, as an isosceles triangle.

i-sos′ce-les tri′an′gle. A triangle having two sides equal. Isosceles

isosotope (*Chem.*) Two nuclei of the same element which have the same charge but different masses, i.e., having the same number of protrons but a different number of neutrons.

i-tal′ic (*Print.*) *Sloping letters;* frequently used for important reference notes or for some item to which particular attention is called.

i′vo-ry (*Furn.*) The tusks of certain animals used for inlay and other decorative work.

i′vo-ry black (*Wood Fin.*) A staining material made from charred bone; also a paint.

J

jack (*Mech.*) A mechanical device used for lifting heavy loads through short distances with a minimum expenditure of manual power.

jack arch (*Masonry*) The ordinary flat arch; also called "French arch."

Jack

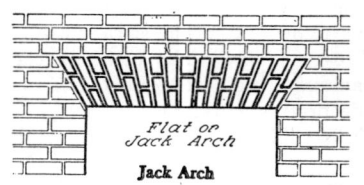
Jack Arch

jack, e-lec′tric. A form of metallic spring contact, connection being made by inserting a plug which is attached to a cord. Commonly used on telephone switchboards and radios.

jack′et (*Mech.*) An outer casing, as around a boiler or tank, to preserve heat or cold, or around a motor cylinder, permitting a flow of water to prevent overheating.

jack, hy-drau′lic (*Shopwk.*) Device for raising weight or exerting pressure by pumping oil or other liquid under a piston or ram.

jack′ing up. The raising up of masses of machinery and heavy structures by means of jacks.

jack, lev′el-ing (*S h o p w k.*) Small jacks (usually screw jacks) for leveling and holding work on planer beds and similar places; practically adjustable blocking.

jack plane (*Woodwkg.*) A plane used for roughing off, bringing the wood down to approximate size, after which it may be finished with a foreplane or a smoothing plane.

Jack Plane

jack raft′er (*Bldg.*) Short rafter with one end terminating against a hip or valley rafter. When one end terminates against the hip and the other against the valley rafter, it is often termed a "cripple."

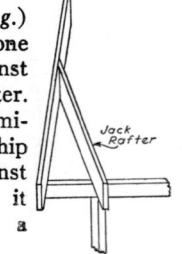
Jack Rafter

jack′screw′ (*Mech.*) Small screw jacks for leveling work in jigs.

Jac′o-be′an (*Furn.*) Of or relating to the time of James I of England. That style of architecture or furniture popular in England during the early part of the seventeenth century.

jamb (jăm) (*Arch.*) One of the upright sides of a doorway or a window frame.

jam nut (*Mech.*) Same as lock nut.

jam plate (*Shopwk.*) Old name for screw plate and in many cases a true one, as the thread was jammed instead of cut.

ja-pan′ (*Wood Fin.*) In the painting trade, a drying agent.

ja-pan′ dri′er. Has no relation to baking japan which is baked on a surface giving a beautiful enamel-like finish. Japan drier is composed of linoleates, a salt of linolenic acid ($C_{17}H_{29}CO_2H$), or resinates of lead or manganese, usually containing free oil and often some resinous varnish, and dissolved to a thin liquid with turpentine or benzine; added to paint in small quantities to hasten drying.

ja-pan′ning (*Paint.*) A method of finishing wood or metal with baking varnish or baking japan, usually applied by dipping, after which it is baked at varying temperatures, on wood at low heat, but on metal at from 300 to 400 deg. F.

jar′di-niere′ (jär′dĭ-nēr′) (*Furn.*) An ornamented wooden, earthenware or metallic bowl for flowers or plants.

Jarno ta′per (*Mach.*) This taper of 0.6 inch per foot is used by a number of manufacturers for taper pins, sockets, and shanks used on machine tools.

jar′ring ma-chine′ (*Fdry.*) A molding machine used for ramming molds by a jarring motion. Also called a jolting machine.

jaw chuck. A lathe chuck consisting of a faceplate equipped with adjustable jaws. A chuck may be universal, in which all jaws move together, or independent, in which each jaw is adjusted separately.

jeff (*Print.*) A game played with em quads thrown in the same manner as dice. The person throwing the greatest number of quads with the nick up wins the game.

Jen′son (*Print.*) A Roman type face named after Nicolas Jenson, a French printer who introduced this face of type during the fifteenth century.

jet. (1) A spout or nozzle. (2) That which spurts out.

jet air′craft′ (*Aero.*) Aircraft or airship (usually a fixed wing airplane) powered by one or more air breathing jet engines.

jet en′gine (*Aero.*) Any engine that ejects a jet or stream of gas or fluid, obtaining all or most of its thrust by reaction of the engine.

jet mold′ing (*Plast.*) A continuous molding operation for thermosetting materials characterized by fully preheating the composition before it is injected, and rhythmical control of heat.

jet′ty (*Naut.*) A structure of stone or wood, projecting into a body of water to divert current, to protect a harbor or shore.

jew′el-ers′ saw. A saw similar to a coping saw but having a saw blade hard enough for cutting metal and other substances.

jew′el-ing (*Furn.*) The carving of an ornament on a surface so as to resemble a jewel.

jib (*Mech.*) The swinging boom of a crane.

jib crane. A crane having a swinging boom or jib.

jig (*Mech.*) A device which holds and locates a piece of work and guides the tools which operate upon it.

jig bor′ing (*Mach.*) A boring operation upon a piece of work which is held in a jig, the tool being guided by some portion of the jig. The term *boring* indicates that the work is performed with a special boring tool, not with a drill.

jig bush′ing (*Mach.*) Hardened-steel

bushing inserted in the face of a jig to serve as a guide for drills.

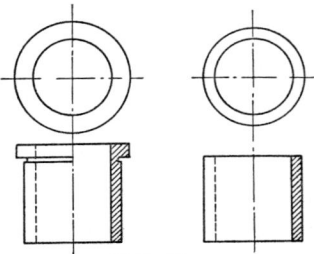

Jig Bushings

jig, drill (*Shopwk.*) A device for holding work while drilling, having bushings through which the drill is guided so that the holes are correctly located in the piece. Milling and planing jigs (commonly called "fixtures") hold the work while it is machined in the milling machine and planer.

jig′ger (*Mach.*) A mechanism which operates with quick up-and-down motion; a jolting device. (*Pot.*) A potter's wheel.

jig saw (*Woodwkg.*) A narrow, thin-bladed saw, to which an up-and-down motion is imparted, either by mechanical or by foot power. It has, to a great extent, been superseded by the band saw.

jim′my. A short crowbar.

job com-pos′i-tor (*Print.*) A typesetter employed on job work.

job press (*Print.*) Any press used for job work.

job print′er (*Print.*) A printer whose main business is small commercial work.

job shop. A shop which specializes on repair work and on odd jobs rather than on a standard line of manufactured products.

job tick′et (*Print.*) The definite instructions relative to a printing job. May consist of notations made directly on the copy but usually is a separate blank form.

job type (*Print.*) Type used for job composition which involves display and variance in faces.

job work (*Print.*) Small, miscellaneous kinds of work.

jog (jŏg) (*Print.*) To level or line up a pile of paper by a jogging motion.

jogged (*Mech.*) A piece which is notched or has a projection or depression is said to be jogged. The term is usually applied only to large work.

jog′gle (*Arch.*) A dowel for joining two adjacent blocks of masonry. (*Mech.*) (1) A projecting pin or ridge, on a casting, which fits into a groove on the piece to which the casting is to be fitted, serving to properly locate the casting and to make a more secure joint. (2) A shoulder to receive the thrust of a brace.

join′er (*Woodwkg.*) A woodworker in the shops. Specifically, one who makes joints.

join′er-y (*Woodwkg.*) The term relates to the various types of joints used by woodworkers.

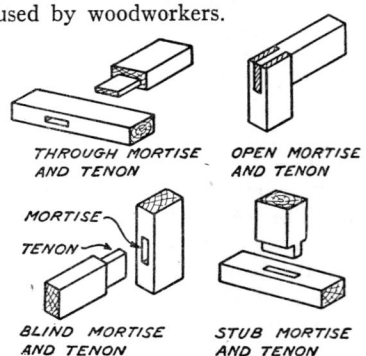

THROUGH MORTISE AND TENON

OPEN MORTISE AND TENON

MORTISE
TENON

BLIND MORTISE AND TENON

STUB MORTISE AND TENON

joint (*Carp. and Shopwk.*) To join, fasten, or secure two or more pieces together by any of the methods well known to artisans.

Combination Brick Jointer

joint'er (*Masonry*) A flat steel tool used for making the various types of joints between bricks upon the face of a wall, as the V, the concave, beaded, square, etc. (*Woodwkg.*) A planing machine for wood.

Jointer Plane

joint'er plane (*Furn.*) Iron plane with wood fittings, used for all kinds of plane work.

joint'ing (*Masonry*) The finishing of the exterior surface of mortar joints.

joint run'ner (*Plumb.*) An incombustible type of packing commonly used for holding lead in the bell in the pouring of lead joints.

joint stool (*Furn.*) A stool of the Tudor period, marked by mortised joints.

joint, u'ni-ver'sal (*Shopwk.*) A shaft connection which allows freedom in any direction and still conveys a positive motion. Most of them can transmit power through any angle up to 45 deg.

joist (*Bldg.*) Heavy piece of planking

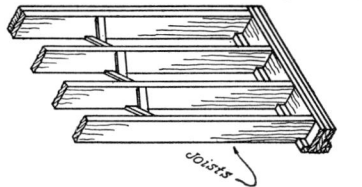

or timber laid edgewise to form a floor support.

jolt–ram'ming ma-chine' (*Fdry.*) A molding machine for all classes of work from light to very heavy. The flask rests on a table which is raised by air pressure, then allowed to drop, thus packing the sand.

Jor'dan en'gine (*Papermkg.*) In papermaking, a refining engine which regulates the length of paper fibers and clears the stuff from the knots coming from the beaters.

joule (joul) (*Elec.*) The practical unit of electrical energy. One joule is equal to .73732 foot pounds. One joule per second equals one watt.

jour'nal (*Mach.*) The supporting portion of a shaft; that part which revolves in the bearing.

jour'nal box (*Mach.*) A bearing or axle box.

jour'ney-man. Properly, one who has gained a thorough knowledge of his trade by serving an apprenticeship, although the term is often applied to any workman who is sufficiently skillful to command the standard rate of mechanic's pay.

joyn'er (*Furn.*) An early form of the word joiner, meaning a furniture maker.

jump (*Forg.*) To shorten and thicken a piece of metal as by hammering on the end of a bar. To upset.

jump spark (*Mech. and Elec.*) A spark produced by electricity jumping across a fixed gap, as between the joints of a spark plug.

junc'tion. Place of union; point of meeting; joint.

junc'tion box (*Elec.*) A metal box where several conduits, etc., enter, and in which electrical conductors can be, or are, spliced.

ju'ris-dic'tion-al dis-pute'. A dispute between two trades, as to which craft a certain kind of work belongs.

jus'ti-fi-ca'tion (*P r i n t.*) Arranging the material to be used in a line so that it will fit a given measure.

jute board (*Bookbndg.*) A tough though usually lightweight board, made largely from jute fiber, much used in check, note, and passbook work; also used as a cover stiffener in semiflexible work.

jute bris'tol (*Papermkg.*) A strong bristol containing jute fiber.

jute fi'ber. The woody fiber of a plant native to India. The plant grows to a height of from ten to fifteen feet and the prepared fibers are from four to eight feet long. Burlap webbing and rope are made from the fibers.

jute Ma-nil'a (*Papermkg.*) A manila-colored paper used for wrapping, envelopes, cards of various kinds, etc.

K

ka′o-lin (kā′ô-lĭn) White burning clays compounded almost wholly of silica, alumina, and chemically combined water with a slight percentage of fluxing material such as iron. Kaolin is used as a filler for paper, and in the manufacture of porcelain, tiles, etc. Also called "china clay."

ka′pok (kä′pŏk) (*Uphol.*) A silky fiber covering the seeds of a tropical tree, used extensively as a filler for pillows and mattresses.

kas (käs) (*Furn.*) A large Dutch cabinet or cupboard.

kau′ri gum (kow′rĭ) An amberlike resin varying from light cream to brownish yellow in color. It is the result of exudation from trees, and is dug in large quantities from the ground in New Zealand. It is used extensively in the manufacture of varnish.

keep down (*Print.*) To use lowercase letters as much as possible.

keep′er (*Elec.*) The bar of soft iron placed across the poles of a permanent horseshoe magnet to prevent loss of magnetism.

keep in (*Print.*) To condense, contract, or space closely.

Keep's test for hard′ness of met′als (*Engin.*) An automatic recording apparatus depending on a definite number of revolutions of a steel drill pressed against the test piece with standard force.

keep up (*Print.*) The free use of capital letters.

kell′a-stone (*Arch.*) A stucco with crushed finish.

kel′vin (*Tel.*) A system of measuring light by temperature. Light for color photography must be 3200 deg. kelvin; in TV studios it usually is above 3200 deg. kelvin.

kemp (*Textile*) Dead wool fibers or coarse inferiors which will not dye well.

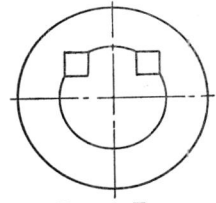

Kennedy Key

Ken′ne-dy key (*Mach.*) Consists of two square-bodied keys so placed that diagonal corners intersect the circumference of the bore. Used for heavy work.

kerf. The cut made by a saw.

kerf′ing (*Woodwkg.*) The process of cutting grooves or kerfs across a board to make it flexible for bending. The kerfs are cut about two thirds of the thickness of the piece. The bullnose of a stair is frequently bent by kerfing.

ke′rite (kē′rīt) A vulcanized insulating compound of tar or asphaltum; and animal or vegetable oil, used in place of rubber.

kern (*Print.*) That part of a letter which overhangs the shank as in f and j. Such letters are said to be kerned.

ker′o-sene′ (*Chem.*) (1) A hydrocarbon oil used for burning and illuminating purposes. (2) A distillate of crude petroleum with specific gravity about .7850, flashing point above 110 deg. F., and a burning point above 125 deg. F.

key (*Mech.*) A wedge-shaped strip of iron or steel used for preventing wheels from slipping around upon their axles. Keys are of various kinds and shapes.

key'board (*Print.*) An arrangement of keys which controls some mechanism so as to permit the assembling of the matrix as in the linotype, or the casting of a letter as in the monotype.

key, cen'ter (*Shopwk.*) A flat piece of steel, with tapered width, for removing taper-shank drills from drill spindle or similar work; also called a drift.

key draw'ing (*Print.*) A master sheet containing instruction for the engraver.

keyed mor'tise and ten'on (*Woodwkg.*) A joint with extended tenon, pierced to receive a tapered key which serves to draw the joint up tightly. Frequently used without glue for massive furniture and for "knocked-down" parts which are to be assembled in position.

Keyed Mortise and Tenon

key'hole cal'i-per (*Shopwk.*) A caliper with one straight leg and the other curved.

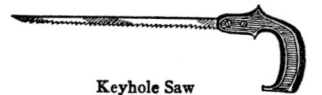
Keyhole Saw

key'hole saw (*Woodwkg.*) A small tapered-blade saw used for cutting keyholes, fretwork, etc.

key'ing (*Furn.*) A process of strengthening a miter joint.

key light (*Tel.*) General illumination also called base light.

key plate (*Furn.*) A small metal plate placed over a keyhole, usually matching the design of the other metal fittings. (*Print.*) The plate of maximum detail in a color set.

key seat (*Mach.*) The recessed groove or space, either in shaft or hub, made to receive a key.

key'-seat rule (*Shopwk.*) A rule used for laying out key seats.

key'stone (*Masonry*) The uppermost stone of an arch which locks its members together.

Key-Seat Rule

key'ston-ing (*Tel.*) When parallel lines tend to converge, usually due to short focal-length lenses used off center of subject.

key'way (*Mech.*) A groove in which a key is placed for the purpose of binding something, as a crank, gear, or pulley, on a shaft.

kick (*Tel.*) Unwanted highlight caused by reflection of light source on polished surface.

kick plate (*Arch.*) A metal plate attached to the lower portion of a door to prevent marring of the finish.

kid fin'ish (*Paper*) A paper or board finish having the appearance of undressed kid leather.

kill (*Print.*) To eliminate, condemn, or indicate that composed matter is not to be used.

killed steel (*Metal.*) Molten steel retained in a ladle or furnace until the gas has left it and the metal is quiet.

kiln (kĭl) An oven or furnace for baking, burning, or drying, as a kiln for drying lumber, a kiln for burning bricks, and a kiln for burning lime.

kiln′-dried′ (kĭl′-drīd′) (*Woodwkg.*) Lumber in which the seasoning process is hastened by placing the boards in a drying room or kiln.

kil′o (kĭl′ō) An abbreviation for kilogram.

kil′o-cy′cle (*Elec.*) One thousand cycles.

kil′o-gram. One thousand grams equal to 2.204 pounds.

kil′o-me′ter (kĭl′ô-mē′tẽr) One thousand meters; equal to 3280 ft. 10 in., or .62137 of a mile.

kil′o-volt′ am-pere′ (*Elec.*) One thousand volt-amperes.

kil′o-watt′ (*Elec.*) A thousand watts.

kil′o-watt′ hour (*Elec.*) The work performed by one kilowatt of electric power in one hour. The unit on which the price of electrical energy is based.

kin′dling tem′per-a-ture (*Chem.*) Temperature at which a substance ignites.

kin′e-mat′ics (*Phys.*) The study of the laws which regulate the actions of bodies in motion.

kin′e-scope (*Tel.*) The cathode-ray or picture tube which may be used in television receivers and at monitor positions in control rooms.

ki-net′ic (*Engin.*) Consisting in or depending on active motion as opposed to potential.

ki-net′ic en′er-gy (*Engin.*) The energy possessed by a moving body by virtue of its motion.

king′pin′ (*Auto. Mech.*) A steel pin or shaft, hardened and ground to size, used in fastening and supporting the steering knuckle to the axle beam, permitting free movement right and left of the front wheels.

king post (*Arch.*) The central upright pieces in a roof truss against which the rafters abut, and which supports the tie beam.

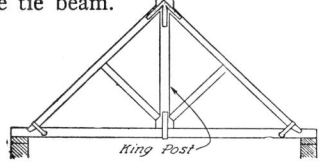

kinks (*Shopwk.*) (1) Short-cut methods or unusual methods of completing a shop job more quickly than by the generally known methods. Spoken of as "shop kinks." (2) A sharp bend or angle made in a piece of metal by a blow or strain.

kip (*Engin.*) An engineering expression meaning one thousand pounds.

kit. A tool box either with or without tools.

kite bal-loon′ (*Aero.*) An elongated form of captive balloon fitted with lobes to keep it headed into the wind; it usually derives increased lift from the inclination of its axis to the wind.

knee (*Furn.*) The projecting upper curve of a cabriole leg. (*Print.*) The adjustable piece on a composing stick which permits setting of type to any measure within the limit of the stick.

knee-ac-tion wheels (*Auto.*) A name given to front wheels independently sprung and where the linkage corresponds to the action of the human knee joint.

kneel′er (nēl′ẽr) (*Masonry*) A stone cut to provide a change of direction.

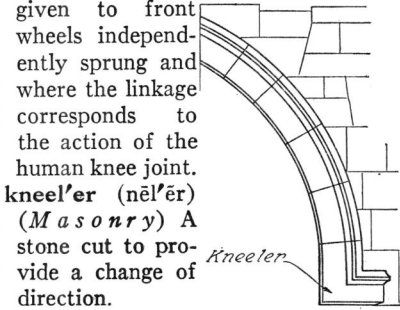

knife. An instrument consisting of a handle to which is attached a blade with a cutting edge.

knife–blade fuse (*Elec.*) A fuse having end connections which resemble the blades of a knife switch and which fit into the contacts of the cutout in the same manner that the blades of a switch fit into the switch contacts.

knife switch (*Elec.*) A switch which opens or closes a circuit by the contact of one or more blades between two or more flat surfaces or contact blades.

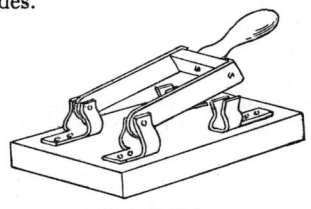

Knife Switch

knob (nŏb) (*Elec.*) A porcelain device for holding electrical conductors in place. (*Furn.*) A form of handle

knob turn′ing (*Furn.*) A turning resembling a series of knobs or balls.

knock (*Mach.*) A jar or pound resulting from a loose fitting of parts.

knocked down. (1) Something complete in its various parts which is shipped or delivered unassembled. (2) Ready for assembling or putting together.

knock′ing (*Auto.*) (*Mech.*) Sounds resulting from worn or improperly fitted pistons, piston (wrist) pins, connecting rod, or main bearings. (*Elec.*) Sound produced in the engine by premature explosion, detonation, of fuel in the cylinder due to improper timing of the spark. (*Gaso-line*) The sound that may be produced in the engine by the detonation of certain types of fuels, carbon, or heat.

knot (*Carp.*) A fault in timber, supposed to be caused by a branch or offshoot when the tree is growing. A live knot is one that cannot be knocked out. A dead knot is one which is loose and can be separated from the timber. (*Naut.*) A nautical mile, equal to 6,080.27 ft., or 1.15 statute miles.

knot′ting (*Paint.*) A compound used by painters for covering knots to prevent them from showing through the paint. Shellac or a compound of red lead and glue may be used satisfactorily.

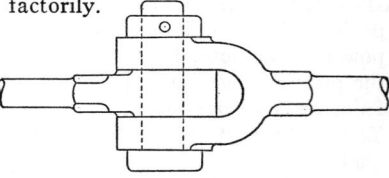

Knuckle Joint

knuck′le joint (*Mech.*) One in which an eye at the end of a rod is engaged by the forked end of a second rod, the two being connected with a joint pin.

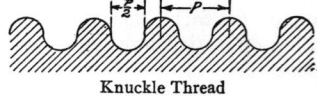

Knuckle Thread

knuck′le thread. A thread which is half round at both root and crest, can be cast in a mold, and is rarely used except on rough work.

knurl (nûrl) To finish by roughing or milling the surface, as on the round head of a thumb screw, to permit a better grip.

ko′a (*Wood*) *Acacia koa*. This tree is found only in the Hawaiian Islands. Weight 52 pounds per cubic foot; color, light brown with wavy streaks across grain. Has a wide variety of uses including fine furniture, musical instruments, and paneling.

ko′ko (*Wood*) *Euphorbia*. Also known as Laurel and East India walnut. It is coarse grained, hard, and brittle; weight 53 lb. per cubic foot; color and grain similar to dark mahogany. Used in furniture, radio cabinets, and paneling.

kraft board (*Paper*) A strong board made from unbleached sulphate pulp or kraft wood pulp.

kraft pa′per (*Papermkg.*) A strong, brown paper, sometimes dyed, used extensively for wrapping purposes.

kraft pulp (*Paper*) A pulp of considerable strength made mainly from pine and spruce trees by the sulphate process.

ky′an-ize. To impregnate wood with mercuric chloride to prevent decay.

Ky′an's proc′ess (*Wood*) A preservative method of impregnating timber with bichloride of mercury.

ky′mo-graph (*Aero.*) An instrument for recording the angular oscillations of an aircraft in flight with respect to axes fixed in space. The reference direction is usually given by a gyroscope or a beam of sunlight.

L

L-head en'gine (*Auto.*) Takes its name from the shape of a section through the head. It is a very popular compact type of motor with all valves, cams, valve lifters, and other moving parts enclosed.

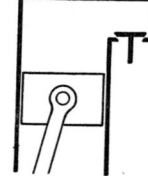
L Head Motor

la'bel (*Arch.*) A projecting molding or dripstone over an opening in a wall.

la'bel pa'per (*Papermkg.*) A paper adequately sized for making labels.

lab'o-ra-to'ry. A place where scientific tests, experiments, analysis, etc., are carried on.

lab'o-ra-to-ry as-sist'ant. A junior engineer whose work consists of routine testing of materials.

la'bor sav'ing (*Print.*) Printing materials prepared for quick use and saving of time.

lac (lăk) (*Wood Fin.*) Often confused with shellac. Lac is the secretion of the lac insect, while shellac is a product manufactured from it. The name is frequently applied to quick-drying wood finishes.

lace'wood'. *Platanus occidentalis.* Sometimes called silky oak. Native of Australia. An inexpensive but decorative wood marked with small evenly distributed silky spots. Used generally in small surfaces and inlays.

lac'ing (*Engin.*) Bars placed diagonally to space and stiffen members, as in a built-up column. (*Mech.*) The fastening together of the ends of a belt with laces, usually of rawhide; metal fasteners, however, are now largely used for the purpose.

lac'quer (*Metal Fin.*) A varnish applied to metalwork to protect it from the tarnishing influence of the atmosphere or from handling.

lac'quer work (*Furn.*) Work coated with lacquer to prevent tarnishing; or decorative work lacquered in imitation of enamel.

lac'tose (*Chem.*) Milk sugar. ($C_{12}H_{22}O_{11}$.) Impalpable, sweet, white powder, derived from whey by concentration and crystallization. Used in infant foods and medicines.

la-cu'nar (*Arch.*) A paneled or coffered ceiling.

lad'der (*Bldg.*) An aid to climbing. Usually made of two parallel uprights connected by regularly spaced rungs.

lad'der back (*Furn.*) A chair back having several horizontal slats.

la'dle (*Fdry.*) Receptacle used for taking the molten metal from the cupola, in transporting it, and in pouring it into the molds. Ladles are of various shapes and sizes with capacities from 25 pounds to 100 tons.

La Farge' ce-ment' (là-färzh' sê-mĕnt') (*Bldg.*) An imported nonstaining by-product cement produced during the calcination of hydraulic lime. It develops nearly the same strength as the Portland cements.

lag (*Elec.*) A retardation. A sine curve lags another curve when its minimum and maximum points are reached la-

lag′ging cur′rent (*Elec.*) Inductance in an electrical circuit causes the current to lag the voltage.

Lag Screw

lag screw. A square-headed, heavy wood screw. It must be tightened down with a wrench as its head is not slotted.

laid pa′per (*Papermkg.*) Any paper containing a watermark which appears as a series of parallel lines, caused by the pressure of the dandy roll on the soft paper pulp.

lake (*Chem.*) A compound of a dye with a mordant.

lake cop′per (*Metal.*) Is obtained by wet concentrating methods from the ores found near Lake Michigan.

lam′bre-quin (lăm′brĕ-kĭn) An ornamental drapery or short decorative hanging, pendant from a shelf or from the casing above a window.

lam′i-nar flow (*Aero.*) A particular type of streamline flow. The term is usually applied to the flow of a viscous liquid near solid boundaries when the flow is not turbulent.

lam′i-nate (*Furn.*) To build up wood in layers, each layer being a lamination or ply. The construction of plywood. (*Plast.*) The plastic product which is laminated.

lam′i-nat′ed brush (*Elec.*) A commutator brush built up of thin pieces of metal, usually spring copper, or bronze.

lam′i-nat′ed con-struc′tion. Work built up in layers to secure maximum strength with minimum weight. In patternmaking, this method eliminates cross-grain wood and provides strength, particularly on thin curved members.

lam′i-nat′ed core (*Elec.*) An armature core built up of layers of insulated iron plates, in order to prevent the formation of Foucault or eddy currents in the metal.

lam′i-nat′ed lin′er (*Auto.*) A shim made up of several layers; proper thickness can be obtained by removing layers.

lam′i-nat′ed plas′tics (*Plast. Art*) A product of impregnating fibrous glass mat or cloth with a binding plastic, usually Polyester Resin, and building up the layers of glass material within the lamination to provide the required strength. The lamination may be flat as in a sheet, or it may be formed, as in a boat hull, or a helmet. The product is said to be as strong as steel, weight for weight, and it is also referred to as the strongest commercial material. Its advantage is lightness with strength.

lamp (*Elec.*) A device having a filament or arc which, when heated to incandescence, gives off light.

lamp a-dapt′er (*Elec.*) A contrivance for making possible the fitting of an incandescent lamp to a socket of a different size.

lamp an-nun′ci-a′tor (*Elec.*) A group of miniature incandescent lamps used on telephone switchboards to attract the attention of the operator.

lamp bank (*Elec.*) A board on which a number of receptacles for lamps are fastened and connected to binding posts.

lamp base (*Elec.*) The brass screw base attached to the end of an incandescent lamp to permit attachment to a socket.

lamp′black. A finely divided carbon derived from natural gas or oil by burning under plates or rollers. Used in paint, ink, and rubber.

lamp cord (*Elec.*) Flexible cord composed of two, stranded, insulated conductors, usually under one sheath.

lamp ef-fi′cien-cy (*Elec.*) An expression used in practice, to mean the power in watts required to produce one candle power of light; watts per candle power (w.p.c.).

lamp sock′et (*Elec.*) A receptacle into which the base of a lamp is inserted, making connection between the lamp and the circuit.

land (*Shopwk.*) Space between flutes or grooves in drills, taps, reamers, or other tools.

land′ing (*Aero.*) The act of terminating flight in which the aircraft is made to descend, lose flying speed, establish contact with the ground, and finally come to rest. (*Arch.*) A platform introduced at some point in a stair run; used to change direction of stair or to break the run.

land′ing an′gle (*A e r o.*) The acute angle between the line of thrust of an airplane and the horizontal when the airplane is resting on level ground in its natural position.

land′ing-a′re-a flood′light (*A e r o.*) A device designed to illuminate the surface of a landing area.

land′ing beam (*Aero.*) A beam projected from the field to indicate to a pilot his height above the ground and the position of the airplane on the proper path for a glide landing.

land′ing–di-rec′tion light (*Aero.*) A light designed to indicate either by itself or in conjunction with other lights, the direction in which landings are to be made.

land′ing field (*Aero.*) A field of such size and surface as to make its use safe for the taking off and landing of aircraft. It may or may not be a part of an airport.

land′ing flap (*Aero.*) An attachment to the rear edge of a wing. When turned down on landing, it acts as an air brake.

land′ing gear (*Aero.*) The structure underneath an aircraft, the purpose of which is to reduce the shock of landing and to support the aircraft while it is on land or in water.

land′ing light (*Aero.*) A light carried by an aircraft to illuminate the ground while landing.

land′ing mat (*Aero.*) A mat, usually of metal mesh or pierced metal strips laid down as a runway.

land′ing new′el (*Bldg. and Arch.*) The post placed at the landing point of a stair and supporting the baluster.

land′ing speed (*Aero.*) The minimum speed at which an airplane can maintain itself in level flight and still be under adequate control.

land′ing strip (*Aero.*) A narrow and comparatively long area, forming part of a landplane airport or of an intermediate or auxiliary field, which is suitable for the landing and take-off of airplanes under ordinary weather conditions.

land′ing T (*Aero.*) A large symbol shaped like a capital T which is laid out on a landing field or on the top of a building to guide operators in landing and taking off.

land'ing tread (*Bldg.*) The front end of a stair landing. Usually it is so built that the front edge has the thickness and finish of a stair tread and the back has the thickness of the flooring of the landing.

land'ing wire (*Aero.*) A wire designed primarily to resist forces in the opposite direction to the normal direction of the lift and to oppose the lift wire and prevent distortion of the structure by an overtightening of those members. Sometimes called "antilift" wire.

land'mark bea'con (*Aero.*) A beacon light, other than an airport beacon or an airway beacon, that serves to indicate a definite geographical location.

land'plane (*Aero.*) An airplane which can rise from or alight on land only.

land'scape pan'el (*Furn.*) A panel with a horizontal grain.

lap (*Mach.*) An accurately finished tool having its surface charged with an abrasive substance.

lap dove'tail (*Woodwk.*) A dovetail joint in which the dovetail tenons are shorter than the thickness of the piece containing the mortises; used in drawer construction to avoid having the joint show on the face of the drawer.

Lap Dovetail

lap joint (*Woodwk.*) A joint produced by the overlapping of contiguous faces of wood or metal, etc.

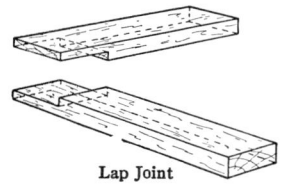
Lap Joint

lap'ping (*Mach.*) The finishing of external or internal surfaces either by hand or by machine. (*Wood. Fin.*) The blemishes in a painted or varnished surface caused by an overlapping of brush strokes.

lap-riv'et-ed joint. A joint formed when the two edges of plates to be joined are overlapped and fastened by one or more rows of rivets.

lap-seam weld'ing. A seam-welding process in which the parts to be welded are overlapped.

lap weld. A weld made on the thinned-down, overlapped edges of plates, maintaining an even thickness of material.

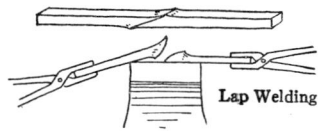
Lap Welding

larch (*Wood*) *Larix*. A medium-size, cone-bearing, deciduous tree. Wood is heavy, hard, and strong, white to red. Used for telephone poles, fence posts, and in shipbuilding.

lard oil (*Mach.*) An oil produced from animal fats. This oil is an efficient lubricant for use on metal-cutting tools.

large knot (*Wood*) A sound knot more than 1½ inches in diameter.

Larry

lar'ry (*Plaster.*) A tool with a curved steel blade provided with a handle about 7 or 8 ft. long. It is used for mixing in the hair with the coarse stuff.

last. A foot-shaped wooden form on which shoes are made.

las′tic (*Chem. Plast.*) A substance which at a certain temperature exhibits the physical properties of rubber.

la′tent heat (lā′tĕnt) That heat which changes the physical state of a substance without changing its temperature, e.g., heat required to melt ice at 32 deg. F. to water at 32 deg. F., or heat required to change water at 212 deg. F. to steam at 212 deg. F.

lat′er-al. Relating to the side, or crosswise of the length.

lat′er-al mo′tion. Motion in a sidewise direction.

lat′er-als (*Engin.*) Diagonal braces between two members to increase rigidity.

lat′er-al sta-bil′i-ty (*Aero.*) Stability with reference to disturbances involving rolling, yawing, or side slipping, i.e., disturbances in which the position of the plane of symmetry of the aircraft is affected.

lat′er-al strain (*Engin.*) A strain which bears against the side of a structure; a transverse strain.

lat′er-al thrust (*Masonry*) The pressure of a load which extends to the sides.

la′tex (*Papermkg.*) A liquid rubber substance employed for strengthening paper.

lath (lăth) (*Arch. and Masonry*) A strip of wood, usually about 1½ in. wide, ⅜ in. thick, and 4 ft. long, used as a foundation for plaster.

lathe (lāth) (*Mach.*) A machine used for the production of circular work.

lathe bed (*Mach.*) The longitudinal supports for the headstock, tailstock, and the slide rest of a lathe.

Lathe Center

lathe cen′ter grind′er (*Mach.*) A grinding device which can be attached to a lathe and used for grinding centers.

lathe chuck (*Mach.*) Form of holding device, attached to spindles of lathes, which grips the work while it is being operated on.

Lathe Chuck

lathe dog (*Mach.*) A carrier; i.e., an attachment which may be fastened to lathe work, and has a projecting tail to engage in a slot or hole in the faceplate.

Lathe Dog

lathe, en′gine (*Mach.*) The ordinary form of lathe with lead screw, power feed, etc.

lathe, gap (*Mach.*) A lathe with a gap or cutout in front of the headstock to increase the swing for faceplate work.

lathe shears (*Mach.*) The machined top of the lathe bed.

lathe tool (*Mach.*) Also called "cutting tool." Used for removing excess stock from metal worked in a lathe. The commonly used lathe tools are: side tool, diamond point, bullnose, inside boring, threading, cutting off. Usually made of high-speed or carbon steel, and ground with wet emery grinder.

lathe work (*Wood and Metalwork*) The work commonly done in the lathe which practically includes almost all branches of turning and boring.

lath′ing (lăth′ing) (*Arch.*) The nailing of laths in position. The material itself.

lat′i·tude. Distance north or south from the equator measured on the earth's surface.

lat′tice (*Arch.*) Open work formed by crossing or interlacing laths or other thin strips.

lat′tice ġir′der (*Arch.*) A truss made up of parallel top and bottom chords with lattice bracing.

lat′tice-work′. Work of wood or metal made of lattices.

laun′dry chute (*Arch.*) An enclosed chute or drop from upper floor to basement for disposal of laundry.

lau′rel-ing (*Furn.*) A decorative feature using the laurel-leaf motif.

la′va (lä′và) (*Chem.*) The material, fine or coarse, fluid or solid, ejected by a volcano. Pumice is a form of lava.

lav′a·to′ry (*Arch.*) A washroom.

lawn (*Pot.*) A fine-mesh gauze used as a sieve for clay.

lay′ing out (*Shopwk.*) The setting off or marking out of work to full size.

lay of the case (*Print.*) The scheme of arrangement of the characters in a type case.

lay′out (*Print.*) A working plan or diagram of a job. (*Shopwk.*) Planning, or marking out to full size, the development or pattern for shopwork Usually the layout is on the metal or other material from which the piece of work is to be constructed.

lay′out bench or ta′ble (*Mach.*) A bench with a level metal top on which work can be laid out.

lay′out man (*Print.*) A man whose duty is to prepare layouts. Sometimes called a "typotect."

lay′out pa′per (*Print.*) Paper having pica squares ruled on it to serve as guides. Used in laying out advertisements and other printing jobs.

lay-up (*Plast.*) In the plastic laminating procedure, the result of laying the reinforcing materials into the mold, or over the mold, by hand. The completed lay-up.

lazy tongs. A system of crossed jointed bars used for picking up articles not within easy reach.

leach (*Plast.*) To dissolve a substance out of another by percolation.

leach′ing cess′pool (*Plumb.*) A cesspool that is not watertight.

lead (lĕd) (*Elec.*) (1) An electrical conductor which projects from an electrical device and to which an electrical connection is made. (2) To be in advance. One sine curve leads another when its minimum and maximum points are reached ahead of the same points on the other curve. (*Mach.*) The distance a screw advances when given a single complete turn. In a single thread the lead is equal to the pitch; in a multiple-thread screw the lead equals the multiple times the pitch; that is, in a triple thread the lead is three times the pitch.

lead (lĕd) (*Min.*) A blue-gray metal, quite soft, ductile, and malleable. Specific gravity 11.34; melting point 327 deg. C. Soluble in nitric acid. Usually found as an ore in combination with sulphur, as lead sulphide or galena. Used for chemical apparatus, storage batteries, etc.

lead burn′ing (*Auto.*) Another name for lead welding. Important for work on storage batteries.

lead cut′ter (lĕd) (*Print.*) A hand-operated device for cutting leads to size.

lead′ed mat′ter (*Print.*) Type with leads between the lines.

lead′er (*Tel.*) Blank film used on either end of subject film for threading projector.

lead′ers (lēd′ẽrz) (*Print.*) Type characters in multiples of em sizes used for printing dotted or intermittent lines.

lead ham′mer (*Mach.*) A hammer with a head made of lead; used in place of a steel hammer to avoid bruising of parts. (*Mech.*) A hammer made of lead and sometimes used for the same purpose as a copper hammer, i.e., for hammering against harder metal which would be bruised if a steel hammer were used.

lead hole (lēd) (*Mach.*) A hole drilled in a piece of metal to facilitate the drilling of a larger hole, or to assist in centering a drill upon an inclined surface.

lead′ing (lēd′ing) (*Print.*) Placing the required number of leads in a piece of composition.

lead′ing cur′rent (lēd′ing) (*Elec.*) An alternating current reaching its minimum and maximum values in advance of the electromotive force causing the current.

lead′ing edge (*Aero.*) The forward propeller blade edge. The leading edge also is called the "entering edge."

lead joint (*Plumb.*) Usually means the making of a joint by pouring molten lead into the annular space between a bell and spigot and then making the joint tight by calking.

lead mon-ox′ide (lith′arge) (*Chem.*) PbO. A yellow to yellowish-red powder obtained by heating lead in air. Used in making lead glass, enamel, and glaze for earthenware. Mixed with glycerin it makes an excellent cement for the stopping of leaking joints. A second variety is known as massicot.

lead paint (*Paint.*) Ordinary paint, so called because white lead is used as a base.

lead per-ox′ide (*Chem. and Elec.*) PbO_2. The lead compound from which the positive plates of electric storage batteries are made.

lead poi′son-ing. A disease affecting painters and workers in lead or lead products.

leads (lĕdz) (*Print.*) Strips of metal used in spacing lines of type; made in multiples of points.

lead screw (lēd) (*Mach.*) The screw which runs longitudinally in front of the bed of a screw-cutting lathe.

lead sponge (*Elec.*) The active element in the negative plate of a storage battery.

lead stor′age cell. A device consisting of plates of lead peroxide and spongy lead in an electrolyte of sulphuric acid. Used for storing chemical energy which on the closing of a circuit will deliver an electrical current.

lead tet′ra-eth′yl (*Chem.*) $Pb(C_2H_5)_4$. The important constituent of anti-knock gasoline.

lead wool (*Plumb.*) A lead fiber used in place of molten lead in making pipe joints.

leaf (*Bookbndg. and Print.*) A single, unfolded piece of paper, or a single division of a folded sheet of paper, as in a book.

leaf′let (*Bookbndg. and P r i n t.*) A folder, a tract, or small printed booklet of only a few pages.

leaf spring. A spring made up of several flat plates superimposed one upon another, such as used on automobiles, wagons, cars, etc.

leaf'work (*Furn.*) Small aggregations of leaves carved upon the legs and splats of chairs and other details of furniture. Extensively used by most of the cabinetmakers of the last quarter of the eighteenth century.

league. 15,840 ft. = 5280 yd. = 3 miles, sometimes considered as 3 knots or nautical miles.

lean mix'ture (*Auto.*) A fuel mixture which contains too much air in proportion to gasoline.

lean'-to' roof (*Arch.*) A wing or extension to a building, with a roof sloping only in one direction.

lease (*Textile*) The crossing made in warp threads in preparing them for the loom.

leath'er (*Furn.*) Dressed hides used for upholstering, often stamped and colored.

leath'er-board'. Made by pulping various fibrous materials, mixed with chalk or whiting. It is molded into form and coated with a glazing solution consisting of starch, gelatin, and turpentine.

leath'er-craft. A trade in which leather is ornamented by means of tools.

leath'er-ette' cov'er pa'per (*Paper*) An imitation leather cover paper.

leath'er fil'let (fĭl'ĕt) A strip of leather glued in the angles of foundry patterns, to increase strength of the casting and to eliminate sharp edges in the foundry sand.

leath'er-oid (*Bookbndg.*) A material resembling leather; usually made by treating vegetable fibers with certain chemicals.

Leclan'ché' cell (lē-klän'shā') (*Elec.*) An open-circuit primary cell using carbon and zinc electrodes, sal-ammoniac electrolyte, and manganese dioxide depolarizer.

lec'tern (*Furn.*) A reading desk.

ledge (*Arch.*) A shelflike projection as from a wall.

ledg'er board (*Arch.*) Same as ribbon strip; attached to studding to carry joists.

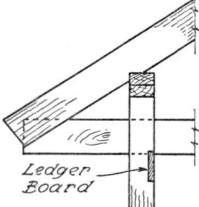

ledg'er pa'per (*Papermkg.*) A strong paper, having a surface adequate for pen writing and erasure which is used for accounting and recording.

left'-hand en'gine (*Aero.*) An engine whose propeller shaft, to an observer facing the propeller from the engine end of the shaft, rotates in a counterclockwise direction.

left'-hand screw (*Mech.*) A screw which advances when turned from right to left.

left'-hand thread (*Mach.*) A screw thread so cut that the bolt, screw, or nut has to be turned in a counterclockwise motion to engage or tighten it.

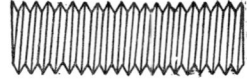

Left-Hand Thread

left'-hand tool (*Mach.*) Side tool ground to an angle on the right-hand side, and which, therefore, cuts from left to right.

leg (*Furn.*) Supporting member of a piece of furniture.

le′gal cap (*Papermkg.*) A size of writing paper, 8½ by 14 in.

leg′end (*Print.*) Descriptive data or specification accompanying or relating to an illustration.

lehr (lēr) An annealing oven used in glass factories in which glass is allowed to cool.

length. The greatest dimension of a body. Distance measured from end to end. Extent in point of time, duration, continuance.

length′en-ing bar (*D r a w.*) An appendage to compasses used in securing a greater radius than could otherwise be had.

Lenz′s law (lĕnt′sĭz) (*Elec.*) The direction of an induced current is always such that the magnetic field belonging to it tends to oppose the change in the strength of the magnetic field which is setting up the induced e.m.f.

leop′ard-wood. *Brosimum aubletti.* A South American tree used for veneering. The wood is hard and beautifully mottled.

let-go (*Plast.*) An area in laminated glass where initial adhesion between interlay and glass has been lost.

let′-in (*Shopwk.*) A shop term, to signify the sinking in of one portion of wood or metal into another.

let′ter board (*Print.*) A flat board used as a storage place for composed type. It usually has strips of wood around three edges.

let′ter-head′ (*Print.*) The printed form at the head of sheets of letter paper; also the sheet after it is printed.

let′ter press. An almost obsolete device for copying letters.

let′ter-press′ print′ing (*Print.*) The making of impressions by means of raised characters on type or plates.

let′ter-size drills (*Metalwk.*) Range from A to Z. A is approximately 15/64 in. diameter. Z is approximately 13/32 in. Diameters are expressed in thousandths.

let′ter spac′ing. The extending of a word by placing spaces between the letters.

Level

lev′el. (1) Horizontal; in a horizontal plane. (2) A tool for testing with regard to the horizontal. (*Tel.*) Power of audio transmission measured in decibels; also voltage of audio-transmission measured in V's.

lev′el-ing in′stru-ment (*Engin.*) A device consisting of a sighting tube with a spirit level so attached that when the bubble is in the center line, the line of sight is horizontal. A graduated arc allows the instrument to swing to read angles in the horizontal plane.

lev′el-ing rod (*Surv.*) There are two general types in common use: target rods and self-reading rods. Target rods are read only by the rodman, while the self-reading rods are read directly by the level man.

lev′el man (*Surv.*) One who operates a surveyor's level.

le′ver (lē′vēr) (*Mech.*) A rigid bar turning upon an axis or fulcrum.

le′ver-age (*Mech.*) The mechanical advantage gained through use of a lever.

lew′is (*Arch.*) A dovetailed tenon inserted in a heavy stone for the purpose of attaching hoisting apparatus.

lew'is bolt (*Bldg.*) An anchor bolt; a bolt having a jagged and tapered tail. It is used for insertion into masonry, where it is held with lead.

Ley'den jar (*Elec.*) A simple form of condenser. It consists of a glass jar coated with tinfoil inside and out for a portion of its height and having a brass rod passing through a wooden stopper. This rod makes contact with the inner coating by means of a loose chain.

li'a-bil'i-ty. The condition of being responsible for a possible or actual loss, penalty, expense, or burden.

lift (*Aero.*) That component of the total air force on an aircraft or airfoil which is perpendicular to the relative wind and in the plane of symmetry. It must be specified whether this applies to a complete aircraft or to parts thereof. (*Print.*) A type form is said to lift when every part is securely locked in the chase.

lift'er (*Fdry.*) A molder's tool, sometimes called a "cleaner." It derives the name of lifter from the use to which it is put in lifting loose, fallen-down sand from the bottoms of molds.

lift'ing mag'net (*Elec.*) An electromagnet, carried by a crane hook, which can lift and deliver masses of iron and steel by a switching on and off of the current.

lift wire (*Aero.*) A wire or cable which transmits the strain or lift on the outer portion of an airplane wing in toward the fuselage or nacelle.

lig'a-ture (*Print.*) Two characters or letters joined together on one body as ff, fi, etc.

light (*Arch.*) A pane of glass; a division in a sash for a single pane of glass.

light bridge (*Tel.*) A platform on which lighting controls and at times lights are mounted.

light cut (*Shopwk.*) In metalwork, a cut is said to be light when the shavings removed are thin and narrow.

light'face (*Print.*) Name given to a type face whose elements are thin or narrow, making the printed matter light, as distinguished from bold or heavy faces.

light flare (*Tel.*) A white spot in a television picture caused by a badly placed floor or spot light.

light lev'el (*Tel.*) The general intensity of illumination on a subject or scene measured in foot-candles.

light'ning ar-rest'er (*Elec.*) A device that causes lightning to pass off to the earth thus serving to protect electrical machines.

ligne (lēn'y) A unit of measure used by watchmakers, equal to .0888 inch.

lig'nin plas'tic (*Chem. Plast.*) Made from wood chips subjected to high steam pressure. Its principal use is for wall panels.

lig'nite (lĭg'nīte) Brown, noncaking coal containing a large proportion of moisture.

lig'num vi'tae (*Wood*) *Guaiacum officinale*. A medium-size tree found in Central America. Wood is extremely hard and heavy, 90 lb. per cubic foot. Used extensively for bearings and bushings.

lime (*Bldg.*) Obtained by the action of heat on limestone, oyster shells. etc. Has many uses in the building arts. Calcium oxide (CaO).

lime'light. An oxyhydrogen flame, or calcium light, which produces brilliant light.

lime'stone (*Bldg.*) A very commonly used stone for buildings of the better type; also used for making lime. Calcium carbonate ($CaCO_3$).

lim'it-er (*Tel.*) An electronic gate used to eliminate noise or amplitude distortion.

lim'it gauge (*Mach. and Shopwk.*) To permit interchangeability, a limit of variation is permitted on each side of the correct dimension, and gauges are made to these limits, and used to test the work; hence the name.

Limit Gauge

lim'its of tol'er-ance (*Mech.*) Refers to limits of accuracy, oversize or undersize, within which a part being made must be kept to be acceptable.

li'mo-nite (li'mô-nīt) ($CaCO_3 \cdot M_gCo_3$) A hydroxide of iron. It is also known as "brown hematite" or "bog iron."

lin'den (*Wood*) Same as "basswood."

line (*Elec.*) The wires running from generating stations or substations to supply transformers or to buildings directly. (*Print.*) A row of written or printed words or figures. (*Tel.*) A horizontal path traced by a moving electron beam on the mosaic of a camera tube or on the fluorescent screen or a picture tube. In a receiver, the intensity of the beam or spot along this path is altered in proportion to the intensity of light and shadow of the scene being televised to create that portion of the picture.

lin'e-al foot. A foot in length as distinguished from square foot or cubic foot.

line am'pli-fi'er (*Tel.*) An amplifier that supplies signal to a transmission line.

lin'e-ar. Pertaining to or of the nature of a line.

lin'e-ar meas'ure.

12 inches (in.)	=	1 foot (ft.)
3 feet	=	1 yard (yd.)
5½ yards	=	1 rod (rd.) or pole
40 rods	=	1 furlong (fur.)
8 furlongs	=	1 statute mile (mi.)
1 mile	=	1760 yd. or 5280 ft.
3 miles	=	1 league

lin'e-ar mol'e-cule (*Plast.*) A molecule of highly elongated form. Generally applied to straight-chain polymers.

line cut (*Print.*) A photoengraving usually on zinc, consisting of solid lines or areas.

lined board (*Paper*) Board lined with lighter paper.

line drop (*Elec.*) The voltage used up in forcing the current through the resistance of the line wires.

line en-grav'ing (*Print.*) A photoengraving or zinc etching reproduced from any drawing or print consisting of distinct lines, dots, or masses of color. It cannot be made from a photograph.

line fre'quen-cy (*Tel.*) The number of lines scanned each second.

line gauge (*Print.*) A printers' measuring rule graduated into picas and nonpareils.

lin'en fin'ish (*Print.*) Paper or card made with a clothlike finish; sometimes called crash finish, also telanian.

lin'en scroll (*Arch.*) A type of ornament used for the decoration of panels, characterized by rolls or convolutions.

line of ac'tion. The line of action of a force is the direction in which it acts upon a material point, which line must be straight.

line pick'up (*Tel.*) Transmission of signals by means of metallic conductors; coaxial cable or equalized telephone cables.

line pipe (*Plumb.*) A special, hightest pipe having recessed and taper-thread couplings, and usually greater length of thread than Briggs' standard.

lin'er (līn'ẽr) (*Mech.*) A replaceable tube to fit inside an engine cylinder, a bushing for a bearing, or the like.

line shaft (*Mach.*) A run of shafting which consists of several lengths coupled together. It may or may not be a main line shaft.

line shaft'ing (*Shopwk.*) The main shafting in a factory from which countershafts and secondary shafts receive their power.

lines of force (*Elec.*) A line of magnetic force indicates the direction taken by a north-seeking pole under the influence of other poles which surround it.

line'-up ta'ble (*Print.*) A precision-built steel table with geared trucks for movable rules, and a ground glass top to enable the operator to "position" sheets to the accuracy of a hairline.

lin'ing (*Print.*) The exact horizontal alignment of a font of type.

link (*Mech.*) (1) One of the loops of a piece of chain. (2) A mechanical device used on engines for controlling valve action.

link fuse (*Elec.*) A fuse wire or ribbon not protected by any outside covering.

link mo'tion. An assemblage of parts for operating the valves of a locomotive.

Lin'o-graph (*Print.*) A slug-casting, typesetting machine similar to the Intertype and Linotype.

lin'o-type (*Print.*) A line of type cast in one piece; a machine for producing the same.

lin'seed oil. Oil from the linseed or flaxseed; used principally in paints.

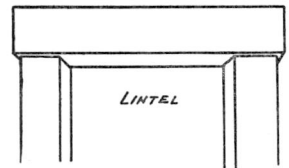

lin'tel (*A r c h.*) The horizontal top piece over a doorway or window opening.

lint'ers (*Uphol.*) The short-fiber cotton which is removed from the seeds. Felted linters are commonly used in upholstery work.

lint'less cot'ton. Long-fiber cotton the seeds of which are not covered with lint as are other cottons.

lip (*Shopwk.*) In machine-shop practice, the cutting edge of a tool.

lip mold'ing (*Furn.*) A small convex molding often placed around drawers.

lip un'ion (*Plumb.*) A special form of union having a lip that prevents the gasket from being squeezed into the pipe so as to obstruct the flow.

liq'ue-fac'tion (*Phys.*) The changing to a liquid state.

liq'uid (*Chem.*) That state of matter which has definite volume and assumes the shape of the containing vessel.

liq'uid air (*Chem.*) Air brought to a liquid condition by a reduction of temperature and an increase of pressure; used chiefly as a refrigerant.

liq'uid meas'ure.

4 gills (gi.)	= 1 pint (pt.)
2 pints	= 1 quart (qt.)
4 quarts	= 1 gallon (gal.)
31½ gallons	= 1 barrel (bbl.)
2 barrels	= 1 hogshead (hhd.)

li′ter (lē′tẽr) The standard French measure for liquids; it contains 61.027 cu. in., equaling 1.0567 liquid quart.

lith′arge. Lead monoxide found in silver-bearing lead ore.

lith′i-um (*Metal.*) The lightest metal. Its specific gravity is only 0.53. It is used to increase hardness of aluminum alloys.

lith′o (*Paper*) Preferred to the names of different papers used in lithography.

li-thog′ra-phy (*Print.*) A method of producing printed matter from a drawing or transfer made on a flat lithographic stone or a metal plate.

lith′o-pone (*Paint.*) A compound of barium sulphate and zinc sulphide. A white pigment with excellent covering qualities; suitable for inside painting, wall finishes, etc.; but is not suitable for outside use. It also is used in the manufacture of linoleum and in the vulcanization of rubber.

lit′mus (*Chem.*) A blue dyestuff made from lichens, a genus of plants. It turns red when treated by an acid and remains blue when treated by an alkali.

lit′mus pa′per (*Papermkg.*) A chemical test paper made with litmus. (See LITMUS.)

live (*Tel.*) (1) Term used for televising *real* things as opposed to film. (2) A set on which action is taking place.

live ax′les (*Auto.*) Axles in which both load and power application is present. These include the semifloating, three-quarter-floating and the full-floating types.

live cen′ter (*Shopwk.*) The center in the revolving spindle of a lathe or similar machine. It is highly important that this should run true or it will cause the work to move in an eccentric path.

live load (*Engin.*) A moving or repeated load which is not constant in its application.

live mat′ter (*Print.*) Matter that is to be printed.

liv′er-ing (*Paint and Lacquer*) Sometimes an acidity sets up in the package, which causes the lacquer enamel to jell or liver.

live spin′dle (*Mach.*) The revolving spindle in the headstock of a lathe as opposed to the dead-spindle of the tailstock.

load (*Elec.*) An electrical device using up electrical power.

load′ed wheel. A grinding wheel which has a glazed or clogged surface from particles of the material being ground.

load fac′tor (*Aero.*) The ratio of any specified load on a member to the corresponding basic load generally applied to the ratio of the breaking load to a basic load.

load′ing (*Papermkg.*) Pigment or mineral filler used to make paper smoother or more impervious to light.

loam (*Fdry.*) A mixture of sand and clay used in molding.

loam molds (*Fdry.*) Forms built of brick and plastered with a loam-clay mortar. These molds which are used mainly for large castings are allowed to dry thoroughly before being poured.

lob′by (*Arch.*) A large entrance room in a building. It may serve as a waiting or lounging room as in a hotel.

lob′lol′ly pine (*Wood*) *Pinus taeda.*

A coarse-grained, soft-fiber pine, with much sapwood; much used in southern United States for framing.

lo′cal ac′tion (*Elec.*) The chemical action which goes on in the positive electrode (negative terminal) under the surface of the electrolyte in a primary cell.

lo′cal cur′rents (*Elec.*) Also known as eddy currents or Foucault currents. (See EDDY CURRENTS.)

lo′cal vent (*Plumb.*) A pipe or shaft serving to convey foul air from a plumbing fixture or a room to the outer air.

lo′cate. To establish or place in a particular situation or spot; place; settle. To fix the position or determine the limit of.

lock (*Furn.*) A device for securing a door, lid, etc., so that it can be opened only by a key, or combination.

lock′er (*Bldg.*) A storage compartment.

lock-in (*Tel.*) The condition existing when the sweep circuits of a television receiver are controlled by the synchronization pulses from the transmitter, resulting in a stationary and clearer picture.

lock′ing bolts (*Mach.*) Bolts of any type used for locking parts in position.

lock′ing stile (*Carp.*) That part of a door to which the lock is attached.

lock nut (*Mech.*) A thin nut screwed down upon another to prevent the slacking back of the main nut under excessive vibration.

lock′pin′ (*Mach.*) Any pin or plug inserted in a part to prevent play or motion in the part so fastened.

lock stitch. A type of stitch accomplished by the use of two threads as in the work done by some sewing machines.

lock′up (*Print.*) Locking up forms for the press.

Lock Washer

lock wash′er. A thin washer whose action is similar to that of a compression spring. Frequently used for the same purpose as a lock nut.

lo′cust (*Woodwkg.*) A hard and very durable wood, used for exposed work.

lode stone. Natural magnetic iron ore.

loft-dried pa′per (*Papermkg.*) Paper which is dried in a drying loft after being surface sized.

log (*Math.*) The logarithm of a number. (*Woodwkg.*) A piece of timber either rough or squared.

log′a-rithm (lŏg′*à*-rĭth'm) (*Math.*) The exponent of the power to which a fixed number, called the "base," must be raised in order to produce a given number.

log′gia (lŏj′*à*) (*Arch.*) A covered gallery or portico having a colonnade open to the air; usually in the upper part of a building.

log′o-type (*Print.*) A syllable or a whole word cast as a unit.

log′wood (*Chem.*) The product of a tree native of Central America and the West Indies, widely used in the dyeing industry and in medicines.

long (*Ceram. and Pot.*) Clay which is very plastic and workable.

long col′umn (*Engin.*) When the length of a column exceeds its diameter by from 25 to 30 times, it comes under the class of long columns, which yield under pressure by bending alone, in the same manner that a beam supported at both ends will yield.

lon′ge′ron′ (lôn′zhā′rôn′) (*Aero.*) In the framing of an airplane fuselage or nacelle, the fore-and-aft member which is continuous across several points of support.

long fold (*Papermkg.*) Term referring to the fact that a sheet of paper will be folded with the grain if it is folded lengthwise. "Broad fold" is the opposite term.

lon′gi-tude. The distance east or west measured from some standard meridian, as that of Greenwich, England.

lon′gi-tu′di-nal di-he′dral an′gle (*Aero.*) The difference in angle of both wing and stabilizer settings. When the angle of the stabilizer setting, referred to the thrust line, is less than the angle of wing setting, this angle is positive.

lon′gi-tu′di-nal sec′tion (*Draw. and Shopwk.*) A section taken through a part in the direction of its length.

lon′gi-tu′di-nal sta-bil′i-ty (*Aero.*) Stability with reference to disturbances in the plane of symmetry, i.e., as in pitching and variation of the longitudinal and normal velocities.

long let′ter (*Print.*) One that has both ascending and descending strokes, e.g., *f*.

long screw (*Plumb.*) A nipple 6 in. long with one thread much longer than the ordinary thread.

long–shunt com-pound′ con-nec′tion (*Elec.*) A type of connection which occurs when the shunt-field winding is connected across or in parallel with the combined armature and series field winding; contrasted with short-shunt connection, where the shunt field is connected directly across or in parallel with the armature only.

long-stroke (*Auto.*) An engine in which the length of stroke considerably exceeds the diameter of the bore.

long ton. 2240 lb.

loom (*Elec.*) Flexible nonmetallic tubing used to protect electrical conductors.

loop (*Aero.*) A maneuver executed in such a manner that the airplane follows a closed curve approximately in a vertical plane.

loop or cir′cuit vent (*Plumb.*) A continuation of a horizontal soil or waste pipe beyond the connection at which liquid wastes from a fixture or fixtures enter the waste or soil pipe. The extension is usually vertical immediately beyond its connection to the soil or waste pipe. The base of the vertical portion of the vent may be connected to the horizontal portion of the soil or waste stack between fixtures connected thereto.

loop wir′ing (*Elec.*) When electrical conductors are looped into and out of each outlet on the circuit.

loose dow′el (*Patmkg.*) A dowel which is not fitted tightly to a part, but made a sliding fit to permit its removal.

loose fit (thread, class 1) (*Mach.*) Used when accuracy is not essential.

loose knot (*Wood*) A knot which is not firmly held in place by growth or position.

loose pul′ley (*Shopwk.*) The idler or carrier pulley of a pair, on which the belt runs when the machine which the belt has to drive is not in use. When the machine has to be driven, the belt is shifted from the loose to the fast pulley.

lop′er (lŏp′ẽr) A swivel used in rope-making.

loss fac′tor (*Elec. Plast.*) The product of the power factor and the dielectric constant.

lost mo′tion (*Mech.*) The difference in the rate of motion of driving and driven parts, due to faulty fittings, slips, etc.

loud–speak′er (*Elec.*) A device for amplifying sound to such an extent that it can be heard at a much greater distance than would be possible without its use.

Louis XV, 1723–1774 (*F u r n.*) A style of French furniture. Light-colored woods were popular; they were decorated with carving, inlay, gilding, or metal ornamentation. Lacquer was much used. Curves were much employed in all shapes and combinations.

Louis XVI, 1774–1793 (*F u r n.*) A style of French furniture easily recognized by the prevalence of straight lines and the slender oval medallions appearing throughout the ornamentation. The woods used were generally painted white or some pale delicate color.

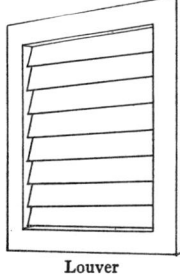
Louver

lou′ver (lōō′vẽr) (*Arch. and Mech.*) A window designed for ventilation, having slats, sloped to keep out the rain. A shrouded opening as on the side of an automobile hood, or on the doors of steel lockers.

low′boy (*Furn.*) An English dressing table or small table with several drawers down the front. They are usually not more than 48 in. high.

low brass (*Metal.*) A yellow brass alloy of 80 per cent copper and 20 per cent zinc. It is ductile and easily drawn, and is used for formed and drawn parts.

low car′bon steels (*Metal.*) Those containing less than 0.30 per cent carbon. Such steels can be casehardened but cannot be tempered.

low case (*Print.*) A type case which contains only a small amount of type.

Lö′wen-herz′ thread (lû′věn-hĕrts′) (*Mach.*) A German thread with flats at top and root, similar in appearance to U.S.S. thread but having a different included angle.

low′er case (*P r i n t.*) Small letters; not capitals.

low fin′ish (*Paper*) A dull paper finish such as eggshell or vellum.

low gear (*Auto.*) The arrangement of change gears which provides the slowest forward speed. (See first gear.)

low in line (*Print.*) Type lower than the adjacent type or material.

low–pres-sure lam′i-nates (*Plast.*) Essentially, laminations made at room temperature, with low pressure or with none.

low re-lief′ (*Furn.*) Carving in which the design projects but slightly from the surface.

low ten′sion (*Auto. Elec.*) The primary circuit (6 volts).

low to pa′per (*Print.*) Worn type, i.e., lower than new type.

low-wing mon′o-plane (*A e r o.*) A monoplane whose wing or wing halves are mounted at or near the bottom of the fuselage.

loz′enge (lŏz′ĕnj) Name applied to a rhombus-shaped figure when used as a unit of decoration as in a lozenge molding.

loz′enge mold′ing (*Arch.*) A molding characterized by lozenge-shaped ornament; used in connection with Norman architecture.

lu′bri-cant (*Engin.*) Oil, grease, graphite, and in general, anything of the sort used to overcome friction and to permit a freer action of parts. (*Mach.*) Also used to exert a cooling action on tool and material that is being cut. The lubricant used for this purpose also removes chips and imparts smoother finish to the parts worked upon.

lu′bri-cant bloom (*Plast.*) Irregular, cloudy, greasy exudation on the surface of a plastic.

lu′bri-ca′tion (*Engin.*) The act of applying lubricants.

Lud′low ty′po-graph (*P r i n t.*) A slug-casting machine used extensively for casting borders, rules, display lines, etc.

lug (*Mach.*) A projection of irregular shape as from a casting.

lug clamp′ing (*Patmkg.*) Clamping action accomplished by passing a bolt through halved or split lugs which are a part of the object to be bound to some other pieces.

lug sill (*Bldg.*) A type of sill longer than the width of the window opening in stone or brick walls. Such a sill differs from a "slip sill" in that its ends are "let in" to the wall.

lum′ber. Timber cut to size in marketable form, as boards, planks, etc.

lum′ber scale (*Lumber*) A graduated measuring scale for determining the number of board feet in rough-sawed lumber.

lu′men bronze (*Metal.*) An alloy of 86 per cent zinc, 10 per cent copper, and 4 per cent aluminum. It is particularly valuable for high-speed bearings which do not carry a heavy load.

lu′mi-nos′i-ty. The quality of emitting or giving out light; shining.

lu′mi-nous. Radiating or emitting light; bright, clear.

lu′mi-nous paint. A paint which makes objects visible in the dark.

lump lime. Lime made from limestone burned or calcined in kilns.

lu-nette′ (lû-nĕt′) (*Furn.*) A chandelier with glass pendants.

lus′ter. Metallic luster is due to the reflection of the light rays on a smooth surface.

lute. (1) To seal a joint as to prevent admission of air. (2) The material used for this purpose.

lye (lī) (*Chem.*) Sodium hydroxide (NaOH), or potassium hydroxide (KOH). A solution or powder derived from a substance containing alkali, used principally in soapmaking.

M

mace (mās) A club-shaped staff used as a symbol of authority.

ma-chin'able. Material capable of being finished by tools or cutters in or on a machine tool.

ma-chine' (*M e c h.*) A device for transforming or transferring energy.

ma-chine' com'po-si'tion (*P r i n t.*) Any type composition done by mechanical method.

ma-chine' draw'ing (*Draft.*) A mechanical drawing of a machine or machine parts provided with notes and dimensions for shop information.

ma-chine' dried (*Papermkg.*) Paper which is dried completely in the web and in contact with the cylinder driers of the machine.

ma-chine' drill'ing (*Mach.*) The drilling of work under a power-driven machine.

ma-chine' fin'ish (*Papermkg.*) A finish intermediate between eggshell and English in smoothness which is produced on the paper machine.

ma-chine' glazed (*Paper*) A paper having a high finish on one side.

ma-chine' mold'ing (*Fdry.*) The use of special machines in the preparation of molds for the production of castings.

ma-chine' rat'ing (*Elec.*) The amount of power a machine can deliver without overheating.

ma-chin'er-y. A group of machines; also, the working parts of an engine or machine.

ma-chin'er-y steel (*Mach.*) An open-hearth steel with 0.15 per cent to 0.25 per cent carbon content. The term is rather general in its use and is frequently applied to any mild steel which cannot be tempered but may be casehardened.

ma-chine' screw. A very commonly used type of screw with clear-cut threads and of a variety of head shapes. It may be used either with or without a nut.

ma-chine' tap (*Metalwk.*) A tap for special use in machines, as distinguished from hand taps which are actuated by a tap wrench.

ma-chine' tool (*Shopwk.*) The name given to any machine of that class which, taken as a group, can reproduce themselves, such as the lathe, drilling machine, planer, milling machine, etc. No other class of machines can be used to build other machines, and because of this, machine tools are known as the "master tools of industry."

ma-chin'ing. The operations performed by machines on metalwork.

ma-chin'ing al-low'ance (*Mach.*) Extra material on the rough part sufficient to permit bringing to finish size by tooling operations.

ma-chin'ist. One who operates machine tools is classed as a machine hand. One who makes and fits parts by hand is called a bench hand. One who assembles machines is often referred to as a floor hand.

mack'le (*Print.*) A spot, blemish, or blurred impression.

mac'ro-mol-e-cule (*Plast.*) A molecule of such size that it exhibits colloidal properties.

---

sāle, surfâce, grăm, humăn, màsk, solár, bär, bâre; mē, êdition, lĕnd, momĕnt, bakēr; kīnd, fĭt; lōde, ômit, ŏlive, cŏnsume, sôrt; dūty, ûtility, nŭt, alŭm, bûrn.

ma-dro′ño (má-drō′nyá) (*Wood*) *Arbutus menziesii.* A flowering tree native to the Pacific Coast. Wood is tough, heavy, and in color light pink with spots of deep red; checks and warps badly. Madroño burl is similar to cherry and has considerable use in furniture manufacture.

mag′a-zine′ (*Arch.*) A protected building or room for the storage of explosives or ammunition. (*Print.*) (1) A paper-bound periodical in book form, usually issued monthly. (2) A part of a composing machine in which matrices or letters are stored ready for assembling into lines.

mag-na′li-um (mă̆g-nā′lĭ-ŭm) (*Metal.*) An alloy of aluminum and from 2 to 10 per cent magnesium. It is very strong and can be easily cast, forged, or machined.

mag-ne′si-a (*Chem.*) A light, white powder derived by calcining magnesium carbonate, used as an antacid laxative.

mag-ne′si-um (*Metal.*) A very light metal with specific gravity of 1.74. It is never used alone but alloyed with aluminum or other metals to produce light-weight airplane parts, etc. The metal ignites very easily and precautions must be taken against fire during machining operations. It is also used in flashlight powders, fireworks, and as a deoxidizer.

mag′net (*Elec.*) A body or substance which has the property of attracting particles of iron to itself. Magnets are of the horseshoe or bar type.

mag′net core (*Elec.*) Usually a soft iron center on which the turns of wire are wound to produce an electromagnet.

mag-net′ic chuck (*Elec., Shopwk.*) A chuck which holds iron and steel work on its face by magnetic attraction. (*Metalwk.*) An important adjunct to surface-grinding machines, especially in holding thin plates during grinding operations. They can be used only with direct current.

mag-net′ic cir′cuit (*Elec.*) The path of magnetic lines of force in a magnetic substance or in magnetic or electric apparatus. A circuit may also include a gap.

mag-net′ic cir′cuit break′er (*Elec.*) An electromagnetic device for opening a circuit.

mag-net′ic coil (*Elec.*) The winding of an electromagnet. A coil of wire wound in one direction, producing a dense magnetic field capable of attracting iron or steel when carrying a current of electricity.

mag-net′ic cut′out′ (*Elec.*) A device for breaking an electrical circuit by means of an electromagnet, instead of by fusing a part of the circuit.

mag-net′ic de-flec′tion (*Tel.*) Movement of electron beam controlled by magnetic fields.

mag-net′ic den′si-ty (*Elec.*) (See FLUX DENSITY.)

mag-net′ic field (*Elec.*) The space in the vicinity of a magnet through which magnetic forces act.

mag-net′ic flux (*Elec.*) Magnetic lines of force set up by an electromagnet, permanent magnet, or solenoid.

mag-net′ic force (*Elec.*) The force by which attraction and repulsion are exerted by the poles of a magnet.

mag-net′ic fu′el pump (*Auto.*) An electrically operated mechanical pump for regulating the fuel supply without the aid of a vacuum system. (See AUTO-PULSE MAGNETIC FUEL PUMP.)

mag-net′ic hoist (*Elec.*) A hoisting device which does its lifting by means of an electromagnet.

mag-net′ic in-duc′tion (*Elec.*) The number of magnetic lines or the magnetic flux per unit of cross-sectional area perpendicular to the direction of the flux.

mag-net′ic nee′dle (*Elec.*) A small slender steel magnet so supported that it can naturally assume a north and south position with regard to the earth's magnetic poles.

mag-net′ic per′me-a-bil′i-ty (*Elec.*) A measure of the ease with which magnetism passes through any substance.

mag-net′ic po-ten′tial (*Elec.*) Is measured by the work involved in moving a unit magnetic pole from the boundary of the field to the point at which the potential is desired.

mag-net′ic screen or shield (*Elec.*) A hollow iron casing, the center of which is free from magnetic lines of force.

mag-net′ic switch (*Elec.*) A switch operated or controlled by an electromagnet.

mag-net′ic whirl (*Elec.*) Around every wire passing electric current a circular magnetic field is built up in the form of whirls or spirals. This does not apply to noninductive winding.

mag′net-ism (*Elec.*) (1) That property of iron, steel, and some other substances, by virtue of which, according to fixed laws, they exert forces of attraction and repulsion. (2) The science that treats of the conditions and laws of magnetic force.

mag′ne-tite (*Min.*) Magnetic iron ore (Fe_3O_4).

mag′net-i-za′tion (*Elec.*) The act of acquiring or communicating magnetism.

mag-ne′to (*Elec.*) A device consisting essentially of permanent magnets and an armature, for generating electricity by electromagnetic induction.

mag′net-o-mo′tive (măg′nĕt-ȯ-mō′tĭv) **force** (*Elec.*) The total magnetizing force integrated over the length of the complete magnetic circuit.

mag′net steel. Usually a good grade of crucible tungsten steel containing some chromium and manganese. Used for permanent magnets.

mag′net wire (*Elec.*) Wire used in winding armatures, field coils, induction coils, etc. It is small, single copper wire, insulated with cotton, silk, or enamel; not impregnated.

Mahlstick

mahl′stick (mäl′stĭk) (*Paint.*) A stick with a ball at one end, used by painters to steady the hand while using the brush.

ma-hog′a-ny (*Wood*) True mahogany Swietenia Mahogani is considered the premier cabinet wood of the world. It grows in southern Florida, the West Indies, Mexico, Central America, Colombia, Venezuela, and in the Upper Amazon region. The heartwood is reddish pink, or salmon, or even yellow when fresh, and turns dark red upon exposure to sun. Weight 25 to 53 lb. per cubic foot; density variable. Grain produces highly attractive figures.

main bear′ings (*Auto.*) The main bearings in an automobile engine are those which carry the crankshaft.

mains (*Elec.*) The electrical conductors from which the branch circuits are supplied.

main shaft (*Mach.*) Is the line of shafting which receives its power directly from the engine or motor and transmits power to other parts.

main sup-port′ing sur′face (*Aero.*) The surface of the wings which makes it possible for an airplane to function.

main′te-nance. Proper care, repair, and keeping in good order.

ma-jol′i-ca (*Pot.*) An earthenware of beautiful luster made by the early Moorish potters, which reached its greatest perfection in Italy in the sixteenth century. It became a lost art, and has been revived with only moderate success.

ma′jor. Greater in number, quantity, or extent. Greater in importance. Principal, leading.

ma′jor ax′is. The long diameter of an ellipse.

ma′jor di-am′e-ter (*Mach.*) Formerly called outside diameter. It refers to the largest diameter of a thread on a screw or nut.

make and break (*Elec.*) The term may be applied to several electrical devices. Primarily, there are a pair of contact points, one stationary, and the other operated by a cam which makes the break in a circuit between these points.

make′–read′y (*Print.*) The operation of making a form ready for printing. It consists of pulling an impression, spotting up, setting guides, etc. Also the paper sheet on which are pasted the overlays for a form.

make′–up (*Print.*) To arrange type matter into pages.

make′–up rule (*Print.*) Steel rule used in making up forms or pages.

mal′a-chite (măl′á-kīt) (*Min.*) One of the ores of copper. A green, basic, cupric carbonate, usually found massive and sometimes as an incrustation; used for ornaments, mosaics, etc. When ground into a powder, it is used as a pigment under the name "mountain green."

ma′lax (*Wood Fin.*) To soften by kneading, rubbing, mixing, or by stirring some thinner substance.

mal′le-a-ble (măl′ê-á-b'l) Capable of being hammered or rolled out without breaking or cracking.

mal′le-a-ble cast i′ron (*Metal.*) Cast iron which has been subjected to partial decarburization. Different from ordinary cast iron in that its structure is fibrous instead of granular. It is used to advantage in parts which are subjected to shock.

mal′le-a-ble-iz′ing (*Metal.*) A method of annealing white cast iron for the purpose of removing most of the carbon or for changing the carbon to temper carbon.

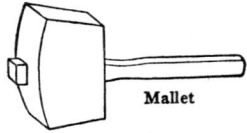
Mallet

mal′let. A wooden hammer.

malt′ose (môl′tōs) (*Chem.*) A crystalline sugar formed from starch in malt, used in breadmaking.

man′age-ment. Administration; direction; superintendence; control.

man′chette′ (män′shĕt′) (*Furn.*) A French term meaning the upholstered cushion on the arm of a chair.

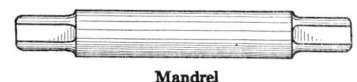
Mandrel

man′drel (*Mach.*) A shaft or spindle on which an object may be fixed for rotation; e.g., when a piece is to be turned in a lathe, it may be carried on a "mandrel" which is supported by the lathe centers. The terms *mandrel* and *arbor* are often used interchangeably.

man′drel stake (*Sheet-Met. Wk.*) A long, straight stake having a rounded face for the greater portion of its length, terminating in a short, flat anvil.

ma-neu′ver (*Aero.*) (1) To operate an aircraft in a skillful manner, so as to cause it to perform evolutions out of the ordinary. (2) To perform tactical or acrobatic evolutions with aircraft.

ma-neu′ver-a-bil′i-ty (*Aero.*) That quality in an aircraft which permits ease of handling.

man′ga-nese′ (*Min.*) A hard, brittle, metallic element, grayish white to red in color, and nonmagnetic; used in the manufacture of steel, glass, and paints.

man′ga-nese′ bronze (*Metal.*) An alloy containing 55-60 per cent copper; 38-42 per cent zinc, and small amounts of tin, manganese, aluminum, iron, and lead. Used for parts requiring strength and toughness.

man′ga-nese′ di-ox′ide (*Elec.*) A depolarizing agent used in primary cells.

man′ga-nese′ steel (*Metal.*) Manganese steel, containing 0.20 to 0.50 per cent carbon and 1.00 to 1.30 per cent manganese, has a high tensile strength and is frequently used to replace 3½ per cent nickel steel. An increase of manganese tends to make the steel very brittle, but with a still greater increase of manganese the ductility, to a certain extent, returns.

man′ga-nin (*Metal.*) An alloy of copper, nickel, and ferromanganese. Much used for standard resistance coils.

man′gling (*Textile*) The pressing of fabric under heated or unheated rollers.

man′hole. An opening through which a workman may gain access to a drain, boiler, sewer, tunnel, etc., or other underground area.

man′i-fold (*Auto.*) Usually a casting or connection containing several branches or parts, as an exhaust manifold on an automobile engine, for conducting the exhaust from each cylinder into a single exhaust pipe.

man′i-fold pa′per (*Print.*) A very thin paper, such as "onionskin," used for duplicating.

man′i-fold vac′u-um (*Auto.*) State of atmospheric tension existing in a manifold when the engine is in operation.

Ma-nil′a (*Papermkg.*) A general term used to describe tan or yellowish paper or paperboard.

ma-nil′a tag (*Papermkg.*) A stiff paper of good folding properties. It is of a light-buff color, its shade varying with the grade.

ma-nip′u-la′tion. The act of working skillfully with the hands.

ma-nom′e-ter (må-nŏm′ê-tẽr) (*Phys.*) An instrument for measuring elastic pressure, as of gases.

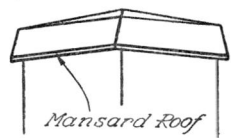
Mansard Roof

man′sard roof (*Arch.*) A rather flat-decked, double-sloped roof, frequently used in placing an additional story on a residence.

man'sion (*Arch.*) A large or pretentious house.

man'tel (*Arch. and Masonry*) The shelf above a fireplace or attached to a chimney breast; also the facing about a fireplace, including the shelf.

man'tel-shelf' (*Masonry*) The shelf of a mantel.

man-tis'sa (*Algebra*) The decimal or fractional part of a logarithm.

man'u-al (*Shopwk.*) (1) Relating to handwork. That which is done by hand. (2) A handbook of instructions.

man'u-al arts. Work performed with the hands.

man'u-al switch (*Auto.*) A hand- or foot-operated switch as opposed to one operated in any other manner.

man'u-script (*Print.*) Material written by hand or by typewriter. Written copy for the printer.

ma'ple (*Woodwkg.*) A hard, light-colored, tough wood much used for flooring and veneers.

mar. To scar or deface.

mar'ble (*Bldg.*) A kind of limestone ranging in color from white to dark gray and to brown; widely used for both interior and exterior finish of buildings; also for switchboard panels. (*Papermkg.*) Paper resembling marble in appearance.

mar'ble dust (*Wood Fin.*) Crushed and pulverized limestone. Large quantities are used in making putty.

mar'bling (*Furn.*) Painting wood in imitation of marble.

mar'gin (*Print.*) A space along an edge or a bounding line; a border. The space on the edge of a printed sheet, which may be blank or contain notes.

mar'gin-al note (*Print.*) Explanatory matter placed in the margin of a page close to the item to which it refers.

ma-rine' glue (*Woodwkg.*) A composition of crude rubber, 1 part; shellac, 2 parts; pitch, 3 parts.

mark'ing awl (*Furn.*) As the name suggests, a pointed steel instrument for "marking out," especially on hardwood.

Marking Awl

mark'ing gauge (*Wood Patmkg.*) A woodworker's gauge, used for gauging lines parallel to the edge of a board. It consists of a bar with an inserted

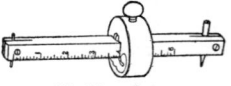
Marking Gauge

pin or scribe, and a sliding head which may be adjusted by means of a thumb screw.

mark'ing knife (*Furn.*) A knife used as the marking awl, especially for softwoods.

mark'ing ma-chine' (*Shopwk.*) A machine for stamping trade-marks, patent dates, etc., on cutlery, gun barrels, etc. Stamps are usually on rolls, and are rolled into the work.

mar'quet-ry (mär'kĕt-rĭ) (*Woodwk.*) An ornamental surface built up of small pieces of various hardwoods to form a pattern. Occasionally ivory, bone, mother-of-pearl, etc., also are used.

marsh gas or meth'ane (mĕth'ān) (*Chem.*) (CH_4) A light, odorless, inflammable, gaseous hydrocarbon, occurring naturally as a product of decomposition of organic matter in marshes and mines, or produced artificially by dry distillation of many organic substances. It constitutes about 30 per cent of coal gas and from 90 to 95 per cent of natural gas.

Mar′ten-sit′ic al-loy′ steels (*Metal.*) Martensitic steels are composed wholly or largely of martensite which is an atomic dispersion of carbon and alpha (crystals of iron). It is very hard, and, therefore, not as tough as annealed or soft steels. It forms by slowly cooling or tempering austenite at about 300 deg. C. It was named for Professor A. Martens, an eminent German metallurgist.

mas′ca-ron (măs′kȧ-rŏn) (*Furn.*) A mask decoration of a human head.

mash seam weld′ing. A seam-welding process wherein the overlap is maintained sufficiently small to permit fusion and plastic reduction of the overlap to approximately the thickness of one of the parts being joined.

mask (*Furn.*) A human, animal, or grotesque face without the rest of the body, used as an ornament.

ma′son-ite. A trade name for an insulating wood-fiber board. It is made with a wide variety of surface finishes. Used extensively for paneling, etc.

ma′son-ry. The work of one who builds with stone, brick, etc.

ma′son's mi′ter (*Furn.*) An early form of joinery used on panel moldings.

mass (*Fine Arts*) A large part of a piece of work consisting of a unity of color. (*Phys.*) Quantity of matter possessed by a body or the measurement of a body's inertia. (*Print.*) Groups of patches of type matter on a page.

mass pro-duc′tion. The manufacture of any article in quantity by the use of special machines and tools.

mas′ter cyl′in-der (*Auto.*) The fluid cylinder containing the piston by means of which the brakes are applied through pressure on the foot pedal.

mas′ter gauge. A gauge of any type kept in reserve for occasional testing the accuracy of similar gauges of everyday use.

mas′ter-keyed′ (*Shopwk.*) A lock is said to be master-keyed when it has been fitted with a special key which will operate it and other locks similarly constructed.

mas′ter switch (*Elec.*) A main switch; a switch controlling the operation of other switches.

mas′ter ta′per (*Mach.*) A standard taper, either inside or outside, by which other tapers are tested.

mas′ter work′man. A workman of more than ordinary skill. The term "master mechanic" is often applied to shop foremen and superintendents.

mas′tic (rock asphalt) Sandstone naturally saturated with bitumen; excellent for paving and floors. (*Plaster.*) A quick-drying cement.

mat (*Plast.*) In plastics, a nonwoven fibrous glass material, blown on a form with binder, and consisting of short length glass fiber, usually cut from Fiberglas roving in the blowing mechanism. Mat is understood as sheet, though the same material is used in Preforms. (See PREFORMS.) The common commercial mat is either 1 or 2 ounce for general use, or it may be overlay mat, a very thin finishing mat. Mat cannot be draped over three dimensional forms, and is therefore used primarily in flat laminations. Draping is accomplished with Fiberglas cloth, which see.

mat board (*Paper*) A thick paper board used for mounting.

matched boards (*Woodwkg.*) Boards finished to secure close joints, by tongue and groove or by rebated edge.

matched met'al mold'ing (*Plast.*) Molding reinforced plastics between two matched metal dies or molds, using a press, and pressure and heat.

matched part'ing (*Wood Patmkg.*) Consists in forming a projection upon the parting surface of the cope part of the pattern and making a corresponding depression in the parting surface of the drag part of the pattern.

match plates (*Fdry.*) Plates of wood or metal on which patterns are mounted to increase production especially when a large number of castings are required.

mat'ed po-si'tion (*Auto.*) When sliding gears are properly meshed they are said to be in mated position.

ma-te'ri-al-ly. In an important manner or degree; substantially; essentially.

ma-te'ri-al well (*Plast.*) Space provided in a compression or transfer mold to care for bulk factor.

mat fin'ish (*Leather and Paper*) A dull, lusterless finish.

math'e-mat'ics. The science which treats of relations between quantities and operations.

ma'trix (mā'trĭcks) In general, a place within which something takes form. (*Print.*) That part of the mold in the type-casting machine which forms the face of the letter. Also a heavy, unsized, and unfinished paper used for making molds for stereotype plates.

matt (*Ceram.*) A glazed finish without gloss.

matte (măt) (*Metal.*) A crude or incompletely refined form of copper. The term is also sometimes applied to a mixture containing many other metals.

mat'ted (*Furn.*) Referring to the rough background of carved oak.

mat'ter (*Phys.*) Anything which has weight and occupies space.

maul. A heavy mallet.

mau'so-le'um (*Arch.*) An elaborate tomb.

mauve (mōv) A delicate purple color or dyestuff.

max'hete (*Metal.*) An alloy steel containing nickel, chromium, tungsten, copper, and silicon. It has a very remarkable capacity for resisting the effects of heat and corrosion. Used very successfully for boiler tubes, furnace parts, etc.

max'i-mum (*Math.*) (1) The greatest quantity, degree, or amount. (2) The highest possible of all the values which a variable or a function can express.

max'i-mum range (*Aero.*) The maximum distance a given aircraft can cover under given conditions, by flying at the economical speed and altitude at all stages of the flight.

max'i-mum rev'o-lu'tions (*Aero.*) The number of revolutions per minute corresponding to the maximum horsepower.

max'i-mum vol'tage (*Elec.*) The highest voltage reached in each alternation of an alternating e.m.f.

mean (*Algebra*) Having an intermediate value between two or more values; an average.

mean chord of a wing *(Aero.)* The quotient obtained by dividing the wing area by the span.

mean line (of an airfoil profile) *(Aero.)* An intermediate line between the upper and lower contours of the profile.

meas'ure *(P r i n t.)* The width of a column, type page, or the width of a job.

meas'ure-ment. Size; area; capacity. The act of measuring.

meas'ures. See apothecaries' fluid measure; avoirdupois weight; circular; cubic; dry; linear; liquid; metric system; square; surveyor's area; time, and troy.

meas'ur-ing ma-chine' *(Shopwk.)* A large bench micrometer caliper of any desired form to measure taps, reamers, gauges, etc. Some are now made to utilize light waves instead of mechanical methods.

meas'ur-ing tape. A graduated tape, steel or linen, usually in 50- or 100-foot lengths, used by engineers, builders, surveyors, etc.

me-chan'ic. A skilled workman who makes, repairs, and assembles machinery or mechanical parts.

me-chan'i-cal brakes *(A u t o.)* Any brake system where pressure on the brake pedal is transmitted to the brake shoes on each wheel by a combination of rods, levers, cams, or cranks.

me-chan'i-cal draw'ing. Drawing accomplished with the use of instruments. Technically, the term includes orthographic projection, architectural and engineering drawing, various kinds of perspectives, and projections.

me-chan'i-cal ef-fi'cien-cy *(Mech.)* The mechanical efficiency of an engine is the ratio of its brake horsepower and its indicated horsepower.

$$\text{m.e.} = \frac{\text{brake h.p.}}{\text{indicated h.p.}}$$

(Phys.) Ratio between "input" and "output."

$$\frac{\text{output}}{\text{input}} = \text{m.e.}$$

me-chan'i-cal en'gi-neer'. One who is expert in the design, construction, and use of machinery or mechanical devices.

me-chan'i-cal en'gi-neer'ing. That science which relates to the designing and constructing of apparatus in which power is generated and transmitted.

me-chan'i-cal lap'ping. (See LAPPING.)

me-chan'i-cal-ly. According to the rules of mechanics. Automatically; by rule; without thought or purpose.

me-chan'i-cal vi'bra-tor *(E l e c.)* A make-and-break device operating mechanically.

me-chan'ic arts. Term usually applied to school-shop training in craftsmanship and the use of tools and machinery.

me-chan'ics. That branch of science which treats of the effect of force upon matter.

me-dal'lion (mê-dăl'yŭn) *(Arch.)* (1) A circular or oval unit of decoration usually surrounded by a frame. (2) A large medal.

me'di-an. The middle; an average.

me'di-um car'bon steel *(Metal.)* Has carbon content between 0.30 and 0.70 per cent.

me'di-um fit (class 3) *(Mach.)* Used for sliding and running fits on

machinery where greater accuracy is necessary than would obtain with "free fit."

me′di-um force fit (class 7)(*Mach.*) Such fits are effected through considerable pressure.

med′ul-lar′y rays (*Wood*) Those fibers or rays which can be seen radiating from the center in a cross section of an exogenous tree. Boards sawed radially from the tree, exposing these rays, have the better grain effects.

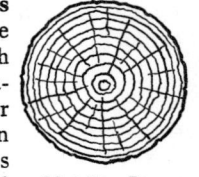
Medullary Rays

meet′ing rail (*Arch.*) The horizontal wood or metal bar which divides the upper and lower sash of a window.

meg or meg′a (*Elec.*) When prefixed to a unit of measurement it means one million times that unit.

meg′a-volt (*Elec.*) A unit of e.m.f. equal to one million volts.

meg′ohm (mĕg′ōm) A unit of electrical resistance equal to one million ohms.

melt′ing point (*Metal.*) The temperature at which a substance changes from a solid to a liquid condition.

melt′ing zone (*Fdry.*) That portion of the cupola above the tuyeres where the metal melts.

men′su-ra′tion (měn′shoo-rā′shŭn) (*Math.*) That branch of mathematics which has to do with the finding of the length of lines, areas of surfaces, and volumes of solids, etc.

mer (*Plast.*) The structural unit in a polymer. (See POLYMER.)

mer′cer-ize (*Chem.*) To treat cotton fiber or fabrics with a solution of caustic alkali which causes the fiber to shrink in length and become stronger and more receptive of dyes. The material assumes a silky luster.

mer′chant bar (*Metal.*) Muck bar is cut into short lengths, piled, reheated, and rerolled into refined bar iron or "merchant bars."

mer′cu-ry (*Chem.*) A silver-white liquid metal with specific gravity of 13.6, obtained principally from cinnabar or mercuric sulphide (HgS), which occurs in brilliant red crystals. Of great use in the forming of amalgams.

mer′cu-ry arc rec′ti-fi′er (*Elec.*) A device invented by Peter Cooper Hewitt for changing alternating into direct current.

mer′cu-ry va′por lamp (*Elec.*) The type of lamp perfected by Cooper Hewitt, in which light is produced by passing a current through mercury vapor.

mesh (*Shopwk.*) Opening formed by crossing strings or wires.

mes-o-col′loids (*Chem. Plast.*) Polymers intermediate between hemicolloids and eucolloids; that is, of a degree of polymerization between about 100 and 1000.

met′al. In the trades the term is used not only to designate the elementary metallic substance but those refined or partially refined products of the ores which have such characteristics as ductility, malleability, fusibility, etc.; also used as a general classification to include a wide variety of alloys.

met′al arc weld′ing. An arc-welding process wherein the electrode supplies the filler metal in the weld.

met′al dip braz′ing. A dip-brazing process wherein the filler metal is obtained from the molten metal bath.

met′a-lene′ nails (*Uphol.*) Nails with large round or flat heads. Used for tacking leather gimp on furniture.

met′al fil′a-ment (*Elec.*) The electrical conductor which glows when heated in an incandescent lamp.

met′al fin′ish-ing. The final step in metalwork in which the piece is given either a dull or glossy finish.

met′al fur′ni-ture (*Print.*) Blocks of type metal, less than type high, in pica lengths and widths, used for filling in space in composition and locking up.

met-al-iz′ing (*Plast.*) Covering plastic with a thin deposit of metal. (See VACUUM METALIZING.)

met′al lacq′uer. Amyl and ethyl acetate solutions of nitrated cotton used as a dipping lacquer for objects made of metal.

me-tal′lic. Consisting of or like metal.

met′al-lur′gy. The art or science of separating metals from ores by smelting or alloying; the study of metals.

met′al pat′tern (*Fdry.*) Foundry patterns are made of metal for durability. They are usually reproduced from wooden patterns.

met′al spin′ning(*Shopwk.*)The process by which light articles in the malleable metals are made to assume circular and molded shapes, through pressure applied to them while in rapid rotation in the lathe.

met′al spray′ing. A protective coating for metals obtained by feeding a wire through a hydrogen-oxygen flame where it is atomized and sprayed on the prepared surface.

met′a-mor′phic rock (*Min.*) Rock which has changed from its original character, as igneous or sedimentary rock.

me′te-or-o-graph′ (*Aero.*) A recording instrument for obtaining meteorological information above the earth's surface. It contains elements to record temperature, pressure, and humidity (also called aerograph).

me-te-or-ol′o-gy (*Phys.*) That branch of physics that treats of the atmosphere and its phenomena, especially conditions that effect the weather.

me′ter (*Mech.*) (1) The fundamental unit of length in the metric system. (2) An instrument or device for measuring fluids, gases, electric currents, as water meter, gas meter, electric meter, etc.

me′ter-ing or′i-fice (*Auto.*) A fixed opening alongside the Venturi through which gasoline flow is regulated to supply fuel on various demands.

me′ter-ing pin (*Auto.*) A pin which seats itself in the metering orifice and regulates the flow of gas through same.

me′ter-ing rod (*Auto.*) The rod linked to the throttle arm by which the gasoline flow is regulated.

meth′ane (*Chem.*) An odorless gas (CH_4) formed by decomposition of vegetable matter or by dry distillation of organic matter. An important component of illuminating gas. (See MARSH GAS.)

meth′an-ol (*Chem.*) CH_3OH. Also known as methyl alcohol, wood alcohol, wood spirit, and by various other names. Used as a fuel, as a solvent for varnishes and paints, and for denaturing alcohol.

meth′yl (*Chem.*) The CH_3 radical. The radical left by the replacement of one hydrogen atom of methane. It is a part of many compounds.

meth′yl ac′e-tone (*Chem.*) A mixture of methyl acetate and acetone. Used as a solvent for rubber.

met′ric gear (mĕt′rĭk)(*S h o p w k.*) Gear designed according to the metric system of measurement.

met′ric plug (*Auto.*) A spark plug on which the screw threads conform to metric standards.

met′ric sys′tem (*Engin.*) A decimal system of weights and measures based on multiples of ten. First used in France, now in universal use in scientific work. (See following tables.)

met′ric threads. Screw threads proportioned to the scale of metric measurement.

mez′za-nine (mĕz′à-nēn) (*Arch.*) A gallerylike floor, usually midway between the ground floor and the one above it.

mez′zo-tint (mĕd′zô-tĭnt) (*Print.*) A process of engraving on copper or steel in imitation of painting in India ink. Invented by Ludwig von Siegen in 1643.

M.F. Abbreviation for machine finish.

mi′ca (mī′kà) (*Min.*) A class of silicates of perfect cleavage; splits into thin scales or sheets.

Length

.03937 in.	0.001 meter	millimeter
.3937 in.	0.01 meter	centimeter
3.937 in.	0.1 meter	decimeter
39.37 in.	1. meter	meter
393.7 in.	10. meters	decameter
328 ft. 1 in.	100. meters	hectometer
.62137 mi.	1.000. meters	kilometer
6.2137 mi.	10,000. meters	myriameter

Surface

1,550 sq. in.	1 square meter	centiare
119.6 sq. yd.	100 square meters	are
2.471 acres	10,000 square meters	hectare

Capacity

United States Measure	Metric Cu. Measure	No. of Liters	Names
.061 cu. in.; 0.27 fl. dram.	1. cu. cm.	0.001	milliliter
.6102 cu. in.; 0.338 fl. oz.	10. cu. cm.	0.01	centiliter
6.1025 cu. in.; 0.845 gill.	0.1 cu. dm.	0.1	deciliter
.9081 qt.; 1.0567 liq. qt.	1. cu. dm.	1.	liter
1.135 pk.; 2.6418 gal.	10. cu. dm.	10.	decaliter
2.838 bu.; 26.418 gal.	0.1 cu. meter	100.	hectoliter
1.308 cu. yd.	1. cu. meter	1,000.	kiloliter, or stere

Weight

Avoirdupois Weight	Weight of What Quantity of Water at Maximum Density	Number of Grams	Names
.0154 gr.	1 cu. millimeter	0.001	milligram
.1543 gr.	10 cu. millimeters	0.01	centigram
1.5432 gr.	.1 cu. centimeter	0.1	decigram
15.432 gr.	1 cu. centimeter	1	gram
.3527 oz.	10 cu. centimeters	10	decagram
3.5274 oz.	1 deciliter	100	hectogram
2.2046 lb.	1 liter	1,000	kilogram, or kilo
22.046 lb.	1 decaliter	10,000	myriagram
220.46 lb.	1 hectoliter	100,000	quintal
2204.6 lb.	1 cu. meter	1,000,000	metric ton, millier, or tonneau

mi′cas (mī′kȧs) (*Papermkg.*) A decorative box-cover paper which has a coating of mica tinted with aniline dyes. It is printed with white intaglio and embossed, as a rule.

mi′cro-am-pere′ (mī′krȯ-ăm-pâr′) (*Elec.*) One millionth of an ampere. 0.000001 amp.

mi′cro-far′ad (mī′krȯ-făr′ăd) (*Elec.*) A unit of capacity, being one millionth of a farad.

mi-crom′e-ter. A device attached to some instrument to permit extreme accuracy in adjustment or in taking measurements, e.g., micrometer caliper.

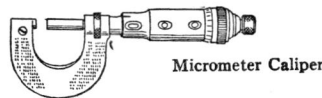
Micrometer Caliper

mi′crom′e-ter cal′i-per. A caliper with graduated screw attachment for measuring minute distances.

mi′cron (mī′krŏn) (*Elec.*) One-millionth part of a meter.

mi′cro-phone (*Elec.*) A device by means of which sound waves produce a fluctuation of current in an electrical circuit.

mi′cro-scope. An instrument containing one or more lenses to permit the observation and study of minute objects which would be invisible without such aid.

a volt. 0.000001 volt.

mi′cro-volt′ (*Elec.*) One millionth of

mi′cro-wave (*Tel.*) Radio waves less than one meter in length for linking remote equipment to station, and stations to other stations.

mi′cro-wave re-flec′tors (*Tel.*) Disklike reflectors used to guide microwave beams.

mid′dle space (*Print.*) Space cast four to an em of any particular body.

mid′wing mon′o-plane (*Aero.*) A monoplane whose wing is mounted approximately midway between top and bottom of the fuselage.

mil. One thousandth of an inch (0.001″).

mild steel. A steel very low in carbon. It welds, but does not temper.

mil′dew. A sort of mold which forms on objects exposed to dampness.

mil foot (*Elec.*) A standard of resistance in wire. The resistance of one foot of wire, one mil in diameter.

milk sug′ar (*Chem.*) (See LACTOSE.)

mill (*Factory*) A building or group of buildings in which manufacturing processes are carried on. The term is commonly, but not universally, used in speaking of various kinds of factories. (*Mach.*) To machine with rotating toothed cutters on a milling machine.

mill file (*Metalwk.*) A single cut file made in any cut from rough to dead smooth. Used for lathe work, draw filing, etc.

mil′li-am-pere′ (mĭl′ĭ-ăm-pâr′) (*Elec.*) One thousandth of an ampere.

mil′li-hen′ry (*Elec.*) One thousandth of a henry. A unit of capacity.

mil′li-me′ter (*Engin.*) One thousandth part of a meter is equal to .03937 in.

mill′ing (*Shopwk.*) The process of operating a milling machine.

mill′ing cut′ters (*Mach.*) All those various types of rotary cutters designed for use on a milling machine.

mill′ing ma-chine′ (*Shopwk.*) A machine in which the operating tool is a revolving cutter. It has a table for carrying work and moving it so as to feed against the cutter.

mill'ing ma-chine', u'ni-ver'sal (*Shopwk.*) The worktable and feeds are so arranged that all classes of plane, circular, helical, index, or other milling may be done. It is equipped with index centers, chuck, etc.

mill'ing ma-chine', ver'ti-cal (*Shopwk.*) It differs from the horizontal machine mainly in having a vertical spindle for carrying the cutter.

mil'li-volt (*Elec.*) One thousandth of a volt. 0.001 volt.

mill'work (*Woodwkg.*) The finished woodwork, machined, and partly assembled at the mill.

mill'wright. A mechanic who installs machinery in a mill or shop.

mim'e-o-graph'. An apparatus in which a thin paper, coated with paraffin, is used as a stencil to reproduce copies of writing or typewriting.

min'a-ret(mĭn'ȧ-rĕt)(*Arch.*) A slender, towerlike structure as on a mosque.

min'er-al'o-gy. The science relating to the properties, classification, etc., of minerals.

min'er-al wool (*Engin.*) A fiber made by sending a blast of steam through molten slag or rock. It is widely used as a heat insulator.

min'er's safe'ty lamp. (See DAVY SAFETY LAMP.)

min'i-mum. The least quantity or amount; the lowest point or amount reached or registered; lowest or least.

min'i-mum fly'ing speed(*Aero.*)The lowest steady speed that can be maintained, with any throttle setting whatever, by an airplane in level flight at an altitude greater than the span of the wings.

min'i-mum glid'ing an'gle (*Aero.*) The acute angle between the horizontal and the most nearly horizontal path along which an airplane can descend steadily in still air when the propeller is giving no thrust.

min'i-mum speed (*Aero.*) The lowest speed at which an airplane can maintain flight.

min'ing. The process of extracting minerals from the earth.

min'ing en'gi-neer'. An engineer whose duties include the opening and working of mines and the extraction of metals from their ores.

min'ion (*Print.*) A type size about equal to 7 point. The name was used prior to the establishment of the point system.

mi'nor. Nonessential; not vital or weighty; inconsiderable.

mi'nor ax'is. The short diameter of an ellipse.

mi'nor di-am'e-ter (screw threads) (*Mach.*) The smallest diameter of the thread on a screw or nut.

mi'nus charge (*Elec.*) A negative charge indicated by the minus sign. Such electrification as is developed on a resinous substance when rubbed with fur or flannel.

min'ute (*Arch.*) A measure used by architects to determine the proportions of a column, or order. It is the sixtieth part of the lower diameter of a column.

mis'a-lign'ment of wheels (*Auto.*) Wheels not in proper alignment make a car hard to steer, cause excessive strains throughout the car, and bring about very rapid wear on tires. Front wheels should be tested for alignment at least once or twice a year.

mis-matched' lum'ber. Worked lumber that does not fit tightly at all points of contact between adjoining pieces, or in which the surfaces of adjoining pieces are not in the same plane.

mis'print (*Print.*) To print incorrectly. Any typographical error.

mis'sion type (*Man. Arts*) Furniture, usually of oak, finished in rather dark tones. Characterized by straight lines rather than curves; frequently massive in structure.

mi'ter. The joining of two pieces at an evenly divided angle, as the corner of a picture frame. (*Carp.*) To match angles; a cut made at an angle for a joint.

mi'ter box. A device used as a guide in sawing miter joints.

mi'ter cut (*Woodwkg.*) A cut made at an angle of 45 deg., so that two pieces similarly cut will form a right angle when joined.

Miter Box

mi'ter-er (*P r i n t.*) The hand- or power-operated device used for mitering borders, rules, leads, etc.

mi'ter gear (*M a c h.*) A bevel gear whose pitch cone is placed at an exact angle of 45 deg. with its axis. Pairs of miter wheels working together are always of equal diameter, pitch, and number of teeth.

mi'ter-ing (*Cabwk.*) The act of joining by the use of miter joints.

mi'ter plane (*Carp.*) A plane for use with a miter board, or for general utility in angle and butt-joint making.

mi'ter–saw cut, or mi'ter–saw'ing board (*Carp.*) An appliance used to guide the saw at the desired angle.

mi'ter square (*Carp.*) A tool similar to the try square, but having a head which permits the laying out of both 90-deg. and 45-deg. angles.

Miter Square

mi'ter wheel. A bevel gear wheel in which the line of the pitch cone makes an angle of 45 deg. with the axis of the wheel. Two such gears meshed together connect shafts running at a right angle. Same as miter gear.

mi-to'graphy (*Print.*) The art of silk screen process printing.

mix'ture (*Chem.*) A combination of two or more substances not chemically united with each other.

M.M.F. (*Elec.*) Magnetomotive force, or magnetic motive force.

mod'el-ing (*Plaster.*) Forming to a desired shape by smoothing the surface.

mock-up (*Aero.*) A mechanical object or device used as an aid in teaching.

Mod'ern (*Print.*) A Roman type having sharper hair lines and longer serifs than the old style.

mod'u-late (*Radio*) The change produced in the carrier wave of a radio transmitter, usually caused by combining it with an A.F. (audio frequency) wave.

mod'ule (*Arch.*) A measure of proportion used by architects in designing columns.

mod'u-lus. A number, coefficient, or quantity which measures a force, function, or effect.

mod'u-lus of e'las-tic'i-ty. The ratio of stress per unit area to the corresponding strain per unit length, the distortion or strain being within the elastic limit.

mod′u·lus of ri·gid′i·ty (*Engin.*) Shearing stress divided by shearing strain.

mo·gul′ (*Elec.*) A socket or receptacle used with large incandescent lamps of 300 watts or over.

mo′hair (*Furn.*) A fabric made of the hair of Angora goats; also an imitation of such fabric.

Mohs′ scale. A numerical grading of hardness of minerals ranging from soft talc with a hardness of 1, to diamond with a hardness of 10.

mois′ture con′tent (*Papermkg.* and *Print.*) The amount of moisture content in finished paper.

mo′lar so·lu′tion (*Chem.*) One which contains the molecular weight of a solute expressed in grams, per 1000 c.c.

mold (*Fdry.*) (*n.*) That in which a shape is reproduced, as the form in which a casting is made. (*Plast.*) In plastics, the receptacle, usually metal, into whose cavities, plastic is shaped, either by chemical reaction alone, but more often, by heat, pressure, and the reaction. Other materials used as molds for plastics are, the resin itself, glass, ceramic, latex, and plastisol. The last two materials are flexible. (*Print.*) That part of a casting machine in which the body of the type is cast.

mold′board (*Wood Patmkg.*) The board on which the pattern is placed preliminary to ramming up the mold.

molded–intake belt course (*Bldg.*) Usually an elaboration of a plain band course of masonry or cut-stone work placed at a point where the thickness of the upper wall is less than that of the wall below it.

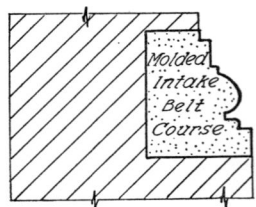

mold′ed plas′tics (*Plast. Art*) Those articles such as, small clock cases, toilet goods, brush backs, mirror frames, etc., made from molding powder, usually in dies under heavy pressure.

mold′er's ram′mer (*Fdry.*) A wooden tool, cylindrical at one end and wedge shaped at the other; used by founders in "ramming up" molds.

mold′ing (*Arch.*) An ornamental strip used in the finishing of buildings. Moldings are of many shapes and sizes. (*Fdry.*) The act of making a casting by means of a pattern from which a mold is made.

mold′ing board (*Plast.*) Pressed sheets, mixed fibers and resins, used to reinforce molded articles.

mold′ing plane (*Furn.*) Small plane of various sizes, shapes, and widths.

mold′ing pow′der (*Plast.*) Uncured plastic granules, compounded with fillers, pigments, plasticizers, etc., prepared for use in compression, injection and extrusion machines, where pressure and heat cause chemical changes that result in hardened products.

mold re·lease′ (*Plast.*) See PARTING AGENT.

mold'ing sand (*Fdry.*) Foundry sand used in the making of molds.

mole (*C h e m.*) (Gram molecular weight) The molecular weight expressed in grams.

mo-lec'u-lar the'o-ry (*Chem., Phys.*) The theory that matter is made up of minute particles called "molecules," and that each molecule has the same properties as has the mass as a whole.

mol'e-cule (*Chem. and Phys.*) The smallest part of any substance that can exist separately and still retain its properties and composition.

mo-lyb'de-nite (mô-lĭb'dĕ-nīt) A greasy graphite like ore of the metal molybdenum occurring in granite, gneiss, and limestone.

mo-lyb'de-num (*Metal.*) This metal, when alloyed with steel, produces a hard steel much used for high speed cutting tools. Also used in cast alloys.

mo'ment (*Engin.*) The product of a force, and the perpendicular of its line of action from the point on which it acts.

mo'ment of a coup'le (*Math.*) The product of the magnitude of one of the forces and the perpendicular distance between the lines of action of the forces.

mo'ment of a force (*Engin.*) The measure of the tendency of the force to cause rotation about the axis. The product of the force and the perpendicular distance from the axis to its line of action. It is measured in foot-pounds or inch-pounds.

mo'ment of in-er'ti-a (ĭn-ûr'shĭ-à) (*Engin.*) The sum of the products of each particle of a moving body multiplied into the squares of the distances of the particles from their neutral axis.

mo-men'tum. The quantity of motion. The product of the mass of a body and the velocity imparted to it equals the momentum.

Mond "sev'en-ty" al-loy (Mônd) (*Metal.*) A nickel copper alloy. Tensile strength runs as high as 90,000 pounds.

Mon'el met'al (Mŏn'ĕl) (*Chem.*) An alloy of 67 per cent nickel, 28 per cent copper, and 5 per cent cobalt and iron. It is practically noncorrosive and is used for acid-resisting chemical equipment, cooking apparatus, screens, etc.

Monkey Wrench

mon'key wrench. An adjustable wrench named for its inventor, Thomas Monkey.

mon'o-bloc (*Mach.*) Cast or made in one piece.

mo'no'coque' fu'se-lage (mô'nô'kôk' fū'zê-lâj) (*Aero.*) A type of fuselage construction wherein the structure consists of a thin shell of wood, metal, or other material, supported by ribs, frames, bell frames, or bulkheads, but usually without longitudinal members other than the shell itself.

mon'o-graph (*Print.*) A booklet or pamphlet in which but one thing is described.

mon'o-lith. A single piece or block of stone, especially of large size, standing alone.

mon'o-mer (*Chem. Plast.*) The basic component, or one of the basic components in the manufacture of plastics whose reaction forms a polymer. (See POLYMER.)

mo-no'mi-al (mô-nō'mĭ-ăl) (*Algebra*) Consisting of a single term.

mon'o-plane (*A e r o.*) An airplane which has but one main supporting surface sometimes divided into two parts by the fuselage.

mon'o-rail' crane (*Engin.*) A traveling crane which is suspended from a single rail.

mon'o-scope (*Tel.*) A television camera tube which contains a simple picture or pattern used for test purposes.

mon'o-tone. (1) Sameness of tone. A style of speech which is characterized by such uniformity of tone. (2) (*Print.*) A type face in which the various elements are all of equal width.

mon'o-tron hard'ness test. A testing machine which registers on dials the depth of penetration of a diamond under certain load conditions.

mon'o-type (*P r i n t.*) A typesetting machine that sets single letters instead of words or lines as in the linotype machine.

mor'dant (*Art*) The corrosive used in etching. (*Chem.*) The name given to compounds which unite chemically with dyestuffs to produce a permanent color, as in the dyeing of wool and silk goods.

Mo-resque' (mô-rĕsk') (*F u r n.*) A Moorish style of decoration, marked by high coloring and gilding.

Mo-roc'co goat-skin (*Leather.*) A thin easily worked leather made from oriental (moroccan) goatskin. Supplied in a variety of colors. Excellent for lining articles made of heavier leathers.

Morse code (*E l e c.*) A system of dots and dashes, transmitted by electricity, to represent letters and numbers in the sending of messages.

Morse ta'per (*Mach.*) Standard taper from 0 to 7 for fitting the shanks of drills and other tools to machine spindles.

mor'tar (*Masonry*) A mixture of sand and slaked lime for joining bricks, stone, etc.

mor'tar board (*Masonry*) A square board, with handle underneath, on which a mason holds mortar. A hawk.

mor'tar box (*Masonry*) The large box or trough in which mortar or plaster is mixed.

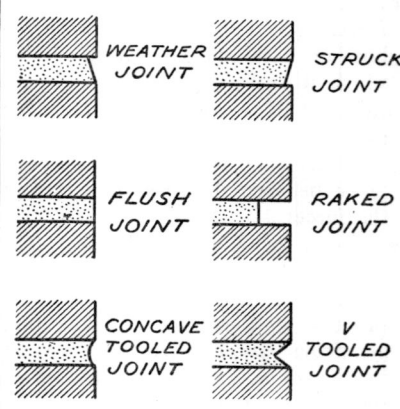

mor'tar joints. A variety of styles of finishing the mortar in brick or masonry work.

mor′tise (*Print.*) An opening in a printing plate in which type characters can be inserted. (*Woodwkg.*) A space hollowed out, as in a piece of wood, to receive a tenon; mortise-and-tenon joint.

Mortise-and-Tenon Joint

mor′tise chis′el (*Woodwk.*) A narrow face, heavy-bodied chisel used in cutting mortises.

mor′tise gauge (*Woodwk.*) A woodworker's tool consisting of a block or head and a bar containing two scratch pins which can be adjusted to the desired width of the mortise to be cut.

mor′tise lock (*Arch.*) Any lock that is fitted into a mortise.

mor′tis-ing ma-chine′ (*Woodwkg.*) A machine for cutting mortises in wood, either by means of a chisel or by a circular cutting bit.

mo-sa′ic. A design formed by small pieces of glass, stone, or tile, usually set in a ground of cement or stucco.

moss edge (*Furn.*) A decorative edge, made of a heavy-pile material, used in upholstery.

moth′er–of–pearl′. The hard iridescent layer on the inner surface of certain shells, as the pearl oysters; used extensively for making buttons and other small articles.

mo-tif′ (mô-tēf′) (*Furn.*) A predominant idea in design, or decoration.

mo′tion (*Phys.*) Change of position which a body undergoes.

mo′tion stud′y (*Masonry*) Relates to a study of the movements of workmen in performing certain operations. Such study is made with the idea of increasing the efficiency of mechanics by the elimination of unnecessary motions.

mo′tive pow′er (*Engin.*) The particular source of energy which is applied to activate a prime mover or a machine.

mo-tom′e-ter (mô-tŏm′ê-tēr) (*Mach.*) A speed counter, as for a steam engine; also a speedometer.

mo′tor (*Elec.*) A machine for transforming electrical energy into mechanical energy. (*Mech.*) An internal-combustion engine, as the gasoline engine of an automobile.

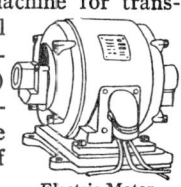
Electric Motor

mo′tor an′a-lyz′er (*Auto.*) A group of instruments, usually assembled in a single case or on a single panel, by which such items as cylinder compression, air-fuel ratio, and ignition timing can be checked.

mo′tor drive (*Shopwk.*) The modern method of supplying power to a machine by a motor, usually directly connected to it, as distinguished from the older style of delivering power from an engine, through the line shaft and countershaft to the machine.

mo′tor gen′er-a′tor (*Elec.*) An electric motor driving a generator changing alternating current to direct current, or the reverse.

mo′tor hoist. A hoisting device operated either manually or by power.

mo′tor jet (*Aero.*) A jet engine having its compressor driven by a reciprocating gas engine. An aircraft having such an engine.

mo′tor start′er (*Elec.*) A variable resistance box connected in series with a motor for starting duty. As the speed of the motor increases, the resistance is decreased until it is entirely cut out of circuit.

mo′tor torque (tôrk) (*Elec.*) Turning effort. The turning moment or pull which causes rotation, or tendency to rotate, in a motor.

mot′tled. Covered with spots of different color or shades of color. (*Paper*) A paper with a variegated finish which is intentionally produced. Also applied to a defect called "crushing" present in the web during pressing which resembles curdled milk in appearance.

mount (*Furn.*) A fitting or other ornamented piece usually made of metal, placed on furniture to decorate and strengthen.

mov′ie-o′la (*Tel.*) A motion-picture device for editing film.

moving–coil gal′va-nom′e-ter (*Elec.*) A sensitive instrument in which a movable coil supported in a strong magnetic field, set up by a permanent magnet, indicates or detects small currents of electricity flowing through the coil.

mov′ing-nee′dle gal′va-nom′e-ter (*Elec.*) An instrument in which a movable magnetic needle indicates the presence of an electric current flowing through a coil of many turns of fine wire wound around or near the needle.

mu′cid (mū′sĭd) Musty; moldy.

mu′ci-lage. An adhesive solution made from a vegetable gum and water.

muck bar (*Metal.*) In the manufacture of wrought iron, the bloom is passed through muck rolls and is then known as "muck bar." Muck bar contains too much slag to permit the use of the metal without further refining.

mud′sill (*Arch.*) A foundation timber of a structure placed directly on the ground.

muf′fle (*Ceram.*) The fire-clay chamber in which ware is placed for firing. (*Mech.*) To reduce the noise of a motor exhaust by passing it through the device known as a muffler.

muf′fle fur′nace (*Art Met.*) A small furnace operated either by electric current or gas. Used for obtaining the high temperature necessary for annealing, hardening, and enameling metals.

muf′fler (*Auto.*) A mechanical device consisting usually of a hollow cylinder attached to the exhaust pipe of a gasoline engine, through which the exhaust is passed in order to partially deaden the sound.

mulch (*Agric.*) Any substance used to protect roots of plants from heat, cold, or drought, or to keep fruit clean.

mule–pul′ley stand (*Mech.*) An arrangement of two loose pulleys on an auxiliary shaft, so placed as to facilitate the transmission of power between two shafts which are at an angle with each other. Often referred to as a device for carrying power around corners.

mul′lion (*Arch.*) The large vertical division of a window opening. In grouped windows, the member which separates the different units.

mul′ti-col′or press (*Print.*) A press on which more than two colors are printed at one time.

mul′ti-fil′a-ment lamp (*Elec.*) Large incandescent lamps are often made with a number of filaments joined in parallel so that the lamp may continue to give service if one filament should burn out.

Mul′ti-graph. A device for printing letters and documents so that they resemble typewritten copies.

Mul′ti-graph pa′per (*Paper*) Any paper appropriate for use on the multigraph machine.

mul′ti-part bear′ings (*Mach.*) Consist primarily of three or more sections in contact with the journal, and arranged to give least interference with oil film. These sections are contained in a housing. Bearings of this type are used on heavy-duty installations.

mul′ti-plane (*A e r o.*) A biplane or triplane; any airplane with two or more main supporting surfaces placed one above another.

mul′ti-ple. Consisting of many parts; repeated many times. A number which contains another an exact number of times without a remainder.

mul′ti-ple disk clutch (*A u t o.*) A clutch consisting of a number of faced disks, one set driving and the other driven; pressure is furnished by a coil spring under compression. The clutch is released by pressure on the clutch pedal. There are two types of these clutches, the wet and the dry. The wet type is essentially the same except that it runs in a bath of lubricating oil mixed with kerosene.

mul′ti-ple drill′ing ma-chine′. A machine in which a number of drill spindles are arranged parallel to each other, and are driven simultaneously.

mul′ti-ple pro-jec′tion weld′ing. A projection-welding process wherein two or more separate welds are made simultaneously in parallel.

mul′ti-ple se′ries (*Elec.*) A parallel connection of two or more series circuits.

mul′ti-ple–thread′ed screw (*Mach.*) A screw with several helixes winding around its body. Used to impart more rapid motion than could be obtained by a single-threaded screw.

mul′ti-pli′er (*E l e c.*) A known resistance used with a voltmeter or a galvanometer to increase their range.

mul′ti-po′lar (*E l e c.*) Having more than two poles.

mul′ti-po′lar mo′tor (*Elec.*) A motor which has four or more field magnet poles.

mul′ti-speed mo′tor (*Elec.*) A motor capable of being driven at any one of two or more different speeds independent of the load.

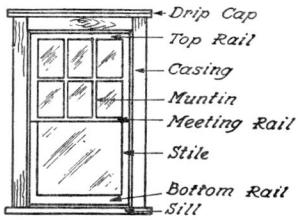

mun′tin (*Arch.*) The small member that divides the glass in a window sash.

Muntz met′al (Mŭnts) (*Metal.*) An alloy of 60–62 parts copper and 38–40 parts zinc. It is used for ship sheathing.

mu′ri-a′tic ac′id (*Chem.*) Commercial name commonly applied to hydrochloric acid (HC1).

Mush′et steel (Mŭsh′ĕt) (*M e t a l.*) Contains 9 per cent tungsten, 2.5 per cent manganese, and 1.85 per cent carbon. It is used mainly for cutting tools, particularly for those used for taking heavy cuts on extra hard material.

mus′lin cov′er (*Uphol.*) An excellent first cover under which the stuffing can be drawn down to desired shape and firmness. This is essential when the top covering is to be of silk or damask.

mut′ton quad (*Print.*) An em quad.

mu′tu-al in-duc′tance (*Elec.*) The effect produced by the magnetic field of one coil acting on, or linking with, a second coil. The voltage induced in one circuit by the current changes in another circuit.

mu′tule (mū′tūl) (*Arch.*) A flat block under the corona of the Doric cornice. The same as rafter ends in wood construction.

myr′tle (*Wood*) *Myrtus*. Also known as California laurel. The wood is hard, strong, greenish yellow with high lights which make it attractive as veneer. On the West Coast of the United States it is a general-purpose wood.

N

N.A.C.A. cowl′ing (*Aero.*) A cowling enclosing a radial air-cooled engine, consisting of a hood, or ring, and a portion of the body behind the engine, so arranged that the cooling air smoothly enters the hood at the front and leaves through a smooth annular slot between the body and the rear of the hood.

na-celle′ (nà-sĕl′)(*Aero.*) An enclosed shelter for passengers or for a power plant. A nacelle is usually shorter than a fuselage and does not carry the tail unit.

nail. A slender piece of metal, one end of which is pointed, the other end having a head, either flattened or rounded. It is a common means of fastening together several pieces of wood or other material by striking the head with a hammer. The term *penny* as applied to nails refers to the number of pounds per 1,000 nails; e.g., six-penny nails means six pounds per 1,000; three-penny means three pounds per 1,000, etc.

nail pull′er (*Mech.*) (1) The ordinary small pinch bar or wrecking bar provided with a forked end which passes about the nail below the head. (2) A mechanical device with two jaws, one of which has a heel, which provides a leverage for gripping the nail and for pulling it from the wood.

nail punch (*Woodwkg.*) Same as NAIL SET.

Nail Set

nail set (*Wood Patmkg.*) A small rod of steel 4 or 5 in. long with one end drawn to a taper and slightly cupped to prevent it from slipping off the head of the nail; used in sinking the head of a nail below the surface.

naph′tha (năf′thà) (*Chem.*) A distillate of petroleum, between gasoline and benzine. It has considerable use as a cleanser.

naph′tha-lene (năf′thà-lēn) (*Chem.*) ($C_{10}H_8$) This compound occurs in coal tar from which it is separated as white, crystalline, volatile flakes. It is used extensively in the preparation of dyestuffs and as an antiseptic and moth preventative.

Na′tion-al coarse thread (*Mach.*) The screw thread of common use, formerly known as the United States Standard thread.

Na′tion-al E-lec′tri-cal Code(*Elec.*) A set of rules to guide electricians when installing electrical conductors, devices, and machinery.

Na′tion-al fine thread (*Mach.*) Same form as National coarse threads but of finer pitch. Much used in automobile work. Formerly known as the S.A.E. thread.

na′tion-al form of screw thread. The profile is the same as the United States Standard.

Na′tion-al Spe′cial threads (*Mach.*) Symbol N.S. Threads of the same form as National Series but divided into three different pitch classifications; the 8-pitch series on diameters 1 to 6 in.; the 12-pitch series ½ to 6

---

sāle, surfâce, grăm, humăn, màsk, solàr, bär, bâre; mē, êdition, lĕnd, momĕnt, bakēr; kīnd, fĭt; lōde, ômit, ŏlive, cŏnsume, sôrt; dūty, ûtility, nŭt, alŭm, bûrn.

in., and the 16-pitch series on sizes ¾ to 4 in.

na′tive cop′per (*Min.*) A very high-grade copper such as is mined in the metallic state in the Lake Superior district. Much used for electrical purposes.

nat′u-ral (*Papermkg. and Print.*) The color of paper obtained from the natural color of the pulp with little, if any, artificial color added.

nat′u-ral ce-ment′ (*Engin.*) As distinguished from Portland cement, is quick setting, cheaper in price, lighter color, and less in strength.

nat′u-ral gas (*Chem.*) Natural gas is formed in the earth, particularly in oil regions in enormous quantities. Has a very high calorific value, and makes an excellent fuel.

nat′u-ral res′ins (*Chem. Plast.*) Solid substances from vegetable excretions exhibiting brittleness, vitreous luster, conchoidal fracture, water-insoluability and varying fusibility and solubility.

nau′ti-cal. Anything relating to navigation.

nau′ti-cal meas′ure. 6080.20 feet = 1 nautical mile or knot; 3 nautical miles = 1 league; 60 nautical miles = 1 degree (at the equator).

nave (*Arch.*) The main body of a cruciform church between the aisles.

N.B. (*Print.*) Means note well. From the Latin *nota bene*.

neat ce-ment′ (*Masonry*) A pure cement mortar, i.e., not cut down by the admixture of sand.

neat's-foot oil. An oil obtained by boiling the feet and shin bones of neat cattle, which are cattle of the ox kind, in water. It is of a pale yellow color, and its chief use is for softening leather.

neck (*Arch.*) The upper part of the shaft of a column immediately below the capital. (*Wood Patmkg.*) That portion of a rod or bar which, for a short piece of its length, is turned down to a smaller diameter than is allowed to remain on either side of such a cut.

neck′ing (*Arch.*) A narrow molding extending around the upper part of a column, pillar, or the like. (*Shopwk.*) The reducing in size of some comparatively short portion of the length of a piece at some place other than at the extreme end.

neck′ing tool (*Shopwk.*) Tool for turning a groove or neck in a piece of work.

nee′dle bear′ing. A roller bearing in which the rollers are thin enough to resemble needles.

nee′dle point′ (*Furn.*) An embroidery of woolen threads upon canvas, used as a covering in upholstery. (*Mech.*) Any tool or instrument drawn to a fine, sharp point is said to have a needle point.

nee′dle valve (*M e c h.*) A valve in which the flow of liquid or gas is regulated by the adjustment of a pin or needle point, which sets in a cone-shaped depression having a small hole at the bottom.

ne′ga-tive brush′es of a dy′na-mo (*E l e c.*) The commutator brushes which are connected with the negative terminal.

ne′ga-tive car′bon (*Elec.*) The lower carbon in a continuous-current arc lamp.

neg′a-tive charge (*Elec.*) A point of potential with an excess of electrons.

ne′ga-tive con-duc′tor (*Elec.*) A conductor leading from the negative terminal.

neg′a-tive ghosts (*Tel.*) Ghost pictures in which the black and white areas are reversed.

ne′ga-tive plate (*E l e c.*) (1) In a storage cell, the spongy lead plate which, during discharge, is the negative plate or terminal. (2) In a primary cell, the carbon, copper, platinum, etc., is the negative electrode.

ne′ga-tive side of cir′cuit (*Elec.*) The conducting path of the circuit from the current-consuming device back to the source of supply.

ne′o–clas′sic (*Arch.*) (1) new classic; (2) revival of classic taste in architecture, furniture, etc., usually applied to early 18th century revival due to Pompeian discoveries.

ne′on light (*Elec.*) A type of lamp with two electrodes instead of a filament. The ionization of neon gas contained in the tube produces illumination. Such lights are extensively used in advertising displays.

ne′on–light ig-ni′tion tim′ing (*Auto.*) By connecting a small neon light by means of wires in the secondary circuit of the ignition wiring in series with No. 1 spark plug, the light flashes on and off as the breaker makes contact and opens. An engine is in proper time when the light flashes directly on a timing mark on the flywheel or vibration dampener.

nep (*Textile*) The small knots in cotton due to inferior bolls or poor ginning.

Nernst lamp (*Elec.*) An incandescent lamp whose lighting element consists of a pencil composed of the refractory oxides of rare earth.

nest′ed ta′bles (*Furn.*) A set of tables, usually four, made to fit one into the other when not in use.

nest of saws (*Woodwk.*) A combination of compass saws consisting of several blades of different lengths for use in the same handle. Used for light work.

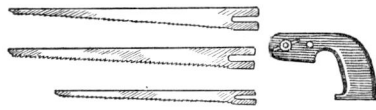

Nest of Saws

nest plate (*Plast.*) A retainer plate with a depressed area for cavity blocks used in injection molding.

neu′tral (*Auto.*) The gear-shift position in which engine power is not transmitted to the driving axle, i.e., the speed-change gears are disengaged. (*Elec.*) Neither positive nor negative.

neu′tral ax′is (*Engin.*) In a simple beam, the top fibers are always in compression and the lower fibers always in tension. There must, therefore, be some point at which the fibers are neither in compression nor tension. The position of these neutral fibers is called the "neutral axis" of the section.

neu′tral flame. A gas-welding flame wherein perfect combustion prevails.

neu′tral-i-za′tion (*C h e m.*) Making neutral or inert, as by the addition of an alkali to acid solution.

neu′tral po-si′tion (*Auto.*) That position of the gear-shift lever which places the change gears out of contact permitting the engine to run idle without giving motion to the car.

neu′tral wire (*Elec.*) The balance wire. The control conductor in a three-wire distribution system. The wire carries the unballanced current.

neu′tro-dyne (*Elec.*) A radio circuit in which control of unwanted "feed back" is effected by neutralizing condensers.

neu′tron (*Phys.*) One of the three basic atomic particles, particles, weighing about the same as the protron, but having no electric change.

new′el (*Arch.*) A post at the top or bottom of a flight of stairs, supporting the handrail.

news (*Papermkg.*) A class of papers made chiefly from ground wood pulp and used for newspapers.

new sand (*Fdry.*) Sand that has not been used for molding.

news′board′ (*Paper*) A cheap paper board made for the most part of waste newspaper.

news cases (*Print.*) Type cases formerly used in newspaper work but now supplanted by the California, New York, and Yankee job cases.

news′print (*Print.*) A plain woodpulp paper used for newspapers and where low-priced stock is required.

news stick (*Print.*) A fixed-measure composing stick used to control column width. Used for newspaper work.

news–tone (*Print.*) A halftone, 100 line or coarser, etched on zinc, usually for newspaper illustration.

New′ton's Laws of mo′tion (*Phys.*) 1st Law — Every body continues in a state of rest or in uniform motion in a straight line, except as it is compelled by a force to change its state of rest or motion. 2nd Law — If a body is acted upon by several forces, it is acted upon by each of these as if the others did not exist. 3rd Law — To every action there is always an equal reaction, i.e., if a force acts to change the state of motion of a body, the body offers a resistance equal and directly opposite to the force.

New York job case (*Print.*) A three-section case, usually 32¼ by 16⅝ in. in size, containing boxes for capitals, lower-case letters, and small capitals.

nib′bler (*Mach.*) A metalworking machine capable of cutting odd shapes from plate and sheet metal by nibbling or biting off small particles.

nibs. Points, as of a pen.

niche (nĭch)(*Arch., Plaster.*) A recess in a wall, generally to receive a statue.

nich′rome (nĭk′rōm)(*Metal.*) A trade name given to an alloy of nickel and chromium. It welds readily and machines well with good high-speed cutting steel. Used for electric heater units and other resistance devices.

nick (*Print.*) A depression made in one side of the type to serve as a guide in setting type right side up.

nick–bend test (*Engin.*) The test specimen should be nicked on one side and then broken. For Class A plates there should be a wholly fibrous fracture, and for Class B plates not more than 10 per cent of the fracture should be crystalline.

nick′el (*Metal.*) (Ni) A hard, white metal with specific gravity of 8.63.

Its chief uses are for nickel plating and the forming of alloys.

nick′el a-lu′mi-num. Eighty per cent aluminum and 20 per cent nickel. Nickel increases the tensile strength of aluminum alloys, and improves the finish in die castings.

nick′el cop′per (*Metal.*) A nickel and copper alloy used in making acid-resistant castings and bearing bronzes. Navy specifications call for 60 per cent nickel, 33 per cent copper, 3.5 per cent manganese, and up to 3.5 per cent iron.

nick′el mo-lyb′de-num i′ron (*Metal.*) A class of alloys containing from 20 to 40 per cent molybdenum and up to 60 per cent nickel with a small amount of carbon. Such alloys are much used on account of high acid resistance.

nick′el plat′ing (*Elec.*) The depositing of a coating of nickel on a metallic surface. Accomplished by immersions in a nickel salt bath through which an electric current of low voltage is passed.

nick′el sil′ver. Also known as German silver. An alloy of copper, nickel, and zinc.

nick′el steel (*Engin.*) A steel containing about 3½ per cent nickel. It is very strong and tough when properly heat treated.

nick′el–tan′ta-lum al-loy′ (*Chem.*) A hard but ductile alloy containing 70 per cent nickel and 30 per cent of tantalum. Used for electrical resistance wires.

nig′gling (*Art*) Work done with too much attention to detail; an overelaborate treatment.

nip′pers (*Print.*) The grippers on a cylinder press. (*Wood Patmkg.*) A pincerlike tool with sharp jaws for cutting.

nip′ple (*Pipe Fittings*) A short length of pipe threaded at both ends.

nip′ple chuck (*Mach.*) A rapid adjusting machine chuck, used in production work for holding pipe while cutting and threading nipples.

ni′trate (*Chem.*) (1) Salt of nitric acid, as silver nitrate. (2) Nitro derivative formed by treating or combining with nitric acid or a compound.

ni′tric (*Chem.*) Obtained from or pertaining to nitrogen.

ni′tric ac′id (*Chem.*) (HNO_3) A colorless, highly corrosive liquid, usually made by decomposing sodium or potassium nitrate with sulphuric acid.

ni′trid-ing (*Chem.*) The process of adding nitrogen to alloys with iron base by heating the alloy in contact with ammonia gas or any other nitrogenous material.

ni′tro-gen (*Chem.*) An odorless, colorless, gaseous element which forms four fifths of the volume of air.

ni′tro-glyc′er-in (*Chem.*) A light yellow or colorless oily liquid made from glycerin, sulphuric and nitric acid. Highly explosive. Mixed with clay to form dynamite.

no′ble met′al (*Chem.*) A term applied to a precious or pure metal, and to metals that do not oxidize readily in the open air.

nodes (*Elec.*) The points of constant potential located between loops of vibration in a circuit through which an oscillatory current is passing.

nog′ging (*Masonry*) The filling in of the spaces between studding with brick.

no–heet met′al. Also known as "tempered lead." It is an antifriction metal composed of lead hardened with sodium.

noil (*Textile*) Short wool fibers left in the combing and used for woolen yarns.

no′men-cla′ture (nō′měn-klā′tûr) (*Engin.*) A list of names or terms common to any particular art or science.

non-bear′ing par-ti′tion (*Bldg.*) One that simply divides the space into rooms and does not carry overhead partitions or floor joists.

non′con-duc′tor (*E l e c.*) Any substance which does not allow electricity to pass through it.

non′cor-ro′sive flux(*Sheet-Met.Wk.*) A flux which does not cause a corrosion when used in soldering or brazing.

non-de-form′ing steel (*Metal.*) An oil hardening steel containing up to 1.5 per cent manganese used for tools and dies.

non′fer′rous met′als (*Engin.*) Metals not containing iron.

non′in-duc′tive cir′cuit (*E l e c.*) A circuit in which the magnetic effect of the current flowing has been reduced by one of several methods to a minimum or to zero.

non′in-duc′tive re-sist′ance (*Elec.*) Resistance free from self-induction.

non′in-duc′tive wind′ing (*Elec.*) A winding so arranged that the magnetic field set up by the current flowing in one half of the coil is neutralized by the magnetic field set up by the current flowing in the opposite directions in the second half.

non′me-tal′lic sheath ca′ble (*Elec.*) A type of wiring material which has two or three conductors encased in a nonmetallic sheath or covering similar to "loom."

non′pa-reil′ (nŏn′pȧ-rĕl′) (*Print.*) A size of type between minion and agate; 6 point.

non-pres′sure (fusion) weld′ing. A group of welding processes wherein the weld is made without pressure.

non-rig′id air′ship (*Aero.*) One whose form is maintained only by internal pressure in the gas bags and ballonets.

Nord′berg key (*Mach.*) A round key for locking a hub to a shaft. It has a taper of 1/16 in. per foot, and the large diameter is about one fourth the diameter of the shaft up to 6 in. For larger sizes, the key is one fifth the shaft diameter.

nor′mal. In accordance with an established law or principle. (*Math.*) A line perpendicular to a curve.

nor′mal-iz′ing (*Engin.*) The heating of steel above the upper critical temperature and then cooling in air.

nor′mal loop (*Aero.*) A loop starting from normal flight and passing successively through a climb, inverted flight; dive and back to normal flight.

nor′mal or three–point land′ing (*Aero.*) A landing in which a path tangential to the landing surface and the loss in flying speed are attained at approximately the instant of contact.

nor′mal so-lu′tion (*Chem.*) A normal solution of an acid contains one gram of hydrogen ions per 1000 c.c. Examples: 36.5 grams of hydrogen chloride (HCL) per 1000 c.c.; 49 grams of sulphuric acid (H_2SO_4) per 1000 c.c., etc. This value is obtained by dividing the molecular weight by the number of hydrogen ions produced. A normal solution of a base contains 17 grams of hydroxyl ions per 1000 c.c. Example: 40 grams of sodium hydroxide (NaOH) per 1000 c.c. Other normal solutions are prepared by using, per liter, the molecular weight of the chemical in grams, divided by a factor which varies with the use of the solution.

nor′mal spin (*Aero.*) A spin which is continued by reason of the voluntary position of the control surfaces, recovery from which can be effected within two turns by neutralizing or reversing all the controls. Sometimes called a "controlled" spin.

Nor′man (*Arch.*) That style of architecture which reached its height in England shortly after the Norman conquest.

nose (*Shopwk.*) The business end of tools or things. The threaded end of a lathe or milling-machine spindle, or the end of a hog-nose drill or similar tool.

nose–down (*Aero.*) To depress the nose of an airplane in flight.

nose′-heav′y (*Aero.*) The tendency of the nose to drop when in normal flight.

nose-o′ver (*Aero.*) An expression referring to the accidental turning over of an airplane on its nose when landing.

nose-up (*Aero.*) To elevate the nose of an airplane in flight.

nose wheel (*Aero.*) A wheel, usually steerable, set ahead of the main wheels to support the nose of a plane equipped with a tricycle landing gear.

nos′ing (*A r c h.*) That portion of a stair tread which projects beyond the riser on which it rests.

no-ta′tion. Act, process, or method of representing by a series of marks, signs, figures, or characters; or, the system so used.

notch′ing (*Furn.*) A form of decoration formerly used on oak furniture.

notch′ing ma-chine′ (*Sheet-Met.Wk.*) A machine used for notching blanks of pieced sheet-metal ware, for cutting the corners of square pans, etc. The notching is accomplished by means of dies.

no′vo-lak (*Chem. Plast.*) A permanently fusible and soluble phenolaldehyde resin. More specifically it is the reaction-product of one molecule of phenol with less than one molecule of formaldehyde, and an acid catalyst.

noz′zle (*Mech. Engin.*) A contracted vent, usually at the end of a flexible tube, as a hose. (*Plast.*) The injection end of a plastic molding machine.

nu′cle-ar en′er-gy (*Phys.*) The energy released in a nuclear reaction.

nu′cle-ar tur′bo-jet (*Aero.*) A turbojet engine having a nuclear reactor rather than a combustion chamber to heat the incoming air for expansion through the turbine and out the jet nozzle.

nu′cle-us (*Chem.*) The inner core of the atom, consisting of tightly locked neutrons and protons.

null′ing (*Carp.*) Turned or carved detail, quadrant shaped in section, used on friezes and moldings in Jacobean work.

num′ber drills (*Metalwk.*) Small drills numbered from 1 to 80, with diameters expressed in thousandths of an inch. No. 1 is 0.228 in. diameter; No. 80 is 0.0135 in. diameter.

num′ber-ing ma-chine′. A machine or device for stamping consecutive numbers on checks, tickets, etc.

num′ber 1 (*Papermkg.* and *Print.*) A prefix used with reference to the best grade of a paper.

nu′mer-als (*Print.*) The most commonly used, or Arabic numerals are 1, 2, 3, 4, 5, 6, 7, 8, 9, 0; the Roman numerals are I, V, X, L, C, D, M.

nu′mer-a′tor (1) In writing a fraction that part above the denominator. It indicates the number of fractional parts taken. (2) One who counts or numbers.

nu′mis-mat′ics. The science which treats of medals and coins with reference to their value, classification, history, etc.

nut (*Mach.*) A small block of metal or other material commonly square or hexagonal in shape, having internal threads to receive a bolt.

nut ar′bor or nut man′drel (*Mach.*) An arbor on which nuts are finished to shape.

nut ma-chine′ (*Shopwk.*) A machine for cutting, drilling, and tapping nuts from a bar or rod.

nut quad (*Print.*) An en quad.

nut shanks (*Shopwk.*) Shanks of bits designed to be used with large wooden handles.

ny′lon (*Plast.*) A family of plastics which consists of many types. The resin is formed by the condensation of dibasic organic acids with diamines. The properties of the resin are toughness, ability to withstand high temperatures, abrasion and chemical resistance. These very desirable properties have opened their field of usefulness, not only in the area of fibers, cords and of knitting; but as molded parts in mechanical and other critical situations, such as in oil field and marine applications. (See PLASTICS.)

O

oak (*Woodwkg.*) A hard, durable, and very strong wood used for many purposes. Especially valuable in places where it may be exposed to the weather; also for furniture, flooring, and trim.

oa′kum (*Plumb.*) Hemp used for calking; usually made by untwisting old rope. Tarred hemp.

ob′e-lisk (ŏb′ē-lĭsk)(*Arch.*) A square monumental shaft with pyramidal top.

ob-lique′ (ŏb-lēk′) Slanting, inclined. neither vertical nor horizontal.

ob-lique′ pro-jec′tion. By this system one face of the object is drawn as parallel to the observer, and the faces perpendicular to this front face are drawn at an angle and to the same scale as the front face, while in cabinet projection the lengths would be drawn at half scale.

ob-long (*Math.*) A rectangular figure having greater length than breadth.

ob′scu-ra′tion (*Paint.*) The covering power of a paint or enamel. The covering of a surface with an opaque paint or finishing material.

ob-sid′i-an (ŏb-sĭd′ĭ-ăn)(*Min.*)A very hard, glassy, volcanic rock, usually black.

ob′so-lete. Gone out of use.

ob-struc′tion light (*Aero.*) A red light designed to indicate the position and height of an object hazardous to the operation of aircraft.

ob-tuse′(*Math.*)Not pointed or acute; greater than a right angle.

ob-tuse′ angle. Greater than a right angle; exceeding 90 deg.

ob′verse. The face side of a medal or coin; the front as opposed to the back.

oc-ca′sion-al fur′ni-ture(*Furn.*)Small furniture of various shapes and uses. In modern times, particularly furniture for the living room and reception hall.

o′cher (ō′kēr) (*Paint.*) A combination of iron and lime formed in marshes by water containing iron in solution. This substance often mixes with clay, and stains it yellow. When dried and ground, this clay forms the yellow ocher of commerce. It is ground to a fine powder and mixed with linseed oil to form paint.

oc′ta-gon. A plane figure having eight sides and eight angles.

oc′tane rat′ing. A measure of the antiknock qualities of gasoline. Iso-octane produces the least knock and is rated at 100. Normal heptane produces the most knock and is rated at zero. A fifty-fifty mixture of these two would produce a knock rated at 50.

oc′tane se-lec′tor (ŏk′tān) (*Auto.*) A scheme for adjusting the timing in order to get maximum efficiency from various grades of gasoline.

oc′tant (*A e r o.*) A variation of the aircraft sextant which measures angles up to 90 deg. Its artificial horizon is usually of the bubble type.

odd–leg cal′i-per (*Mach.*) Calipers with moderately curved legs, both curved in the same direction, used for measuring shoulder distances, etc.

o-de′um (*Arch.*) A roofed theater of

---

sāle, surfâce, grăm, humăn, màsk, solàr, bär, bâre; mē, êdition, lĕnd, momĕnt, bakēr; kīnd, fĭt; lōde, ômit, ŏlive, cŏnsume, sôrt; dūty, ûtility, nŭt, alǔm, bûrn.

ancient Greece. In modern usage, a hall, gallery, etc.

o-dom′e-ter (ŏ-dŏm′ĕ-tẽr) A device for measuring distance traveled; it is attached to the hub of the wheel.

o-don′to-graph (*Mech.*) A table of radii for making or laying off the outlines of gear teeth.

O.D. pipe (*Engin.*) Indicates outside diameter. Used to designate nominal sizes of boiler tubes, also wrought pipe of over 12 in. diameter.

Oersted, Hans Christian (ûr′stĕd) (1777–1851). Danish physicist noted for discovery of effects of electric current on magnetic needle.

off′-cen′ter (*Mach.*) A term applied to a part which does not "run true."

off its feet (*Print.*) Type which leans and would not give a sharp impression.

off′set (*Bldg.*) A recess or sunken panel in a wall. (*Print.*) A smudge resulting from carrying too much ink on a sheet. (*Steel*) Bent out of line in order to clear another structural member.

off′set pa′per (*Paper.*) The prefix "offset" denotes a paper which has properties rendering it suitable for offset lithography.

off′set print′ing. A printing process in which the ink from the form, instead of being transferred directly to the sheet, is first offset on a rubber blanket.

off′set rod (*Auto.*) A connecting rod which has a greater length of bearing projecting from one side of the center line than from the other.

off time (*Weld.*) The time in the resistance-welding process that one or both electrodes are separated from the parts welded.

o-gee′ (ô-jē′) (*Arch.*) A molding having in section a reverse curve or long S curve.

o′give (ō′jīv) (*Furn.*) A pointed arch.

ohm (*Elec.*) The unit of electrical resistance.

ohm′me′ter (*Elec.*) A type of galvanometer which directly indicates the number of ohms of the resistance being measured.

ohm re-sist′ance (*Elec.*) A circuit (d.c.) is said to have a resistance of one ohm when one volt (e.m.f.) will produce a current of one ampere through it.

Ohm's law (*Elec.*) A law which states that the current flowing in a circuit is proportional to the e.m.f. and inversely proportional to the resistance or opposition. More frequently it is expressed in mathematical form:

$$I = \frac{E}{R}; \quad R = \frac{E}{I}; \quad E = IR.$$

oil (*Chem.*) A greasy or unctuous liquid of animal, vegetable, or mineral origin; in addition to its use as a lubricant, oil has a very wide use in the industries.

oil bloom (*Paint and Lacquer*) Iridescent appearance generally due to rubbing or polishing with a material that contains free oil which floats to surface of film.

oil con-trol′ ring (*Auto.*) A type of piston ring designed to scrape from the cylinder wall, oil which passes through slots in the ring and small holes in the piston wall, and then drains to the crankcase. Such rings are usually placed next above the piston-pin bosses.

oil cup (*Mach.*) Consists of a hollow

glass cylinder contained between brass top and bottom plates, so designed that it may be attached by screw threads to a bearing; used to permit a constant and uniform dripping of oil when desired.

oil′er. A small-size oil can.

oil fil′ter (*Auto.*) The cylinder containing screens or filtering material, attached to the motor in such a manner that when the motor is running, the lubricating oil is constantly passing through the filter, thus removing grit and foreign matter. The filtering unit should be renewed at every 8,000 miles.

oil gauge (gāj) (*Auto.*) These gauges are of two kinds; one is used to indicate the amount of oil in the sump; the other indicates the pressure of flow of the oil. An oil pressure gauge usually is mounted on the instrument board and indicates the amount of pressure by the position of a hand on a graduated dial.

oil grind′er (*Wood Patmkg.*) A type of power-driven grinder used for grinding plane bits and other edged tools.

oil groove (*Mech.*) Small, semicircular groove, cut in the internal face of a brass and on the sliding surface of machinery, for the distribution of oil for lubricating purposes.

oil hard′en-ing (*Mech.*) The hardening of steel by quenching it in oil instead of water.

oil hole (*Mach.*) A hole through which oil is admitted to a bearing.

oil′-hole drills (*Metalwk.*) Drills with one or two oil holes running from shank to cutting point; used principally for drilling deep holes.

oil′less-type bear′ings (*Auto.*) (1) Bearings which require oiling only at long intervals. Usually made of some oil-absorbing porous metal. The warmer the bearing, the more actively it lubricates. (2) Bronze bearings with graphite inserts.

oil line (*Auto.*) The tubing and devices connected therewith which comprise the circuit for lubricating oil.

oil pan (*Auto.*) The lower half of the crankcase, made either of pressed steel or cast aluminum.

oil pump (*Auto.*) Oil pumps are of the gear, vane, or plunger type. They are usually an integral part of the engine. Their purpose is to lift oil from the sump to the upper level in the splash and circulating system, and in forced-feed lubrication they pump the oil to the tubes leading to the bearings and other parts.

oil′slip (*Woodwkg.*) A small unmounted oilstone held in the hand while whetting the cutting edges of gouges.

oil′stone (*Woodwkg.*) A smooth stone used, when moistened with oil, for sharpening tools, etc.

oil-tank vent (*Aero.*) A large tube used to conduct oil vapors from the engine to the oil tank.

oil tan′nage (*Leather.*) The oldest tanning method of which there is any record. The present method consists of kneading the skins in contact with certain oils and soft fats. Oil tannage is used in the manufacture of chamois, buff, and buck leathers.

oil tight. Constructed or packed so as to prevent oil leakage.

oil var′nish (*Wood Fin.*) Contains drying oils such as linseed oil and tung oil. The hardening process takes place slowly through oxidation.

old man (*Shopwk.*) A shop term applied to a portable frame or support, used in connection with a ratchet drill, for drilling "in the field" or "on the job."

old style (*Print.*) A type face distinguished by oblique serifs; in common use during the eighteenth century.

o′le-ag′i-nous (ō′lẻ-ăj′ĭ-nŭs) (*Chem.*) Oily; pertaining to oil.

o′le-fine (*Chem.*) A member of the ethylene series.

o′le-o gear (*Aero.*) An oil-damping device that depends on the flow of oil through an orifice for its shock-absorbing effect in a landing gear.

ol′ive (*Wood*) Olea europaea. A slow-growing, close-grained, heavy wood, light yellowish brown with dark brown spots and streaks. Much used for novelties.

o-me′ga (ỏ-mē′gả) The last letter of the Greek alphabet.

om′ni-graph. A machine which is an automatic acetylene cutter. A mechanical pointer traces the pattern which is attached to the machine thus controlling the motion of the cutter tip. By this method several duplicate plates can be cut simultaneously.

one–side coated (*Papermkg.*) A litho paper or a blank which has a coating only on one side.

on′ion foot (*Furn.*) A bulbous foot of oval shape.

on′ion-skin (*Paper*) A very thin paper used for duplicating on a typewriter.

on′lay (*Furn.*) Ornament laid on surface woods.

on′yx (ŏn′ĭks) (*Chem.*) A form of chalcedony; a variety of quartz consisting of layers of different colors, usually in even planes.

o′ö-lit′ic lime′stone′ (ō′ȯ-lĭt′ĭk) (*Bldg.*) A granular variety of limestone made up of minute spherical particles.

ooze (*Verb*) To discharge or leak out gradually. (*Noun*) Mud, miry earth.

ooze leath′er. Denotes the kind of finish or the process by which it is produced. The soft velvety finish given to the flesh side of calfskin, sheepskin, or goatskin.

o-pac′i-me′ter. An instrument for measuring the opacity of paper.

o-pac′i-ty (*Papermkg. and Print.*) The degree of nontransparency of a paper.

o-paque′ (ỏ-pāk′) Impervious to light; not translucent.

o′pen bub′ble (*Plast.*) Bubble which has partly broken through the surface of a plastic.

o′pen cir′cuit (*Elec.*) A circuit which is not electrically complete and in which there is no current.

o′pen–cir′cuit cell (*Elec.*) Cells normally kept on open circuit for intermittent work. They exhaust quickly on closed circuit, but recover when the circuit is opened.

o′pen cy′cle en′gine (*Aero.*) The ordinary kind of aircraft gas-turbine engine in which air is drawn in from the outside, heated by the combustion of fuel and discharged, together with the combustion of products into the open.

o′pen hearth (härth) Refers to steel-making furnaces built on the reverberatory type, being termed open-hearth furnaces, and their method of manufacture open-hearth processes.

o′pen mat′ter (*Print.*) Widely spaced lines of type.

o′pen mold (*Fdry.*) Used in casting bars, plates, and large flat work without the use of a flask. An absolutely level bed of sand is built up and the pattern placed on it and rammed up. When the pattern is removed the mold is ready to pour.

o′pen punc′tu-a′tion (*Print.*) Refers to the sparing use of punctuation marks.

o′pen shop. An establishment in which both union and nonunion workmen may be employed, as opposed to the closed shop which employs only members of trade-unions.

o′pen–side plan′er (*Mach.*) Not in common use. It has only one upright housing to carry the arm. With this type of machine it is possible to machine work which is wider than the bed of the planer.

o′pen string stairs (*Arch. and Bldg.*) A stair having a wall on one side and a balustrade or handrail on the other. The stair is so constructed that the treads and risers are visible from the side.

o′pen wash′er (*Mach.*) Also called "slip washer." A washer partly cut away so that it may be slipped around a bolt without entirely removing the nut.   **Open Washer**

o′pen wir′ing (*Elec.*) Exposed electrical conductors mounted on porcelain knobs or cleats.

o′pen-work′ (*Furn.*) Any form of decoration that pierces or cuts through the surface leaving open spaces.

op′er-at′ing speed (*Aero.*) The speed in level flight corresponding to 87.5 per cent of the rated speed of the engine.

op′er-a′tor (*Mach.*) One who manipulates a machine or controls the working thereof.

op′po-site. Facing; set over against; contrary; diametrically different.

op′ti-cal al-tim′e-ter (*Aero.*) An altimeter, the indications of which depend on the manipulation of a suitable optical system.

op′ti-cal cen′ter (*Print.*) That point on a page of printed matter or drawing which the eye seems to seek as the center; it is about one eighth of the total height above the actual center.

op′ti-cal dis-tor′tion (*Plast.*) An apparent distortion of anything viewed through a transparent plastic, caused by the nonuniform optical character of the plastic and not by its shape.

op′ti-cal py-rom′e-ter. A device used for measuring high temperature by the comparison of the color brought about by intense heat, with the color of a wire heated to a known temperature by means of an electric current.

or′ange peel (*Paint and Lacquer*) A pebble effect in spray coats of paint or lacquer, similar to the peel of an orange, caused by too much air pressure, holding the gun too close to the surface, spraying lacquer that is cooler than the room temperature, or using a too-quick-drying thinner, which prevents the proper flow of the solids.

or′der (*Arch.*) The general style of a column and its parts as distinguishing a style of architecture.

or′ders of ar′chi-tec′ture (*Arch.*)

There are five classic orders: Tuscan, Doric, Ionic, Corinthian, and Composite.

or'di-nate (*Math.*) The distance of any point from the axis of abscissas; also the line indicating such distance.

ore (*Mineral*) Metal-bearing rock in such form or amount as to make it practical for use as a raw material from which to extract a metal.

Or'e-gon pine or Doug'las fir (*Wood*) *Pseudotsuga taxifolia.* Strong, but light in weight; used extensively for masts, flagpoles, long framing, etc.

o'ri-el (*Arch.*) A window built out from a wall and resting on a bracket or on corbels; distinguished from a bay window.

o'ri-ent. To find or fix the position of, with reference to the east.

o'ri-en'tal wal'nut (*Wood*) *Endiandra palmerston.* Also known as oriental wood. An Australian tree of large size. Suitable for producing great quantities of veneer with grain similar to American walnut. Used for furniture and paneling.

o'ri-en-ta'tion. Specifically, construction with reference to the East; generally, the term is applied to the determining of the direction in which a building is to face. The layout of an athletic field in such a manner as to keep the sun from the eyes of contestants, etc.

or'i-fice. A small opening into a cavity.

o-rig'i-nal. Novel; new; ability to produce works requiring thought, without copying or imitating those of others. (*Plaster.*) The name is given to the model from which a mold is taken. An original for a gelatin molding needs to be coated with shellac or some other substance which will render its face impervious. An original for a wax molding must be well soaked in water to prevent absorption.

or'mo-lu (ôr'mȯ-lōō) (*Furn.*) Bronze or other metal gilded and used in mounts for furniture.

or'na-ment (*Furn.*) Any addition or part so treated that it adds to the beauty or elegance of a thing. (*Print.*) Any decorative device, as a rule, border, or design used as an embellishment.

or'na-men-ta'tion (*M a s o n r y*) The laying of stone, bricks, tiles, or other masonry, in such a manner as to form a decorative design.

or'ni-thop'ter (*Aero.*) A heavier-than-air craft with flapping wings.

o-rom'e-ter (*S c i e n c e*) An aneroid barometer which records elevations above sea level.

or'phan (*Mach.*) Some odd or obsolete machine or item for which repair parts are not available.

or'tho-graph'ic. (1) Relating to the arrangement of views in a mechanical drawing. (2) Pertaining to correct spelling.

or'tho-graph'ic pro-jec'tion (*Draw.*) A system of graphically presenting an object by means of several views, each view showing a face of the object, such as the front view, top view, right-side view, etc.

or'tho-style (*Arch.*) An arrangement of columns in a straight line.

o-sage' or'ange (*Wood*) A small- to medium-size tree. Wood is yellow, streaked with red; very hard, strong, and durable. Used for fence posts, wagon felloes, police clubs, and tobacco pipes.

os′cil-la′tion (*Mech. Eng.*) A backward and forward motion as in a pendulum; a vibration.

os′cil-la′tor (*Radio*) A high-frequency circuit used to generate alternating current.

os-cil′lo-graph (*Elec.*) An instrument used for studying wave forms of current or voltage either by means of a screen or photograph.

os′mi-um (*Metal.*) A rare metal used for the tips of gold pens and for the production of corrosion resistant alloys.

os-mo′sis (*Phys.*) The intermingling of two fluids separated by a porous membrane, the greater flow being toward the denser liquid.

ot′to-man. A stuffed seat without a back, originally used in Turkey.

out′board Ben′dix drive (*Auto.*) A Bendix starter drive in which worm, spring, and gear permit engagement with engine flywheel from the outboard end of the starting motor shaft.

out′board mo′tor. A detachable gasoline engine which can be readily fastened to the stern of small boats. Such motors are capable of driving racing boats at very high speeds.

out′board sta′bi-liz′ing float (*Aero.*) A stabilizing float placed relatively far out from the main float or hull, usually at or very near the tip of the wing.

out′let (*Elec.*) Any point on the wiring system from which current may be taken for consumption.

out′let box (*Elec.*) An iron box inserted in a conduit system, from which current is taken to supply some apparatus as, for instance, a lamp.

Outlet Box

out′lined half′tone (*Print.*) A halftone from which the screen surrounding any part of an image has been cut away. A silhouette.

out′lin-ing. (1) Drawing the outline of. (2) To describe in general terms. (3) To sketch.

out of gear (*Mech.*) When the teeth of gear wheels, which usually mesh together, are disengaged, or when the driving mechanism of a machine is disconnected from the rest of the machine by clutch or other means, they are said to be out of gear.

out of reg′is-ter (*Print.*) When the printed matter on both sides of a sheet does not occupy the same position on the page the sheet is out of register. Or in color work when the different colors do not strike in proper relation.

out of sorts (*Print.*) Refers to the type case when the supply of any letter or character is exhausted.

out of true (*Bldg. and Shopwk.*) Inaccurate, twisted, varying from the exact.

out-put (*Elec. and Mach.*) Amount of energy delivered to an external device from the source of generation. (*Phys.*) Work accomplished which is equal to input less various losses.

out′side cal′i-per (*Shopwk.*) A caliper used for gauging outside measurements or sizes.

Outside Caliper

out′side gouge (*Woodwk.*) A firmer gouge on which the bevel is ground upon the outside or convex face.

out′side loop (*Aero.*) A loop starting from normal flight and passing successively through a dive, inverted flight; climb, and back to normal flight; the pilot being on the outside of the flight path.

out′side roll (*Aero.*) A roll executed while flying in the negative angle-of-attack range.

o′val (*Math.*) An egg-shaped figure, the curves of whose ends are unequal.

o′ver–all (*Draw. and Shopwk.*) A common term in shopwork meaning an outermost or total dimension.

o′ver–all length (*Aero.*) The extreme length from front to rear including propeller and tail unit.

o′ver–cast′ing (*Bookbndg.*) The sewing over the back of the sections of a book.

overdrive (*Auto. Mech.*) An arrangement of gearing which produces more revolutions of the driven than of the driving shaft.

o′ver–hand work (*Masonry*) Work on the outside of a wall performed from a scaffold built on the inside of a wall.

o′ver–hang (*Aero.*) Used in two senses. (1) One half of the difference in span of any two main supporting surfaces of an airplane. The overhang is positive when the upper of the two main supporting surfaces has the larger span. (2) The distance from the outer strut attachment to the tip of the wings. (*Print.*) Any part that projects beyond the main body of the type or slug. (*Wood Patmkg.*) The projection of the cope half of a core print beyond the drag half, to give clearance, and to prevent the cope from touching the end surfaces of the core during the closing of the mold.

o′ver–hang′ing pul′ley. A pulley carried on an overhanging shaft; that is, supported by a bearing on one side only.

o′ver–haul′ (*Mech.*) To take apart, inspect, repair, and reassemble, as a piece of machinery.

o′ver–head cost. The cost of operating a business, as for rent, interest on investment, maintenance and depreciation of equipment, etc.; over and above the actual cost of labor and material.

o′ver–head shaft′ing (*Shopwk.*) Line shafting or counter-shafting suspended from the ceiling, from which power is transmitted to machines.

o′ver–head–valve mo′tor (*Auto.*) A motor with all of the valves located in the head.

Overhead Valve Motor

o′ver–heat′ing (*Auto.*) The heating of an engine beyond the point of safe operation. Usually due to a defective cooling system or poor lubrication.

o′ver–lay (*Print.*) A piece of paper placed on the tympan of a press to compensate for a depression in the form or to make that part of the impression heavier.

o′ver–lay sheet (*Plast.*) Thin Fiberglas mat used as a top or finishing layer in a fibrous glass mat or cloth lay-up. (See MAT.)

o′ver–load (*Elec.*) More than a normal amount of current flowing through an electrical device.

o′ver–load switch (*Elec.*) An automatic switch for breaking a circuit in case of an overload.

o′ver–run′ (*Papermkg.*) A quantity of paper made over and above the amount ordered.

o'ver-run'ning (*Print.*) Carrying words over from the end of one line to the beginning of the next.

o'ver-run'ning clutch (*A u t o* .) A clutch designed with inner and outer rings; the inner is milled with several triangular slots in which hardened steel rollers are inserted. By this construction the inner ring will drive the outer, but if the outer ring moves faster than the inner, it will slide or overrun the inner ring.

o'ver-shoot' (*Aero.*) To fly beyond a designated mark or area, such as a landing field, while attempting to land on the mark or within the area.

o'ver-shot' wheel. A water wheel which is turned by the weight of water shooting over its top, filling buckets which cover its circumference.

o'ver-time. Time spent in working beyond specified working hours.

o'vo-lo (*A r c h.*) A convex molding; a quarter round. **Ovolo**

ox-al'ic ac'id (*Chem.*) Made from wood chips or sawdust and a mixture of caustic soda and caustic potash; used principally as a bleach, and in dyeing and calico printing.

Ox'ford cor'ner (*Print.*) A border with overlapping corners, thus (✝).

ox'i-da'tion (*Chem.*) The act of uniting, or causing a substance to unite with oxygen chemically.

ox'ide (*Chem.*) Any binary compound of oxygen with an element or with an organic radical, as iron rust.

ox'i-diz'ing. Finishing metalwork by means of an acid solution.

ox'i-diz'ing a'gent (*Chem.*) A substance which by giving up some of its oxygen changes another substance to an oxide or some other compound.

ox'i-diz-ing flame. A gas welding flame having oxygen in excess of that required to produce perfect combustion.

ox'y-a-cet'y-lene (ŏk'sĭ-à-sĕt'ĭ-lēn) (*Engin.*) A mixture of oxygen and acetylene gas in such proportions as to produce the hottest flame known for practical use. Oxyacetylene welding and cutting is much used in almost every metalworking industry.

ox'y-gen (*Chem.*) A tasteless, colorless, gaseous element. It constitutes one fifth of the air by volume. It is closely related to combustion.

oys'ter-ing (*Furn.*) The using of a veneer cut from the roots and boughs of certain trees.

o'zone (*Chem.*) A colorless gas with a pungent odor. (O_3) It is used for bleaching oils, waxes, flour, starch, etc., and sometimes for sterilizing drinking water. It is produced by the discharge of high-tension electricity through dried and cooled air in a special apparatus.

P

pack'age la'bel (*Print.*) A gummed slip either printed or plain, placed on packages to carry the address or to indicate contents.

pack hard'en (*Metal.*) (1) to carbonize or caseharden. (2) The process of giving a hard outer surface to mild steel.

pack hard'en-ing (*Metal.*) Consists in treating steel with some carbonaceous material and quenching it in oil. The term "pack hardening" and "casehardening" are often used interchangeably.

pack'ing (*Engin.*) (1) The material which is enclosed in a stuffing box for the purpose of preventing leakage around a piston rod. (2) The act or process of inserting packing material. (3) Blocking up. (*Print.*) The heavy sheet used under the drawsheet of a press to build up the impression.

pad (*Paper*) A number of sheets of paper held together in tablet form by gumming one or more edges.

pa'dauk (*Wood*) *Pterocarpus macrocarpus*. Native to Burma and Andaman Islands. It is hard and heavy, with large open pores; characterized by reddish streaks. Used in furniture, paneling, and in railway coaches.

pad'lock. A detachable lock, usually used in connection with a hasp and staple.

pad lu'bri-ca'tion. Lubrication accomplished by contact with an oil-saturated pad as distinguished from any of the many other methods.

pad saw (*Carp.*) A type of handsaw with narrow tapering blade. The pad or socket into which the blade fits when not in use also serves as a handle.

page. One side of a leaf of a book.

pa-go'da (*F u r n.*) A tower-shaped roof or top; a feature of cabinets, cupboards, etc., designed by Chippendale and others, showing Chinese influence.

paint (*Chem.*) (1) Pigment or color, either dry or mixed with oil or water. (2) The act of applying the same.

paint base (*Chem.*) The body matter of paint, as white lead or zinc.

paint dri'er. Most paint driers are composed of lead and manganese. A limited amount of drier serves a good purpose, but too much is harmful.

paint for con'crete. Paint made of zinc oxide or barium sulphate mixed with tung oil are much used for this class of work.

paint'ing. Decorating with paint.

paint thin'ner. Turpentine or petroleum spirits may be used to thin heavy-bodied paints in order to make application easier. Petroleum spirits are much used on account of lower cost.

pak'tong. A metal composition of nickel, zinc, and copper, resembling German silver, and made in China, used for candlesticks, fire irons, and other metalwork.

Palette Knife

pal'ette knife (păl'ĕt)(*Print.*) A very

thin-bladed, flexible, steel knife used for mixing ink or colors.

pal·la′di·um (pă-lā′dĭ-ŭm) (*Chem.*) A rare, white, ductile, malleable metal occurring with platinum.

palm fi′ber (*Uphol.*) Made from the outer husks of coconuts. It makes a firm, springy filler for upholstery and is a cheap substitute for hair.

pal′nut (*Aero.*) A single-thread nut stamped out of spring steel or other suitable materials. The locking part of the palnut is essentially a cone with a hole in the center, whose inner edges are formed to the pitch of the screw thread. This inner edge is slotted to form spring jaws which close in on the root of the thread and grip the screw thread when the palnut is tightened.

pam′phlet (păm′flĕt)(*Print.*) A booklet of but few pages and without covers, or bound in paper.

pan (*Tel.*) (1) A camera movement which shows a panorama of a set. (2) A reflecting unit using one or more lights, usually fluorescent tubing.

pan′cake (*Aero.*) To level off an airplane at a greater altitude than normal in a landing, thus causing it to stall and to descend on a steeply inclined path, with the wings at a very large angle of attack and without appreciable bank.

pan′chro·mat′ic (păn′krô-măt′ĭk) Sensitive to all colors.

pan′el (*Aero.*) A portion of an airplane wing constructed separately from the rest of the wing to which it is attached. (*Bldg. and Cabwk.*) A raised or sunken portion surrounded as by a frame, especially applicable to woodwork.

pan′el board (*Elec.*) An electrical control board carrying switches and fuses.

pan′el saw (*Carp.*) A handsaw with fine teeth, for cutting thin wood.

pan′el strip (*Bldg.*) A strip of molded wood or metal to cover a joint between two sheathing boards to form a panel; or, any strip of material used for forming panels.

pan′tile (*Arch.*) A roofing tile whose cross section is an ogee curve; a curved roofing tile laid alternately with convex covering tiles. A flat paving tile, Dutch or Flemish.

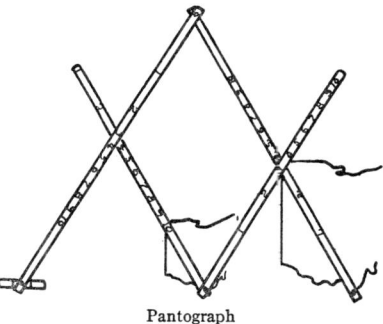

Pantograph

pan′to·graph (*Draw.*) An instrument for copying drawings on an enlarged or reduced scale.

pan-tom′e·ter (*Math.*) Instrument for measuring angles, elevations, etc.

pa′per (*Draft.*) White and buff are commonly used for finished drawings; both may be had either in sheets or rolls. Good paper should be tough, take pencil and ink well, and have good erasing qualities. For fine work a paper similar to Whatman's handmade is usually used. It is made in three surfaces: hot pressed, with a smooth surface; cold pressed, with a moderately rough surface; and rough, for water-color sketches.

pa′per birch (*Wood*) *Betula papyrifera*. Also spoken of as white birch. A large tree growing to a height of 50 to 75 ft. Wood is strong and hard; light brown in color. Used in the manufacture of spools, shoe lasts, and for paper pulp.

pa′per con-dens′er (*Elec.*) A condenser having a dielectric of impregnated paper.

pa′per cut′ter (*Print.*) A machine, either power or hand operated, for cutting paper stock.

pa′per drill (*Print.*) Used for drilling holes in piles of paper.

pa-per ma-chine′ (*Papermkg.*) The machine on which the elements of paper are formed, pressed, dried, calendered, wound on reels, cut into widths, and wound into rolls or in some instances, cut into sheets.

pa′per-mak′ing. The manufacture of paper.

pap′e-terie pa′per (păp′ĕ-trĭ) (*Paper*) A class of papers used in the box stationery trade.

pa′pier–mâ′ché′ (pā′pēr-mă-shā′) Paper pulp mixed with size, glue, rosin, or clay, molded into various forms while moist.

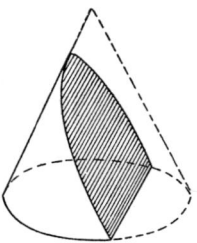

Parabola

pa-rab′o-la (pá-răb′ô-lá) (*Math. and Engin.*) A conic section or curve as would be obtained by passing a plane through a cone parallel with its side.

par′a-bol′ic gird′er (*Engin.*) A form of bowstring girder, the outline of whose bow is that of a polygon inscribed in a parabola; used on bridge work.

par′a-chute (*Aero.*) An umbrella-like device used to retard the descent of a falling body by offering resistance to its motion through the air.

par′a-chute can′o-py (*Aero.*) The main supporting surface of a parachute.

par′a-chute flare (*Aero.*) A pyrotechnic device attached to a parachute and designed to illuminate a large area when released from an aircraft at an altitude.

par′a-chute har′ness (*Aero.*) A combination of straps, buckles, and fastenings used to attach a parachute to the wearer.

par′a-chute pack (*Aero.*) A parachute and its container.

par′a-chute rig′ger (*Aero.*) A person who packs, repairs, and inspects parachutes.

par′a-chute vent (*Aero.*) A distendable opening in the apex of the canopy of a parachute designed to relieve excess pressure and to stabilize the parachute in descent.

par′a-dox. Something seemingly incredible, yet true.

par′af-fin (păr′ă-fĭn) (*C h e m.*) A translucent, waxy, solid substance derived principally in the distillation of petroleum.

par′al-lax (*Elec.*) This occurs when the scale of an electrical instrument, the needle and the eye, are not in correct alignment. This is overcome by covering the reflection of the needle in the mirror by the needle.

par′al-lel. Lying side by side; extending in the same direction and equidistant at all points; having the same direction; similar.

par′al-lel cir′cuit (*Elec.*) A circuit having a common feed and a common return, between which two or more pieces of apparatus are connected, each receiving a separate portion of the current flow from the common feed.

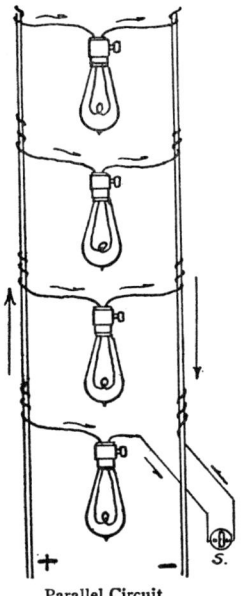

Parallel Circuit

par′al-lel con-nect′ed trans-form′er (*Elec.*) When two or more transformers have their primary windings connected to the same source of supply in such a manner that the impressed voltage in each case is the same as that of the line.

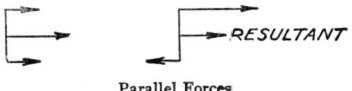

Parallel Forces

par′al-lel for′ces (*Mech.*) When two forces are parallel and act in the same direction but do not start from the same point, the resultant is parallel to both and equal to their sum. When the forces act in opposite directions the resultant is equal to the difference between the two.

par′al-lel jaw pli′ers (*S h o p w k.*) Pliers equipped with a toggle joint which permits the jaws to remain parallel regardless of the extent of opening.

par′al-lel′o-gram (*Math.*) A four-sided figure whose opposite sides are parallel. Area equals base times perpendicular height.

Parallelogram

par′al-lel′o-gram for′ces (*M e c h.*) The result of two forces operating at an angle which can be enclosed in a parallelogram. The diagonal is the resultant.

par′al-lel rul′ers (*Draft.*) A draftsman's tool consisting of two rulers or straight edges connected by pivoted arms in such a way that the edges of the rulers are always parallel, regardless of the distance between.

par′al-lels (*Mach.*) Accurately machined bars or strips of metal, rectangular in section, used for blocking up or leveling work for some machine operation.

par′a-mount. Superior to all others.

par′a-pet (*Arch.*) A low wall about

the edge of a roof, a terrace, or at the side of a bridge.

par′a-site drag (*Aero.*) That portion of the drag of an aircraft exclusive of the induced drag of the wings.

par′a-sol mon′o-plane (*A e r o.*) A monoplane in which the wing is above the fuselage.

parch′ment (*Papermkg.*) A glossy, transparent, durable paper produced in imitation of animal parchment. It is common in a sized paper which is made tough and waterproof by being soaked in a weak solution of sulphuric acid.

par′get-ing (pär′jĕt-ĭng) (*Arch.*) (1) Ornamental plaster or stucco work in relief. (2) The plastering of the inside of flues to give a smooth surface and help the draft.

par′ing (*Woodwk.*) A method of wood turning employed by wood turners as opposed to the scraping method of turning usually followed by patternmakers.

par′ing chis′el (*Wood Patmkg.*) A long chisel used by patternmakers in making, paring, or slicing cuts, thus obtaining a smoother surface than would result if the cuts were taken directly across the grain.

par′ing gouge(*WoodPatmkg.*)A woodworker's bench gouge which has the angle of the cutting edge ground on the inside or concave face of the blade.

par′is green (*Chem.*) (CuHAsO$_3$) A poisonous copper arsenite used as a pigment and for destroying insects.

park′ing lamp (*Auto.*) The term was formerly applied only to those lowpowered lamps mounted where they could be seen from either direction, usually on the left rear fender, showing white from the front and red from the rear. The term now covers both cowl lights and rear lamp taken collectively.

par′quet-ry (pär′kĕt-rĭ)(*Bldg.*)Wooden mosaic for floors or furniture.

part′ed core box(*Patmkg. and Fdry.*) A core box made up of two or more parts.

part′ed pat′tern (*Patmkg.*) A pattern made up of two or more parts, to facilitate its withdrawal from the sand. The parts of the pattern take their name from the section of the flask in which they are molded, as the cope or drag of the pattern.

par′ti-cle. Small part, atom.

part′ing (*Fdry.*) The joint or surface which separates two sections of a mold.

part′ing a′gent (*Plast.*) A material applied to plastic molds to facilitate parting the casting from the mold. When it is remembered that most plastics are adhesives, the need for this agent will be understood. Waxes and plastic film applied as liquids, are examples of parting agents.

part′ing sand (*Fdry.*) Burned molding sand or a manufactured parting compound dusted over the surface of the sand in the drag to avoid having sand in cope stick to it.

part′ing strip (*Arch.*) In a sash window, one of the thin strips of wood let into the pulley stile to keep the sashes apart.

part′ing tool (*Wood Turn.*) A narrowblade turning tool used for cutting grooves, recesses, and for cutting off.

par-ti′tion (*Bldg.*) A permanent interior wall which serves to divide a building into rooms. In dwellings

partitions are usually made of studding covered with lath and plaster. In factories, office buildings, and institutions, concrete, hollow tile, brick or even glass is used.

par-ti′tion plate (*Bldg.*) The horizontal member at the top of a partition wall, serving as a cap for the studs and as a support for joists, rafters, or studs.

par′ty wall (*A r c h.*) A partition of brick or stone between adjoining properties.

Pas′cal's law (*Phys.*) Pressure applied to a given area of a fluid enclosed in a vessel is transmitted undiminished to every equal area of the vessel.

paste′board (*P a p e r m k g.*) Today, used commonly with reference to any stiff paperboard of medium thickness. Originally applied to material made by pasting several sheets of paper together.

past′ed core (*Fdry.*) A core made in halves and pasted together after having been dried.

past′ed plate (*Elec.*) The kind of plate used in the cheaper types of lead storage cells. A grid of lead and antimony has forced into its interstices a chemical compound which, after a short period of forming, becomes either the positive or negative plate according to the chemicals used.

past′ed stock (pās′ted) (*Paper*) Card stock built up by pasting together several thicknesses. Rated as two ply, three ply, etc.

pas′tel (*Art.*) A kind of colored crayon made of a paste composed of colors ground and compounded with gum water, etc.

Patch Bolt

patch bolt. A flathead bolt threaded the full length of the body. The square shank, which projects from the head to permit setting the bolt with a wrench, is removed after the bolt is in position. Patch bolts are used in making repairs to boiler plate, structural shapes, etc.

pat′ent. The sole right in an invention granted by the government.

pat′ent ap′pli-ca′tion. The drawings, claims, and forms submitted to the Patent Office by the inventor, usually through his attorney, when seeking a patent.

pat′ent base (*Print.*) A honeycomb or slotted metal base whereon unmounted electrotypes can be fastened at any desired angle.

pat′ent grant. This grant gives to the patentee for the term of the patent, the sole and exclusive right to manufacture, sell, and use the article so patented.

pat′ent-ing. Alloys with iron base are heated above the critical temperature range and then are cooled to below that range in air or in molten lead which has a temperature of about 700 degrees Fahrenheit.

pat′er-a (*A r c h., Furn., Plaster.*) A circular ornament often worked in relief on friezes.

Patera

path line (*Print.*) The line which connects the proof mark with the error in correcting proofs.

pat′i-na (păt′ĭ-nȧ) (*Furn.*) The dark color and rich appearance of the wood in furniture, caused by age.

pat′tern (*Fdry.*) A model or specimen; something made for copying, or for reproducing similar articles. The model from which metal castings are reproduced.

pat′tern let′ter (*Fdry.*) A letter made of cast lead, tin, or brass and attached to a pattern in order that the name or number of the part may be reproduced on the casting.

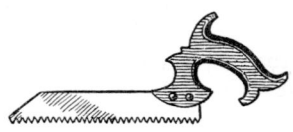
Patternmaker's Saw

pat′tern-mak′er's saw (*Woodwk.*) A small saw with a very thin blade; designed for accurate work in patternmaking and cabinetmaking.

pat′tern-mak′ing. The making of a model or plan for foundry projects.

pat′tern shop (*Patmkg.*) The shop where wooden patterns are made which are used in the production of castings.

pave′ment (*Masonry*) A hard-surface covering for road or sidewalk.

pa-vil′ion (*Arch.*) Usually a roofed structure not entirely enclosed by walls, used as a gathering place or place of amusement.

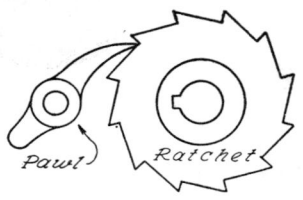

pawl (*Mech.*) A hinged or pivoted arm having a pointed edge or hook made to engage with ratchet teeth.

pay load (*Aero.*) That part of the useful load from which revenue is derived, viz., passengers and freight.

Payne's proc′ess (*Wood*) A method of fireproofing wood by injecting sulphate of iron followed by the injection of a solution of sulphate of lime or soda.

peak load (*Elec.*) The heaviest load which a generator or system is called on to supply at regular intervals, as once every twenty-four hours.

pearl (*Chem.*) A gem composed of calcium carbonate, formed in the pearl oyster. (*Print.*) A 5-point type.

pearl′ing (*Furn.*) The carving of a series of small circles or ovals.

pearl′ite (*Metal.*) The eutectoid alloy of carbon and iron, containing 0.9 per cent carbon, which is the iron-carbon alloy of lowest transformation point in the solid.

pear′wood. *Pterocelastrus rostratus.* A light-brown, close-grained, medium-hard wood extensively used for draftsmen's T squares, triangles, etc.

peat (*Chem.*) Partially carbonized vegetable material used as fuel. It has a very heavy water content when dug from the bogs, and must be pressed and dried before it will burn freely.

peb′ble dash (*Bldg.*) A finish for exterior walls made by dashing pebbles against the plaster or cement coating.

peb′bles (*Paint and Lacquer*) A rough, uneven, wavy effect in a spray coat of paint, etc., can be charged to insufficient atomization or too low air pressure.

peb′bling (*Print*.) The process of graining or imparting a surface of irregular roughness to paper to improve its attractiveness and to reduce the shiny effect.

peck (*Wood*) Channeled or pitted areas of localized decay (found in cedar and cypress).

ped′es·tal. A base of or for a column, statue, or other object.

ped′es·tal ta′ble (*Furn*.) A table supported by a column or pedestal.

ped′i·ment (*Arch*.) A triangular member framed in by a cornice and surmounting a portico; usually of low altitude as compared with the width of its base.

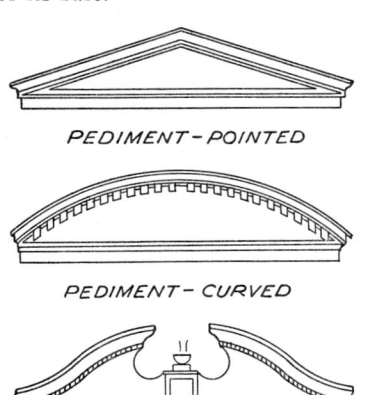

PEDIMENT – POINTED

PEDIMENT – CURVED

PEDIMENT – BROKEN

pe·dom′e·ter. An instrument for recording distance walked.

peen (*Mech*.) The small end of the head of a hammer, as the ball-peen hammer for metalworkers.

peen′ing (*Metalwk*.) Beating over or smoothing over a metallic surface with the peen end of a hammer.

peen ram′ming (*Fdry*.) Ramming done with the wedge or peen end of the rammer.

peg (*Furn*.) A wooden pin, or spike, used for fastening together the parts of furniture in lieu of nails.

pel·lu′cid (pĕ-lū′sĭd) Perfectly clear; transparent.

pend′ant (*Furn., Plaster*.) A hanging ornament.

pend′ant switch (*Elec*.) A small push-button switch attached to a drop cord hanging from the ceiling; used for operating a ceiling light.

Pendant

pen′du·lum. An object suspended from a fixed point, being free to swing to and fro, as the pendulum of a clock.

pen′e·trat′ing (*Wood Fin*.) Having power to penetrate or permeate. In wood finishing, a penetrating stain is one that forces its way below the surface into the fibers of the wood.

pen′e·trat′ing oil. A special oil used as an aid in loosening parts that have become rusted or corroded.

pen′e·trom′e·ter (*Plast*.) Instrument for measuring ease of penetration of surfaces of solid bodies.

pen′ta·gon (*Math*.) A five-sided plane figure.

pent roof (*Arch*.) A roof with a slope on one side only.

pe·num′bra (pĕ-nŭm′brà) A sort of secondary shadow. That area between complete shadow and the unshaded area.

per·cent′age (*Math. and Mech*.) Proportion in a hundred parts. Rate per hundred. A part considered in relation to the whole.

perch. In stonework, a variable measure, usually about 25 cu. ft.

per-cus′sive weld′ing. A resistance-welding process wherein a relatively intense discharge of electrical energy and the application of high pressure (usually a hammer blow) occur simultaneously or with the electrical discharge which occurs slightly before the application of the pressure or hammer blow.

per′fect-ing press (*Print.*) A machine with two impression cylinders able to print both sides of a sheet at one time.

per′fo-rat′ing (*Print.*) The punching of small holes in a sheet of paper to aid in separating it into parts.

per′fo-rat′ing ma-chine′ (*Print.*) A machine for punching a row of small holes in paper to permit even separation of the parts; used in checks, billheads, etc.

per′fo-rat′ing rule (*Print.*) A piece of rule put into a type form so the job may be printed and perforated in one operation.

per-form′ance–type glid′er (*Aero.*) A glider having a high degree of aerodynamic refinement and low minimum sinking speed.

per-im′e-ter (*Math.*) The outer boundary of a plane figure.

pe-ri-od′i-cal (*Print.*) Such a publication as a magazine or journal issued at regular intervals.

pe′ri-od′ic ar-range′ment (*Chem.*) An arrangement of elements in the order of their increasing atomic numbers. As a result of this arrangement the elements fall into nine natural groups, the members of each resembling each other very strongly.

pe-riph′er-al speed (*Mach.*) The speed, usually registered in feet per minute of the circumference of a part, as a wheel or a shaft.

pe-riph′er-y (*Math.*) The circumference of a circle, ellipse, or similar figure.

per′i-scope. An instrument containing an arrangement of mirrors which permits the observer to see over intervening objects.

per′i-style (*Arch.*) A system of columns encircling a building.

per′ma-nent load (*Engin.*) A load which is constant and unvarying; a dead load as the weight of the structure itself or a load imposed, or both taken together.

per′ma-nent mag′net (*Elec.*) A piece of magnet steel which retains the acquired property of attracting other pieces of magnetic material after being under the influence of a magnetic field.

per′ma-nent set (*Engin.*) The amount of deflection from which a beam or structure is unable to return to its original form.

per-man′ga-nate (*Chem. and Wood Fin.*) A dark purple salt of permanganic acid ($HMnO_4$).

per′me-a-bil′i-ty (*Elec.*) The ratio of flux density to magnetizing force.

per′mu-ta′tion (*Math.*) The arrangement of any determinate number of things or letters in all possible orders, one after another.

per′pend (*Masonry*) A header brick extending through the wall so that one end appears on each side of it.

per′pen-dic′u-lar. Meeting a given line or surface at right angles.

per′ron (*Arch.*) A staircase outside of a building, leading to the first floor.

per-sim′mon (*Wood*) *Diospyros vir-*

giniana. Belongs to the ebony family. Does not grow large enough to be of great commercial value. Wood is yellowish, often streaked with black; hard and strong, and takes high polish. Used for brush backs, billiard cues, and veneer.

per-spec′tive (*Draw.*) The art or science of representing on a plane surface objects as they actually appear to the eye.

per-suad′er. A common term for crowbar, lever, or some such article used as a manual aid in moving heavy objects.

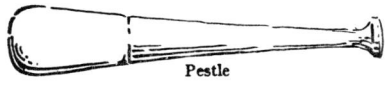
Pestle

pes′tle. A tool for pounding substances in a mortar.

pet cock. A drain cock which, when open, permits the release of gas, air, or liquid from the vessel to which it is attached.

pet′rol. European name for gasoline. The term is little used in the United States.

pe-tro′le-um (*Chem.*) A natural oil taken from the earth, used extensively for heating and lighting. By distillation, it yields many products valuable in the industries, such as gasoline, kerosene, paraffin, etc.

pew (*Arch.*) One of the long benches used as seats in a church.

pew′ter (*Metal*) An alloy of tin, lead, and antimony, formerly much used for tableware.

pha′e-ton (fā′ĕ-t'n) (*Auto.*) An open-type body with two cross seats. Has folding windshield and weatherproof top and side curtains.

phan′tom draw′ing (*Draft.*) Usually refers to some "dotted in" part added to a drawing to show the relation, method of connection, assembly, etc., of or to the project being drawn.

phar′ma-ceu′ti-cals (*Chem.*) Drugs and similar chemicals sold through drugstores.

phase (*Elec.*) The time instant when the maximum, zero, or other relative value is attained by an electric wave.

phase ang′le (*Elec.*) The angle which expresses the phase relation in an alternating-current circuit.

phase me′ter (*Elec.*) A meter which indicates the frequency of the circuit to which it is attached. A frequency meter.

phe′nol (fē′nōl)(*Chem.*) A crystalline substance (C_6H_5OH), a limited supply of which is obtained from coal tar. Also produced synthetically by fusing sodium benzine sulphonate with caustic soda, and then neutralizing with hydrochloric acid. Used also in the manufacture of dyestuffs and pharmaceutical products, antiseptics, etc.

phe′nol–fur′fur-al res′ins (*Chem. Plast.*) Made principally from oat hulls and coal. Used in pressure molding, positive, flash, transfer and injection molding, and laminating. Have wide range of application for electrical articles, cabinets, etc. Desirable from standpoint of superior moldability; permanence of dimensions during molding, high heat resistance, and stability of color.

phe-nol′ic res′ins mold′ing type (*Chem. Plast.*) One of the oldest and most important family of plastics because of its low cost and combination of useful properties, outstanding of which are its resistance to heat and most corrosive agents. It is a nonconductor of electricity, and from the beginning and now, electrical plugs, sockets, connectors, handles, and enclosures are made of it, together with a host of other familiar housings and appliance parts. Phenolics result from a controlled reaction between phenol and formaldehyde. (See PLASTICS.)

phe′no-plast (*Chem. Plast.*) A general term for phenol-aldehyde resins. Synonymous with popular term "phenolics."

Phil′lips ma-chine′ screw. A metal or wood holding screw made in a variety of head forms and having a four-point star shaped recess in the head which requires a special tool for setting. Much used on automobile body work.

phos′phor bronze (*Metal.*) An alloy composed of copper and tin to which a little phosphorus is added. It is largely used as a bearing metal.

phos′pho-rus (*Chem.*) A light yellow, waxlike solid; specific gravity 1.83; melting point 44.4 deg. C. It is marketed in the form of sticks which, being highly inflammable, must be kept under water.

pho′to-com-pos′ing (*Print.*) Offset lithography.

pho′to-e-las′tic′i-ty (*Plast.*) Study of elastic strains by photographic measurement of strains sufficient to cause double refraction in a celluloid or glass model.

pho′to-e-lec′tric cell (*Elec.*) A device which changes light energy to electrical energy. Also called "electric eye." Principal use is for automatic control through light source.

pho′to–en-grav′ing (*Print.*) Any engraving process accomplished by means of photography.

pho-tog′ra-phy (*Chem.*) The process of fixing an image of an object on a sensitized plate, film, or paper, by exposure to light, after which it is made permanent by treating with certain chemicals.

pho′to-gra-vure′ (fō′tô-grá-vūr′) (*Print.*) An intaglio plate for printing, in which there are no sharp lines but very small depressions; the high parts show white and the depressions produce shadows.

pho-tom′e-ter (fô-tŏm′ê-tĕr) (*Phys.*) An instrument for measuring the intensity of light or for comparing the relative intensity of different lights.

pho′to-mi′cro-graph (*Metal.*) A picture taken by a combination microscope and camera for the purpose of studying specimens. The usual magnification is 100 to 500 times for metallic sections.

pho′to-stat. A photographic process for rapid duplication of maps, drawings, charts, and records on sensitized paper.

pho-to-syn′the-sis (*Chem.*) Process whereby plants produce carbohydrates from water and carbon dioxide when the leaves of plants are exposed to sunlight.

phu′goid os′cil-la′tion (fū′goid ŏs′ĭ-lā′shŭn) (*Aero.*) The oscillatory longitudinal disturbance in the motion of an aircraft commonly called "hunting."

phys′i-cal change (*Phys.*) A change by which the identity of the substance is not altered; e.g., sawing a board into small pieces is a physical change.

phys′i-cal met′al-lur′gy. Has to do with the physical and chemical properties of metals being worked on as well as their action in service.

phys′ics (fĭz′ĭks) The science which treats of the constitution and properties of matter.

pi (pī) (*Math.*) The ratio of the circumference of a circle to its diameter, or 3.1416. (*Print.*) Loose type matter badly mixed.

pi-an′o wire (*Metal.*) An exceptionally strong wire with tensile strength of from 300,000 to 340,000 lb. per square inch. Its composition is as follows: carbon, 0.570; silicon, 0.090; sulphur, 0.011; phosphorus, 0.018; manganese, 0.425.

pi′ca (pī′kȧ) (*Print.*) A type size equivalent to twelve point. It is also the unit of length for rules, leads, slugs, etc.

pick (*Textile*) A filling thread. The relative value of cotton cloth is determined by the number of picks to the inch.

pick′et (*Carp.*) A narrow board used in making fences. It is often pointed at the top; sometimes called a pale or paling.

pick′ing of pa′per (*Print.*) The pulling off of the surface of coated or enameled papers due to tacky ink.

pick′ing sort (*Print.*) When a compositor is setting up a job and finds needed letters missing, he is compelled to pick "sort" from other jobs to supply his own.

pick′le. The solution in which castings are dipped for cleansing. Dilute sulphuric acid is used for iron castings and iron plates; nitric acid for brass.

pick′ling (*Fdry.*) A process by which sand and foreign matter are removed from rough castings.

pic′ric ac′id. A monobasic acid $(C_6H_2(NO_2)_3, OH)$ prepared by treating phenol-sulphonic acid with nitric acid. It forms yellow crystals used in the manufacture of explosives and to some extent in dyeing.

pic-to′ri-al. Representing as in a picture; containing or illustrated by pictures or drawings.

pic′ture mold (*Arch.*) A molding attached to a wall, from which pictures are hung.

pic-ture noise (*Tel.*) Interference signals causing spots of light and other irregular patterns on the receiver picture.

pic′ture sig′nal (*Tel.*) The electrical impulses which represent the video or picture elements being transmitted. (See signal.)

pic′ture tube (Kinescope) (*Tel.*) A cathode-ray tube used to produce an image by variation of the beam intensity as the beam scans a raster.

piece′ work (*Print.*) Work paid for at the rate of so much per thousand ems.

pie′crust′ ta′ble (*Furn.*) A table, usually round, having a raised, carved, or molded edge.

pier (*Arch.*) A mass of masonry supporting an arch, bridge, etc.

pier glass (*Bldg.*) A large mirror placed between two windows.

pie′tra du′ra (pyā′trä dōō′rä) (*Arts*) Hard and fine stones as those used for inlay and the like.

pi-e′zo-e-lec′tric′i-ty (pī-ē′zō-ê-lĕk′-trĭs′ĭ-tĭ) (*Elec.*) Electrification produced by pressure in particular directions on certain crystals.

pi′e-zom′e-ter. A gauge for measuring the pressure of fluids or liquids.

pig (*Metal.*) Cast iron in the form of a bar ingot.

pi′geon-hole′. Small open compartment, as in the upper portion of a roll-top desk, used as receptacle for letters, envelopes, etc.

pig i′ron (*Metal.*) The cast iron of commerce as it comes from the smelting furnace; usually in bars of about 100 lb.

pig′ment (*Chem., Color, and Print.*) That substance added to paint or ink to give body and color.

pig′skin (*Leather.*) A leather of high quality and durability made from the skin of the domestic pig. Desirable for wallets, billfolds, cigarette cases, gloves, etc.

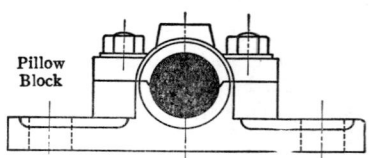
Pigtail Splice

pig′tail′ (*Elec.*) A splice made by twisting together the bared ends of parallel conductors.

pike pole. A pole tipped with a sharp metal point; used in supporting poles in an upright position during "planting" or removal.

pi-las′ter (*Arch.*) A right-angled columnar projection from a pier or wall.

pile driv′er. A vertical framework provided with guides for carrying a weight which, after being elevated to the top of the framing, is allowed to fall, by force of gravity, on the head of a pile.

Pilaster

pil′ing (*Engin.*) Large timbers or poles driven into the ground or the bed of a stream to make a firm foundation.

pil′lar (*Arch.*) A column to support a structure.

pil′lar file (*Shopwk.*) Used on narrow work, cutting grooves, etc. Same general shape as a hand file but not as wide and is obtainable in any cut.

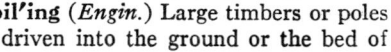
Pillow Block

pil′low block (*Mech.*) A bearing or support for a shaft.

pi′lot (*Aero.*) An operator of an aircraft. This term is applied regardless of the sex of the operator. (*Mech.*) A projecting part entering a hole or opening, thus serving as a guide for alignment of work.

pi′lot bal-loon′ (*Aero.*) A small balloon sent up to show the direction and speed of the wind.

pi′lot drill (*Mach.*) A small drill used to start a hole in order to insure a larger drill running true to center.

pi′lot light (*Elec.*) A small light set in a wall case or receptacle at or near a control switch and wired to it to indicate whether the fixture or appliance connected to it is operating.

pi′lot par′a-chute (*Aero.*) A small, auxiliary parachute attached to the apex of the main parachute, designed to pull the latter out of its pack when the rip cord is pulled.

pi′lot plane (*Aero.*) An auxiliary airfoil pivoted near the leading edge of a main airfoil and free to take up a position in line with the wind.

pim'ple (*Plast.*) Undesirable small, sharp or conical elevation on the surface of a plastic.

pin (*Carp.*) A small peg or wooden nail.

Pincers

pin'cers (pĭn'sẽrz) A jointed instrument with two handles and a pair of grasping jaws for holding an object.

pinch (*Auto.*) A leak in an inner tube caused by the tube being caught between the casing and the rim or by fold or crease in a tube too large for the casing.

pinch bar (*Shopwk.*) A shop name for crowbar.

pinch dog (*Wood Patmkg.*) A small bar of steel, with two sharpened points projecting from it at right angles; used by woodworkers for clamping pieces together when hand screws cannot be used.

pine (*Wood*) *Pinus.* Includes a wide variety of woods, ranging from the soft, easily worked white pine to the hard, heavy, long-leaf yellow pine which is used in heavy construction work. White pine is used principally for patternmaking and for facework in dwelling construction. Short-leaf yellow pine is used as a substitute for the long-leaf variety in places where great strength is not so necessary.

ping (*Auto.*) A short, sharp sound resulting from too rapid detonation of gas in the engine cylinders.

pin'hole' (*Papermkg.*) An imperfection in paper which may be caused by froth or foreign particles.

pin'hol'ing (*Paint and Lacquer*) Minute holes in sprayed paint and lacquer film due to bubbles which persist until the film has dried. Caused by draughts, sealed air pockets, humid spray booth, moisture or oil in air line, porous undercoatings, difference in temperature between surface being sprayed and the lacquer itself, or use of too-quick-drying thinner.

pin'ion (*Gear.*) The smaller gear of a pair, either bevel or spur, regardless of size.

pin'ion gear and shaft (*Auto.*) The pinion gear and shaft, made as a unit from one piece of steel, carries the power from the propeller shaft to the rear axle. The unit is supported by two tapered roller bearings; all are contained in a housing attached to the front of the rear-axle housing.

pin knot (*Wood.*) This term is applied to a knot not over $\frac{1}{2}$ in. in diameter.

pin'na-cle (*Arch.*) (1) A high or topmost point. (2) A small turret or tall ornament, as on a parapet.

pin punch (*Engin.*) A long, slender punch used for driving out tight-fitting pins.

pin seal (*Bookbndg.*) A very small fine-grained leather effect resembling natural grain on a young sealskin.

pin span'ner (*Mach.*) Used on round nuts having holes in the periphery to receive the spanner pin.

pint. A measure of capacity; one half a quart; one eighth of a gallon. Used in both liquid and dry measure.

pin'tle (*Mech.*) A pivot pin, such as is used in attaching a rudder to the stern of a boat.

pin vise (*Mach.*) A small hand vise with a V notch in each jaw for gripping wire or round objects.

pin wrench (*Mach.*) Used on round nuts which have two holes in their face to receive the pins of the wrench.

pipe (*Metal.*) In general, pipe is made of wrought steel, seamless steel, wrought iron, cast iron, alloys, copper, and brass.

pipe cou′pling (*Plumb.*) A threaded sleeve used to connect two pipes.

pipe cut′ter (*Plumb.*) A tool for cutting wrought iron or steel pipes. The curved end which partly encircles the pipe carries one or more cutting disks. Feed of the cutter is regulated by a screw as the tool is rotated around the pipe.

pipe die (*Plumb.*) A screw plate used for cutting threads on pipe.

pipe fit′tings (*Plumb. and Steam Fit.*) A general term referring to ells, tees, various branch connectors, etc., used in connecting pipes.

pipe hang′er (*Plumb. and Steam Fit.*) Device for suspending pipe. Malleable iron hanger consists of a lag screw, a piece of pipe, a socket, and an adjustable ring. An adjustable hanger consists of a beam clamp, an adjustable rod, and an adjustable ring. A strap hanger consists of a metal strap or band nailed or screwed to ceiling or rafter and slung around pipe.

pipe thread (*Mach.*) The V-type thread used on pipe and tubing, cut on a taper of ¾ in. per foot, which insures a thoroughly tight joint.

pi-pette′ (pĭ-pĕt′) (*Chem.*) A small tube used for the accurate measuring of small quantities of a liquid. Frequently not of the same diameter throughout, being widened into a bulb about midway between the two ends.

pipe vise (*Plumb.*) Pipe vises are of two kinds: the hinged side type with V jaws for small pipes, and the chain type used for large pipes.

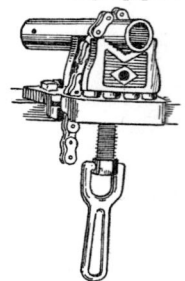

Pipe Vise

pi′qua (*Wood*) An African tree belonging to the cedar family. It is a light brown, medium-hard wood, with grain somewhat like mahogany.

pique (pēk) (*Furn.*) French inlay.

pis′ton (*Engin.*) The plunger which moves within the cylinder of an engine or pump. The efficiency of compression depends very largely on the proper fitting of the piston.

pis′ton head (*Auto.*) The top, closed end of a piston.

pis′ton pin (*A u t o.*) A hollow steel shaft, hardened and ground, which connects the upper end of the connecting rod to the piston. It also is called "wrist pin."

pis′ton–pin boss′es (*Auto.*) Those parts of a piston which carry the ends of the piston pins.

Piston Ring

pis′ton ring (*Mach.*) A spring packing ring for a piston.

pis′ton rod (*Mech.*) The rod which moves the piston and is connected to the crosshead or crankshaft.

pis′ton skirt (*Auto.*) That part of a piston below the piston pin.

pis′ton stroke (*Auto.*) The complete length of travel of a piston in its cylinder.

pis′ton valve (*Engin.*) A piston operating in a cylindrical case having ports which are opened and closed by motion of the piston.

pit (*Plast.*) Small, regular or irregular hole in the surface of a plastic, usually having approximately the the same diameter and depth, and often dull or rough at the bottom.

pitch (*Chem. Plast.*) A dark-colored, fusible, viscous to solid bituminous or resinous substance, insoluble in water but more or less soluble in carbon disulphide, benzol, etc. (*Mech.*) A term used to denote the number of threads per inch, or in gearing, to indicate the size of teeth.

pitch′blende (*Mineral.*) A dark mineral with pitchlike luster. An ore containing uranium and radium.

pitch board (*Bldg.*) A template of thin wood or metal, in the shape of a right-angle triangle, for marking out and testing the cuts of a stair string. The shorter side is the height of the riser cut; the next longer side is the width of the tread cut.

pitch cir′cle. The circumference of the pitch line; the circle of contact in meshed gears.

pitch di-am′e-ter (*Gear.*) The diameter of the pitch circle of a gear wheel.

pitch in′di-ca′tor (*Aero.*) An instrument for indicating the existence of a pitching velocity of an aircraft.

pitch of a roof (*Arch.*) The angle which the slope of a roof makes with the horizontal.

pitch of a screw (*Mach.*) The distance from a point on a screw thread to a corresponding point on the next turn. In a single thread the pitch is the amount of advance in one revolution.

pitch of gears (*Mach.*) Refers to the size of gear teeth.

pitch ra′tio (*Aero.*) Ratio of propeller pitch (geometrical, unless otherwise stated) to diameter P/D.

pitch speed (*Aero.*) The product of the mean geometrical pitch by the number of revolutions of the propeller in unit time; i.e., the speed the aircraft would make if there were no slip.

pith knot (*Wood*) A knot with a pith hole not more than ¼ in. in diameter.

pit′man (*Mech.*) A rod or arm which connects a rotary with a reciprocating part; a connecting rod.

Pitman

pit mold′ing (*Fdry.*) A method of making large castings in a pit in the foundry floor.

pi-tot′–stat′ic tube (pē-tō′ stăt′ĭk) (*Aero.*) Parallel or coaxial combination of pitot and static tubes. The difference between impact pressure and static pressure is a function of the velocity of flow past the tube.

pi′tot′ tube (pē′tō′ tūb) (*Aero.*) A cylindrical tube with an open end which is pointed upstream, i.e., so that the air meets the instrument head-on or is met head-on by the instrument.

pit′ted (*Auto.*) Pock-marked. Caused by burning or rusting.

pit′ting (*Paint and Lacquer*) Spraying lacquer in a room where the temperature is less than 65 deg. F., especially with high pressure.

piv′ot-ed case′ment (*Arch.*) A casement window pivoted on its upper and lower edges.

piv′ot pin. A point supporting something which turns.

plain saw′ing (*Woodwkg.*) Saw cuts taken parallel to squared side of log.

plain turn′ing (*Mach.*) Straight or cylindrical turning.

plan. A draft or form drawn on a plane surface as a map; especially a top view or a view of a horizontal section; a diagram.

planch′et (*Shopwk.*) Blank piece of metal punched out of a sheet before being finished by further work, such as the blank from which coins are made.

plan-cier′ (plăn-sēr′)(*Arch.*) The underside of the corona in a cornice.

plane (plān) (*a.*) Level, flat, even. (*n.*) (*Woodwk.*) (1) A surface in which, if any two points are taken, the straight line which joins them lies wholly in that surface. (2) A tool for smoothing boards or other surfaces of woods. (*v.*) (*Mech.*) To machine work on a planer. (*Woodwk.*) To handsmooth a wooden surface by means of a plane, or to machine it on a jointer.

plan′er (plān′ēr) (*Mach.*) A metal-working machine for producing plane surfaces. The work is fastened to a table which moves back and forth under the tool. (*Print.*) A block of hardwood with a smooth surface, used with a mallet for leveling forms in a chase.

plan′et-a-ry gear (*Auto.*) Consists of an internal ring gear, a pinion on a short shaft through which power is applied, and three pinions carried on a plate or spider; these three pinions mesh both with the shaft pinion and the ring gear.

plane tree (*Wood*) *Platanus*. Same as buttonwood or sycamore.

plane trig′o-nom′e-try (*Math.*) A branch of mathematics dealing with the measurement of triangles. Six functions are developed and the relationship existing among these six functions and their application to the solution of the right and oblique triangles are of great mathematical importance.

plan form, de-vel′oped (*Aero.*) The plan of an airfoil, as drawn with the chord lines at each section rotated about the airfoil axis into a plane parallel to the plane of projection, and with the airfoil axis rotated or developed and projected into the plane of projection.

plan form, pro-ject′ed (*Aero.*) The contour as viewed from above.

pla-nim′e-ter (*Math.*) An instrument for measuring the area of any plane surface, by moving a pointer around its boundary and reading the indications of a scale.

plan′ing mill (*Woodwk.*) A mill or woodworking establishment equipped with planing and other machines for surfacing, matching, and fitting boards or planks.

plan′ish (*Metal.*) To smooth or polish metallic surfaces by hammering or rolling.

plan′ish-ing ham′mer (*Art Met.*) A finishing hammer, the style of head being selected to suit the needs of the work. Used for removing irreg-

ularities and for making bright faceted surfaces.

plank (*Woodwkg.*) A wide piece of sawed timber thicker than a board, usually 1½ to 6 in. thick and 6 in. or more wide.

plank truss (*Arch.*) A roof truss or bridge truss built of planking.

pla-nom'e-ter (plà-nŏm'ê-tēr) (*Mach.*) A name sometimes given a surface plate.

plans and spec'i-fi-ca'tions (*Shopwk.*) Drawings and a full set of directions accompanying them.

plant en'gi-neer'. Usually a mechanical engineer whose practice follows the line of some particular industry. His duty consists principally of the construction of plant equipment.

plaque (plàk) An ornamented plate or disk, of metal, wood, ivory, porcelain, etc.

plas'ter (*Bldg.*) Made by heating gypsum sufficiently to drive off most of the combined water which it contains and grinding finely the dehydrated residue. Mixed plaster is mortar to which a binder is added and is used for plastering walls and ceilings.

plas'ter board (*Arch.*) A building board made of plaster and faced with paper on both sides.

plas'ter cast. A plaster of Paris model which has been reproduced by use of a mold.

plas'ter-ing. The act of applying plaster.

plas'ter-ing trow'el. A thin rectangular piece of steel 4 to 5 in. wide and 10 to 12 in. long, with handle attached, offset but parallel to the blade.

plas'ter lath (*Arch.*) The thin strips of wood nailed to studding, joists, or rafters to receive plaster.

plas'ter of Par'is (*Chem. and Bldg.*) Calcined gypsum, marketed in the form of a white powder. When mixed with water, it sets quickly, and is useful in making casts and models.

plas'tic (*Ceram.*) Capable of being molded or modeled. Moldable material.

plas'tic art. Ceramics or sculpture in which things are modeled.

plas'tic flow (*Plast.*) Flow which is proportional to the pressure in excess of a certain minimum pressure (yield value) necessary to start the flow.

plas-tic'i-ty (*Phys.*) That property of a body which permits a change of shape without fracture. (*Plast.*) Susceptibility to and retention of deformation. Capacity of taking and retaining the form of a mold.

plas'ti-cize (*Plast.*) To soften a material and make it plastic or moldable.

plas'ti-ciz'ers (*Plast.*) Chemical agent added to plastic compositions, especially those to be used as coatings, to make them softer and more flexible.

plas'tics. In the broad sense there are many plastic substances, from pitch to Portland cement, and on, through the synthetics. All flow at some stage of use. The common acceptance of the term, however, refers to the synthetics. These are a large group of variously based types of high molecular weight, which solidify in the finished state, and though they resemble the natural resins in some respects, they are chemically and physically different. There are many combinations of plastic source ma-

terials; therefore, there is a large and growing number of members in the plastics family. The major divisions are:
1. The thermosets, which set permanently under heat, catalysts, ultraviolet light, etc. The members of this group are the Aminos (ureas and melamines), most polyesters, alkyds, epoxies, and phenolics. (See POLYESTER, etc.)
2. The thermoplastics, which can be repeatedly softened and shaped, and hardened by cooling are: styrene polymers and copolymers, acrylics, cellulosics, polyethylenes, vinyls, nylons, and various fluorocarbons. (See POLYMERS, etc.).

Each member of the plastic family has properties suitable to certain particular demands; some are hard surfaced, some abrasion resistant, some flexible, some tough, and some are high in dielectric strength. Of the two plastics most common in schools, acrylics (plexiglas and lucite), and polyesters; the former is supplied as sheet and is sawed, filed, and worked much like wood; while the polyesters, under various trade names such as Castolite, Castoglas, Vibrin, Hetron, etc., are chemically treated and hardened from liquid in the classroom, and they are used to produce castings and laminations by simple classroom methods. Polyesters are the familiar boat laminating resins.

plas′tic tool′ing. Dies, jigs, and fixtures for metal forming, boring, assembly, and checking, made at a saving of time and labor, of laminated and cast components, and cemented into highly stable industrial tools, chiefly with epoxy and some with polyester resins. Epoxies are strong adhesive resins, particularly useful because of their low shrinkage factor. Polyesters have a cost advantage and are easy to handle. (See EPOXY RESIN.)

plas′tic wood (*Woodwk.*) A wood compound which quickly hardens on exposure to air, for filling in cracks and defects. It can be painted over almost immediately after applying:

plas′ti-sol (*Plast.*) Vinyl dispersions in mixtures with plasticizers, which can be molded or converted into film. Often used for flexible molds.

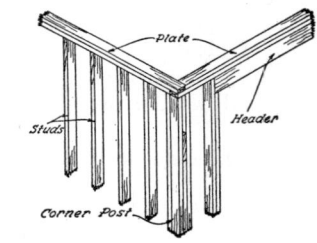

plate (*Arch.*) The top horizontal timber of a wall on which rest, and are fastened, attic joists, roof rafters, etc. (*Print.*) A stereotype or electrotype of material to be printed. (*Radio*) A solid metallic element of a vacuum tube which attracts the electrons from the cathode and acts as an output electrode for the external circuit.

plate cir′cuit (*Radio*) The complete circuit the plate current would make from the plate, through the reproducer or coupling devices, power supply, ground, and back to the cathode of the same tube.

plate clutch (*Auto. Mech.*) A clutch which transmits power through two or more plates which are held in contact by the pressure of springs.

plate con-dens'er. A condenser, in which the alternating sheets of metal are joined to give two terminals. The separators may be of mica, paraffined paper, air, etc.

plate cur'rent (*Radio*) The pulsating direct current which flows in the plate circuit of any stage I_p (plate current).

plate cyl'in-der (*Print.*) The revolving section of a rotary press to which curved printing plates are attached.

plat'ed bar (*Metal.*) This is blister steel in the form of bars which have been rolled or hammered while hot. This treatment flattens down the blisters and tends to toughen the metal.

plate fin'ish (*Papermkg.*) A term applied descriptively to English finish or lightly supercalendered papers because of the similarity to a plated finish.

plate glass (*Bldg.*) A high-grade glass cast in the form of a plate or sheet and subsequently polished; usually thicker than window glass, of smoother surface, and better quality.

plat'en (*Mach.*) A flat working surface for laying out or assembling metal work, or the movable table of a planer or similar machine. (*Print.*) That part of a job press on which the sheet takes the impression from the type.

plat'en press (*Print.*) One in which both paper and form lie flat during the process of printing.

plate rail (*Arch.*) A narrow shelflike molding attached to an interior wall for the support of dishes, etc.

plate volt'age (*Radio*) The D.C. voltage impressed between the ground and plate of any vacuum tube by the power supply.

plat'form (*Bldg.*) A horizontal structure usually covered with wood or metal and set on uprights to form an elevated flooring or stand.

plat'form fram'ing (*Bldg.*) In this type of construction the floor platforms are framed independently; the second and third floors are supported by studs one story in height.

plat'ing (*Metal.*) The depositing of a metallic coating on another material or metal either by dipping or by the electrolytic process.

plat'i-nite (*M e t a l.*) A 46-per-cent nickel steel which has the same thermal coefficient of expansion as platinum for which it is substituted, especially in the manufacture of electric lamp bulbs.

plat'i-noid (*Metal.*) An alloy of German silver and tungsten, used in the manufacture of electrical appliances, particularly resistance coils.

plat'i-num (*Metal.*) A very heavy, rare, white metal, specific gravity 21.5. It is very ductile, and does not oxidize readily. It is used in the manufacture of jewelry, and for the little connecting wires in the tops of incandescent lamps.

play (*Mach.*) The motion between poorly fitted or worn parts.

pli'ant. Flexible; easily bent without breaking.

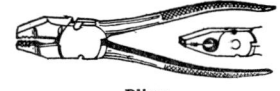

Pliers

pli'ers (*Mech.*) A pincerlike tool having broad, flat, roughened jaws.

plinth (*A r c h.*) The lowest square-shaped part of the base of a column or pedestal.

plot′ting points (*Math.*) The determining of the position of, and the locating of points as in a graph.

plow (*Carp.*) (1) A grooving tool. (2) To cut a groove.

plow′ing (*Aero.*) Taxiing a seaplane at low speed before rising on the step.

plug (*Elec.*) A device with conducting projections which fit into slots, making electrical contact, usually between a portable device and a source of supply.

plug fuse (*Elec.*) A type of fuse which is held in position by a screw-thread contact instead of spring clips as is the case with a cartridge fuse.

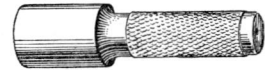

Plug Gauge

plug gauge (*Mach.*) A very accurately made plug for testing the size of holes or internal diameters in machine work.

plug tap (*Mach.*) The intermediate tap in a series of three: (1) starting tap, (2) plug tap, (3) bottoming tap. See TAPS.

plug weld (*Weld.*) A method of attaching plates or fixtures by welding through a hole in one or both of the parts.

plumb (plŭm) (*Bldg.*) To test or true up vertically, as a wall by means of a plumb line.

plum-ba′go (plŭm-bā′gō) Graphite or black lead, used for pencils, crucibles, and for lubricating purposes; also for coating nonconducting surfaces, as gutta-percha.

plumb and level (*Bldg.*) A piece of well-finished hardwood or metal with bubble set lengthwise for testing horizontal accuracy and another bubble set crosswise for testing vertical accuracy.

plumb bob (*M a s o n r y*) The weight used at the end of a plumb line.

Plumb Bob

plumb′ing. Installation and repair of water pipes, tanks, bathroom fixtures, sewage lines, etc.

plum′met. A piece of lead attached to a line for adjusting to the vertical; also for sounding depths.

plung′er–type oil pump (*Auto.*) Similar in operation to any cylinder and plunger pump. On one plunger stroke oil is drawn into the cylinder and a check valve closes after it. On the return stroke the piston forces the oil out of the cylinder into the oil lines of the engine past another check valve.

ply (*Paper*) A layer or thickness, as in something built up of several layers, each thickness being termed a ply.

ply′wood (*Woodwk.*) Veneered sheets glued together, the wood grain alternating in each sheet.

pneu-mat′ic (nû-măt′ĭk) (*Engin.*) Pertaining to, or operated by, air pressure.

pneu-mat′ic brakes (*Auto.*) Brakes operated either by air pressure or vacuum, the pressure being on a large piston to get the proper force.

pneu-mat′ic tire (*Auto.*) A tire usually consisting of an outer casing or shoe and an inner tube which, when inflated to proper pressure, enables the tire to retain its shape under load.

pneu-mat′ic tools (*E n g i n.*) Tools operated by air pressure.

pock′et rot (*Wood*) Decay which appears in the form of a hole, pocket, or area of soft rot, usually surrounded by apparently sound wood.

pock marks (*Paint and Lacquer*) Air bubbles that are trapped in a porous surfacer coat, and which show up as pock marks when the surfacer is sanded. In spraying, too much surfacer is applied or too much air pressure employed, or the combination of two result in this condition.

po′di-um. A small, raised platform, such as used by a leader when conducting an orchestra.

point (*Print.*) The unit on which type sizes are based. One point is .013837 of an inch.

point′ing (*Arch.*) The finishing of joints in a brick or masonry wall.

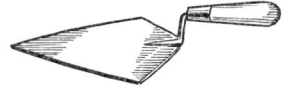

Pointing Trowel

point′ing trow′el (*Masonry*) A small trowel used by bricklayers for pointing and striking up joints and for removing mortar from the face of the wall.

point line (*Print.*) Type is said to be "point line" when the faces of various sizes may be made to align with the aid of point-size spacing materials.

points (*Print.*) Punctuation marks in type.

point sys′tem (*Print.*) The unit of size in the casting of type bodies.

poke or push weld′ing. A spot-welding process where pressure is applied manually to one electrode only.

po-lar′i-ty (*Elec.*) A means of designating the poles of a magnet or magnetic circuit, the kind of charge of static electricity, or the positive or negative terminal of a d.c. electrical circuit.

po′lar-i-za′tion (*Elec.*) In a primary cell, the collection of hydrogen bubbles on the positive plate, which increases the internal resistance, and diminishes the current strength.

po′la-rized light (*Plast.*) That phenomenon whereby light rays are limited to one plane of vibration.

poles (*Elec.*) The positive and negative terminals of an electric circuit.

pole shoes (*Elec.*) The outer part of the pole pieces curved concentrically with the armature.

pol′ish. To make smooth or bright by friction.

pol′y-chrome (pŏl′ĭ-krōm)(*Furn.*) A form of painted ornamentation, originating in Egypt and much used in Italy during the sixteenth century.

pol′y-es′ter (*Plast.*) A plastic family of many types. It has grown rapidly to great importance in the industry. The unsaturated polyesters, whose two basic ingredients are dihydric alcohols and dibasic acids are cross linked with the monomer Styrene and others. They are easily handled in liquid form and cure easily with no liquid or gaseous by-product. They have good weathering, heat, corrosion, electrical and physical properties, and they are dimensionally stable. They are used extensively for laminating such products as huge boat hulls, truck tanks, hampers, radomes, swimming pools, chairs, auto bodies, small electrical components, and architectural panels. Much polyester is also used in foamed plastics. (See FOAMED PLASTICS.) Polyesters are highly recommended for school use because of their versatility, and ease of use. The resin comes in liquid form, and by adding a hardener, it solidifies in simple molds or on glass surfaces at room temperatures, and without pressure. Other forms of polyesters are used for fibers (Dacron) and film (Mylar), the latter, very strong, was used in the now famous earth-circling "Ecco." (See PLASTICS.)

pol′y-eth′yl-ene (*Plast.*) A thermoplastic, composed of polymers of ethylene: tough, waxy, and uneffected by water. It is commonly seen in flexible bottles, and in builders', agriculturalists', and manufacturers' protective, weatherproof sheets. (See PLASTICS.)

pol′y-gon. A plane figure of many sides and angles, especially more than four.

pol′y-gon of for′ces. An expansion of the triangle of forces. If any number of forces are represented in magnitude and direction by the sides of a polygon taken in order, they are in equilibrium.

pol′y-mer (*Plast.*) A chemical compound of high molecular weight formed by the combining of simpler compounds having the same chemical elements in the same proportion. Polymers may be made by condensation or by successive addition of numbers of relatively small monomers.

pol′y-mer-i-za′tion (*Chem.*) Union of two or more molecules of the same substance to form a different substance without loss of anything from the original substance; e.g., change of 6 formaldehyde molecules (CH_2O) into 1 of sugar ($C_6H_{12}O_6$) by chlorophyll (green coloring matter in plants) during photosynthesis.

pol′y-mers (*Chem. Plast.*) The products of reaction in polymerization.

pol′y-phase (*Elec.*) Two or more phases or circuits associated electrically with each other.

pol′y-sty′rene (*Chem. Plast.*) An acid-resisting thermoplastic resin easily molded by the injection process producing a high gloss and luster on molded pieces. Used for acid containers, refrigerator parts, instrument panels, novelties, etc.

pol′y-tech′nic. Including many of the arts and sciences; as a polytechnic school.

pol′y-vi′nyls (*Plast.*) The family includes polyvinyl chloride, p.v. acetate, p.v. acetals, and p.v. alcohol: the first being a thermoplastic material composed of polymers of vinyl chloride. It has outstanding resistance to water, alcohol, acids and alkalies, and therefore it is found in film and sheet vapor barriers, shower curtains, silo covers and upholstery. (See PLASTICS.)

pop′lar (*Woodwkg.*) A common tree whose wood is soft, light in weight, and from white to a light-greenish-yellow in color. It is easy to work and is much used in the arts.

pop′pet (*Mach.*) (1) The headstock of a lathe. (2) A lathe center. The term is not generally used.

pop'pet valves (*Engin.*) The disk and stem type of valves as used in an automobile motor.

pop'py heads (*Arch.*) The ornaments which form the tops of the ends of benches or pews.

por'ce-lain. China or chinaware. A translucent kind of ceramic ware, usually glazed.

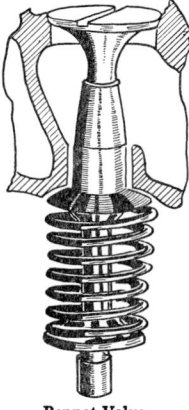
Poppet Valve

porch (*Arch.*) A covered structure, outside of a building, and with separate roof, forming an entrance to the building.

po-ros'i-ty. The tendency to permit air, gas, or fluid under pressure to ooze through metal or other material. A tire is porous when many small holes allow the escape of air. A cylinder is porous if the metal is not dense enough to prevent leakage through its walls.

por'pois'ing (pôr'pŭs'ĭng) (*Aero.*) An undulatory movement of a seaplane consisting of a combination of a vertical oscillation and an oscillation about its transverse axis, which occurs at certain stages of planing.

port (*Auto.*) An opening through which fuel may be admitted to the combustion chamber of the engine or one from which exhaust gases are released.

port'a-ble. That which may be easily moved or carried.

port'a-ble crane (*Shopwk.*) A hoisting device carried by a frame mounted on wheels. It is particularly useful for quick moving about in a shop for the handling of parts too heavy for a man to lift.

port'a-ble fire'box' boil'er (*Engin.*) Widely used type of steel heating boiler, fitted with water-jacketed firebox. May be of welded or riveted construction, and have fire tubes or water tubes. Designated portable because it is shipped complete, in one piece, ready for installation.

por'tal (*Arch.*) A door, also a gateway or entranceway. Usually applied to imposing structures.

port-fo'li-o. A portable case for carrying papers and drawings.

por'ti-co (*Arch.*) A space with a roof supported by columns; usually a porch before the entrance to a building.

por'tiere' (pôr'tyâr') (*Furn.*) A curtain for use in a doorway.

Port'land ce-ment' (*Masonry*) The building cement of common use, made by heating clay and lime substance. The vitrified product, when ground, forms a very strong hydraulic cement.

pos'i-tive car'bon (*Elec.*) In direct-current arc lamps the positive carbon has formed in it a crater. This carbon is usually the top one.

pos'i-tive-driv'en-type su'percharg'er (*Aero.*) A supercharger driven at a fixed speed ratio from the engine shaft by gears or other positive means.

pos'i-tive feed (*Mach.*) When the feed motion is communicated directly by means of gears, without friction clutches or belts.

pos'i-tive group (*Elec.*) A number of storage-battery plates, welded to a common terminal, which forms the positive element for a single cell.

pos′i-tive mold (*Plast.*) A mold designed to trap all the molding material to prevent its escape when it closes.

pos′i-tive mo′tion (*Mech.*) Motion obtained by use of gears, linkages, levers, etc., in which there is no loss by slipping or friction.

pos′i-tive plate (*Elec.*) The plate of a storage cell, usually brownish in color, from which the current flows to the negative plate during the process of discharging.

pos′i-tive ter′mi-nal (*Elec.*) The point of connection of a circuit or battery from which electricity flows when a circuit is completed.

post drill (*Mach.*) A drilling machine constructed for attachment to a post or column. Often used in small shops, service stations, etc.

post′er (*Print.*) A large printed sheet used for outdoor or window-display advertising.

post′-of′fice bridge (*Elec.*) A type of Wheatstone bridge, where the galvanometer and known resistances are all enclosed in a box. The balance is obtained by removing brass connecting plugs which insert certain known resistances into the circuit. The name comes from the rows of plugs inserted in the face of the box.

po-tas′si-um (*Chem.*) A soft, waxlike, silver metal, which rapidly oxidizes in moist air; melting point 63.5 deg. C.; specific gravity 0.8621. The metal itself has no uses in the arts, but its many salts are of great value.

po-ten′tial (*Elec.*) An electrical state or the electrical state of a point. It is measured by the work done in bringing a unit charge from an infinite distance up to the point. It is measured in practical units called volts. (*Phys.*) A condition at a point in space, due to local attraction or repulsion, such, that a mass, electric charge, etc., at such point becomes capable of doing work.

po-ten′tial dif′fer-ence (*Elec.*) The difference in the electrical state of two points, measured in volts.

po-ten′tial en′er-gy (*Phys.*) Stored energy or energy of position.

po-ten′ti-om′e-ter (pô-tĕn′shĭ-ŏm′ê-tẽr) (*Elec.*) An instrument used for comparing voltages with a constant standard; also a form of rheostat.

pot life (*Plast.*) See WORKING LIFE.

pot′ter-y. Earthenware or porcelain, or the factory in which it is made.

pounce (*Draft.*) The fine powder sometimes applied to the surface of tracing linen to facilitate inking.

pow′der met′al-lur′gy. This process is accomplished without melting. The fine powdered metals are placed in a steel mold and subjected to heavy pressure, producing a fragile metal shape which under heat-treatment results in a perfect alloy. The method is well adapted to the making of alloys of metals or nonmetals having a great difference in melting temperature.

pow′er (*Elec.*) The unit of electric power is the watt, in which is measured the rate of doing work by electricity in motion. (*Mech.*) The rate of working or expending energy. In mechanics power is measured: force $\times$ distance $\div$ time. It is expressed in foot-pounds per minute or second. (*Phys.*) The rate at which work is performed or the amount of work done in a unit of time.

pow′er am′pli-fi′er (*Radio*) A type of amplifier used to deliver a large amount of power to the loud-speaker or on an antenna.

power brakes (*Auto. Mech.*) Brakes operated hydraulically through a booster system. When engine is running brakes respond to light pressure on brake pedal.

pow′er fac′tor (*Elec.*) The ratio of the true power (watts as read by a wattmeter) to the apparent power (volts times amperes as read by a voltmeter and ammeter respectively)

$$p.f. = \frac{\text{true power (W)}}{\text{apparent power (V} \times \text{A)}}$$

pow′er feed (*Mech.*) The automatic feed of a lathe, planer, screw-cutting, or other machine.

pow′er ham′mer. A hammer operated by air, water, or mechanical power, used on heavy work.

pow′er land′ing (*Aero.*) Any landing during which the engine is kept running at more than idling speed.

pow′er load′ing (*Aero.*) The gross weight of an airplane fully loaded, divided by the normal brake horsepower of the engine computed for air of standard density unless otherwise stated.

pow′er pack (*Elec.*) A device to supply the necessary filament or heater power, and also the plate power and grid bias for the operation of a radio set, public-address system, etc. In some cases, a direct current for the dynamic-speaker field is supplied.

pow′er plant (*Auto.*) Consists of the motor with the fuel, carburetion, ignition, cooling, and lubrication systems.

power steering (*Auto. Mech.*) Permits free steering when the engine is running; hydraulically operated through a booster built into the steering unit attached to the steering linkage.

pow′er stroke (*Auto.*) (1) The arc of crankshaft travel while the pressure of ignited gases is exerted on the piston. (2) The piston stroke on which the engine is delivering power.

pow′er trans-form′er (*Elec.*) A device for connecting power from a high voltage and low current to a low voltage and high current, or vice versa. the amount of power so changed remaining theoretically the same. The frequency in which these are used is usually 60 cycles.

pow′er tube (*Radio*) The vacuum tube used in the last stage of the AF (audio frequency) amplifier. Provides large AF for the speaker operation.

pow′er u′nit (*Elec.*) The watt is the unit of power in electrical circuits. The product of the voltage times the amperage gives the wattage.

pow′er ven-tu′ri (*Aero.*) A venturi tube used to operate gyroscopic turn indicators and other instruments.

prac′tice (1) To do, carry on, act, or exercise. (2) To follow or work at, as a profession.

Pratt Truss

Pratt truss. A popular form of truss for both roof and bridge construction.

The vertical members are in compression and the diagonals in tension.

pre-ca'ri-ous. Risky; doubtful; perilous.

pre-cip'i-tate (*n.*) (*Plast.*) A solid substance thrown out of solution as the result of a chemical change effected by addition of a reagent. (*v.*) To separate a substance from a solution by chemical action of a reagent.

pre-ci'sion grind'ing (*Mach.*) Machine grinding in which the tolerances are exceedingly close.

pre-ci'sion lathe (*M a c h.*) A small bench lathe used for very accurate work.

pre-fab'ri-cat-ed (*Arch.*) Something completely or in part built in a factory or elsewhere to be finally erected at the place where it is to be used.

pre-form' (*Plast.*) In plastic lamination, to save time and labor, rather than drape the mold with glass cloth, difficult mold forms are filled with a fibrous glass liner, preformed by various methods, but chiefly by blowing cut fiber, together with a binder, over a screen form which approximates the contour of the mold. When dried, it is inserted into the mold, charged with resin, and pressed into the finished product.

pre-form'ing (*Plast.*) The process of condensing molding compounds to insure easier and quicker filling of the molds with a minimum amount of waste.

pre'ig-ni'tion (*Auto.*) A condition of detonation brought about by either hot carbon deposits, or faulty ignition, in which gas is exploded prematurely.

pre-lim'i-na-ry. Introductory; preceding the main discourse, business, or subject; something done at the outset.

pre-mix' (*Plast.*) In plastic molding, the plastic is mixed with fillers, pigment and glass fiber, and forced into a die under pressure and heat. The term refers to mold ingredients mixed in the plant, rather than to those ready-mixed outside the plant.

pres'en-ta'tion. The act of offering for acceptance, approval, etc.; introducing or bringing forward.

press'board (*P r i n t.*) Hard, smooth cardboard used where a solid packing is needed in the tympan of the platen press.

pressed brick (*Masonry*) A high-grade brick used for exposed surface work.

pressed steel (*Metalwk.*) The great variety of articles shaped or pressed from steel sheets or plates by dies or forms.

press fit (*Mach.*) A fitting together of parts by pressure; slightly tighter than a sliding fit.

press pol'ish (*Plast.*) A finish for sheet stock produced by contact, under heat and pressure, with a very smooth metal which gives the plastic a high sheen.

press re-vise' (*Print.*) A final proof; one taken after all revisions and corrections have been made.

press'room (*Print.*) The room where printing is done.

pres'sure (*Elec.*) Electromotive force (e.m.f.) commonly spoken of as voltage. (*P h y s.*) Force per unit area.

pres'sure air'ship (*Aero.*) An airship that maintains its form either wholly or in part by internal pressure. Non rigid, semi rigid, and pressure rigid are pressure airships.

pres′sure al′ti-tude (*Aero.*) (1) The altitude corresponding to a given pressure in a standard atmosphere. (2) The altitude at which the gas bags of an airship become full.

pres′sure cir′cu-lat′ing sys′tem of lu′bri-ca′tion (*Auto. Mech.*) A pump is so located that it can lift oil from a reservoir in the lower part of a machine or engine and deliver it under pressure through pipes or drilled holes to the parts to be lubricated. Commonly used on automobile engines.

pres′sure noz′zle (*Aero.*) An instrument which, in combination with a gauge, is used to measure the indicated speed of an aircraft relative to the air. It may be a pitot-static or a venturi tube, or a combination of a pitot tube and a venturi tube.

pres′sure pads (*Plast.*) Reinforcements of hardened steel distributed around the dead areas in the faces of a mold to help the land absorb the final pressure of closing without collapsing.

pres′sure re-duc′ing (*Steam Heat.*) Device for reducing steam pressure in heating systems where boilers are operated, for power purposes, at high pressure.

pres′sure–rig′id air′ship (*Aero.*) An airship combining the principles used in both rigid and nonrigid airships to maintain shape and skin tautness.

pres′sure sys′tem for fu′el sup-ply′ (*Auto.*) The system used before the invention of the vacuum tank, for supplying gas when the tank was lower than the carburetor. A small hand pump is used to provide initial pressure. The engine, when running, operates a small pump thus maintaining pressure. In this system the gas tank must not be vented.

pres′sure weld′ing. A group of welding processes wherein the weld is consummated by pressure.

prick′punch (*Mach.*) A small center punch. Also known as a layout punch.

Prickpunch

pri′ma-ry (*Auto. Elec.*) Refers to the low-tension (6 volts) circuit.

pri′ma-ry cell (*Elec.*) A device for transforming chemical energy into electrical energy. It consists essentially of a jar containing the solution, or electrolyte, and two plates or electrodes.

pri′ma-ry coil (*Elec.*) The coil into which the original energy is introduced and which sets up magnetic lines of force to link with another coil in which energy is induced.

pri′ma-ry col′ors. The fundamental colors from which all others are made, specifically red, yellow, and blue.

pri′ma-ry–type glid′er (*Aero.*) A ruggedly built glider designed for use in elementary training of student glider pilots.

pri′ma-ve′ra (prē′mä-vâ′rä) (*Wood*) *Tabebuia donnellsmithii*. A Central American tree. Incorrectly called white mahogany. It is creamy white in color and darkens with age. Much used in veneered store interiors, window paneling, and for bedroom furniture.

prime num′ber (*Math.*) Number having no common factors but unity.

prim′ing (*Paint.*) Laying a first coating, color, or preparation upon a surface as in painting.

prim′ing paint (*Paint.*) The first or ground coat of paint applied to a piece of work, to fill the pores of the surface.

prin′ci-ple of mo′ments (*E n g i n.*) The algebraic sum of any number of forces with respect to a point, equals the moment of their resultant about that point.

prin′ci-ples. Fundamental or general truths.

print′er's mark (*Print.*) A design or emblem used by a printer as a trademark.

print′ing. The act or art of making, under pressure, an impression on paper or other material, as from type or printing plate .(See TYPOGRAPHY.)

print′ing back (*Fdry.*) Consists of replacing the pattern in the mold and tapping it lightly after the pattern was first removed and the cavity dusted with facing material. This method produces smooth castings.

print′ing press. Any machine or press on which rapid reproduction can be made on paper or other material by transferring ink from an original (as from type or a plate) by the application of pressure.

prism (priz′m) (*Math.*) A solid whose ends are plane surfaces, equal and parallel, and whose sides are plane parallelograms.

pris′moid. A body resembling a prism in form.

proc′ess an-neal′ing. Alloys with iron base are heated below or almost to the lower limit of the critical temperature range, and then cooled.

proc′ess con-trol′ en′gi-neer′. A chemical engineer whose duty it is to check and supervise the use of materials used in the manufacturing processes.

pro′cess or chem′i-cal met′al-lur′gy. Has to do with melting and refining of metals.

proc′ess work (*P r i n t.*) A halftone process, by means of which colored pictures are obtained, by the use of three or four color plates prepared by the photo-engraving process.

prod′uct (*Engin.*) In industrial work, the quantity of output or the output itself.

prod′uct con-trol′ en′gi-neer′. One who looks after the testing and control of raw materials.

pro-duc′tion (1) Act of producing. (2) That which is produced or made. (3) In factory work, the quantity of output.

pro-duc′tion ba′sis. The manufacture of parts in quantities by the most economical methods.

pro-duc′tion en′gi-neer′. One who is responsible for the maintenance of production. He also directs tooling operation and the design of fixtures and appliances to secure the most efficient manufacturing methods.

pro′duc-tiv′i-ty. The efficiency with which economic resources (men, materials, and machines) are employed to produce goods and services.

pro′file. An outline, or contour.

pro′file drag (*Aero.*) The difference between the total wing drag and the induced drag.

profileometer. An exceedingly accurate instrument for measuring the smoothness or roughness of a surface. As a diamond-pointed tracer arm is moved across a surface, the arm, by moving a coil in an electric field, causes the generation of a current in proportion to the roughness of the surface, which is registered by an indicating needle.

pro′file thick′ness (*Aero.*) The maximum distance between the upper and lower contours of an airfoil, measured perpendicularly to the mean line of the profile.

pro′fil-ing ma-chine′ (*Mach.*) A type of milling machine in which the cutter can be made to follow a profile or pattern. A very valuable machine for certain classes of work.

pro-gres′sion (*Arith.*) A progression in which a series of numbers increases or decreases by addition or subtraction. (*Geom.*) A progression in which each of a series of numbers increases or decreases by multiplication or division.

pro-gres′sive proofs (*Print.*) Colorplate proofs which serve as a guide to the pressman in selecting the exact shades of color and in determining their sequence in printing.

pro-ject′ed pro-pel′ler a′re-a (*Aero.*) Projected blade area times the number of blades.

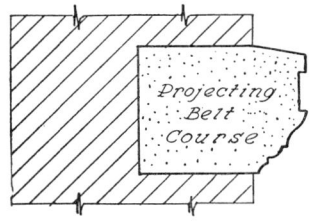

pro-ject′ing belt course (*Bldg.*) Usually an elaboration of a plain band course of masonry or cut-stone work projecting several inches beyond the face of the wall.

pro-jec′tion (1) A jutting out, a prominence. (2) In drawing, the method by which one or more views of an object are used as an aid in securing additional views.

pro-jec′tion re-ceiv′er (*Tel.*) Television receiver incorporating a principal of optical projection as distinguished from direct-viewing television receiver.

pro-jec′tion weld′ing. A resistance-welding process wherein localization of heat between two surfaces or between the end of one member and the surface of another is effected by projections.

pro-jec′tor. A device for projecting a beam of light, as a searchlight projector.

pro-mot′er (*Plast.*) A chemical catalytic additive which increases the speed of gelation provided by a normal catalyst in a resin mix.

Pro′ny brake (prō′nĭ brāk) (*Elec.*) A mechanical device consisting of a spe-

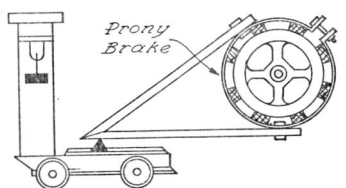

cial pulley, braking attachment, and a weighing scale, which is attached to a motor, to determine the horsepower it will deliver under load.

proof (*Print.*) A printed impression made for inspection and correction.

proof mark (*Print.*) Mark or symbol used to designate correction to be made in a proof.

proof plan′er (*Print.*) A block of hardwood faced with felt. Used for taking stone proofs.

proof press (*Print.*) Any printing

press upon which type forms may be proofed without locking in a chase.

proof-read′er (*Print.*) One who reads the proofs and checks the errors.

pro-pel′ler. The helical segment used for the propulsion of vessels. A propeller may be two-, three-, or four-bladed.

pro-pel′ler–blade an′gle (*Aero.*) The acute angle between the chord of a propeller section and a plane perpendicular to the axis of rotation of the propeller. Usually called "blade angle."

pro-pel′ler–blade a′re-a (*Aero.*) The area of the blade face, exclusive of the boss and the root, i.e., of a portion which is usually taken as extending 0.2 of the maximum radius from the axis of the shaft.

pro-pel′ler–disk a′re-a (total)(*Aero.*) The total area swept by a propeller, i.e., the area of a circle having a diameter equal to the propeller diameter.

pro-pel′ler ef-fi′cien-cy (*Aero.*) The ratio of thrust power to power input of a propeller.

pro-pel′ler hub (*Aero.*) The central portion of a propeller, often containing a pitch changing mechanism from which the blades radiate and by means of which the propeller is mounted on its drive shaft.

pro-pel′ler rake (*A e r o.*) The mean angle which the line joining the centroids, or center, of the sections of a propeller blade makes with a plane perpendicular to the axis.

pro-pel′ler root (*Aero.*) That part of the propeller blade near the boss.

pro-pel′ler shaft (*Auto.*) Also called "drive shaft." It is the shaft which delivers the power from the transmission to the rear axle.

pro-pel′ler thrust (*Aero.*) The component parallel to the propeller axis of the total air force on the propeller.

pro-pel′ler tip′ping (*Aero.*) A protective covering of the blade of a propeller near the tip.

pro-pel′ler tur′bine (*Aero.*) Or propeller turbine engine; same as turbopropeller engine.

prop′er-ties (*Plast.*) In plastics, refer to physical strength, dimensional stability, electrical, light, and weather stability, color, heat and structural stability, machinability, and hardness. (See references given under individual plastic names.)

prop′er-ty. That to which a person has a legal title, protected in that title by public authority.

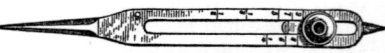

Proportional Divider

pro-por′tion-al di-vid′ers. A divider or compass for drawing purposes, provided with two slotted and double-ended legs, united by a sliding pivot and screw, by the regulation of whose position it is possible to copy measurements at an increased or decreased proportional scale.

pro-por′tion-al lim′it (*Metal.*) That point at which elongation or deformation ceases to be proportional to the load.

pro-por′tion-ate-ly. Having proper relation as to size, degree, quantity, value or importance; in proportion to.

pro-pul′sive ef-fi′cien-cy (*Aero.*) The ratio of the product of effective thrust and flight speed to the actual power input to the propeller as mounted on the airplane, consistent units being used throughout.

pro-sce′ni-um (prô-sē′nĭ-ŭm) The front part of a theater stage including the arch over the stage, in front of the curtain.

pro′te-in (prō′tê-ĭn) (*Chem.*) A class of compounds containing carbon, oxygen, hydrogen, and nitrogen, with sulphur usually present and sometimes phosphorus, iron, etc. Example: egg albumen.

pro′ton (*Elec.*) The positive nucleus of an atom around which the electrons revolve.

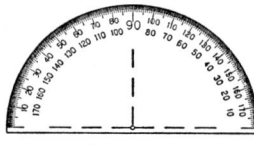

Protractor

pro-tract′or. An instrument for measuring and laying off angles on paper, used in drawing and plotting.

Prus′sian blue (*Chem.*) $Fe_4[Fe(CN)_6]_3$. Made by action of potassium ferrocyanide on ferric salt. An intense blue precipitate used as a pigment, in dyes, coloring of paper, etc. Also, mixed in oil, it is used in the fitting of bearings to indicate high spots which must be removed by scraping.

psy-chrom′e-ter. (1) Usually a thermometer having wet and dry bulbs for measuring atmospheric humidity. (2) In sling psychrometers there is only one bulb; readings are taken before and after moistening the bulb cover, to determine rate of evaporation.

pud′dle (*Engin.*) To settle loose dirt by application of water. (*Metal.*) The batch of molten iron in the puddling furnace.

pug′ging (*Arch. and Masonry*) A coarse mortar laid between floor joists to prevent passage of sound.

pull a proof (*Print.*) To take a stone proof; or a proof of a form on a hand press.

pull′back′ (*Plast.*) Device to bring the press platen to the open position by the operation of hydraulic cylinders; also used to operate ejection devices. See PUSHBACK.

pull broach (*Mach.*) A tool for cutting internal grooves or finishing holes of some shape, usually other than round, by being pulled through the work. See BROACH.

pull′er (*Auto.*) Any mechanical or hydraulic device for removing, by pulling action, parts which are tightly fitted; e.g., wheel puller or gear puller.

pul′ley (*Mech. Engin.*) A wheel used to transmit or receive power through a belt which travels over its face.

Pulley Blocks

pul′ley block (*Mech.*) A sheave pulley or series of such pulleys, enclosed between metal or wooden side plates which carry the shaft or pin on which the pulleys revolve.

pul′ley lathe (*Mach.*) A lathe used for turning either a straight or crowned face on pulleys.

pul′ley stile (*Arch.*) The vertical sides of a double-hung window frame, on which are fastened the pulleys for the sash weights.

pul′ley tap (*Mach.*) A tap with a very long shank, used for tapping setscrew holes in the hubs of pulleys.

pull–out (*Aero.*) The maneuver of transition from a dive to horizontal flight. (*Print.*) Anything pulled out from a form by the suction of the rollers of a press.

pull pin (*M a c h.*) A device for throwing mechanical parts in or out of gear, or for readily shifting in or away from a fixed relative position.

pull–up (*Aero.*) A maneuver, in the vertical plane, in which the airplane is forced into a short climb, usually from approximately level flight.

pulp (*Paper*) A mixture, as of wood fibers or rags, reduced to a soft, wet mass and forming the basis from which paper is made.

pulp'board' (*Papermkg.*) A crude board made of mixed paper stock, mechanical wood pulp, or a mixture of such materials.

pul'pit (*A r c h.*) A raised platform, with enclosed front, for a preacher in a church.

pul'sat-ing cur'rent (*Elec.*) A direct current in which the value is not constant but the flow is in one direction.

pul-sa'tion weld'ing. A spot, projection, or seam-welding process wherein the welding current is interrupted one or more times without release of pressure or change of location of electrodes.

pulse–jet en'gine (*Aero.*) A type of compression jet engine in which combustion takes place intermittently, producing thrust by a series of explosions commonly occurring at the approximate resonance frequency of the engine. Often called a pulse jet.

pul-som'e-ter (pŭl-sŏm'ê-tẽr) (*Engin.*) A type of steam siphon frequently used on construction work for pumping out cofferdams.

pul'vi-nat'ed frieze (pŭl'vĭ-nāt'ĕd) (*Carp.*) A swelled or convexly curved frieze.

pum'ice (pŭm'ĭs) (*W o o d F i n.*) Powdered lava used as a polishing material.

pump (*Mech.*) A machine for lifting or forcing liquids, either by means of a bucket or of a piston working in a closed cylinder.

pump buck'et. The piston of a lift pump.

punch (*Mech.*) (*n.*) A shearing tool made of steel, used for removing a piece of metal or other material whose shape is the same as that of the punch. (*v.*) To perforate or cut with a punch, as opposed to drilling or boring.

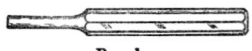

Punch

punch'ing. The making of holes through plates by means of a punching machine, as on boiler plate.

punch press (*Mach.*) A machine designed for punching holes or forming metals. A ram moves a punch against the die held on the bed.

punc'tu-a'tion (*Print.*) The separation of words into clauses and sentences by the use of marks, each of which has a definite use.

Pu'ri-tan (*Furn.*) A period in English furniture better known as Cromwellian.

pur'lins (*A r c h.*) Timbers spanning from truss to truss, and supporting the rafters of a roof.

pur'ple-heart (*Wood*) *Peltogyne purpurea*. A tree native to Dutch Guiana.

It is a hard, close-grained wood, varying in color from light to reddish purple. Used for unusual veneers.

push′back (*Plast.*) Device used to open the press and supply the force necessary to eject the molded parts. The hydraulic cylinders are usually connected to the high-pressure supply at all times, and the effective force of the main ram is proportional to their respective areas.

push broach (*Mach.*) Performs the same operations as a "pull broach" but is pushed through the work. See BROACH.

push but′ton (*Elec.*) A device which completes an electric circuit as long as a small button or knob is depressed.

push-button drive (*Auto. Mech.*) A system of gear shift control operated manually or electrically by a set of push buttons mounted as a unit on the instrument panel.

push′–but′ton start′er (*Auto.*) A starting system in which the starting motor circuit is closed by a push button instead of a foot switch.

push–but′ton switch (*Elec.*) A switch in which the electrical contacts are closed by pushing one button and are opened by pushing another.

push–down (*Aero.*) The opposite of pull-up.

push′er air′plane (*Aero.*) An airplane with the propeller or propellers aft of the main supporting surfaces.

push′er pro-pel′ler (*Aero.*) A propeller mounted to the rear of the engine or on the rear end of the propeller shaft.

push rods (*Auto.*) In overhead-valve engines, the rods between the outer end of the rocker arms and the cam followers.

put′log (*Masonry*) A crosspiece in a scaffolding, one end of which rests in a hole in the wall.

put′ty (*Chem. and Bldg.*) A composition of whiting and linseed oil, used for filling small holes in woodwork, and securing panes of glass in sash.

puz′zo-lan or slag ce-ment′ (pŏz′-zuo-lä′na) (pŏt′swô-lä′nä) Cement made of volcanic ash or from blast-furnace slag. It is slow-setting and slow-hardening, and not as strong as natural Portland cement. It is not extensively used.

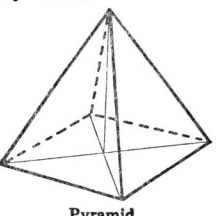

Pyramid

pyr′a-mid (*Math.*) A figure having for its base a plane polygon, and for its sides several triangles with a common vertex.

pyr′i-dine (pĭr′ĭ-dĭn) (*Chem.*) A nitrogenous base (C_5H_5N) obtained as a yellow oil from the dry distillation of bones. It is used in denaturing alcohol.

py′rite (pī′rīt) (*Chem.*) A naturally occurring sulphide of iron, FeS_2, brass yellow in color. Also known as fool's gold or sulphur diamonds.

py′ro-graph-ing (pī′rȯ-grȧf-ĭng) The producing of a design, as on leather or wood, by means of a red-hot needle or fine flame.

py′ro-lu′site (*Metal.*) An important manganese ore of iron-black color found in many countries. Besides being a source of metal manganese, it has use in electric batteries and as a paint dryer.

py-rom′e-ter (*Mech. Engin.*) An instrument for measuring very high degrees of heat, as in furnaces.

py-rox′y-lin (pī-rŏk′sĭ-lĭn) (*Chem.*) A solution of nitrocellulose in ether, ethyl acetate, and amyl acetate. Used in the manufacture of photographic films, celluloid, rayon, etc. It is inflammable and explosive.

Q

quad (*Print.*) A type body, less than type high, cast in multiples of em lengths, used for spacing out lines at the end of paragraphs and for indentions.

quad'ran-gle (*Arch.*) A square or quadrangular space surrounded by buildings, as on college grounds.

quad'rant. (1) The quarter of a circle, or of its circumference. (2) An instrument for measuring altitudes.

Quadrant

quad'rant stay (*Furn.*) A band of metal used for supporting flaps, falls, and secretary fronts.

quad-rat'ic e-qua'tions (*Algebra*) An equation which contains the square of the unknown quantity but no higher power; a pure quadratic contains the square only; an effected quadratic, both the square and the first power.

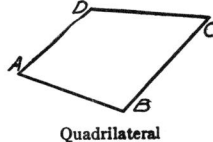

Quadrilateral

quad'ri-lat'er-al. A plane figure with four sides and four angles.

quad'ru-plane' (*Aero.*) An airplane with four sets of wings placed one above the other.

quad'ru-ple–ex-pan'sion en'gine. A compound engine in which steam is expanded four times; first, in a high-pressure cylinder, and afterwards in three low-pressure cylinders in succession. The initial steam pressure should be at least 200 pounds.

quad'ru-ple thread (*Mech.*) A thread in which there are four distinct helices, making the lead four times the pitch. A quadruple thread is usually of the square or acme type.

qual'i-ta-tive a-nal'y-sis (*Chem.*) The determining of how many and what elements or ingredients are present.

qual'i-ty. (1) Degree of goodness. (2) Peculiar power or property.

quan'ti-ta-tive a-nal'y-sis (*Chem.*) The determining of the bulk or amount of each element or ingredient.

quan'ti-ty. A certain mass, volume, or number; that property of anything that may be increased or diminished.

quar'ry. (1) An excavation from which stone is removed by blasting, cutting, etc. (2) A small square or lozenge-shaped pane of glass, plain or decorated, used in forming the glass fronts of eighteenth-century bookcases.

quar'ry–faced ma'son-ry. That in which the face of the stone is left unfinished just as it comes from the quarry.

quar'ry tile (*Masonry*) Also called "promenade" tile. A name for machine-made, unglazed tile, ¾ in. or more in thickness.

quart. Two pints; ¼ gallon. In dry measure one eighth of a peck.

quar'ter. One of four equal parts of anything. One of the four principal points of the compass.

quar'ter bend. A bend through an

sāle, surfâce, grăm, humăn, màsk, solȧr, bär, bâre; mē, ėdition, lĕnd, momĕnt, bakēr; kīnd, fĭt; lōde, ȯmit, ŏlive, cŏnsume, sôrt; dūty, ūtility, nŭt, alŭm, bûrn.

329

arc of 90 deg.; as in a piece of pipe.

quar′ter saw′ing. Signifies that the log is first cut into quarters. In sawing into boards, the cuts are made parallel with the medullary rays.

quar′ter–turn belt (*Mech.*) The arrangement of a belt to drive two shafts which are at right angles to each other.

quar′tile. Refers to a quarter part of.

quar′to (kwôr′tō) (*Print.*) A sheet of paper measuring 18 by 24, which is folded twice to make four leaves and eight pages. Also, the size of any sheet folded or cut into four parts. Abbreviated 4to by publishers with reference to a book size.

quartz (*Min.*) A hard, crystalline mineral occurring as a rock (SiO_2). It is usually colorless, but is often colored by impurities.

qua-ter′na-ry steel (*Metal.*) That class of alloy steel which consists of iron, carbon, and two other special elements.

qua-ter′ni-on (*Bookbndg.*) Four sections or sheets inserted into each other, after folding, to make one section for gathering and sewing.

quat′re-foil′ (*Arch.*) A unit of decoration in the form of a four-leaved flower.

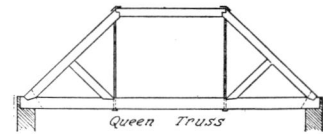
Quatrefoil

Queen Anne, 1702–1714 (*Furn.*) This style of furniture was much influenced by the Dutch, Flemish, French, and Chinese. Lacquer was freely used, and the style was similar to the William and Mary although the carving was much simpler.

queen clos′er (*Masonry*) A half brick, made by cutting the brick lengthwise.

queen truss (*Arch.*) A truss framed with two vertical tie posts, as distinguished from the king truss which has but one.

Queen Truss

quench′ing (*Mech.*) The dipping of heated steel into water, oil, or other bath, to impart necessary hardness.

quench′ing oils. Oils used in heat treating. Fish oils are much used but have offensive odors. Mineral, fish, vegetable, and animal oils are often compounded and sold under trade names.

quick–break switch (*Elec.*) Usually of the knife-blade type. The blade is made of two pieces. As the switch is pulled out, the first half of the blade is withdrawn, and as the throw increases, the second half is drawn out by the action of a spring attached to the first blade.

quick change (*Mach.*) The arrangement of gears on a lathe in such a manner as to permit change of feed by shifting levers instead of removing and replacing gears.

quick′lime (*Bldg.*) Unslaked lime made from nearly pure limestone.

quick re-turn′ (*Mach.*) A term applied to shapers, planers, and other metalworking machines, which are so constructed that the return stroke is much more rapid than the forward or cutting stroke.

quick′sand. A mass of loose sand

mixed with water to such an extent that it is not capable of supporting the weight of a heavy body.

quick'sil'ver (*Metal.*) The common name for mercury; also the amalgam of tin used on the backs of mirrors.

quill (*M a c h.*) A hollow shaft or spindle.

quill gear (*Mach.*) A gear or pinion cut on a quill or sleeve.

quire (kwīr) (*Papermkg.*) A term used to describe a group of 24 or 25 sheets of paper. One quire equals one twentieth of a ream.

quire'fold (*Papermkg.*) A package of paper made up of folded quires. If folded lengthwise the sheet is termed "quirefold long way."

quirk (kwûrk) (*Plaster.*) A small groove in, beside, or between moldings or beads.

quirk bead (*A r c h.*) A bead molding separated from the surface on one side by a groove. A double quirk bead means a groove on each side of the beads.

Quirk Bead

quirk mold'ing (*A r c h.*) One which has a small groove, although frequently applied to a molding having a convex and a concave curve, the two separated by a small flat.

quoin key (koin; kwoin) (*Print.*) A T-shaped key used to adjust quoins in locking up a form.

quoins (koins) (*Arch.*) Large squared stones set at the angles of buildings, buttresses, etc. (*Print.*) A wedge or pair of wedges used in locking up type in a chase or galley.

quo-ta'tion fur'ni-ture (*Print.*) Small metal pieces used for filling blank spaces.

R

rab'bet (*Woodwkg.*) A corruption of the term *rebate*. A groove or cut made in the edge of one plank, etc., so that another, similarly cut, may fit into it; rabbet joint.

race ro-ta'tion (*Aero.*) The rotation, produced by the action of the propeller, on the stream of air passing through or influenced by the propeller.

race'way (*Elec.*) The term is applied to conduits, moldings, and other hollow material, often concealed, through which wires are fished from one outlet to another.

rack (*Furn.*) A framed shelf on which objects may be placed. (*Gear.*) A straight strip of metal having teeth to engage with those of a gear wheel as in a rack and pinion. (*Print.*) The metal or wooden framework used to hold type storage cases.

rack and le'ver jack (lē'vẽr) A housing to which is pivoted the lever and pawl, and a rack bar which is raised by the pawl actuated by the lever.

rack feed (*Mach.*) Tool feed accomplished by "rack and pinions" as on a lathe.

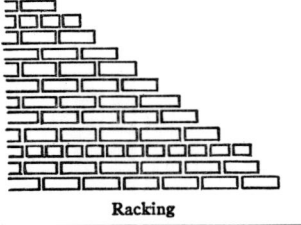

Racking

rack'ing (*Masonry*) In approaching a corner where two walls meet, "racking" is the making of each course shorter than the course below it, in order that the workmen on the walls may tie in their courses in the easiest manner.

radar. The name given to a radio detection device employing the principle of the deflection of high frequency radio waves. Its use determines the presence, approach, speed, direction, etc., of enemy planes and ships long before their presence is detected by any other means.

ra'di-al. Extending outward from a center or axis.

ra'di-al arm (*Mach.*) The movable cantilever which supports the drilling saddle in a radial drilling machine.

ra'di-al bar. A wooden bar to which a point and pencil are attached in order to strike large curves.

ra'di-al bear'ing (*Auto.*) Bearing made with cylindrical or with barrel-shaped rollers.

ra'di-al drill'ing ma-chine' (*Mach.*) A heavy drilling machine, so constructed that the position of the drill can be adjusted to the work without moving the latter.

ra'dial en'gine (*Aero.*) An engine which has stationary cylinders arranged radially around a common crankshaft.

ra'di-ant heat (*Phys.*) A loosely applied term referring to baseboard, panel, and piping encased in floor types of heating.

ra'di-at'ing sur'face. The amount in

---

sāle, surfâce, grăm, humăn, màsk, solár, bär, bâre; mē, ėdition, lĕnd, momĕnt, bakēr; kīnd, fĭt; lōde, ômit, ŏlive, cŏnsume, sôrt; dūty, ûtility, nŭt, alŭm. bûrn.

square feet of effective heating area of a radiator.

ra′di-a′tion (*Mech. Engin.*) The act of radiating, as of heat. The amount or area of radiating surface in a building is spoken of as so many feet of radiation. (*Radioactivity*) The emission of very fast atomic particles or rays by nuclei.

ra′di-a′tor (*Mech. Engin.*) A heating unit.

ra′di-a′tor hose (*Auto.*) The hose which connects radiator and engine.

rad′i-cal (*Algebra*) Relating to the root or roots of numbers; being or containing a root. (*Chem.*) A group of atoms which retain the action of single atoms.

ra′di-o (*Elec.*) A preferred name for wireless. Often incorrectly used where a compound word would be more proper, as radiotelephone, radiotelegraph, etc.

ra′di-o-ac′tive (*Elec.*) Giving off positive and negative charged particles.

ra′di-o-ac-tiv′i-ty (*Chem.*) The change that takes place when one kind of atom is changed into a different kind. Energy is emitted from the nucleus of the atom.

ra′di-o broad′cast′ing. The changing of auditory energy to radio energy to be transmitted in the form of radio waves.

ra′di-o chan′nel (*Tel.*) The "space" in the radio-frequency spectrum allocated to each station or service. In present television standards a channel is 6 megacycles wide.

ra′di-o com-mu′ni-ca′tion. The transmission of voice or a coded message by means of radio energy.

ra′di-o com′pass (*Aero.*) A compass which receives its directions from the radiation principles of the loop antenna. It does not point north but toward the radio broadcasting station on which it is set.

ra′di-o-fre′quen-cy (*Elec.*) The frequency of the electric waves used in the transmission of radio signals which are just beyond audible frequencies, approximately between 40,000 and 30,000,000 vibrations per second.

ra′di-o-gram′. A message transmitted through the medium of radio and relayed by some means to the addressee.

ra′di-o-i′so-tope (*Chem.*) That form of an element which is radioactive. It may be natural to the element, or produced by fission or other nuclear changes.

ra′di-o-marker bea′con (*Aero.*) A radio transmitter of low power emitting a characteristic aural signal to indicate course positions with respect to a landing field or an airway.

ra′di-o net′work. The grouping of a number of radio broadcasting stations for the purpose of transmitting a common program, usually originating at one of the affiliated stations.

ra′di-o op′er-a′tor. The individual who is charged with the responsibility of operating a radio transmitter and receiver for the purpose of carrying on communication either in code or voice.

ra′di-o-phone′. The apparatus necessary to carry on voice communication by means of radio, from either a fixed or movable location.

ra′di-o-range bea′con (*Aero.*) A radio transmitter supplying directive radio waves that provide a means of

keeping an aircraft on its proper course.

ra′di·o re-ceiv′er. The equipment necessary to change radio energy, being received, into auditory energy.

ra′di-o sta′tion. The location of the apparatus used in the transmitting and receiving of radio communications.

ra′di-um (*Chem.*) A naturally radioactive element, far more radioactive than uranium and found in the same ores.

ra′di-us. A straight line from the center of a sphere or circle to its circumference or surface.

ra′di-us gauge (*Mech.*) An instrument for measuring the radii of fillets and rounded corners.

ra′di-us of gy-ra′tion (jī-rā′shŭn) (*Engin.*) Equals the square root of the quotient of the moment of inertia divided by the area of the section.

$$R = \sqrt{\frac{I}{A}\frac{I}{A}} = R^2$$

When R = radius of gyration, I = moment of inertia, and A = area.

ra′di-us plan′er (*Mach.*) A special planer used for planing arcs, links for locomotives, etc.

ra′di-us rod (*Auto.*) A bracing member fitted to either front or rear axle assembly (housing) to maintain perfect running alignment of wheels.

raf′fi-a (răf′ĭ-à) (*Furn.*) A fiber used for making woven furniture.

raf′ters (*Arch.*) The ribs which run from hip, or ridge, to eaves in a roof.

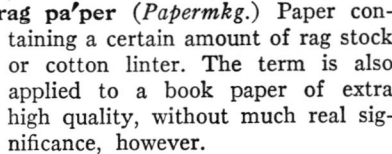

rag pa′per (*Papermkg.*) Paper containing a certain amount of rag stock or cotton linter. The term is also applied to a book paper of extra high quality, without much real significance, however.

rail (*Arch.*) The top member of a balustrade; also the horizontal member of a door or window.

rail′road fur′ni-ture (*Print.*) Metal furniture whose two side walls are joined through the center with a sustaining web.

rail′road-ing (*Print.*) The marking over of words at the ends of successive lines.

rail′road ma′nil-a (*Papermkg.*) A term applied to a groundwood grade of writing paper which comes in yellow and other colors. Used commonly for cheap tickets and manuscript paper.

rail′way en′gi-neer′. One who selects, surveys, and lays out right of ways for railroads, supervises the construction of road beds and the laying of ties and rails.

rail′way track gauge. The standard gauge to which American railway track is laid is 4′ 8½″ measured between the inner sides of the rail heads.

raised print′ing (*Print.*) The printing process by which an embossed effect is obtained.

rais′ing (*Paint and Lacquer*) A wrinkled or blistered condition in a surface due to reaction of lacquer solvents on unoxidized oil in oil-base undercoaters, or in the application of lacquer over old paint or varnish.

rais′ing ham′mer (*Art Met.*) Small hammers of various shapes to suit the needs of the work. Used for forming thin metal into shape over anvils or stakes.

rake (*Shopwk.*) The amount of set on a cutting tool.

rake an'gle (*Mach.*) In a milling cutter, the angle measured between the face of the tooth and a radial line in a diametral plane. In a lathe tool the angle between the upper side of the cutting face of the tool and horizontal face of the tool holder or shank.

rak'ing bond (*Masonry*) Brick laid in an angular or zigzag fashion.

ram (*Mach.*) (1) The movable part of a shaper which carries the tool. (2) The piston of a hydraulic press (3) Also see HYDRAULIC RAM.

ram-jet en'gine (*Aero.*) A type of compressorless jet engine consisting of a specially shaped tube or duct open at both ends, the air necessary for combustion being shoved into the duct by the forward motion of the engine. The ramjet cannot operate under static conditions.

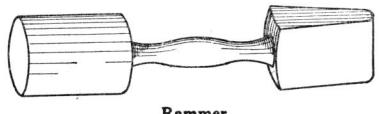

Rammer

ram'mer (*Fdry.*) A tool used by molders for ramming the sand around a pattern.

ram'ming (*Aero.*) The effect obtained when the air intake to the engine is placed in the slip stream in such a manner as to take advantage of the difference in velocity of this air intake and the slip stream, in order to increase the pressure in the induction system.

ramp (*Arch.*) A slope or inclined way used in place of steps.

ran'dom. (1) Without apparent method or system. (2) Odd sizes, considered together, are spoken of as random sizes, as shingles of different widths.

ran'dom joints (*Furn.*) Joints made in veneer without reference to the veneer being of equal width.

ran'dom work (*Arch.*) Stonework laid up in irregular order; as a wall built up of odd-sized stones.

range at e'co-nom'ic speed (*Aero.*) The maximum distance a given aircraft can cover while cruising at the most economical speed and altitude at all stages of the flight.

range at full speed (*Aero.*) The maximum distance a given aircraft can cover at full speed at sea level.

range at max'i-mum speed (*Aero.*) The maximum distance a given aircraft can fly at full speed at the altitude for maximum speed under given conditions.

rape'seed oil. A heavy, brown oil obtained from the seed of rape, which is similar to a turnip and is used as a forage crop for hogs and sheep. Used as a lubricant, and in the heat treatment of steel.

rap'ping bar (*Fdry.*) A bar of iron or steel inserted in a pattern in order to lift it from the mold.

rasp (*Mech.*) A filelike tool having coarse projections for abrasion.

ras'ter (*Elec.*) The illumination of a picture tube screen produced by sweeping the electron beam across its face.

ratch'et (*Mach.*) A gear with triangular-shaped teeth, adapted to be engaged by a pawl, which either imparts intermittent motion to the ratchet, or locks it against backward movement when operated otherwise.

ratch′et bar (*Mech.*) A straight bar with teeth like those of a ratchet wheel to receive the thrust of a pawl.

Ratchet Bit Brace

ratch′et bit brace (*Woodwk.*) A bit brace with ratchet attachment to permit operating in close quarters.

ratch′et drill (*Mach.*) A hand drill in which a lever, carrying at one end a drill holder, is revolved by a ratchet wheel and pawl.

ratch′et feed. An intermittent motion accomplished by pawl and ratchet.

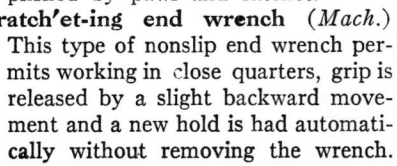

Ratchet Drill

ratch′et-ing end wrench (*Mach.*) This type of nonslip end wrench permits working in close quarters, grip is released by a slight backward movement and a new hold is had automatically without removing the wrench.

rat′ed horse′pow′er of an en′gine (*Aero.*) The average horsepower developed by a given type of engine at the rated speed when operating at full throttle, or at a specified altitude or manifold pressure.

rat′ed rev′o-lu′tions (*Aero.*) The number of revolutions corresponding to the rated horsepower.

rate fix-ing. Settling the cost of individual operations in a machine shop as a basis for mechanics' wages.

rate of climb (*Aero.*) The vertical velocity of an aircraft with reference to the air.

rate-of–climb in′di-ca′tor (*Aero.*) An instrument that indicates the rate of ascent or descent of an aircraft.

rate of com-bus′tion. The number of pounds of coal burned per square foot of grate per hour.

rate of speed (*Mach.*) In machine work rate of speed may be expressed in revolutions per minute; r.p.m. or in feet per minute.

rat′ing of al′ter-na′tors (*Elec.*) The rating of alternators or alternating-current generators is usually expressed in Kva, or kilovolt-amperes, which is the product of the voltage times the amperage, divided by 1,000.

ra′ti-o (rā′shĭ-ō) Relative value; proportion.

ra′ti-o of trans′for-ma′tion. Ratio of the number of turns on the primary coil to the number of turns on the secondary coil of a transformer, affecting both voltage and current.

rat′tail file. Name commonly applied to round files.

rat–tail splice (*Elec.*) (See PIGTAIL SPLICE.)

raw′hide (*Leather.*) Untanned, dressed skin.

raw′hide gears (*Mach.*) Noiseless gears made of tightly compressed disks of rawhide.

raw′hide ham′mer. A hand hammer having a rawhide head which serves to prevent bruising metal parts against which it is used.

raw ma-te′ri-al. The ingredients before being processed, which enter into a finished product.

ray′on (*Textile*) Formerly called artificial silk. It is a manufactured fiber of regenerated cellulose.

ray′on-nant (*Furn.*) Ornamented by radiating lines. A term applied to French Gothic ornamentation of the middle period.

raze. To tear down; to demolish; as to raze a building.

re-act′ance (*Elec.*) In an alternating-current circuit, that component of the resistance that does not oppose the current, but tends to cause a difference of phase between it and the electromotive force. The measure of resistance to the flow of an a.c. current through a coil or a condenser.

re-ac′tion en′gine (*Aero.*) Or reaction motor. An engine or motor that develops thrust by its reaction to a substance ejected from it.

re-ac′tion tur′bine (*Aero.*) A type of turbine having rotor blades shaped such that they form a ring of nozzles, the turbine being rotated by the reaction of the fluid ejected from between the blades.

re-ac′tor (*Elec.*) Any device which offers opposition to the flow of alternating currents; usually consists of turns of wire on iron cores.

read′y print (*Print.*) Those sections of newspapers bought printed ready for issue, such as magazine sections, sheets of comics, etc.

re-a′gent (*Chem.*) Term used in analytical chemistry. A chemical used to bring about a desired change in another substance, or to detect the presence of another substance.

ream (*Shopwk.*) To smooth the surface of a hole and finish it to size with a reamer as for a running fit. (*Paper*) Twenty quires or 480 sheets of paper. A printer's ream is 516 sheets.

ream′er (*Metalwk.*) A tool with cutting edges, square or fluted, used for finishing drilled holes.

ream′ing (*Metalwk.*) The process of smoothing the surface of holes with a reamer.

rear ax′le (*Auto.*) Consists of rear-axle housing, gears, axle shafts, and drive, also such accessory parts as are needed for operation, as bearings, washers, etc.

Re′au-mur ther-mom′e-ter (*Phys.*) A thermometer used in a number of European countries. Zero, 0 deg. is given as the melting point of ice and 80 deg. as the boiling point of water.

re-bate′ (*Woodwkg.*) A recess in or near the edge of one piece to receive the edge of another piece cut to fit it.

re′ca-pit′u-late. To summarize; to review.

re-ceiv′er (*Elec.*) The instrument which is held to the ear in receiving a telephone message. It consists of a

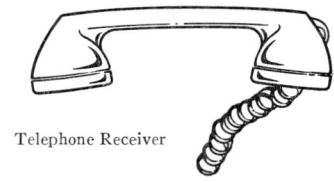

Telephone Receiver

hard-rubber container or shell, which holds a permanent horseshoe or U magnet with a thin iron diaphragm close to its poles.

re-cep'ta-cle (*Elec.*) A porcelain, fiber, or composition device into which a lamp may be screwed or an attachment plug pushed, and which is fastened in place with screws. A wall socket for an incandescent electric lamp.

re-chuck'ing (*Shopwk.*) The resetting of a piece of work in a chuck for further operations.

re-cip'ro-cat'ing (*Mech.*) A forward and backward motion.

re-cip'ro-cat'ing-type su'per-charg'er (*Aero.*) A positive-displacement reciprocating pump in which the air or mixture is compressed by a piston working in a cylinder.

re'con-di'tion. To repair and adjust so as to be usable.

re-con'nais-sance (*Surv.*) The operations preliminary to the actual survey. Making notes, sketches, and a general study of the problem.

re-cord'ing ther-mom'e-ter. A thermometer which makes a permanent record of variations in temperature, usually by an inked line traced automatically on a paper disk or roll.

re'crys-tal-li-za'tion (*Metal.*) The return to normal condition of properties and structure of work hardened metal by annealing.

rec'tan'gle (*Math.*) A plane figure of four sides; the angles are right angles, opposite sides are equal and parallel; the adjacent sides need not be equal.

rec-tan'gu-lar (*Geom.*) Having one or more right angles.

rec'ti-fi'er (*Elec.*) A device that changes alternating current into direct current.

rec'ti-fi'er tube (*Radio*) A vacuum tube used to change A.C. to D.C.

rec'to (rĕk'tō) (*Bookbndg.*) A right-hand page, as of a book.

red brass (*Metal.*) A high copper brass of good casting and machining qualities. Usually the composition consists of about 85 per cent copper and varying percentages of tin, lead, and zinc.

red ce'dar (*Wood*) *Juniperus virginiana*. Grows to height of 30 to 40 ft. in north; southern variety reaches height of 100 ft. Wood is soft and easily worked, durable in contact with soil. Used for fence posts, lead pencils, cedar chests, and closets. The large red cedar of northwestern United States is extensively used for shingles.

red lead (*Chem.*) Pb_3O_4. Made by heating lead monoxide or litharge; used in making flint glass; red paint for prevention of rusting of ironwork, also for leakproofing pipe joints.

red oak (*Woodwkg.*) An oak, darker than white oak and of coarser grain, also more brittle and porous; used extensively for interior trim in buildings and in the manufacture of furniture.

red–short'ness or hot–short'ness (*Engin.*) That condition of wrought iron or steel in which they are incapable of being rolled or worked at red heat. The presence of sulphur is largely responsible for red-shortness.

re-duc'er (*Plumb.*) Any one of the various pipe connections so constructed as to permit the joining of pipes of different sizes, such as reducing sleeve, reducing ell, reducing tee, etc.

re-duc′ing. The use of a device or fixture for making the size of one part smaller so as to fit another, as a reducing coupling, or a drill socket.

re-duc′ing a′gent (*C h e m.*) A substance which removes oxygen or some other element from a second substance.

re-duc′ing glass. A double concave lens for viewing objects in reduced sizes.

re-duc′tion (*Chem.*) (1) In metallurgy, generally the removal of oxygen by means of coke or other forms of carbon. (2) Removing oxygen or some other element.

re-duc′tion gears (*Engin.*) Gears used on a shaft to reduce the speed.

red′wood (*Woodwkg.*) A giant tree of California. The wood is soft, reddish in color, and light in weight.

reed′ing (*Arch.*) A general term applied to half-round moldings of various kinds; also ornamentation by the use of such moldings. Reeding is the reverse of fluting.

Reed ta′per (*Mach.*) One of the several standard tapers used on lathe spindles.

re-face′ (*Auto.*) To true up a valve face by grinding or turning.

ref′er-ence gaug′es. Test gauges used to check the accuracy of inspection gauges.

ref′er-ence marks (*Print.*) Any numeral, character, or mark used to direct attention to a note in the margins or at the foot of a page. For example: Asterisk or star (*), dagger (†), double dagger (‡), section mark (§), parallels (||), paragraph mark (¶).

re′flex re-flec′tors (*Auto. Mech.*) An optical device that reflects light which may come from an angle and which makes the object appear luminous. Taillights, road markers, and signs use reflex reflectors.

re-frac′tion (*Physics*) The bending of a ray of light as it travels through a transparent substance.

re-frac′to-ry (*Pot.*) A piece of ware covered with a vaporable flux, placed in a kiln to impart a glaze to other articles being fired.

re-frig′er-at′ing (*Mech. Engin.*) The method employed for the preservation of foodstuffs by cold storage.

Re′gen-cy (*F u r n.*) A period (1715–1723) in French furniture.

re-gen′er-a′tion (*Elec.*) Refers to energy "fed back" to the input of the radio tube usually from the plate circuit to the grid circuit.

re-gen′er-a-tive quench′ing (*Metal.*) Double quenching of carburized parts to refine case and core.

reg′is-ter (*Print.*) (1) Correct relation of the colors in color printing. (2) The exact correspondence of lines, etc., on opposite sides of a sheet.

reg′let (rĕg′lĕt) (*Print.*) A thin strip of wood used for spacing forms in poster work, and as furniture around the outside of metal type forms.

re-ground′ (*Auto.*) A refinished surface produced by grinding.

reg′u-la (rĕg′ū-là) (*A r c h.*) In the Doric order, the flat block from which the "guttae" drop.

reg′u-lar pol′y-gon (*Geom.*) Area equals sum of sides times one-half perpendicular distance from center to sides.

reg′u-late. To make adjustment or

to correct the position of, as to change the feed or depth of cut.

reg′u‑la′tor (*Weld.*) The arrangement of valves and gauges which control the flow of oxygen and acetylene in oxyacetylene welding.

re′in‑forced′ (*A r c h.*) Strengthened by the addition of extra material. Reinforced concrete has within its mass iron or steel rods, bars or shapes to give it additional strength.

re′in‑forced′ con′crete (*Engin.*) Concrete work increased in strength by iron or steel bars imbedded in it.

re‑in‑force′ment (*P l a s t.*) Embedments within a plastic sheet or form which give the product strength, toughness, and rigidity. Reinforcement refers principally to laminated plastic, where the chief ingredient is glass fiber, either in cloth or mat form, and in certain applications, cut-glass-fiber is the added material. Glass fiber lends great strength to the product, but other reinforcement material, such as resin fiber, sisal, asbestos, and others, are also employed.

re′in‑forc′ing steel (*E n g i n.*) Steel bars of various shapes used in concrete construction to give added strength.

re‑lat′ed trades. The various trades whose work is necessary for the completing of a project.

re‑lat′ing. Having reference to; referring.

rel′a‑tive in′cli‑nom′e‑ter (ĭn′klĭ‑nŏm′ē‑tēr) (*A e r o.*) An instrument which indicates the attitude of an aircraft with reference to apparent gravity, i.e., to the resultant of the acceleration of the aircraft and that due to gravity.

rel′a‑tive mo′tion (*Phys.*) Motion of one object with respect to another.

rel′a‑tive wind (*Aero.*) The velocity of the air with reference to a body in it. It is usually determined from measurements made at such a distance from the body that the disturbing effect of the body upon the air is negligible.

re‑lay′ (*Elec.*) A device for opening or closing a local circuit under given conditions in the main circuit.

re′lay sta′tion (*Tel.*) A station used to receive picture and sound signals from a master station and to transmit them to a second relay station or to a television station transmitter.

re‑lief′ (*Engin., Draw., and Print.*) That which stands out prominently from a surface is said to be in relief.

re‑lief′ print′ing (*P r i n t.*) Printing done by the letterpress process; i.e., from movable type or plates.

re‑liev′ing (*Mach.*) Removing of material back of the cutting edge of a tool to reduce friction, as on milling cutters, etc.

rel′ish (*Carp.*) The shoulder on a tenon.

re‑luc′tance (*E l e c.*) The resistance offered to the magnetic flux by the substance magnetized.

re‑mote′ (*Tel.*) Any program originating outside of studios.

re‑mote′ con‑trol′ (*Aero.*) Control from a distance, especially by means of electricity or electronics; a controlling switch, lever, or other device used in this kind of control. (*Elec.*) The control of electrical apparatus or machinery from a distance by the use of a relay or other electromagnetic device.

re-mote pick′ups (*Tel.*) Events televised away from the studio by a mobile unit or by permanently installed equipment at the remote location.

ren′ais-sance′ (*Arch.*) A style of building and decoration which follows the medieval. It originated in Italy during the fifteenth century.

re-new′a-ble fuse (*Elec.*) An enclosed fuse, so constructed that the fusing material can be readily replaced.

ren′verse′ment′ (rän′vĕrs′män′) (*Aero.*) A maneuver consisting of a half roll and a half loop in the order named.

rep (rĕp) (*Uphol.*) A reversible fabric used extensively for draperies and for the upholstering of seat cushions.

re-pair′ kit. A container or kit of tools and/or parts suitable for repair and adjustment of objects in some particular field.

rep′e-ti′tion. (1) The doing, making, or saying of something again or repeatedly. (2) Recital from memory.

re-plac′ing. Renewing; restoring to a former place, condition, or the like; taking the place of.

rep′li-ca. An exact copy or reproduction.

re-pous′sé′ (rē-pōō′sā′) (*Metal.*) A pattern on thin metal beaten up from the reverse side and modeled by working from the other side.

rep′re-sent′a-tive. Typical; being of the best style or type.

re′print (*Print.*) A new printing, as for an additional supply after the original edition has been exhausted.

re′pro-duc′ing. Producing again; copying; bringing forward or exhibiting again.

re′pro-duc′tion (*Furn.*) A term referring to reproduced furniture, usually of the historic periods.

rep′tile calf (*Leather.*) A lizard grain produced on calfskin. It is mostly used for ladies' purses, wallets, billfolds, etc.

re-pul′sion (*Elec.*) The action of a force by which two similarly charged bodies tend to repel each other.

req′ui-si′tion. A formal request, as for supplies.

rere′dos (rēr′dŏs). The screen or ornamental work behind an altar.

re-search′ chem′i-cal en′gi-neer′. One whose work is along the line of examination and original investigation generally under the direction of the chief engineer.

re-search′ en′gi-neer′. One who engages in the investigation of materials to increase the efficiency of the product. He also may investigate market conditions for the sales department or manufacturing conditions.

re-seat′ (*Auto.*) To refinish a valve seat by means of a special reamer, by lapping process, or by specially mounted abrasive stones.

re-sid′u-al mag′net-ism (*Elec.*) The small amount of magnetism left in a piece of iron after the magnetizing force has been removed.

res′i-due (*Auto.*) A sediment or deposit. That which remains after burning or pouring.

re-sil′i-ence. The act or power of springing back; capability of a strained body to recover its size and shape after deformation.

res′in (rĕz′in) Any of various oily gummy substances obtained from certain trees, soluble in alcohol, ether, etc., but not in water.

res′in-oid (*Plastics*) A general term applied to synthetic resinous substances as distinguished from natural resins.

re-sist′al (*Metal.*) A very high grade of stainless steel. It is nonmagnetic and resists acid and rust.

re-sist′ance (*Elec.*) That property of a substance that opposes the flow of an electric current through it.

re-sist′ance box (*Elec.*) A box containing known resistances, the amount of which can be varied by means of plugs or dials.

re-sist′ance braz′ing. An electric brazing process wherein the heat is obtained from the resistance to the flow of an electric current.

re-sist′ance butt weld′ing. A group of resistance-welding processes wherein the fusion occurs over the entire cross-sectional area.

re-sist′ance coil (*Elec.*) A coil of wire of high specific resistance, such as nichrome or iron, inserted in a circuit to decrease the current flow.

re-sist′ance u′nit (*Auto.*) A small coil of wire made of a metal highly resistant to the flow of electrons, or a small bar of carbon. (Both types are used interchangeably.) These units are introduced in certain auto electrical circuits to reduce the flow of electric current through the circuit.

re-sist′ance weld′er. A resistance welding machine. (The term "welder" has sometimes been used to denote an operator of welding equipment for which the term "welding operator" is greatly to be preferred.)

re-sist′ance weld′ing. A pressure-welding process wherein the heat is obtained from the resistance to the flow of an electric current.

re-sist′ance wire (*Elec.*) Nickel-chromium electrical resistance wire sold under a number of trade names.

re-sist′ing mo′ment (*E n g i n.*) The resistance to rotation by the moment of tensile and compressive stresses in that section which act as an internal couple.

re-sist′ing shear (*E n g i n.*) The internal opposing force equal to the vertical shear of a section.

re-sist′ print′ing (*Textile*) A dyeing process in which portions of the fabric are covered with a dye-resistant paste.

res′o-lu′tion (*Tel.*) Picture fidelity (better than 16mm.).

res′o-lu′tion of for′ces (*Phys.*) The operation of finding two or more forces whose combined effect is equivalent to that of a given force.

res′o-nance (*E l e c.*) A condition reached in an electrical circuit when the inductive reactance just neutralizes the capacitance reactance leaving ohmic resistance as the only opposition to the flow of current.

res′tor-a′tion (*F u r n.*) The bringing back of an article of furniture as nearly as possible to its original state.

re-tain′ing wall (*Engin.*) A wall of masonry erected to prevent the sliding of earth or other material.

re-tard′. To hinder, delay, to prevent from acting. (*Auto.*) To set the time of spark to have it occur later with regard to the piston position.

re-tard′ing the spark (*Auto.*) Causing the spark to occur after the piston has passed its top point and is moving downward on its working stroke.

re-tic′u-late (*Furn.*) To make into or have the form of network.

re-tort′. A container in which a substance is distilled or decomposed by heat.

re-tract′a-ble land′ing gear (*Aero.*) A type of landing gear which may be withdrawn into the body or wings of an airplane while it is in flight, in order to reduce the parasite drag.

re-tract′a-ble wheel (*Aero.*) A part of that type of landing gear which may be withdrawn into the body or wings of an airplane.

re-turn′ bend (*Plumb.*) A pipe bend or a fitting shaped like the letter U.

re-turn′ nos′ing (*Bldg.*) In stair construction the mitered, overhanging end of a tread, outside the balusters.

re-veal′ (*Arch.*) The vertical side of an opening in a wall, especially that portion of the side of a door or window between the line where the window frame or doorframe stops and the outer edge of the opening.

re-verse′ curve. An S curve.

re-verse′ mold (*F d r y.*) A dummy mold on which a portion of an actual mold is to be rammed.

re-verse′ plate (*P r i n t.*) A printing plate which prints white and black in reverse, producing a white design on a black background.

re-verse′ turn (*Aero.*) A reverse in flight produced by a half loop and a half roll.

re-vers′i-ble pro-pel′ler (*Aero.*) A propeller whose pitch may be changed to a negative angle so as to give reverse thrust used for braking action.

re-vers′ing gear (*Mech.*) The gear by which the reversal of an engine or machine is accomplished.

re-vise′ (*Print.*) (1) To check for error; to alter or change with the idea of improving. (2) A proof taken after corrections have been made.

rev′o-lu′tion (*Shopwk.*) The act of revolving, as the turning in a complete circuit of a body on its axis. Usually distinguished from rotation, which may mean a revolution or a part of a revolution, while the term revolution is applied to something having continuous motion, as a revolution of a shaft.

rev′o-lu′tion count′er (*Mech.*) Also called "speed indicator." It is a device for counting the revolutions of a shaft. By pressing a pointer against the end of a shaft, the revolutions are registered on a dial.

rev′o-lu′tions per min′ute. An expression referring to rate of speed of machines. Abbreviation, r.p.m.

re-volv′ing door (*Arch.*) A door with four vanes operating in a curved frame and mounted on a central vertical axis about which it revolves. Commonly used at store entrances to permit easier access by a greater number of people and to retain an even temperature within the store.

re-volv′ing field (*Elec.*) When the field coils and poles revolve instead of remaining stationary.

rf pick′up (*Tel.*) Radio-frequency transmission of a video or audio signal.

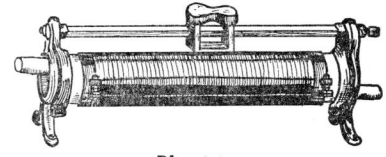

Rheostat

rhe′o-stat (rē′ô-stăt) (*Elec.*) A device

for regulating electrical current, in which the current is made to flow through wires having considerable resistance.

rhe-o-stat'ic con-trol' (*Elec.*) A system of control which is accomplished by varying resistance and/or reactance in the armature and/or field circuit of the driving-machine motor.

rho'di-um (*Metal.*) A hard, white rare metal resistant to corrosion but hard to work; mostly used to form an alloy with platinum.

rhom'boid (rŏm'boid) (*Geom.*) A parallelogram whose adjacent sides are unequal in length, but whose angles are oblique.

rhom'bus (rŏm'bŭs) (*Geom.*) A parallelogram whose adjacent sides are equal in length, but whose angles are oblique.

rib (*Arch.*) A skeleton arch which is part of the frame work that supports a vault. (*Ceram.*) A small hand tool used in shaping or smoothing ware on a potter's wheel. (*Mech.*) A flange extending across or around the edges of a casting, in order to strengthen a portion which would otherwise be weak.

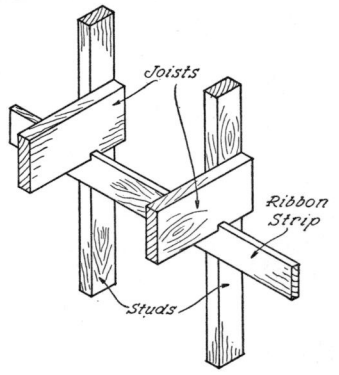

rib'bon ef'fect (*Furn.*) A stripe in wood, manifested in mahogany by the softer and more feathery portion alternating with the plainer, harder portions.

rib'bon strip (*Arch.*) A board attached to studding to carry floor joists.

rid'dle (*Fdry.*) A sieve for sifting sand or other material.

rid'er (*Print.*) A piece of type higher than adjacent type, thus having a tendency to make a heavier impression.

ridge (*Arch.*) The top of the roof where two slopes meet. (*Bookbndg.*) The outer joint of a book along the parallel to the backbone, against which the cover boards are fitted.

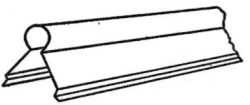
Ridge Capping

ridge cap'ping (*Arch.*) The covering which runs along the ridge of a roof.

ridge pole (*Arch. and Carp.*) The highest horizontal timber in a roof to which the rafters are fastened.

ridge roof (*Arch.*) A roof whose rafters meet in an apex; its end view is that of a gable.

ridge tiles (*Arch.*) Those roofing tiles used to cap the ridge of a roof.

rif'fler (*Metal. Fin.*) A small rasp or file, usually curved, used for filing inside surfaces or for enlarging holes.

Riffler

rig'ger. One who, with special equipment and tackle, moves and transports heavy machinery, etc.

rig'ging (*Aero.*) The assembling and adjusting of the parts of an airplane.

right angle. An angle of 90 deg. formed by one straight line standing perpendicular to another.

right-hand en'gine (*Aero.*) An engine whose propeller shaft, to an observer facing the propeller from the engine end of the shaft, rotates in a clockwise direction.

right-hand screw (*Mech.*) A screw which advances, when turned in clockwise rotation.

right-hand tools (*Shopwk.*) (1) In hand tools, those made to be operated with the right hand. (2) In tools for machine use, those which cut from the right toward the left.

right line. A straight line; the shortest distance between two points.

rig'id air'ship (*Aero.*) One whose form is maintained by a rigid framework.

ri-gid'i-ty. Stiffness, resistance to change of form.

rim lock (*Carp.*) Any lock the body of which is attached to the inside face of a door.

rim'ming steel (*Metal.*) A steel much used in the form of sheets for difficult forming operations. This steel is cast with very little degasification, the ingot containing many deep-seated blowholes but with sound and pure surface.

ring (*Math.*) A plane figure included between two circumferences having the same center.

ring bolt. An eyebolt with a ring through the eye.

ring cowl'ing (*Aero.*) A ring-shaped cowling, placed around a radial air-cooled engine to reduce its drag and improve cooling.

ring gauge (*Mach.*) A gauge in the shape of a ring used for checking external diameters.

ring gear (*Auto.*) (1) The large gear on the flywheel which is engaged by the pinion gear when the starting motor is in action. (2) Any gear in the form of a ring, having no hub or central bore.

ring mark (*Print.*) A proofreader's mark. A circle is drawn around any indicated change to show that the compositor is not at fault.

ring oil'er (*Mach.*) A bearing in which the journal carries a loose-fitting ring, the lower half being immersed in oil, as the shaft rotates the ring is given a circular motion, picking up oil and distributing it to the bearing.

ring shake (*Wood*) A separation of the wood between the annual rings.

ring-type re-tain'er (*Auto.*) A ring which can be sprung into position in order to hold some part in its proper place.

rip cord (*Aero.*) Device for manual operation of a parachute.

rip'ping (*Woodwkg.*) The sawing of timber longitudinally as distinguished from crosscutting.

rip'ping tool (*Uphol.*) A small tool like a tack lifter, used for removing tacks and small nails in taking off upholstering.

rip'rap (*Engin.*) A foundation of broken stones loosely thrown together in deep water or on a soft bottom.

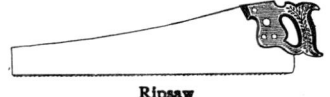

Ripsaw

rip'saw (*Woodwkg.*) An ordinary handsaw, used for sawing in the direction of the grain. Its teeth are so formed that the action is similar to that of a chisel.

rise (*Arch.*) (1) The vertical distance between the springing of an arch and the center or highest point of the intrados. (2) The height of a stair step.

rise and run (*Carp.*) Term used to indicate the degree of incline.

ris′er (*Arch.*) A board set on edge which connects the treads of a stair. (*Bldg.*) A vertical pipe in a system for conducting steam, water, gas, etc. (*Elec.*) Vertical conduits containing wires or cables running from floor to floor of a building. (*Fdry.*) A tube-like opening in a mold for the passage of air. (*Mech. Engin.*) A vertical pipe leading from a steam main to the radiators above.

riv′et (*Metalwk.*) A short, metal, boltlike fastening, without threads, which is clinched by hammering. Rivets are designated by the shape of the heads as flat or pan-head, buttonhead, countersink, mushroom, or swollen neck.

riv′et forge. A portable forge, used by boilermakers and ironworkers, for heating rivets near the work for which they are required.

riv′et-ing. The heading over or clinching of rivets. Small rivets are headed when cold, large ones when hot.

riv′et set. A steel punch with a hollow or cupped face, used in the setting of rivets.

riv′nut (*Aero.*) An internally threaded and counterbored tubular rivet that can be headed in a blind application. Rivnuts are machined from one of the corrosive-resistant aluminum alloys and are of a one-piece construction. They are normally supplied anodized and ready for use in the "as received" condition. They are intended primarily for blind applications where a nut is required on the reverse side of a sheet.

roach (*Aero.*) A heavy jet or vertical sheet of water thrown above the water surface behind a seaplane float.

road clear′ance (*Auto.*) The distance from the lowest point of a car to the road.

road drag (*Agric.*) Any one of the various devices dragged over a soft surfaced road for the purpose of leveling; distinguished from road scraper.

road′ster (*Auto.*) An open-type body with accommodations for two people. Has a luggage compartment in rear deck.

roast′ing (*Metal.*) The treatment of ores or metals in order to volatilize and drive off deleterious gases, carbonic acid, sulphur dioxide, etc.

ro′bot. An automatic or self-acting apparatus or mechanism that performs operations ordinarily done by man. A vehicle or machine operated by such an apparatus.

rock crys′tal (*Min.*) Colorless, transparent quartz.

rock′er arm (*Mech.*) (1) An arm pivoted at one end, the other end moving back and forth in an arc. (2) An arm pivoted at or near its middle point, as the rocker arms which operate the valves in an overhead-valve automobile motor.

Rock′well test (*Engin.*) A modification of the Brinell test. A hardened steel ball or a diamond cone is pressed into the article to be tested and the depth of the impression is measured with a dial micrometer.

ro·co′co (rô-kō′kō) (*Arch.*) Style of decoration distinguished by a delicately executed ornament in imitation of rockwork, shells, foliage, and scrolls massed together, in vogue during the seventeenth and eighteenth centuries. It was meaningless and unrelated to structural forms, and was applied in unsymmetrical and extravagant manner.

rod (*Carp.*) A measuring device, consisting of a piece of wood, used for determining the exact height of risers in a flight of stairs. Sometimes called story rod. (*Masonry*) A piece of hardwood about 2 by 4 in. and of any desired length, used as a tool rest when striking joints which project beyond the faces of the wall. (*Measure*) 5½ yards.

rod as·sem′bly (*Auto.*) Consists of connecting rod, piston, piston pin, and piston rings ready for installation.

rod ends (*Engin.*) The end portion of connecting rods which carry the bearings or brasses. The strap, solid head, and marine are the main types.

rod′man (rod′man) (*Engin.*) One who uses or carries a surveyor's leveling rod.

roe (*Furn.*) Mottled markings in veneer resembling fish roe.

roll (*Aero.*) A maneuver in which a complete revolution about the longitudinal axis is made, the horizontal direction of flight being approximately maintained.

roll edge on wood (*Uphol.*) Used on wood frames to keep stuffing from working away from the edges. A strip of burlap is blind-tacked to the frame, then filled with the desired amount of stuffing, after which the loose end of the burlap is tacked, thus forming the roll. A half-round wood molding is often used for the same purpose.

rolled iron (*Engin.*) Sheets, bars or formed shapes that have been made to their desired form by the rolling process.

rolled threads (*Mach.*) Threads formed by hardened rolls or dies having threads or ridges which, by rolling grooves into the stock, raise enough metal on the blank to form threads.

roll′er bear′ing (*Engin.*) A bearing made of hardened-steel rollers instead of the round steel balls used in ball bearings.

roll′er chain. A chain in which the links are built with cylinders or rollers to reduce noise and friction.

rol′ler com′po·si′tion (*Print.*) A mixture of glycerin and glue melted and cast about a central core in varying proportions. More glue and less glycerin are used for hot-weather rollers and more glycerin and less glue for cold-weather rollers.

roll′er ram′ming ma·chine′ (*Fdry.*) A type of molding machine especially adapted to long thin work.

roll′er trucks (*Print.*) The steel wheels at the ends of platen-press rollers that travel over the "tracks" when the press is in motion.

roll′ing (*Aero.*) Angular motion about the longitudinal axis.

roll′ing fric′tion (*Mech.*) Is the resistance developed when a spherical or cylindrical body is rolled over a plane surface. Rollers and ball bearings are used to reduce rolling friction.

roll–leaf stamp′ing (*P r i n t.*) The process by which designs and titles are placed on covers of books either in gold leaf or its substitute.

roll ti′tles (*Tel.*) Series of titles on drum which, when revolved, moves titles in front of camera in continuous flow.

Ro′man (*Print.*) Type usually characterized by prominent serifs.

Ro′man-esque′ (*Arch.*) The architectural style which grew out of the Roman. It preceded the Gothic. It was used chiefly in ecclesiastical buildings between the seventh and twelfth centuries.

roof boards or roof′ers (*Arch.*) The sheathing or undercovering of a roof which serves as a foundation for shingles, slate, or other roofing material.

roof line (*Arch.*) (1) The contour of the extreme top of a roof. (2) The top of a wall from which the roof is sprung.

roof truss (*Arch.*) Timbers or structural iron fastened together for the support of a roof.

root (*Mach.*) That surface of a thread which lies between adjacent threads.

root di-am′e-ter (*M e c h.*) (1) The diameter at the bottom of a thread. (2) The diameter of a gear wheel taken at the bottom of the teeth.

rope driv′ing (*Mech. Engin.*) The transmission of power by means of rope gearing, as distinguished from belt drive.

rose′bit (*Mach.*) A solid, cylindrical, parallel boring tool used for finishing drilled holes. (See ROSE REAMER.)

rose cut′ter (*Shopwk.*) The hemispherical cutter, known as a "rose mill," is one of a large variety of forms employed for working out dies and other parts in the profiler. Cutters of this form are also used for making spherical seats for ball joints, etc.

Ro′sen-dale ce-ment′. The name given to a natural cement made from rock found near Rosendale, New York.

rose ream′er (*Mach.*) A heavy-duty machine reamer, designed so that cutting is done by its end, which is beveled, instead of by its sides.

rose win′dow (*Arch.*) A circular window with divisions radiating from the center.

ro-sette′ (*Arch.*) A circular unit of ornamentation with parts radiating from the center.

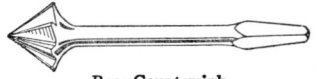

Rose Countersink

rose–type coun′ter-sink′. A countersink with a fluted, cone-shaped point, for use on either wood or metal.

rose′wood (*Woodwkg.*) A dark-colored wood, heavy, hard, and brittle, used as a veneer.

ros′in (rŏz′ĭn) The product of several species of pine from which it exudes in the form of gum. It is much used as a flux in soldering tinwork, and for making varnishes and soaps.

ros′ter (rŏs′tẽr) A tabulated schedule or list of names.

ros′trum (*Bldg.*) A pulpit or platform for public speaking.

ro′ta-ry. Turning on its axis, like a wheel.

Rotary Blower

ro′ta-ry blow′er (*Engin.*) An incased rotating fan such as is used for forced draft in furnaces.

ro′ta-ry con-ver′ter (*Elec.*) A single machine connected to an a.c. circuit which delivers d.c., or vice versa.

ro′ta-ry cut′ter (*Mach.*) A cutter which rotates with the spindle to which it is attached, to produce a cut on the work with which it comes in contact.

ro′ta-ry en′gine (*Aero.*) An engine in which the radially arranged cylinders revolve around a fixed crankshaft.

ro′ta-ry in-duc′tion sys′tem (*Aero.*) A carburetor induction system used on radial engines, in which a rotary fan assists in distributing the fuel charge to the cylinders.

ro′ta-ry press (*Print.*) A press in which the printing surface is fastened to a revolving cylinder and the paper is fed from a roll.

ro′tate (*Shopwk.*) To turn, or cause to turn or revolve, as on its axis.

ro′to-gra-vure′ (*Print.*) Intaglio printing on a rotary press from an etching made on a copper cylinder.

ro′tor (*Aero.*) The complete rotating portion of a rotary wing system. (*Elec.*) The rotating member of an a.c. motor or generator.

ro′tor-craft (*Aero.*) An aircraft which in all its flight attitudes is supported wholly or in part by a rotor or rotors, i.e., by airfoils rotating or revolving about an axis.

ro′tor plane (*Aero.*) A form of aircraft whose support in the air is chiefly derived from the vertical component of the force produced by rotating airfoils.

rot′ten-stone (*Wood Fin.*) Decomposed limestone marketed in the form of a fine powder and used in the polishing of varnished surfaces.

ro-tun′da (*Arch.*) The circular room under a dome.

rouge (rūzh) (*Chem.*) A ferric oxide, Fe_2O_3, produced by heating copperas, $FeSO_4$. It is used as a pigment, and for polishing glass, metal, or gems.

rough′cast (*Bldg.*) Stucco thrown against a wall to form a rough finish.

rough cut (*Mach.*) Usually the first or heavy cut taken in preparation for the finish cut.

rough′ing out (*Mach.*) To speedily remove excess material without regard to finish. (*Metalwk.*) To make a quick, approximate layout for a job.

rough′ing tool (*Mach.*) The ordinary tool used by machinists for removing the outer skin and generally for heavy cuts on cast iron, wrought iron, and steel.

rough lum′ber. Lumber undressed as it comes from the saw.

roun′del (*Furn.*) A term used in furniture to refer to any circular ornament, such as a medallion, patera, rosette, etc.

round′nose tool (*Mach.*) A type of tool used for roughing cuts and for turning fillets.

round-point chis′el (*Mach.*) Used for cutting oil grooves, etc.

round-tube ra′di-a′tor (*Auto.*) A very commonly used type in which round tubes, set closely together, run from an upper to a lower tank. The tubes are sweated to a series of thin plates through which they pass, thus insuring a more complete radiation of the heat generated in the cooling system.

rout (*Woodwkg.*) To cut or gouge out with a router.

rout′er (*Woodwkg.*) A two-handled tool for smoothing the face of depressed surfaces in woodwork.

rout′ing (*Print.*) The cutting away of unnecessary parts of a printing block which would mark the printed sheet if allowed to remain.

rov′ing (*Plast.*) A comparatively heavy bundle of filaments of fibrous glass, continuous, used as an unspun yarn in woven roving, or as single rope, fed into a chopping mechanism which cuts glass fiber into short lengths for preforms or mat.

row′lock (*Masonry*) A course of brick laid on edge is called a "row-lock" course.

row′lock-back wall (*Masonry*) A wall made with the bricks of the exterior face laid flat, and the bricks of the backing laid on edge.

roy′al (*Papermkg.*) A flat writing paper size 19 by 24.

roy′al draw′ing pa′per. Drawing paper in sheets 19 by 24 in.

r.p.m. An abbreviation for revolutions per minute.

rub′ber (*Chem.*) A hydrocarbon obtained from the milk juice of certain tropical plants. Commercial rubber is widely used in the industries, mainly because of its great elasticity and its impermeability to water and gases. Enormous quantities are used for automobile tires, waterproofing, and insulating.

rub′ber ce-ment′. There are many formulas for making rubber cement for different purposes. Plain rubber cement is made by cutting crude rubber in small pieces and adding a solvent. Carbon disulphide is best; benzol is good and much cheaper. Gasoline is also extensively used.

rub′ble (*Arch.*) Roughly broken quarry stone.

rub′ble ma′son-ry. Uncut stone, used for rough work, foundations, backing, etc.

ru′bri-ca′tion (*Arch.*) The coloring of a background by enamels or paint.

rud′der (*Aero.*) The plane surface attached to the rear of an aircraft for the purpose of controlling left and right direction of flight.

rud′der an′gle (*Aero.*) The acute angle between the rudder and the plane of symmetry of the aircraft. It is positive when the trailing edge has moved to the left with reference to the normal position of the pilot.

rud′der bar (*Aero.*) The foot bar by means of which the control cables leading to the rudder are operated.

rud′der ped′als (*Aero.*) The foot pedals by means of which the controls leading to the rudder are operated.

rud′der torque (*Aero.*) The twisting moment exerted by the rudder on the fuselage. The product of the rudder area by the distance from its center of area to the axis of the fuselage may be used as a relative measure of rudder torque.

rule (*Print.*) A strip of type-high metal, usually brass, one long edge of which has been prepared for printing a line.

rule cut′ter (*Print.*) A small hand-lever machine used for cutting leads, slugs, and rules to desired length.

rule joint (*Woodwkg.*) A type of knuckle joint with projecting shoulders, which abut when the joined pieces are fully opened, as in the ordinary two-foot rule used by woodworkers.

rul′ing ma-chine′ (*Print.*) A machine equipped with pens for ruling lines on papers.

rum′ble or tum′bler(*Fdry.*)A hollow, revolving cylinder used for the purpose of cleaning sand from castings.

run (*Plumb.*) That portion of a pipe or fitting continuing in a straight line in the direction of flow of the pipe to which it is connected.

rung (*Wood Turn.*) Rounded cross strip as on a ladder or chair.

ru′nic (*Print.*) A style of modern type.

run in (*Print.*) A proofreader's term meaning to keep in one paragraph.

run-ner (*Plast.*) In an injection mold, the groove that connects the sprue with the gate through which the plastic composition flows.

run′ning fit (*Mach.*) Refers to the fitting together of parts with just sufficient clearance to permit freedom of motion.

run′ning gear (*Auto.*) Consists of front and rear axles, wheels, springs, and frame.

run′ning head (*Print.*) The headlines used at the top of each page in a book.

run′ning in. The operation of new or repaired machinery or equipment for the detection of faults and to insure smooth, free operation of parts before delivery to the purchaser or user.

run′ning or stretch′er bond (*Masonry*) The surface of the wall is made up of stretchers which break joint at the center with a header on each alternate course at the corner.

run of stairs (*Bldg.*) Horizontal part of a step without nosing; horizontal distance of face of one riser to another; horizontal distance of a flight of steps.

run of work. (1) A number of jobs following one another in steady succession. (2) A repetitive job calling for the production of a quantity of the same article.

run out (*Print.*) Same as hanging indention.

runs (*Paint and Lacquer*) Applying too much material in one spot, or using too much thinner, resulting in sags or curtains.

run′way (*Aero.*) An artificial landing strip permitting the landing and take-off of airplanes under all weather conditions.

run′way lo′cal-iz′ing bea′con(*Aero.*) A small radio-range beacon giving accurate lateral direction along the runway of an airport or landing field and some distance beyond.

rup′ture–stress (*E n g i n.*) The unit stress at the time of failure.

rush (*Furn.*) The stems of a marsh-growing plant, used for chair seats since early times.

rust (*Chem.*) Hydrated ferric oxide, $2Fe_2O_3 3H_2O$.

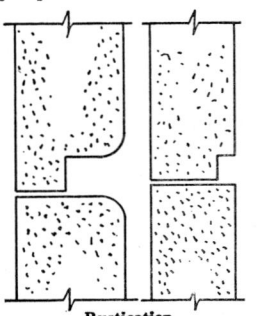
Rustication

rus′ti-ca′tion (*B l d g.*) Ashlar work with roughened surface and deeply sunk grooves at the joints.

rust′ing (*Chem.*) Dipping bright metal patterns into a solution of sal ammoniac or a weak hydrochloric-acid solution. Such patterns are rusted in order that they may be shellacked without risk of the varnish peeling off.

rust joint (*Plumb.*) A joint in which some oxidizing agent is employed; either to cure a leak or to withstand high pressure. (*Shopwk.*) A joint made by packing with a stiff paste which oxidizes the iron, the whole rusting together and hardening into a solid mass.

ru-the′ni-um (*Metal.*) A rare metal used for pen-point alloys and for hardening platinum.

S

sad′dle (*Ceram.*) Rod made of fire clay, used for supporting glazed ware during firing. (*Mach.*) The base of a slide rest which lies on the lathe bed; also the sliding plate which carries the drill spindle and gear wheels of a radial drill; or, the crossbar which carries the toolhead on a planer or boring mill.

sad′dle stitch (*Print.*) A method of fastening the sheets of a pamphlet together by stitching through the middle fold, either with thread or wire.

S.A.E. (*Auto.*) The Society of Automotive Engineers' standard formula for computing horsepower of gasoline engines may be stated as follows:

$$\text{h.p.} = \frac{D^2 \times N}{2.5},$$

based on 1,000 feet per minute piston speed. D is the cylinder bore in inches, N the number of cylinders, and 2.5 a constant.

S.A.E. or So-ci′e-ty of Au′to-mo′-tive En′gi-neers′. These initials, prefixed to the name of any mechanical part, indicate that the article is built in accordance with the standards laid down by this society.

S.A.E. steels. A numerical system has been adopted by the Society of Automotive Engineers to designate the steels included in S.A.E. specifications. The first figure of the number indicates the general class to which the steel belongs: e.g., (1) indicates carbon steel; (2) nickel steel; (3) nickel chromium, etc. The second figure usually indicates (in cases of alloys) the percentages of the main alloying element. The last two or three figures indicate the carbon content in hundredths of 1 per cent. Thus, specification 2345 calls for a nickel steel having 3 per cent nickel and 0.45 per cent carbon.

S.A.E. threads (*Auto. Mech.*) Of the same form as U.S. Standard, but of finer pitch now known as Nat'l Fine Series.

safe car′ry-ing ca-pac′i-ty (*Bldg.*) Anything so constructed as to carry a certain weight without a breakdown. (*Elec.*) The National Board of Fire Underwriters established a table of safe carrying capacities for all sizes of copper wire. This safe carrying capacity, in amperes, may not be exceeded when installing electrical conductors.

safe edge (*Shopwk.*) The uncut edge of a file which makes possible the protection of an adjacent surface when operating in a corner.

safe load (*Engin.*) The load that a piece can support without exceeding the working unit stress.

safe′ty fac′tors (*Engin.*) The allowance made for overloads and unforeseen circumstances in order to insure ample strength in a machine, material, or type of construction under all conditions.

safe′ty lamp (*Min.*) An incandescent lamp used by miners.

safe′ty pa′per (*Papermkg.*) A durable writing paper used for negotiable certificates which is so made as to expose alterations.

safe′ty switch (*Elec.*) A knife-blade

switch enclosed in an iron box and operated externally.

safe′ty valve (*Engin.*) A safety device for allowing steam or water to escape from a boiler when the pressure may become dangerous. Usually adjusted to permit not more than 5 pounds of pressure above maximum allowable working pressure of the boiler.

sag. (1) To dip, bend, or cause to bend downward, a depression, especially in the middle. (2) A departure from original shape by its own weight, as the sag of a door.

sag′ger (*Pot.*) A fire-clay box in which delicate pieces are placed while being baked.

sail′plane (*Aero.*) A performance-type glider.

sal am-mo′ni-ac (*Chem.*) Ammonium chloride (NH_4Cl.) Obtained as a by-product in gas manufacture. Used as a flux in soldering, in the manufacture of dyestuffs, in calico printing, etc.

sales en′gi-neer′. Not a salesman, but a builder of good will. He helps the consumer solve his problems. He reports on the performance of his company's product in the field, aids in developing new markets, and should fully cooperate with the sales department.

sa-lon′ (*Arch.*) A large and magnificent room; usually a room for holding receptions, or displaying exhibits, as distinguished from an assembly room.

sal so′da (*Chem.*) Washing soda. Used in glass and soap manufacture, bleaching and washing linen, dyeing, papermaking, etc.

salt (*Chem.*) A product formed by the neutralization of an acid by a base. A compound containing a metal and a nonmetallic element.

salt of tar′tar (*Chem.*) Potassium carbonate. $K_2CO_3.H_2O$.

salt′pe′ter, or po-tas′si-um ni′trate (*Chem.*) (KNO_3) Chile saltpeter is mineral sodium nitrate. Saltpeter is used as a preservative, in the manufacture of gunpowder and matches, as a flux in smelting ores, and to some extent in dyeing.

sa′mite (sā′mīt) (*Furn.*) A silk fabric generally interwoven with gold, as was used in medieval times.

sand. Small grain of mineral, largely quartz, which is the result of disintegration of rock.

san′dal-wood (*Furn.*) A heavy close-grained wood, of fragrant odor, native of the East Indies.

sand′blast′ing (*Engin.*) The driving of sand against an object or surface by air pressure. Used extensively for cleaning castings, removing scale and dirt from forgings preparatory to tooling, brazing, galvanizing, etc., also for renovating stonework buildings.

sand fin′ish. Refers to sandpaper finish on wood surfaces and to the sand-blast method of renovating the exterior of stone buildings.

sand hole (*Fdry.*) A cavity formed in a casting by loose sand or by the facing which is washed into the mold during the pouring operation.

sand′ing (*Wood Fin.*) The finishing of a surface on or by a sanding machine, which consists essentially of a revolving disk faced with sandpaper or by a sanding belt carried on rollers.

sand match (*Fdry.*) A shallow frame of the same size as the flask with which it is to be used. It has a bottom board fastened on with screws, and sockets to receive the pins of the flask. The "match" is rammed up and the pattern set in to the parting line, being coped out where necessary. The drag is rammed up on the "match." The best use of a sand match is for making a number of castings from a one-piece pattern of irregular shape.

sand′pa′per (*Shopwk.*) Paper coated with sharp sand; used as an abrasive, particularly for finishing surfaces of woodwork. Also called "garnet paper."

sand′stone (*B l d g.*) Is composed of grains of fine sand cemented together by silica, oxide of iron, or carbonate of lime; used as a building stone. (*Mech.*) Grindstones are made of natural sandstone.

sand′wich (*Plast.*) In laminating employing layers of materials. The lamination itself is, in a sense, a sandwich. When used in sandwich panels, the outer faces are laminated sheets enclosing cores of various kinds, each designed to fulfill a purpose. If urethane foam is the core, the use is probably sound or refrigeration insulation. The core may be honeycomb (see HONEYCOMB), or it may be wood in pieces arranged as decoration. The wood components may be pigmented. An unlimited variety of architectural panels for walls, screens, dividers, and partitions are a possibility.

san′i-ta-ry. Pertaining to, or tending to promote health.

san′i-ta-ry en′gi-neer′. One who supervises the planning and construction of water supply, sewage systems, etc.

san′i-ta-ry sew′er (*Plumb.*) Underground pipe or tunnel for carrying off domestic sanitary wastes.

san′i-ta′tion (*Engin.*) The neutralization or removal of conditions injurious to health. Sanitary engineering; purification of water supply; disposal of sewage, etc.

sans′–ser′if (*Print.*) Type, such as the modern Gothic, made without serifs.

sap (*Wood*) The juice of plants which is necessary to growth.

sap streaks (*Wood Fin.*) Streaks which show through a finished wood surface due to sapwood. For a uniform finish, they must be "toned out."

sap′wood. The new wood next to the bark of a tree.

sash (*Bldg.*) A frame in which window glass is set or retained.

sash bars (*Bldg.*) The strips in a sash which separate the narrow panes of glass.

sash chain (*Arch.*) The chain used to carry the weights in double hung window sash. Used especially on heavy sash.

sash pul′ley (*Arch.*) The small pulley set in a window frame, over which the sash cord or chain runs.

sash weight (*A r c h.*) The counterweight used to make easy the raising and lowering of window sash.

sas′sa-fras (*Wood*) *Sassafras variifolium*. A soft, brittle, porous wood, dull orange brown in color, with light sapwood. Sometimes substituted for ash and chestnut.

sat′el-lite tel′e-vi′sion sta′tion (*Tel.*) A station, all of whose live talent programming comes from a network. It may supplement this network program schedule by local newsreel films or remote pickups. Such a station may serve a community outside the service area of a master station.

sat′in-wood. *Chloroxylon swietenia.* One of the finest cabinet woods; found principally in Ceylon. It is heavy in weight, light in color, and close grained with silky streaks. Used for high-grade furniture and paneling.

sat′ur-ated steam. Water vapor at the temperature of the boiling point corresponding to a given pressure. (*Engin.*) Steam which is in contact with the water from which it is generated.

sat′ur-a′tion (*Elec.*). A magnetic material is said to be saturated, when, upon increasing the ampere turns, no increase in the number of magnetic lines of force is obtained.

saw ar′bor (*Woodwkg.*) The spindle (arbor) on which a circular saw is mounted.

saw bench (*Woodwkg.*) The frame or table which carries a circular saw.

saw gull′et. The throat at the bottom of the teeth of a circular saw.

saw gum′ming. Shaping the teeth of a circular saw.

saw′horse (*Woodwkg.*) The ordinary trestle used by carpenters; also X-shaped framework used while sawing cordwood.

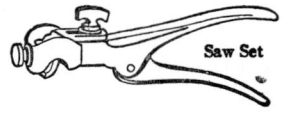
Saw Set

saw set (*Woodwkg.*) A tool for giving the proper "set" to the teeth of saws.

saw′-toothed sky′light (*A r c h.*) A skylight roof whose profile is shaped like the teeth of a saw.

saw trim′mer (*P r i n t.*) A machine used for the sawing and trimming of type slugs and plates.

saw′yer (*Woodwkg.*) One who operates a circular saw; either in a mill or in the field.

scab (*Fdry.*) Small wartlike projection formed on the surface of a casting when small patches of the mold face wash off. Caused by too much slicking.

scab′ble (*M a s o n r y*) To dress off rough stones for rubble work.

scaf′fold (*Bldg.*) A temporary structure for the support of workmen and materials.

scaf′fold height (*Masonry*) The distance between various stages of scaffolding, usually about 4 or 5 ft., representing the height within which a bricklayer can carry on his work efficiently.

scagl-io′la (skăl-yō′lá) (*A r c h.*) An imitation of colored marble obtained in plastering, used for floors, columns, and other ornamental interior work.

scale (*Draft.*) (1) A piece of wood or other material graduated into divisions, used for measuring. (2) The

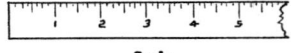
Scale

size of a drawing in relation to the size of the object represented. (3) In architecture or building, drawings are usually made to a scale of ⅛ or ¼ in. equals one ft. (*Metal.*) The outside coating of a casting.

scaled draw′ing (*Draw.*) A drawing made smaller than the work which it represents, but to a definite proportion, which should be specified on the drawing itself.

sca-lene′ (*Math.*) A triangle in which no two

Scalene

sides are equal; also a cone or cylinder in which the axis is inclined to the base.

scal'y (*Plast.*) A flaked appearance of the surface.

sca-mil'lus (skå-mĭl'ŭs) (*Arch.*) The small groove which separates the necking of the Greek Doric column from the shaft.

scan'ning (*Tel.*) The process of deflecting the electron beam in a camera or picture tube so that it moves at high speed left to right in a sequence of rows or lines from top to bottom, thus changing light and shadows of a scene into electrical impulses to form the image on the receiver tube.

scan'ning line (*Tel.*) One line from left to right of a picture being transmitted.

scant'ling (*Bldg.*) Small timber as 2 by 3, 2 by 4, etc., used for studding.

scare'head' (*P r i n t.*) A large and prominent news-article heading.

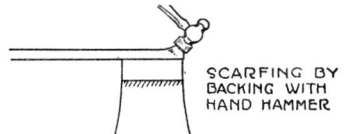
SCARFING BY BACKING WITH HAND HAMMER

scarf'ing (*Forg.*) Tapering the ends of two pieces to be joined to avoid an enlarged joint.

scarf joint (*Bldg.*) A joint made by notching and lapping the ends of two timbers, fastening them together with bolts or straps. (*Metalwk.*) A tapered joint made by beveling off the edges of the parts to be joined.

scar'i-fy (skăr'ĭ-fī) (*E n g i n.*) To roughen up, as a road, for repairs.

sci'en-tif'ic. According to exact and accurate rules; systematic.

scis'sors truss (*Arch.*) A type of roof truss, so named from its resemblance to a pair of scissors. It is frequently used for supporting roofs over halls and churches.

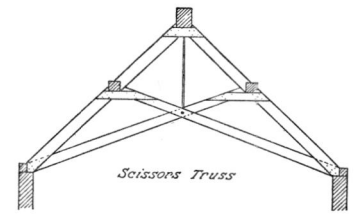
Scissors Truss

scle-rom'e-ter (s k l ē-r ŏ m'ē-t ē r) (*Engin.*) An instrument for determining the hardness of metals by drawing a diamond once forward and once backward over a smooth surface; the resulting scratch is compared with a standard scratch.

scle'ro-scope (sklē'rô-skōp) (*Engin.*) An instrument for measuring the hardness of metal. A diamond pointed plunger is dropped vertically on a test specimen. The height of rebound is a measure of the hardness of the material.

sconce (skŏns) (*Bldg.*) An ornamental bracket holding candles or lantern.

scoop (*Tel.*) A type of single lamplight reflector.

score (*Auto.*) A groove, scratch, or mark caused by burning or abrading in moving parts.

scored cyl'in-ders (*A u t o. M e c h.*) Cylinders of automobile or other engines in which the smooth polished surfaces of the cylinder walls have been cut into or scored by broken piston rings or loose wrist pins, or by the admission of some foreign substance into the cylinders.

scored drum (*Auto.*) A brake drum

scored or grooved. This often occurs when the brake lining becomes badly worn due to harsh braking effort or exposed heads of rivets, or both, which produce grooves and ridges inside the surface of the drum.

scor′ing (*Cabwk.*) Striking lines or grooves across the grain on a piece of wood with any steel instrument, for the purpose of roughing the surface, in order to make a firmer glued joint. (*Print.*) Grooving heavy paper or cardboard with a plane rule upon a press, by a heavy uninked impression, for the purpose of folding.

scor′ing of pis′tons and cyl′in-ders (*Auto.*) Roughening surfaces of these parts due to improper lubrication.

scor′ing or creas′ing rule (*Print.*) A rule printed to secure exact creasing and folding. When given a heavy impression the resulting crease makes cover stock or board less likely to break on the fold.

Scotch tape. A strip of paper supplied with an adhesive on one side, used in the drafting room for holding down drafting paper, and by painters for covering surfaces not to be touched by the paint. Also a transparent adhesive for sealing packages, etc.

sco′ti-a (skō′shĭ-à) (*Arch.*) A concave molding often found in the base of a column.

Scotia

scrap (*Fdry.*) Pig iron that has been melted in the cupola and is to be melted again.

scrap iron (*Metal.*) A term covering all grades of salvaged iron or steel to be used in making new steel.

scrape (*Mach.*) To finish a surface or to fit a bearing, etc., by the use of a hand tool called a scraper.

scraped joint (*Mach.*) A joint, as a bearing brought to a perfect fit by means of a scraper.

scrap′er (scrāp′ẽr) (1) A flat plate of steel used by woodworkers to smooth wood surfaces. (2) A tool used by metalworkers for fitting bearings, and for truing surfaces. Metalworkers' scrapers are of a variety of shapes, depending on the work to be done.

scrap′er plane (*Woodwk.*) A plane which carries a scraping blade. Used in scraping floors and smoothing large surfaces.

scrap′ing (*Mach.*) A method of finishing flat surfaces and bearings, etc., by the use of a hand tool called a scraper.

scratch. Shallow mark, groove, furrow, or channel on a surface.

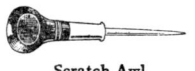

Scratch Awl

scratch awl (*Shopwk.*) A sharp-pointed piece of steel used for marking on metal.

scratch brush. A wire brush used for removing rust, dirt, and foreign matter from metal surfaces.

scratch coat (*Masonry*) The first coat, which is scratched in order to give a better hold for succeeding coats.

screeds (*Masonry*) Strips of plaster about 8 in. wide and the depth of the first two coats, which are put on first and are used as thickness guides in applying the remainder of the plaster.

screen (*Print.*) The ruled glass screen used in halftone engraving. Its close

screen′ings (*Papermkg.*) A cheap paper, often specked, sometimes glazed; used for packing and wrapping.

screw (*Mech.*) A screw may be considered as a helix wound around a cylinder; the helix may be single as in a common screw, or double, or multiple.

screw ad-just′ing cal′i-per (*Mach.*) Similar in construction to the firm joint caliper but has in addition a spring and screw control for securing delicate adjustments.

screw–and–nut steer′ing gear (*Auto.*) The lower end of the steering-gear shaft has a double screw thread cut on it; one a right-hand, and the other, crossing it, a left-hand thread. When assembled, the threaded end of the shaft is engaged by two half nuts, one right-hand and one left-hand. When the steering wheel is turned one half of the nut moves upward and the other half downward; this motion is transmitted to the cross shaft through rollers which operate against the lower ends of the half nuts.

screw chuck (*Woodwk.*) A chuck for a wood-turning lathe, having a projecting screw which serves as live center.

screw clamp (*Shopwk.*) Same as hand screw or hand clamp.

screw–cut′ting lathe (*Mach.*) A lathe adapted to thread cutting, being equipped with lead screw and change gears.

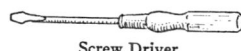
Screw Driver

screw driv′er. A bar or rod of steel with handle at one end and flattened at the other to fit the slots in screwheads.

screw eye. A wood screw with the head formed into a completely closed ring or circle.

screw jack (*Engin.*) A lifting jack actuated by a square-threaded screw.

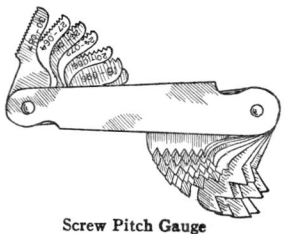
Screw Pitch Gauge

screw pitch gauge (*Mach.*) A gauge usually made up of many leaves, the edge of each being cut to a thread of indicated size. Used for determining the number of threads per inch on a given screw, bolt, or nut.

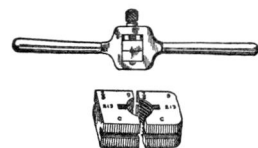
Screw Plate

screw plate (*Mach.*) Originally a steel plate having holes of different sizes which are internally threaded for making screw threads by forcing up the metal. The present use of the term refers to a stock and a halved or solid die.

screw–slot cut′ter (*Mach.*) A milling cutter used for slotting screw heads.

screw′stock (*Metal.*) A shop term for soft steel used for small screws and parts made on screw machines.

screw threads (*Mach.*) Projections left by cutting a helical groove on a cylinder are known as screw threads. Threads may be internal or external.

Scriber

scribe awl or scrib′er. A pointed steel instrument for making fine lines on wood or metal for layout work.

script (*Print.*) Type matter in imitation of handwriting.

scroll (*Furn.*) Ornamentation characterized by free-flowing curves.

scroll saw (*W o o d w k g.*) A thin-bladed saw for cutting curved designs. A jig saw is a power-driven scroll saw.

scroll shears (*Sheet-Met. Wk.*) A hand-operated, gap-shearing machine designed to cut irregular shapes.

scroll′work. Ornamental work suggesting a parchment roll, or work characterized by designs of many curves.

scutch (*Masonry*) A tool resembling a pick on a small scale, with flat cutting edges, for trimming bricks for particular uses.

scutch′eon or es-cutch′eon (skŭch′ŭn or ĕs-kŭch′ŭn) A metal plate, as around a keyhole.

sea coal (*Fdry.*) Finely ground soft coal.

sealed–beam head′light (*Auto.*) The combined assembly consisting of lens, reflector, and lamps in a sealed vacuum or gas container. A much used form for auto-road lighting.

seal′ing com′pound (*E l e c.*) Plastic, nonconducting, acid-resisting compound used to seal-in tops and terminals of a storage cell to prevent spilling of acid electrolyte.

seal′ing wrap′pers (*Papermkg.*) A wrapping paper of smooth finish and good strength used for packaging paper or cardboard.

seam. (1) The joining of two edges as by sewing. (2) A sheet-metal joint in which the edge of one piece is folded or turned over the edge of another.

seam′ing i′ron (*Sheet-Met. Wk.*) Also called grooving tool. Used for setting seams in sheet-metal work.

seam′less tub′ing (*M e c h.*) Drawn tubing without joints, as distinguished from pipe or tubing with welded longitudinal joints.

seam weld′ing. A resistance-welding process wherein overlapping or tangent spot welds are made progressively.

sea′plane (*Aero.*) Any type of airplane which can rise from or alight on water.

sea′plane hull (*Aero.*) That portion of a flying boat which furnishes buoyancy when in contact with the surface of the water. It contains accommodations for the crew and passengers, usually combining the functions of both float and fuselage.

sea′son-ing mod′el-ing. The process of coating plaster models for molds; the molds themselves, and the cases for gelatin molds, with a preparation which will stop absorption.

sea′son-ing of lum′ber (*Woodwkg.*) By the kiln-drying process, boards are placed in a drying room or kiln to hasten the seasoning. By the air-drying process, lumber is allowed to dry naturally under sheds.

seat (*Auto. Mech.*) (1) That part of an engine with which the valve comes in contact to make a tight joint. (2) In valves generally, that stationary part which when the valve head or plunger is in a closed position provides a leakproof contact.

se′cant (sē′kănt) (*Math.*) The secant of the angle is the quotient of the hypotenuse divided by the adjacent side.

sec′ond-a-ry (*Elec.*) A winding or coil which is magnetically coupled with another coil called a "primary."

sec′ond-a-ry col′or (*Paint.*) The colors obtained by mixing red, yellow, and blue pigments together in pairs; e.g., red and yellow make orange, yellow and blue produce green, etc.

sec′ond-a-ry–type glid′er (*Aero.*) A glider designed to have better aerodynamic performance than the primary type, but rugged enough for the use of pilots with limited training.

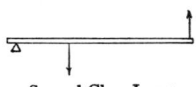
Second-Class Lever

sec′ond–class le′ver (*Mech.*) A lever with the weight applied between fulcrum and power.

sec′ond cut (*Metalwk.*) This refers to the spacing of teeth on a file. Second cut indicates a degree of roughness between bastard and smooth, and may be either single or double cut.

sec′onds. Any articles not of first quality. In the printing trade "seconds" is usually applied to paper.

sec′tion (*Bldg. and Mech. Drg.*) A drawing representing the internal parts of an object as if it had been cut straight through vertically or horizontally. Also partial sections may be taken through particular parts.

sec′tion-al. (1) Of, or pertaining to, a section or district; local; consisting of sections; divisible into sections. (2) A drawing which shows some portion cut away, in order that the drawing may be more easily understood, is called a "sectional view."

sec′tor (*Geom.*) (1) A part of a circle bounded by two radii and the arc subtended by them. (2) Any mechanical part of similar shape.

se-dan′ (*Auto.*) An enclosed four-door permanent-type body with full-width cross seats front and rear.

sed′i-ment. The matter which settles at the bottom of a liquid.

sed′i-men′ta-ry rock (*Min.*) Rock formed under water by pressure or by cementation.

seg′ment. The part of a circle included between the chord and its arc.

seg-men′tal arch (*Masonry*) An arch whose curve is an arc of a circle, but less than a semicircle.

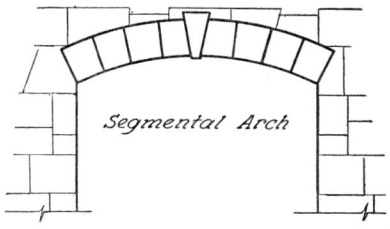
Segmental Arch

seg-men′tal rack or **seg-men′tal wheel** (*Mach.*) An arc or portion of a gear wheel, used for imparting reversible motion to a spindle.

seg′re-ga′tion. The separating of parts as from a main body and bringing these parts together as a unit.

seis′mo-graph (sīz′mȯ-gràf) (*Phys.*) An instrument which automatically records an earthquake shock.

seize (sēz) The sticking together or adhering of surfaces, which normally move freely against each other, due to heat generated by friction caused by lack of lubrication. Such parts are often said to be "frozen." See GALLING.

se-lec′tiv′i-ty (*Radio*) The ability of a set to clearly receive one radio station signal while eliminating all others.

self′–act′ing. Operating automatically; performing an operation without outside assistance.

self′–a-lign′ing bear′ing. A bearing supported in such a manner that it can readily adjust itself to the alignment of its shaft.

self′–cen′ter-ing (*Mech.*) The automatic setting, locating, or marking of a cylindrical piece of work.

self′–cen′ter-ing chuck (*Mach.*) A chuck which automatically centers a piece of work through the simultaneous movement of the jaws.

self′–cen′ter-ing or bell cen′ter punch (*Mach.*) A center punch which slides in a bell-mouthed casing. A fairly accurate centering is secured by placing the bell mouth over the end of the piece to be marked, then tapping the punch with a hammer.

self′–en′er-giz′ing (*Auto.*) The tendency of a brake mechanism to increase the brake pressure, due to the rotation of the brake drums.

self–ex′ci-ta′tion (*Elec.*) Direct current gotten from the brushes of a d.c. generator to provide current for its electromagnetic field. In alterna-tors the term refers to a d.c. generator built on the alternator shaft. Used to provide direct current for the alternator field.

self′–ex-cit′ed (*E l e c.*) A machine which generates its own current for supplying its field.

self–ex-cit′ed al′ter-na′tor (*E l e c.*) An alternating-current generator which also produces through one of several ways a direct current for magnetizing its main fields.

self′–hard′ening steel (*Metal.*) An alloy tool steel which hardens when cooled in air.

self-in-duced′ cur′rent (*Elec.*) The current produced by the self-induced e.m.f., set up in a coil when the magnetic field of the same coil changes in direction or intensity.

self–in-duct′ance (*Elec.*) The phenomena of electro magnetic induction which takes place between the turns of a coil in a circuit.

self′–in-duc′tion (*Elec.*) The reaction of the magnetic field of a coil upon itself.

self′–lock′ing setscrews (*M a c h .*) There are several patented types of setscrews which resist the loosening effect due to vibration. One type has left-hand spiral knurling at the point, another has a deeply slotted head, the slot being spread to offer resistance.

self′–o′pen-ing die (*M a c h.*) A die which opens automatically to permit its removal after the thread-cutting operation is finished.

self′–tap′ping screw. A type of screw designed to cut its own threads in metal. Such screws are used most satisfactorily on the softer metals of not too heavy gauge.

Sell′ers screw thread (*Mach.*) The

U. S. Std. or National coarse thread of V type, with flats at top and bottom, equal to one eighth of the pitch. The included angle is 60 deg.

Sell'ers ta'per (*Mach.*) This taper is 0.75 inch per foot. It is not as much used as the Brown and Sharpe or the Morse tapers.

sem'a-phore (sĕm'á-fōr) An apparatus, with movable or stationary arms for giving signals.

sem'i-chord. Half the length of the chord of an arc.

sem'i-cir'cle. A half circle, bounded by the circumference line and diameter.

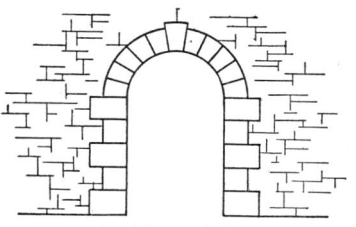
Semicircle

Semicircular Arch

sem'i-cir'cu-lar arch (*Arch.*) An arch whose intrados is a half circle.

sem'i-el-lip'tic spring (*Auto.*) As indicated by the name, the shape of this spring is approximately that of half an ellipse. It is much used on automobiles.

sem'i-float'ing ax'le (*Auto.*) The outer ends of the axle shafts are carried in bearings and the inner ends by the differential side gears. The wheels are keyed to the tapered outer ends of the shafts. Formerly a broken shaft meant the loss of a wheel.

sem'i-pos'i-tive mold (*Plast.*) A mold which allows a small amount of excess material to escape when it is closed.

sem'i-rig'id air'ship (*Aero.*) One whose form is maintained by a rigid or jointed keel and the internal pressure in the gas containers and ballonets.

sem'i-steel' cast'ings (*Metal.*) Produced by adding soft steel or wrought-iron scrap to the charge in the cupola. These castings are made in the same manner as ordinary castings. They are used for machine parts, large gears, etc., where both strength and finish are essential. The usual amount of scrap in the mixture is about 20 per cent. The carbon content of the finished product runs about 3 per cent.

sem'i-trans-par'ent. Translucent, allowing the passage of light, but not permitting a clear view of any object.

sen'si-ble heat (*Engin.*) Heat which is measured by the thermometer, as opposed to latent heat.

sen'si-tive drill'ing ma-chines (*Mach.*) Those designed for operating small drills of about ½ in. and under, at high speed.

sep'a-ra-ble plug (*Auto.*) A spark plug so constructed that it can be disassembled for cleaning or repair.

sep'a-rate-ly ex-cit'ed (*Elec.*) A machine which gets the current needed for the excitation of its field from some source outside of itself.

sep'a-ra'tors (*Auto., Elec.*) Used as insulators between the plates of a battery. They may be of wood or special composition, and must be porous to allow circulation of electrolyte.

se'pi-a (sē'pĭ-á) (*Color*) Dark brown tinged with red.

sep'tic tank (*Plumb.*) A plumbing unit used for decomposing solid sewage matter. It is designed to dispose of these wastes in a completely sanitary and odorless manner by natural bacterial action which dissolves most of the solids into liquids and gases.

se′quence. In regular order, or systematic arrangement.

se′ri-al taps (*Mach.*) A set of taps usually numbered 1, 2, and 3. No. 1 is a tapered tap, No. 2 is slightly tapered near the end, and No. 3 is a full-threaded tap, called a "bottoming" tap.

Lamps in Series

se′ries (*Elec.*) When two or more pieces of electrical material or apparatus are so connected that the current feeding one must pass through the others, they are said to be in series. (One after another, as in a string.) (*Print.*) A quantity of type of the same style in a number of sizes and faces.

se′ries dy′na-mo (*Elec.*) A direct-current dynamo in which the armature and field are connected in series internally.

se′ries mo′tor (*Elec.*) A direct-current motor with the armature and field connected in series. Used on elevators and other machines where variable loads occur. The speed varies with the load.

se′ries par′al-lel cir′cuit (*Elec.*) A circuit made up of two or more simple parallel circuits all joined in series.

se′ries weld′ing. A resistance-welding process wherein two or more welds are made simultaneously by a single welding transformer with the total current passing through every weld.

ser′if (*Print.*) A light line or stroke crossing or projecting from the end of a main line in a letter.

ser-ra′tion. Like the toothed edge of a saw.

serv′ice (*Elec.*) That part of an electrical installation between the pole transformers and the meters and their associated equipment.

serv′ice ceil′ing (*Aero.*) The height above sea level, under normal air conditions, at which a given airplane ceases to be able to rise at a rate in excess of 100 feet per minute in the United States and England. This specified rate varies in different countries.

serv′ice ell (*Plumb.*) An elbow having an outside thread on one end.

serv′ice pipe. The small pipe which conveys liquid or gas from a main pipe to its places of use.

serv′ice switch (*Elec.*) The switch inserted at the point of entrance of the wiring to a building, controlling the whole installation in the building.

serv′ice tank (*Aero.*) A fixed full tank near each power unit, into which fuel from other tanks is pumped and from which the fuel supplying the engine is drawn.

serv′ice tee (*Plumb.*) A tee having inside thread on one end and on the branch but outside threads on the other end of the run.

serv′ice wires (*Elec.*) The supply wires connecting the load in a building to the source of supply from a transformer.

ser′vo con·trol′ (*Aero.*) A control devised to reinforce the pilot's effort by an aerodynamic or mechanical relay.

ses′qui-plane (*Aero.*) A form of biplane in which the area of one wing is less than half the area of the other.

set (*Carp.*) (1) A small tool for sinking nail heads below the surface. (2) To adjust a tool, as to set a plane bit. (*Plast.*) In plastics, the moment of solidification in a curing cycle.

set at ze′ro (*Mach.*) To set to a given point from which other adjustments can be made. In lathe work when the gauge line on the tailstock is set at zero the live and dead centers are in alignment.

set′ting time (*Plast.*) The time required to solidify the fluid resin.

set′o′ver (*Mach.*) Transverse movement of a lathe tailstock center on its base to obtain a taper on a turned piece.

set′screw′ (*M e c h.*) A plain screw having a square or other shaped head, used for tightening purposes, and for locking adjustable parts in position. Setscrews are usually heat treated.

set′ting–down ma·chine′ (*Sheet-Met. Wk.*) A machine used to close down the seams left by the burring machine.

set′ting ham′mer (*Art Met.*) Made of square stock with one end of the head bevelled to a sharp edge; the other end is flat. Used for working in corners or against an angle.

set′tle (*Furn.*) A bench or seat.

set′tle-ment (*Carp.*) The unequal sinking or lowering of any part of a structure, usually caused by weakness of foundation, skimping of materials used in the structure, or by unseasoned lumber.

sev′er-y (*Arch.*) A compartment in a vaulted ceiling, especially in Gothic construction.

Sè′vres (sâ′vr') (*Furn.*) A costly porcelain manufactured at Sevres, France, used for plaque decoration.

sew′er (*Plumb.*) Pipe or tunnel for carrying away sewage or storm water for sanitary purposes.

sex′tant (*Math.*) An instrument for measuring angles in any plane. It is particularly useful on boats as it can be used by an observer who is on a moving object.

shac′kle (*Mech.*) A connecting link or device for fastening parts together; usually in such a manner as to permit of some motion.

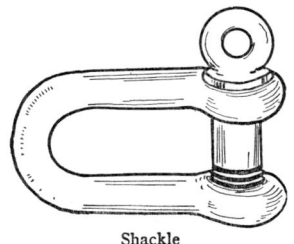

Shackle

shac′kle bolt (*Mech.*) A bolt passing through a shackle and some other part fastening the two together.

shade. Degree of luminosity of a color, as darker or lighter, as produced by mixture of black or white with pure color.

shaft (*Mech.*) An axle or bar, usually cylindrical, used to support rotating pieces, or to transmit power or motion by rotation.

shake. A split or check in timber which

usually causes a separation of the wood between annual rings.

shakes (*Arch.*) Handmade shingles.

shank (*Mach.*) That part of a tool by which it is connected to its handle or socket.

shape (*Shopwk.*) To plane metal on a shaper.

shap'er (*Mach.*) A metalworking machine on which the work is fastened to a table or "knee," and the tool is moved back and forth over it by means of a sliding ram.

shapes (*Engin.*) A general term applied to rolled structural metal, as I beams, channels, Z bars, angles, etc.

sharp sand (*Bldg.*) A clean sand containing coarse angular grains.

shat'ter-proof' glass (*Auto.*) Glass now commonly used in automobiles. It consists of two pieces of glass with plastic between to prevent shattering.

shear (*Engin.*) The resistance of a body to being cut by the action of two parallel forces or loads acting in opposite directions. (*Mech.*) (1) To cut with shears. (2) A part is said to be "in shear" when it is subject to shearing stress.

shear'ing strength (*Engin.*) Indicates the strength of a material against a sliding failure.

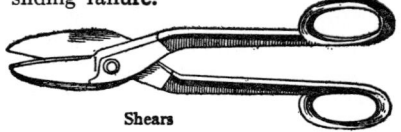
Shears

shears (1) A tool with two blades for cutting metals. (2) The ways on which the lathe carriage and tailstock move are called "shears" by some. They may be either V, flat, or any other shape.

sheath'ing (*Arch.*) Usually wide boards nailed to studding or roofing rafters, to form a foundation for the outer surface covering of the side walls or roof in a dwelling.

sheave wheel (*Engin.*) A grooved wheel in a block over which a rope or chain runs.

shed (*Arch.*) A one-story structure open on at least one side, either attached to or detached from a building.

shed'der (*Mach.*) A sort of stripper which ejects the blanks from a compound die.

sheet'er lines (*Plast.*) Parallel scratches or projecting ridges distributed over a considerable area of a plastic sheet, such as might be produced during a slicing operation.

sheet'ing (*Arch.*) Same as sheathing.

sheet-met'al gauge (*Mech.*) A gauge used for measuring the thickness of sheet metal.

sheet-met'al work'ing. Work performed on metal in sheet form.

sheet steel (*Sheet-Met. Wk.*) Thin sheets of steel used by sheet-metal workers. Thickness is gauged by number. Heavy sheets are called plates.

sheet tin (*Sheet-Met. Wk.*) Thin sheets of iron or steel, coated with tin which serves to prevent corrosion.

sheet wise (*Print.*) The printing of two forms or pages one at a time as opposed to the work-and-turn method wherein both forms are printed at one time and then backed up.

shel-lac' (*Wood Fin.*) A flake material made from the secretion of the lac insect. This flake shellac, when cut with alcohol, is known both as shellac and shellac varnish; white and orange are the usual colors.

shel′lac var′nish (*Wood Fin.*) A varnish very generally used by pattern-makers. It is made by dissolving flake shellac in alcohol.

shell drill (*Mach.*) A hollow drill carried on an arbor when in use. It is used for enlarging holes through which a drill has been passed.

shell–end cut′ter (*Mach.*) A heavy-duty cutter designed for use on a tapered arbor to which it is attached by a nut which fits into a recess at the outer end. The back end of the cutter is slotted to receive a projection on the arbor, thus giving additional driving strength.

shell ream′er (*Mach.*) A hollow reamer which is mounted on an arbor when in use.

sher′ard-ize (*Metal.*) To galvanize with zinc by a dry heating process.

Sher′aton (*Furn.*) That style of furniture developed in England by Thomas Sheraton, 1751–1806.

shield′ed car′bon arc weld′ing. A carbon arc-welding process wherein the welding arc and/or weld metal is protected from the atmosphere by a shielding medium.

shift′er forks (*Shopwk.*) Arms straddling a belt and guiding it from loose to tight pulley, or vice versa.

shift′ing dogs (*Auto.*) In a transmission, lugs or projections on short splines which engage and/or disengage the second- and the high-speed gear.

shift′ing fork (*Auto.*) A steel fork or yoke mounted on a sliding rod, used to move gears in and out of mesh.

shim (*Mech.*) A thin piece of metal or other substance, used in fitting a bearing to a shaft. (*Engin.*) A piece of wood or metal placed beneath an object for the purpose of leveling up or truing up.

shim′my (*Auto.*) Name commonly applied to "front-wheel wabble."

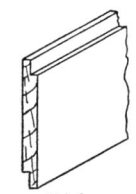

Laminated Shims

This very annoying condition may be due to one or more of several causes such as improper spring suspension, uneven pressure in tires, loose king-pins, or improper adjustments.

shin′gles (*Bldg.*) Small pieces of wood or other material used for covering roofs and side walls. Wood shingles are 16, 18, or 24 in. long and of varying widths. Thickness varies from 1/16 in. at the thin end to 1/4, 3/8, or 1/2 in. at the butt end.

ship (*Aero.*) Slang for airplane. In view of the confusion with "airship" it should not be used.

ship′lap′ (*Carp.*) Boards which are rebated on both edges, the two rebates being cut on the opposite sides. Shiplap is used as sheathing, siding, and sometimes for flooring.   Shiplap

ship′ping meas′ure. For measuring entire internal capacity of a vessel. 1 register ton = 100 cu. ft. For measuring cargo: 1 U. S. shipping ton = 40 cu. ft. = 32.143 U. S. bushels.

ship′plane (*Aero.*) An airplane of the land type, so built that it may rise from or alight on the deck of a vessel.

shock (*Engin.*) The result of a sudden application of force.

shock ab-sorb′er (*Aero.*) That portion of the landing gear which reduces shock when landing or taking off.

shoe (*Mech.*) A protective covering,

as an adjustable plate, to offer sliding surface and to take up wear.

shoot'ing board (*Woodwk.*) A device of wood or metal with swivel attachment and groove or runway for a plane, used in planing to any angle from zero to ninety degrees.

shop'work. Mechanical work performed in a shop.

shore (*E n g i n.*) To support as by a stout timber, usually as a prop.

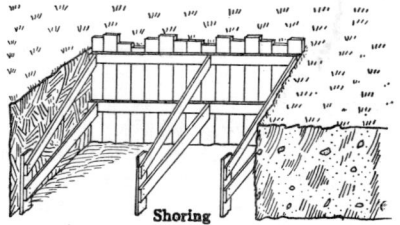
Shoring

shor'ing (*A r c h.*) Timbers braced against a wall as a temporary support. Also the timbering used to prevent a sliding of earth adjoining an excavation.

short (*Plast.*) Marks on the surface of a molded article indicating incomplete filling of the mold.

short cir'cuit (*Elec.*) A path of low resistance placed across an electrical circuit causing an abnormal flow of current.

short length (*Wood.*) Refers to lumber less than eight feet in length.

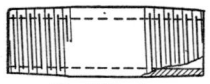
Short Nipple

short nip'ple (*Plumb.*) Shoulder nipples are referred to as long or short nipples depending on the length of blank space between the threaded ends.

short pour-ing (*F d r y.*) When the metal in the ladle is not sufficient to completely fill the mold.

short–time du'ty (*Elec.*) That demand which requires operation at a constant load for a definitely specified short time.

short ton. Two thousand pounds.

short'–wave' ra'dio. Radio reception or transmission employing high-frequency radio energy in the form of short waves as a means of communication.

shot (*Plast.*) The yield from one complete molding cycle.

shoul'der (*Mech.*) That portion of a shaft, or of a stepped or a flanged object, where a sudden increase of diameter occurs.

shoul'der nip'ple (*Plumb.*) A nipple of any length which has an unthreaded portion of pipe between the two threaded ends.

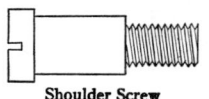
Shoulder Screw

shoul'der screw (*Mach.*) Acts as a pivot pin for levers. The shouldered portion must be slightly longer than the hub of the lever through which it passes in order to avoid binding.

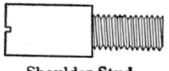
Shoulder Stud

shoul'der stud (*Mach.*) An easily removable threaded stud used for mounting levers and other parts.

show card (*Print.*) A large advertising card such as is often displayed in store windows.

show raft'er (*Arch.*) A short rafter,

often ornamented where it may be seen below the cornice.

Show Rafter

shrine (*Arch.*) (1) A receptacle of sacred relics. (2) A tomb or chapel.

shrink'age (*Fdry.*) The failure of a casting to retain its exact size, weight, and shape during the process of cooling in the mold. Shrinkage is much greater in large castings than in small.

shrink'age crack (*Fdry.*) Crack in a casting caused by unequal cooling of its parts.

shrink fit (*Mech.*) A tight fit accomplished by heating a collar or like part, and permitting it to cool in position; made tight by contraction.

shrink holes in cast'ings (*Fdry.*) Cavities caused by unequal cooling. They frequently occur in thick parts of castings which have sudden changes in dimension.

shrink'ing (*Mech., Fdry.*) Drawing together; contracting; diminishing. The contraction of a casting in cooling.

shrink rule (*Patmkg.*) The rule used by patternmakers when making patterns in order to properly allow for the shrinkage of the metal in which the pattern is to be cast.

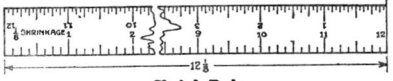

Shrink Rule

shroud (*Mech.*) A flange cast against, or attached to, the ends of gear-wheel teeth in order to increase their strength or to promote smoothness of motion.

shroud'ed wheels (*Auto.*) Wheels almost enclosed, on streamline automobiles, by means of side skirts on the fenders.

shroud line (*Aero.*) The suspension cords of a parachute which attach the harness to the canopy.

shunt (*Elec.*) Usually a comparatively low resistance connected in parallel, with, or across a device or part of a machine.

shunt for am'me'ter (*Elec.*) A predetermined known resistance connected in parallel with the galvanometer; used to limit the current through the meter. An ammeter is basically a galvanometer connected in parallel with a known resistance.

shunt gen'er-a'tor (*Elec.*) A machine for generating an electric current, in which the winding for producing the magnetic field is connected in shunt, or parallel, with the armature or rotating part.

shunt'-wound mo'tor (*Elec.*) Used when the motor speed must be constant, irrespective of variation in load.

side bars (*Plast.*) Loose pieces used to carry one or more molding pins, and operated from outside the mold.

side draw pins (*Plast.*) Projections used to core a hole in a direction other than the line of closing of a mold, and which must be withdrawn before the part is ejected.

side'head' (*Print.*) A heading set to one side instead of centered.

side-mill′ing cut′ter (*Mach.*) Cutter of comparatively narrow face which cuts both on the periphery and the sides. When two or more cutters are set up on an arbor, they are called "straddle mills."

side rake (*Mach.*) The amount of transverse slope away from the cutting edge on the top face of lathe, planer, shaper tools, etc.

sid′er-ite (*Metal.*) $FeCO_3$. An ore of low iron content.

side′slip′ping (*Aero.*) The opposite of skidding when it occurs while turning. When the lateral axis of the airplane is inclined and a slipping takes place in the direction of the lower end of the axis.

side stick (*Print.*) A long wedge-shaped piece of wood used in forms and galleys, and locked in place with wooden quoins.

side stitch (*Print.*) Wire staples affixed by machine along the binding edge.

sid′ing (*Arch.*) Lumber used for finishing the exterior walls of a building.

sieve (*Masonry*) A screen used for removing stones and large particles from sand.

sight-feed lu′bri-ca′tor (*Mech.*) A lubricator in which the flowing or nonflowing of the oil is always apparent at sight.

sight′ing pend′ant (*Aero.*) A steering mark on an airship. A vertical wire on center line forward of control car used as a sight.

sig′nal (*Tel.*) Two signals are involved in transmitting a television program, the picture or video signal and the sound or audio signal. Each signal, therefore, contains the electrical impulses which represent the sound or picture elements being transmitted.

sig′nal flare (*Aero.*) A pyrotechnic signaling device of distinctive color and characteristics.

sig′na-ture (*Print. and Bookbndg.*) The small numbers printed on each form of pages of a book, to show in what order the different sections should be assembled. Also one of the sections of a book.

sig′na-ture press (*Print. and Bookbndg.*) A device used by binders for pressing signatures together.

si′lent chain (*Engin.*) A transmission chain, each link of which is made up of a number of thin plates interlocked with the plates of the adjoining links and connected with pins or rivets. These plates are so designed that they conform to the shape of the teeth of the sprocket or wheel over which they run. This type of chain is much used for timing-gear drive on automobiles and in many other places where only short lengths are required.

sil′i-ca (*Pot.*) (SiO_2) Silica and infusorial earth are usually either ground quartz or the native infusorial earth washed and powdered. China clay and kaolin are silicates of alumina.

sil′i-con (*Min.*) A nonmetallic element derived by heating quartz and carbon in an electric furnace. It is used for hardening and deoxidizing in the manufacture of steel.

sil′i-con car′bide. A product of the resistance-type, electric furnace, made by fusing sand and coke with sawdust, using salt as a flux. It is used as a refractory material and as an abrasive. It is sold under a variety of trade names such as Carborundum,

Crystolon, Carbofrax, Carbora, Carborite, and Crystolite. (*Chem.*) SiC. In granular form used in grinding or cutting materials of low tensile strength such as cast iron, aluminum, copper, bronze, and non-metallic materials.

sil′i-con cop′per (*Metal.*) A rich copper alloy added to molten copper in order to secure clean, solid castings free from blow holes, swellings. etc. When used in the proper amount (about 1½ to 2 lb. per hundred) not a trace of silicon remains in the metal.

sil′i-cone (*Plast.*) A plastic family based on silica with a wide range of physical forms, from simple fluids and greases to flexible rubbers and hard, durable resins. Since they offer excellent weather, heat, and wear properties, they are used in gaskets, circuit breakers, and aircraft parts where high temperature operation is required. They are also used in lubricants, and adhesives. (See PLASTICS.)

sil′i-con steel (*Metal.*) Steel containing from 1 to 2 per cent of silicon is used in the manufacture of springs Steel containing 3 to 5 per cent possesses magnetic qualities which make it valuable for electromagnets.

sill (*Arch.*) A foundation of timber or stone at the bottom of a door or window.

sill high (*Masonry*) The height from floor to sill.

silt. A finely divided earthy material deposited from running water.

silumin (*Metal.*) A German alloy of aluminum silicon which is much used for intricate castings on account of its high ductility and slight shrinkage.

sil′ver (*Min.*) Symbol *Ag*. A white, ductile, malleable metal; an excellent conductor of heat and electricity. Melting point, 1750° F.; specific gravity 10 to 11 according to purity.

sil′ver sol′der. Consists of 1 part copper and from 2 to 4 parts silver. It is used by jewelers.

sil′ver white (*Wood Fin.*) A pure variety of white lead, but more commonly known to painters as filler materials; a fine grade of pulverized silica.

sim′i-lar poles (*Elec.*) When two magnetic poles repel each other, they are magnetically similar or like.

sim′ple e-qua′tion (*Math.*) A mathematical expression of equality between two or more quantities.

sim′ple ma-chine′ (*Mech.*) One whose operating principle is based on the action of any one of the following: the lever, pulley, inclined plane, screw, wheel and axle, or wedge.

sine (sīn) (*Math.*) The function of an angle in a right-angled triangle; the ratio of the side opposite that angle to the hypotenuse.

sine bar (*Math.*) A device used for measuring angles accurately or for locating work to a given angle. It consists of a straightedge to which are attached two hardened and ground plugs.

sine curve (*Elec.*) A curve is said to be sinusoidal when each instantaneous ordinate equals the maximum ordinate times the sine of the angle that the maximum ordinate is from the horizontal. $e = E \sin \angle$.

sin′gle–act′ing (*Mech.*) A machine, or device, in which the motive power is applied in one direction only; action is effective in one direction only.

sin-gle belt′ing (*Mech.*) A belt formed of only a single thickness of leather.

sin′gle–con′tact lamp (*Elec.*) A type of lamp used principally on automobiles, having but one contact in the end of the base. The sides of the base and socket complete the circuit.

single–cut file (*Metalwk.*) A file having parallel lines of teeth running diagonally across its face in one direction only, at an angle of 65 degrees as distinguished from a double-cut file which has a double series of teeth crossing each other at an oblique angle.

sin′gle float (*Aero.*) A single central float fitted under a seaplane and usually requiring two stabilizing floats to give adequate stability and complete the float system.

sin′gle phase (*Elec.*) A single, independent a.c. circuit or winding.

sin′gle–phase al′ter-nat′ing cur′rent (*Elec.*) When the output from an alternating-current generator is obtainable from a coil or coils in series, the current is single phase. In one revolution of the generator the current will evidence one complete set of values.

sin′gle–phase in-duc′tion mo′tor (*Elec.*) An alternating-current motor in which the field magnetism sets up an opposing field in the armature windings, causing rotation. Since the current in the armature is set up by induction, no commutator or brushes are required.

sin′gle–plate clutch (*Auto.*) A popular clutch consisting of three plates, usually two driving plates and one driven plate. So called because of the single driven plate.

sin′gle–pole switch (*Elec.*) A switch that opens and closes only one side of a circuit.

sin′gle riv′et-ing (*Engin.*) Refers to a riveted joint made with only one row of rivets.

sin′gle–thick cov′er (*Papermkg.*) A cover paper of medium thickness made without pasting.

sin′gle–thread screw (*M a c h.*) A screw having a single helix or thread. Its pitch and lead are equal.

sink′age (*P r i n t.*) The blank space which occurs at the beginning of a chapter in a book.

sink′ing (*Paint and Lacquer*) When the color sinks in, resulting in flat or semigloss spots, it is due to a porous undercoating.

sink′ing speed (*Aero.*) The rate at which an aircraft loses altitude, especially the rate at which a heavier than air aircraft descends in a glide in still air under given conditions of equilibrium.

sink mark (*Plast.*) Dimplelike depression in the surface of a molded piece indicating that it has retracted from the mold. The mark has well-rounded edges and shows a surface film.

si′phon (*Mech. Engin.*) A bent tube or other device for drawing off liquids by making use of atmospheric pressure.

si′sal fi′ber (sī′săl) The hemplike fiber of several Mexican and Central American plants, next to manila hemp in strength and durability.

site (*Arch.*) The location of a building or the place on which a building is to be erected.

size (*Papermkg.*) (1) Water-repellent material used in papermaking stuff such as resin size, or applied to the surface of a weblike gelatin. (2) Customary dimensions of typical papers. Flat writings and bond papers are:

Cap	14 x 17	Double Folio	22 x 34
Crown	15 x 19	Double Cap	17 x 28
Demy	16 x 21	Royal	19 x 24
Folio	17 x 22		

The following is a less used list of sizes referring to ledger papers:

Crown	15 x 19	Double Demy,	
Super Royal	20 x 28	long	16 x 42
Medium	18 x 23	Double Demy,	
Imperial	23 x 31	broad	21 x 32
Double Royal	24 x 38	Double Medium,	
Elephant	23 x 28	broad	23 x 36
Columbier	23 x 34	Double Medium,	
Atlas	26 x 34	long	18 x 46
Antiquarium	31 x 53	Double	
Emperor	48 x 72	Elephant	27 x 40

The following are common book paper sizes:
24 x 36   28 x 42   32 x 44   35 x 45
25 x 38   30½ x 41   34 x 44   38 x 50

size con-trol' (*Tel.*) Controls on a television receiver for increasing or decreasing the picture size, both horizontally and vertically.

sized and su'per-cal'en-dered (*Print.*) Paper made with the sizing mixed in with the other ingredients. It is surfaced by steaming and polishing. Abbreviation S. & S.C.A.

siz'ing (*Papermkg.*) A term having reference to those qualities of paper by virtue of which it resists water or ink. Addition of resin to the beater stuff is one way of producing it. (*Plast.*) One of the uses of plastic resins. The closing of surface pores with resin.

skel'e-ton-ize (*Print.*) To remove the color sections of a form and lock the same to register.

skel'e-ton-iz'ing (*Print.*) The arrangement of the various parts of a job in such a manner as to permit its being printed in different colors.

skelp (*Metal.*) Steel or iron plate from which pipe or tubing is made.

sketch. A suggestive presentation, either graphic or literary.

sketched. Outlined; rough drafted, a slight preliminary draft; generally used to refer to freehand drawing.

skew (skū) (*Mech.*) Oblique; not at a right angle. Work is said to be askew when it is out of square.

skew'back (*Arch.*) The surface at each end of an arch upon which the first bricks are laid, and from which an arch springs.

skew'back saw. A handsaw whose back is curved in order to lighten its weight without lessening its stiffness.

skew chis'el (*Wood Patmkg.*) A chisel with a straight cutting edge made at an angle other than a right angle with the center line of the tool; used in turning.

skew'er (*Uphol.*) Small wire bent into a ring at one end and sharpened at the other, used to fasten covering temporarily while being worked.

skew gear (*Gear.*) Gears with spiral teeth. Skew bevel gears are now largely used on the rear axles of automobiles; they increase strength and promote smooth and quiet action.

skew nail'ing (*Carp.*) The driving of nails obliquely.

skid (*Aero.*) A runner which is a member of the landing gear and which acts as an aid to the aircraft in taxiing or landing. (*Auto.*) Small piece of metal used as an aid in sliding parts into place. (*Papermkg.* and *Print.*) A platform with runners on which about 3000 lb. of paper can be packed and secured for shipping.

skid fin (*Aero.*) A fore-and-aft vertical keel surface usually placed above the upper wing for the purpose of increasing lateral stability.

skid′ding (*A e r o.*) Slipping sidewise when turning; caused by insufficient bank; opposite to side-slipping.

skim′mer (*Fdry.*) A piece of iron used to hold back dirt on the surface of molten metal to prevent it from entering the mold.

skim′ming (*Fdry.*) Holding back the dross or dirt on molten metal when pouring.

skin (*Leather.*) The dressed or undressed hide of an animal, as a whole or in part. (*Shopwk.*) A term applied to the thin film of hard metal on the surface of castings.

skin–dried mold (*Fdry.*) A green sand mold made with a facing an inch or more thick composed of molding sand and some binding material. By thoroughly drying this facing before pouring the mold danger of formation of steam is eliminated.

skin′ning (*E l e c.*) Removing insulation from electrical conductors before making splices or connections.

skin′tled brick′work (*Masonry*) An irregular arrangement of bricks with respect to the normal face of the wall, the bricks being set in and out to produce an uneven effect; also the rough effect caused by mortar squeezed out of the joints.

skirt (*F u r n.*) The horizontal band which connects the legs of a chair beneath the seat, or the legs of a table beneath the top, sometimes called the "apron."

skirt′ing (*Arch.*) The finishing board which covers the plastered wall where it meets the floor. Same as baseboard.

skiv′er (skīv′ēr)(*Bookbndg.*)(1) Split leather used in bookbinding. (2) One who skives, or the knife or machine with which it is done.

skiv′er leath′er (*Leather.*) A thin, split leather used extensively for lining such articles as card cases, coin purses, billfolds, etc.; also for bookbinding.

sky′light′ (*Arch.*) A glassed area in a ceiling or roof to provide for light.

sky′scrap′er (*Masonry*) A term applied to high and lofty buildings of many stories, as the modern office building.

sky writ′ing (*A e r o.*) Directing the course of flight of an aircraft in such a manner, while a trail of smoke is being emitted, that the trail forms letters or symbols.

slab. (1) A thin piece of stone, marble, concrete, or the like, having a flat surface. (2) The outside pieces cut from a log when sawing it into boards. (3) (*Metal.*) A thick rectangular piece of steel for rolling into plates.

slab′bing cut′ter (*M a c h.*) A wide-faced, milling cutter with nicked teeth to permit an easier cut than would be possible with a plain-toothed cutter.

slack (*Mech.*) Loose; that looseness of parts which must be removed before applied power becomes effective.

slag (*Fdry.*) Impurities fluxed from the cupola in foundry work. (*Engin.*) The fused refuse separated in the reduction of ores, used in concrete work and in road construction.

slag ce-ment′. Cement made with blast-furnace slag.

slag hole (*Fdry.*) A hole 2 or 3 in. in diameter placed opposite the tap hole in a cupola for the drawing off of slag.

slag wool. This material somewhat resembling asbestos is made by blowing a jet of steam through fluid slag. It is nonconducting and noncombustible. Used for insulating. (*Engin.*) Used as a packing material. It is produced from molten slag just out of the iron blast furnace.

slam′ming stile (*Carp.*) The vertical strip against which a door abuts when closed, and into which the bolt of the lock engages.

slash′ing (*Textile*) The dressing or sizing of yarns in order to prevent them rubbing rough in the weaving process. (*Wood*) The tops, branches, and trimmings which remain after a logging operation.

slat (*Aero.*) A movable auxiliary airfoil, attached to the leading edge of a wing, which, when closed, falls within the original contour of the main wing and which, when opened, forms a slot. (*Furn.*) A thin piece of wood used in the seat or back of a chair.

sledge. A long-handled heavy hammer used with both hands.

sleek′er (*Mold.*) A molder's tool of a variety of shapes, used for smoothing rough spots and for removing loose sand from the mold. Also called slicker.

sleep′er (*Arch.*) Heavy beam or joist.

sleeve (*Mech.*) A hollow tube or cylinder which surrounds a rod or shaft.

sleeve nut (*Engin.*) A long adjusting nut with right- and left-hand threads used to connect two rods.

sleeve valve mo′tor (*Auto.*) A motor in which the valve mechanism consists of sleeves and pistons. The valve strokes are controlled by means of eccentric rods worked from an eccentric shaft.

slice or slice bar (*Engin.*) A firing tool, used for breaking up and separating the clinkers on a furnace grate.

slic′ing cut (*Mech.*) A cut taken with a sliding or slicing motion for the purpose of removing thin pieces.

slick′ing (*Fdry.*) Smoothing the surface of foundry molds.

slide. A glass plate used in a projecting lantern for throwing a picture on a screen.

slide cal′iper (*Mach.*) A pocket caliper consisting of a graduated bar which slides in a retaining piece.

slide rest (*Mach.*) On a lathe, the parts above the saddle which support the compound rest.

slide rule (*Engin.*) A rule provided with logarithmic numbers arranged on a sliding scale.

slide valve (*Engin.*) A valve operating with a sliding motion, so adjusted that the cylinder ports are opened and closed in proper relation to the piston stroke.

slid′ing fit (*Mech.*) A running fit. A fitting together of moving parts so snugly that there is no looseness, yet not so tightly as to interfere with free motion.

slip (*Ceram.*) Clay reduced to a fluid state by addition of water. (*Elec.*) The difference in speed between a rotating magnetic field and a rotor rotating in the field.

slip bush′ing (*Mach.*) A jig bushing which is easily removed in order to permit the use of a different size bushing in the same position.

slip fu'el tank (*Aero.*) A fuel tank so attached to either airship or airplane that, in case of emergency, the tank and contents may be dropped.

slip func'tion (*Aero.*) The ratio of the speed of advance through the undisturbed air to the product of the propeller diameter and the number of revolutions per unit time, i.e., V/nD.

slip jack'et (*Fdry.*) A box, open top and bottom, placed over a mold after removal of the snap flask.

Slip-Joint Pliers

slip–joint pli'ers. Pliers which permit adjustment to a greater range of opening by a slipping motion of the two halves about the pin or rivet which connects them.

slip'ping clutch (*Auto.*) A clutch which, from wear or glazing or improper pedal adjustment, is not able to transmit full engine power due to a slipping between the pressure plate and the driven plate.

slip plane (*Plast.*) A plane within transparent plastic material due to poor welding and shrinkage on cooling. It is visible in reflected light.

slip rings (*Elec.*) The means by which the current is conducted to a revolving electrical circuit.

slips (*Bookbndg.*) The ends of the cord or tape on which a book is sewed.

slip'–sheet'ing (*Print.*) The placing of sheets of rough paper between printed sheets, so that the printed face of any sheet will not smudge the lower side of the next sheet above it.

slip sill (*B l d g.*) A simple slab of stone of the required window width, set in the walls between jambs of the masonry opening. Easier to set than "lug sill."

slip speed (su'per-charg'er) (*Aero.*) The supercharger speed necessary to maintain a given pressure difference between intake and discharge when there is no air delivery.

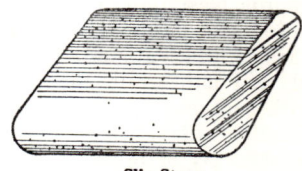

Slip Stone

slip stone (*Wood Turn. and Wood Patmkg.*) A small wedge-shaped oilstone with rounded edges. It is held in the hand and used for whetting gouges.

slip stream (*Aero.*) The stream of air driven astern by the propeller.

slip wash'er (*Mach.*) Same as open washer.

slit'ter (*Print.*) A rotary cutting device used on cylinder presses to deliver finished sheets in sections. It is also used on folding machines.

slit'ting cut'ter (*Sheet-Met. Wk.*) Thin rotary cutters, intended for cutting off, or for slitting purposes.

slit'ting saw for met'al (*Mach.*) Thin milling cutters used for splitting bushings, etc.

slit'ting shears (*Sheet-Met. Wk.*) Usually a sturdy shear designed to operate by short cuts on rather heavy sheets or for cutting off rods or bars. A slitting shear may also have rotary cutters and be used for dividing a sheet into a number of strips, e.g., the dividing of a sheet of tin into a number of pieces each of a width suitable for the height of a tin can.

slot (*Aero.*) The nozzle-shaped passage through a wing whose primary object is to improve the flow conditions at high angles of attack. It is usually near the leading edge and formed by a main and an auxiliary airfoil or slat. (*Wood Patmkg.*) A long, narrow groove, particularly one cut to receive some corresponding part of a mechanism.

slot screw′ing. A method of fixing whereby the screwheads are not seen.

slot′ted ai′le-ron (ā′lê-rŏn) (*Aero.*) An aileron having a nose and axis arrangement somewhat similar to a Frise aileron but having a smooth air passage between the nose portion of the aileron and the wing for the purpose of maintaining a smooth air flow over the upper surface of the aileron when its trailing edge is deflected downward.

slot′ting ma-chine′ (*Mach.*) A machine used for shaping metals and cutting mortises, the arm which carries the cutters moving in a vertical direction.

slow dry′ing (*Paint and Lacquer*) When a finishing material does not set up or dry hard within the drying time specified by the maker, it indicates that either the surface was not clean and dry, the wrong type of reducer was employed, or the drying conditions were not normal.

slow sand fil′ter (*E n g i n.*) A filter for the purification of water. It is different in construction, and is built in larger units than a rapid filter.

Sloyd knife (*Woodwk.*) Knife used in the Swedish Sloyd systems of woodwork; the forerunner of the American manual training.

sludge. Muddy deposit such as accumulates in a boiler. Also dirty oily deposit as in a crankcase.

slug (*Print.*) (1) A type-high bar of metal with type cast on it by the linotype. (2) Strip of metal less than type high, used as spacing material between lines of type.

slug cast′ing ma-chine′ (*Print.*) (See LINOTYPE; also LUDLOW.)

slur (*Print.*) A blur, blemish, or smear.

slush′ing oil. Used to coat metals, machine parts, etc., to prevent corrosion. It usually is nondrying oil or grease which coats the metal very well but is easily removed when desired.

slush mold′ing (*Plast.*) A method of casting thermoplastic resin into a hot mold, a skin solidifying against the mold, the remaining resin being poured out. The skin is peeled out when the mold cools.

small caps (*Print.*) Capital letters in an assortment of book type, of a smaller size than regular capitals.

small pi′ca (pī′kȧ) (*Print.*) A type size equivalent to 11 point.

smalt (*Paint.*) A vitreous sand furnished in various screenings and colors for painters' and signwriters' use. It produces a brilliant and sparkling decorative effect. Also used by painters for the protection of a painted surface subjected to wind and weather.

smash′ing (*Print. and Bookbndg.*) Compressing signatures to make them lay flat.

smelt′ing (*Metal.*) The obtaining of

metal from the ore by means of heat and fluxing agents.

smok′ing (*Ceram.*) The first stage of firing in which the moisture is removed from green ware.

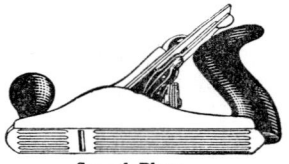
Smooth Plane

smooth′ing plane (*Woodwk.*) A small plane usually not over 9 in. long with an iron width varying from 1¾ in. to 2¼ in.

smooth′ing trow′el. Used by plasterers and cement workers for finishing surfaces.

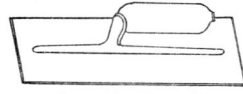
Smoothing Trowel

snake′wood. *Piratinera guianensis.* A heavy, hardwood timber of northern South America. Wood often colored like snakeskins.

snap flask (*Fdry.*) A flask provided with hinges and catches to permit its removal after the mold is made.

snap gauge. A nonadjustable gauge for testing internal and external sizes.

snap hook. A self-closing hook operated by a spring; used on harnesses and on dog leashes.

Snap Gauge

snap′ping lines (*S h o p w k.*) Lines transferred to a floor or other surface by means of a chalked cord which is held taut, raised at some place along its length, and allowed to snap down. A common method used by workmen.

snap rings (*Auto.*) Hardened metal rings (broken circles) fixed in recessed parts to act as retainers.

snap roll (*Aero.*) A roll executed by a quick movement of the controls, in which the motion is maintained by auto-rotational couples on the wings.

snap switch (*E l e c.*) The common type of switch which opens or closes electrical contacts with a quick movement when the knob or thumb piece is turned in a clockwise direction.

snarl′ing i′ron (*A r t M e t.*) A tool used in forming hollow objects, such as vases. It is gripped in a vise, and is used to back up the work while it is being hammered.

snips (*Sheet-Met. Wk.*) Another name for sheet-metal workers' hand shears.

snow load (*Engin.*) The load caused by accumulated snow on a roof, provision for which is made when a roof is designed.

snub′ber (*Auto.*) A mechanical device consisting essentially of a drum, spring, and friction band. Connection is made between axle and frame. The purpose is to slow the recoil of the spring and reduce jolting.

snug fit (*M e c h.*) In machine work, the closest fit that can be assembled by hand.

soak′ing (*Metal.*) Holding steel at a fixed heat until a complete and uniform penetration is obtained.

soar (*A e r o.*) To perform sustained free flight without self-propulsion; it is called "up-current soaring" if performed in ascending air; "dynamic soaring" in other cases.

sock′et (*Elec.*) The receptacle into which the threaded portion of an incandescent lamp or plug is fitted. A term which often means, in electrical practice, a portable receptacle.

Socket Chisel

sock′et chis′el (*W o o d w k g.*) The strongest kind of woodworker's chisel. The upper end of the shank terminates in a socket into which the handle is driven.

sock′et-ing (*Furn.*) A method of joining by means of wedging one piece of wood into the cavity of another.

sock′et wrench (*Auto. Mech.*) Consists of a socket which fits over and completely encircles the nut or bolthead, a handle or lever, with or without ratchet, and sometimes an extension to permit working in places not easily accessible.

so′cle (sŏk′'l) (*A r c h.*) A projecting member at the foot of a wall or pier, or beneath the base of a column.

so′da ash (*Chem.*) (Na_2CO_3) Practically pure sodium carbonate. It is much used for cleansing purposes and in solution as a lubricant for grinding and cutting and as a rust preventive.

so′da or so′di-um car′bon-ate (*Chem.*) Soda is a very general term applied to various commercial compounds used in the household and in the industries. The sodas of commerce are manufactured from salt. Sodium carbonate is used in the manufacture of glass and as a cleansing agent.

so′da pulp (*Papermkg.*) A wood pulp prepared by the soda process used for blotters, bulk book papers, etc.

so′da-wa′ter mix′ture (*Mach.*) A solution of sal soda and water to which soft soap or lard oil is added to increase lubricating value. Used as a coolant and lubricant in turning and milling work.

so′di-um chlo′ride (*Chem.*) NaCl. Ordinary table salt or rock salt.

SOF (*Tel.*) Sound on film.

sof′fit (*Arch.*) The underside of an arch, staircase, cornice, or the like.

soft (*Ceram.*) Glazes or clays which are fusible at low temperatures.

soft an-nealed′ (*Metal.*) Completely annealed.

soft brass (*Metal.*) Brass which has been annealed after drawing and rolling; used where ductility is essential.

soft i′ron (*Metal.*) Iron which can be worked with ordinary cutting tools or which can be readily abraded with files. It is gray in color, as distinguished from the harder cast iron which is lighter in color.

soft sol′der. Solder such as is used for tin plate and other metal sheets. The composition varies from "half and half"; half lead and half tin to 90 parts tin and 10 of lead. A very small percentage of antimony is often added.

soft steel (*Engin.*) A general term applied to steels of low carbon content which do not temper. Mild steel.

soft wa′ter. Water free from carbonate and sulphate of lime.

soft′wood′. Some of the group of trees which have leaves in the form of needles or scales. The term does not refer to the softness of the wood.

soil pipe (*Plumb.*) Term generally applied to cast-iron pipe in 5-ft.

lengths used for house drainage.
sol (sŏl) (*Plast.*) Solution or suspension of colloid in a liquid.
so'lar en'gine (*Mech. Engin.*) Engine operated by heat generated by the sun shining on large areas of glass; not extensively used.
so-lar'i-um (*Arch.*) A glassed-in sunroom.
sol'der (sŏ'dẽr) (*Metal.*) An alloy used for joining metals together under heat. Solder is usually an alloy of equal parts of lead and tin. Melting point about 188 deg. C., 370.4° F.
sol'der-ing (*Mech.*) The uniting under proper heat, of pieces of metal by means of a dissimilar metal or alloy.

Soldering Copper

sol'der-ing cop'per (*Mach.*) A tool, also called soldering iron, used for applying heat to melt the solder and heat up the metals that are to be joined by soldering.

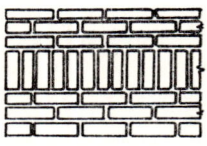

Soldier Course

sol'dier course (*Masonry*) A course in which the bricks stand on end.
sole (*Arch.*) A foot piece or rest such as would be laid on top of a subfloor to carry studding.
so'le-noid (*Elec.*) An electromagnetic helix. A system of equal circular currents flowing in uniform direction about a single straight or curved axis.

so'le-noid re-lay' (*Auto. Elec.*) The switch used to complete the starting-motor circuit, operated by a push button on the dash.
sole plate (*Engin.*) A foundation plate to which a piece of machinery is bolted.
sol'id bear'ing (*Mach.*) A one-piece rigid bearing. Its use is limited as it must be slipped over the end of the shaft which it is to support. When solid bearings are pressed into the parts to which they are applied they are called bushings.
sol'id fric'tion (*Mech.*) That friction which results when the surface of one solid body is moved across the surface of another solid body.
so-lid'i-ty (*Aero.*) The ratio of the total blade area of a rotor to the area of the disk swept by the blades.
sol'id mat'ter (*Print.*) Type matter without leads or slugs between the lines.
so'lo (*Aero.*) Flight, when the operator of an airplane is unaccompanied or when the operation of the airplane is under the operators' complete command.
sol'u-ble. Capable of being dissolved in a fluid.
sol'ute (*Chem.*) The material which passes into solution when mixed with a solvent. (See SOLUTION.)
so-lu'tion (*Chem.*) A clear mixture of two or more substances in which neither separates on standing.
sol'vent (*Chem.*) A substance used to dissolve another substance, as the water in a solution of salt in water.
soot. Finely divided carbon.
sorts (*Print.*) Characters or type considered as separate elements in a font.

sound'ing bal-loon' (*Aero.*) A small balloon used to send up a meteorograph.

sound knot (*Wood*) One which is solid across its face and is as hard as the wood surrounding it. It may be black or red, and must be so fixed that it will retain its position.

sound-rang'ing al-tim'e-ter (*Aero.*) An altimeter, the indications of which depend on the measurement of the time required for a sound wave to travel from the aircraft to the earth and back.

south'ern moss (*Uphol.*) Also known as Louisiana moss and Spanish moss. It grows on trees, hanging in long festoons, and derives its sustenance from the air. It is extensively used by upholsterers.

south'ern pine (*Wood*) Long-leaf, yellow pine used principally in heavy construction work. Is often spoken of as southern pine although there are a number of varieties native to the southern states.

spac'es (*Print.*) Type bodies less than type high which are subdivisions of the em quad, used for spacing between words and for justification of lines.

space wash'er (*Mach.*) A washer used for spacing rather than to provide bearing for a nut.

spac'ing (*Print.*) The arrangement of words, lines, and other material to give the most pleasing effect.

spa'cious. Extending far and wide; roomy.

spall (spôl) (*Masonry*) Bad or broken brick or chips of stone.

span (*Aero.*) The maximum distance, measured parallel to the lateral axis, from tip to tip of an airfoil, of an airplane wing inclusive of ailerons, or of a stabilizer inclusive of the elevator. (*Arch.*) The distance between abutments or supports. The horizontal spread of a roof between exterior walls.

span'drel (*Arch.*) (1) The irregular triangular space between an arch and the beam above the same, or the space between the shoulders of two adjoining arches. (2) The angle of rise of a stairway.

span load'ing (*Aero.*) The ratio of the weight of an airplane to its equivalent monoplane span.

span'ner. A type of wrench used for the tightening up of nuts. Especially, a flat wrench with projecting pins which are inserted in holes drilled in round nuts or threaded collars.

spare (*Shopwk.*) Extra, as a spare part; some part held in reserve.

spark (*Auto. Mech.*) A discharge of hot electrical energy in air; used to produce combustion of fuel gas in engine cylinders.

spark coil (*Elec.*) A spark coil is used to produce a spark of high intensity. It may be of the make-and-break type of one winding on an iron core, the spark occurring as the break contacts; or of the jump type, two separate windings, the spark jumping across two stationary points as in a spark plug.

spark'ing at brush'es (*Elec.*) Small sparks or flashes between commutator and brush due to poor contact, improper position of brush, irregular surface, dust on commutator, etc.

Spark plug (*Auto.*) A device for conducting the high-tension current to the combustion space where the charge is fired by the spark as it jumps the gap of the plug.

spark-plug e-lec'trodes (*Auto.*) The metal points between which the electric spark jumps. Also the metal conductor which passes through the center of the spark-plug insulator.

spat'u-la. A knifelike instrument with flexible blade used for mixing small quantities of chemicals, paints, etc.

spe'cial. Designed for a particular purpose.

spec'i-fi-ca'tion. A detailed statement of particulars.

spe-cif'ic grav'i-ty (*Phys.*) The density of weight of a substance; estimated relatively to that of water for solids and liquids, and air for gases.

spe-cif'ic heat. The relative amount of heat required to raise the temperature of a unit mass of different substances one degree compared with the amount of heat required to raise the temperature of the same weight of water one degree.

spec'i-fy. To designate so as to distinguish from other things.

spec'i-men bar (*Engin.*) A length of bar of any material, especially prepared for testing in a testing machine.

spec'tro-pho-tom'e-ter. A color-measuring device.

spec'tro-scope (*Chem.*) An instrument for forming and studying spectra. Spectra produced by vaporized substances are useful in the study of their composition.

spec'trum (*Phys.*) The band of color which results when sunlight is broken up into its component parts, producing the seven colors of the rainbow.

spec'u-lum met'al (*Metal.*) A hard brittle alloy of two parts copper and one part tin. It takes and retains a high polish and is therefore much used for reflectors.

speed (*Phys.*) The rate at which a body travels.

speed con-trol' (*Tel.*) Controls on a television receiver, sometimes called the hold controls, which can be regulated to hold the received picture in horizontal and vertical synchronization.

speed-in'di-cat'ing ven-tu'ri (*Aero.*) A venturi tube may be combined with a pitot tube or with a tube giving static pressure to form a pressure nozzle which may be used to determine the indicated speed of an aircraft through the air. The pressure difference is measured by a suitable gauge.

speed in'di-ca'tor (*Engin.*) A term applied to any of the many devices for recording speed, as a speedometer on an automobile. A small mechanism for recording the r.p.m. of shafts; also the elaborate tachometer which makes an autographic diagram.

speed lathe (*Mach.*) A metalworker's lathe, not equipped with mechanical feed.

speed-om'e-ter (*Auto.*) An instrument for recording distance traveled and the rate of speed in miles per hour. Usually mounted in such a position as to be clearly visible by the car operator.

spel'ter (*Metal.*) The commercial name for zinc ingots; also an alloy of zinc and copper in equal parts.

sphal′er-ite (sfăl′ēr-īt) (*Mineral.*) The most important ore of zinc.

sphere (*Geom.*) A solid having every part of its surface equally distant from its center. Area = diameter squared x 3.1416. Volume = diameter cubed x 0.5236.

sphe′roi-diz-ing (sfē′roi-dīz-ĭng) Alloys with iron base are given an extended heating at a temperature a little less than the critical temperature range and then slowly cooled.

spi′der gears (*Auto.*) The two, three, or four gears (as the case may be) fitted free running on the spider, by means of which the differential action is obtained in the rear axle.

spie′gel-ei′sen (spē′gĕl-ī′zĕn) (*Chem.*) A hard, white cast iron containing a high percentage of carbon and of manganese. When the percentage of manganese exceeds 15 to 20 per cent, it is known as ferromanganese.

spig′ot (*Plumb.*) The end of a pipe which fits into a bell. Also a word used synonymously with faucet.

spike (*Bldg.*) A large nail, but thicker in proportion.

spike knot (*Woodwk.*) A knot sawed lengthwise.

spile (*Engin.*) A large timber driven into the ground, used as a foundation; a pile.

spills (*Metal.*) Cracks or seams which occur in iron bars of inferior quality, due to careless rolling.

spin (*Aero.*) A maneuver in which an airplane descends along a helical path of large pitch and small radius while flying at a mean angle of attack greater than the angle of attack at maximum lift.

spin′dle (*Furn.*) A slender turned rod tapering toward each end, as in the back of a chair. (*Mach.*) A rotating rod or arbor, either hollow or solid.

spin′et (*Furn.*) A keyed musical instrument in use from the sixteenth to the eighteenth century.

spin′ner (*Aero.*) A fairing of approximately conical or paraboloidal form which is fitted coaxially with the propeller boss and revolves with the propeller.

spin′ner-et (*Plast.*) A metal extrusion die with many minute holes for plastic or glass filament extrusion.

spin′ning (*Sheet-Met. Wk.*) The forming of circular articles in thin sheet metal by pressure applied while it is being rotated in a lathe.

spin′ning lathe (*Sheet-Met. Wk.*) A lathe used for spinning operations on sheet-metal work.

spi′ral. A curve formed by a fixed point moving about a center, and continually increasing the distance from it. (*Aero.*) A maneuver in which an airplane descends in a helix of small pitch and large radius, the angle of attack being within the normal range of flight angles.

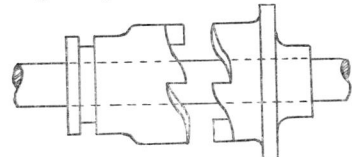

Spiral Coupling

spi′ral coup′ling (*Mach.*) A type of jaw coupling which remains engaged only when rotating in one direction.

spi′ral gear (*Gear.*) Sometimes called "screw gear." One in which a tooth constitutes a part of a helix. (See HELICAL GEAR.)

spi'ral in'sta·bil'i·ty (*Aero.*) A type of instability inherent in certain airplanes which becomes evident when the airplane, as a result of a yaw, assumes too great a bank and sideslips; the bank continues to increase and the radius of the turn to decrease.

spi'ral spring (*Mach.*) A spring of the type of clock or watch springs.

spire (*Arch.*) A tapering tower; a steeple.

spir'it lev'el (*Bldg.*) An instrument for testing the horizontal and vertical accuracy of work. It consists of a glass tube or bulb nearly full of spirit and enclosed in a wood or metal case. When the bubble in the tube is in a central position, it indicates the accuracy of the work being tested.

spir'it var'nish (*Wood Fin.*) One which dries through evaporation and contains volatile solvents such as turpentine and alcohol.

splash lu'bri·ca'tion (*Auto. and Mach.*) A method of lubrication accomplished without the aid of a pump, by which a moving part passing through a reservoir of oil is itself lubricated and at the same time throws oil to other parts needing lubrication.

splat (*Furn.*) A broad, flat, upright member in the middle of a chair back.

splay (*Arch.*) To make with a bevel, to spread out, to broaden; a slanted or beveled surface.

splice (*Elec.*) The joining of electrical conductors by twisting or by a separate splicing device.

splic'ing (*Print.*) The process of joining two or more leads or slugs, for the purpose of obtaining a length equal to their total.

splic'ing com·pound' (*Elec.*) A rubber tape required as the first insulating covering over a splice.

spline (*Draw.*) A flexible rod or rule used by draftsmen in drawing curved lines. (*Mach.*) An arbor fitted with a key or keyway.

spline mi'ter (*Woodwk.*) A miter joint strengthened by a feather (thin strip of wood) inserted in matching grooves (splines) cut on the joining faces.

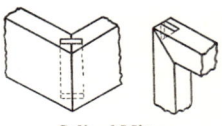

Splined Miter

spline shaft (*Auto.*) A shaft with a series of lengthwise grooves a portion of its length to make a sliding engagement with corresponding internal divisions permitting a positive rotation of parts but with a varying length of shaft; e.g., drive shaft of an automobile.

split bush'ing (*Auto.*) Any bushing divided lengthwise into two halves, such as a main bearing, or the big end connecting-rod bearing.

split cot'ter pin (*Mech.*) A pin made of wire whose section is semicircular, bent around until the flat surfaces meet. It is inserted in a hole near the end of a shaft or bolt to prevent the nut from backing off.

split field (*Elec.*) (Auto generator) A 2-pole field winding in which one field is connected to a third brush, the other to the main brush. In this type of generator the current-limiting features of the third brush are retained.

split flap (*Aero.*) A hinged plate forming the rear upper or lower portion of an airfoil.

split nut (*Mach.*) A nut split lengthwise to permit sliding over a screw for quick movement. Final adjustment is made by turning in the usual manner. Often used on spring calipers.

split phase (*Elec.*) Causing currents to differ in phase in several circuits connected to the same single-phase e.m.f.

split-phase mo′tor (*Elec.*) A single-phase motor which is made self-starting by causing the current to lead or lag in one of its windings with respect to the other winding.

split pul′ley (*Mach.*) A pulley made in halves and bolted together.

split ring (*Mach.*) A piston ring.

split-ring mold (*Plast.*) A mold in which a split cavity block is assembled in a chase to permit the forming of undercuts in a molded piece. These parts are ejected from the mold and then separated from the piece.

split S (*Aero.*) A maneuver consisting of a half snap roll followed by a pullout to normal flight, thus obtaining a 180-deg. change in direction accompanied by a loss of altitude.

split-skirt pis′ton (*Auto.*) A piston with longitudinal slit in the side wall to allow for expansion w i t h o u t binding.

split′ting (*Paint and Lacquer*) Too much

Piston Split-Skirt

or too hard sanding fractures the old lacquer film, and when the solvents of the new lacquer penetrate into the old lacquer, these sanding scratches are opened up, resulting in what is generally termed as splitting.

spoil′er (*Aero.*) A small plate arranged to project above the upper surface of a wing to disturb the smooth air flow, with consequent loss of lift and increase of drag (interceptor).

spoke (*Mech.*) One of the arms of a wheel connecting the hub with the rim.

spoke′shave′ (*Woodwkg.*) A kind of double-handled plane for dressing curved woodwork.

Spokeshave

spon′gi-ness (*Fdry.*) Sponginess in a casting is due to the formation of gas bubbles in the iron at the instant of solidification.

spong′i-ness of cast′ing (*F d r y.*) Caused by gas bubbles forming in the casting at the time of solidification. Likely to occur in castings in which some parts are very thin and others very thick.

spon′son (*A e r o.*) A protuberance from a seaplane hull designed to increase the beam or give lateral stability at rest.

spon-ta′ne-ous com-bus′tion. The ignition or combustion of a substance by heat generated within itself.

spoon bit. A boring bit with a crescent-shaped section with sharp edges. Used for drilling holes in paper, cardboard, etc.

spoon stake (*Art Met.*) A small stake used in forming spoons, ladles, etc., by hand.

sport road′ster (*A u t o.*) Similar to roadster except rear deck is provided with a rumble seat instead of luggage space.

spot (*Tel.*) The light produced by the beam of electrons on the fluorescent screen of the cathode-ray picture tube as the beam scans a line or an image from left to right.

spot face (*Mach.*) To finish a round spot on a surface, usually around a drilled hole, to give a good bearing for a screw or bolt head.

spot'ting the cen'ter (*Mach.*) Spotting work with a center punch, then starting a hole with a much smaller drill than the one with which the hole is to be finished.

spot'ting tool (*M a c h.*) Also called "centering and facing tool." Used to "spot" a center and to face the end of stock.

spot'ting up (*Print.*) The marking out and patching of a make-ready sheet.

spot weld'ing. A resistance-welding process wherein coalescence is produced by the heat obtained from resistance to the flow of electric current through the work parts held together under pressure by electrodes. The size and shape of the individually formed welds are limited primarily by the size and contour of the electrodes.

spout (*Fdry.*) The projecting trough through which metal flows from the cupola to the ladle.

spray'ing li'quid (*Auto. Trade*) A general term applied to those liquids or finishes that can be atomized readily, including oils, cleansing liquids, paints, and other finishes.

spread (*Plast.*) Amount of adhesive or of plastic, in pounds per square feet, required for area coverage.

sprig (*Woodwkg.*) A small, headless wire nail or brad.

spring bal'ance. A weighing device consisting of a calibrated tension spring contained in a casing. As the spring is extended, weight is indicated by a pointer on a graduated scale.

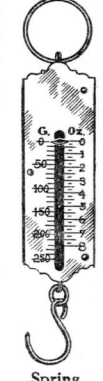

Spring Balance

spring chuck or spring col'let (*Mach.*) A type of chuck used on screw machines. It consists of a sleeve slotted through a portion of its length, and is closed on the work by being drawn or pressed into a conical cap into which it fits. When released, it springs open sufficiently to free the stock.

spring clip (*Auto.*) A U-shaped bolt used for securing the spring to the axle. Two clips are used for clamping each spring. Spring Crp

spring cot'ter (*Mech.*) Same as split cotter.

spring'er (*A r c h.*) The stone from which an arch springs.

spring hang'ers (*Auto.*) Those brackets or fixtures attached to an automobile frame to which the springs are connected.

spring hinge (*Bldg.*) A hinge with a spring built into it. Used for self-closing of screen doors, etc.

spring leaf (*Mech.*) One of the flat members of a built-up spring as used on automobiles, buses and trucks.

spring perch or pad (*Auto.*) One of the flat surfaces on the axles to which the springs are attached.

spring twine (*Uphol.*) Used for tying down the heavy upholstery springs in seats. It is very essential that twine of good quality be used. Spring twine is sold in one-pound balls.

sprin′kler sys′tem (*Arch.*) An arrangement of overhead piping equipped with sprinkler heads or nozzles which automatically release sprays of water in case of fire.

sprock′et (*Mach.*) A toothlike projection on a wheel shaped so as to engage with the links of a chain.

spruce (*Wood*) *Picea*. An evergreen which grows abundantly throughout the eastern states. An inexpensive wood used extensively in the building trades.

sprue (*Fdry.*) The opening or channel through which molten metal may enter the "gate" and into the mold. Also the solidified iron which filled that opening or channel.

sprung mold′ing (*Carp.*) A curved molding; also a thin molded piece of wood used for cornices, and attached to blocks or brackets fixed to the cornice frame.

spur (*Carp.*) A sharp-pointed tool used for cutting various lengths of rotary veneer as it is cut from a log of longer length.

spur cen′ter (*Wood Turn.*) The center used in the headstock of a wood-turning lathe.

Spur Center

spur wheel (*Gear.*) A gear wheel whose teeth are on the outer diameter and at right angles with the sides of the wheel.

spy (*Pot.*) The small hole, kept plugged, through which tests and cones are observed.

squab (*Furn.*) A loose seat resembling a cushion.

square (*Math.*) Multiplying a number by itself. To be at right angles. A plane figure of four sides, all sides are equal and opposite sides are parallel; angles are right angles and their sum is 360 deg. (*Mech.*) An instrument having at least one right angle and two or more straight edges, used to lay out or test square work.

square meas′ure.

```
144   square inches  = 1 square foot (sq. ft.)
                       (sq. in.)
  9   square feet    = 1 square yard (sq. yd.)
 30¼  square yards   = 1 square rod (sq. rd.)
160   square rods    = 1 acre (A.)
640   acres          = 1 square mile (sq. mi.)
 36   square miles   = 1 township
```

square root (*Math.*) A quantity which, when multiplied by itself, produces the given quantity.

square–thread′ed screw (*Mech.*) A screw, the section of whose thread is rectangular in form.

squar′ing shears (*Sheet-Met. Wk.*) A foot- or power-operated machine for cutting metal from the original sheets or for straight cutting in trimming work to exact size.

squeeze pe′ri-od (*Weld.*) The time interval in a resistance-welding process between the application of pressure and the application of welding current.

squeez′er (*Fdry.*) A type of molding machine.

squinch (*Arch.*) A small arch or corbeled set-off, running diagonally, and cutting off a corner of the interior of a room or tower, to bring it from the square to the octagon, to carry the spire.

squir′rel–cage ro′tor (*Elec.*) The revolving part of the ordinary induction motor.

sta-bil′i-ty. The state or quality of being firm or stable. (*Aero.*) That property of a body which causes it, when disturbed from a condition of equilibrium or steady motion, to develop forces or moments which tend to restore the body to its original condition.

sta′bi-liz′er (*Aero.*) Also called tail plane. An airfoil usually located at the rear of an aircraft for the purpose of lessening the pitching motion. Mechanical stabilizers include gyroscopic, pendulum, inertia types, etc. (*Plast.*) In plastic manufacture, an additive to a resin compound which keeps the product stable, in respect to its essential properties, throughout its service life.

sta′ble os′cil-la′tion (*Aero.*) An oscillation whose amplitude does not increase.

stack (*Arch.*) A large chimney usually of brick, stone, or sheet metal for carrying off smoke or fumes as in a factory. (*Engin.*) A chimney usually of steel and generally short.

staff bead (*Bldg.*) The molding strip used between the masonry and window frame to shut out the weather.

stag′ger (*Shopwk.*) (1) To arrange parts in an uneven line. (2) To place in rows, as rivets, one row alternating with the spaces of another.

stag′ger wire (*Aero.*) A wire connecting the upper and lower surfaces of an airplane and lying in a plane substantially parallel to the plane of symmetry. Also called "incidence wire."

stag′ing (*Bldg.*) A temporary structure of boards and posts. (*Paint.*) A wood platform hung in ropes to be used as a scaffold for such work as painting or scraping a building wall.

stain (*Shopwk.*) A wood finish which usually does not obscure the grain as would be the case with paint. There are oil stains (which are classed as pigment stains), also acid, penetrating, and water stains which contain dyestuffs in solution.

stain′less steel (*Metal.*) An alloy steel containing a high percentage of chromium, with the addition sometimes of nickel and copper. This steel is hard and tough and retains a polish.

stair (*Bldg.*) A stair is a single step in a flight of stairs.

stair′case (*Arch. and Bldg.*) A flight of stairs with landings, newel posts, handrails, and balustrade.

stairs (*Bldg.*) Means the complete set of steps between two floors of a building and may consist of one or more flights. Simplest type is the "straight stair or straight run stair so called because it leads from one floor to another without a turn or landing. "Close string" stairs are built with a wall on each side. "Open string" stairs have one side open to a room, so that a handrail is necessary. "Doglegged" stairs or "platform" stairs have landings near the bottom or top, usually introduced to change direction.

stair treads (*Bldg.*) The horizontal boards of a stair.

Stake

stakes (*Sheet-Met. Wk.*) Small anvils of various shapes and sizes, used on the bench by sheet-metal workers for bending and forming.

stak′ing out (*Bldg.*) The driving of stakes into the earth to indicate the foundation location of the structure to be built. The stakes are often connected by a cord in order to secure a clean edge in the excavation.

stall (*Aero.*) The condition of an airplane when the speed necessary for support or control has been lost. (*Arch.*) A small booth or compartment, as in a market.

stal′ling speed (*Aero.*) The speed of an airplane in steady flight at its maximum coefficient of lift.

stamp′ing press (*Print.*) An embossing press.

stan′chion (stăn′shŭn) A support or post of iron or wood.

stand′ard. (1) Accurate; authoritative. (2) Any established measure; a type, model, or example for comparison.

stand′ard at′mos-phere (*Aero.*) An arbitrary atmosphere used in comparing the performance of aircraft. The standard atmosphere in use in the United States at present represents very nearly the average conditions found at latitude 40 deg.

stand′ard in′ter-na′tion-al at′mos-phere (*Aero.*) The atmosphere used as an international standard presumes for mean sea level and a temperature of 15 degrees C., a pressure of 1,013.2 millibars, lapse rate of 6.5 degrees C. per kilometer from sea level to 11 kilometers, and thereafter a constant temperature of — 56.5 degrees C.

stand′ard-ized cell (*Elec.*) For accurate testing, a cell in which the voltage remains constant is desirable. In use, no appreciable amount of current is drawn from the cell. The Clark cell was the first standardized cell. The Weston is in general use today.

stand′ard knot (*Wood*) A sound knot not over $1\frac{1}{2}$ in. in diameter.

stand′ard pres′sure (*Plumb.*) Term applied to valves and fittings suitable for a working steam pressure of 125 pounds per square inch.

stand′ing mat′ter (*Print.*) Type composition kept standing to be used for further printings.

stand′pipe (*Engin.*) A large vertical pipe or water tower which serves as a reservoir, and is used to secure a uniform pressure in a supply system.

stan-nif′er-ous (*Ceram.*) An opaque white glaze.

sta′ple. A U-shaped piece of wire or iron with sharpened points for driving into wood.

star con-nec′tion (*Elec.*) Three-phase generators and transformers have three coils which may be connected, star, Y, or delta. When one terminal of each coil is connected together and the other three terminals are brought out separately, the connection is called star or Y.

star drill. A tool with a star-shaped point used for drilling in stone or masonry.

star feed (*Mach.*) An intermittent feed accomplished by a star wheel attached to the cross slidescrew. A bolt or pin fastened to the lathe faceplate on each revolution strikes a point on the star wheel causing the cutting tool to advance. The same principle has various applications.

star′ling (*Arch.*) An enclosure made by driving piles close together as for protection about a bridge or pier.

star shake (*Carp.*) A radial split or crack in a log or timber as a result of being cut green and drying too rapidly. The cracks or splits which may be seen radiating from the center in an end view of a timber.

start′er (*Auto., Elec.*) A series electric motor used on automobiles to turn over the gasoline engine until it starts under its own power.

starterator (*Auto.*) A linkage which makes it possible to operate the starting motor by depressing the accelerator pedal.

start′ing box (*Elec.*) A rheostat contained in a case having a switch arm and contact points for delivering the current gradually by cutting out one resistance after another.

start′ing cir′cuit (*Auto.*) On closing the starting switch, the current flows from the positive post through the heavy lead to the switch, to the starting-motor-field winding, to the brushes, to the armature winding then off the commutator through the two remaining brushes to the ground of the starting motor. It then returns to the battery through the car frame, and up through short grounding cable to the negative post of the battery.

start′ing crank (*Auto.*) A crank formerly used for turning over the engine in order to start it. Since the invention of selfstarters, the starting crank is rarely used except during certain types of repair jobs.

start′ing mo′tor (*Auto.*) The electric motor by means of which the engine is cranked by closing the electric circuit.

start′ing new′el (*Arch. and Bldg.*) The post at the bottom of a stair, supporting the balustrade.

start′ing step (*Bldg.*) The lowest step at the bottom of a stair.

start′ing torque (tôrk) (*Elec.*) The turning effort produced by a motor upon its shaft through the electromagnetic effect at the initial flow of current.

startix (*Auto.*) A solenoid which automatically closes the starting-motor switch as soon as the ignition switch is turned on.

stat′ic bal′ance. That state of balance which exists when the weight of a pulley or shaft is so distributed that when lightly supported there is no heavy side to roll to the bottom.

stat′ic bal′anced sur′face (*Aero.*) A control surface whose center of mass is in the hinge axis.

stat′ic ceil′ing (*Aero.*) The altitude in standard atmosphere at which an aerostat is in static equilibrium after removal of all dischargeable weights.

stat′ic e-lec-tric′i-ty. Differs from current electricity in that it is electricity at rest. One method of generation is by frictional contact, as the charge placed upon a glass rod by rubbing with silk or fur.

stat′ic fric′tion (*Engin.*) That friction between two bodies when there is a tendency to, but not an actual slipping of, one with regard to the other.

stat′ic load (*Engin.*) A load at rest.

stat′ics (*Engin.*) That branch of mechanics which treats of the equilibrium, pressure, weight, etc., of bodies at rest.

stat′ic sta-bil′i-ty (*Aero.*) Stability of such a character that, if the airplane is displaced slightly from its normal attitude by rotation about an axis through its center of gravity, moments come into play which tend to return the airplane toward its original attitude.

stat′ic thrust (*Aero.*) The thrust developed by a propeller when rotating without translation.

stat′ic turn in′di-ca′tor (*A e r o.*) A turn indicator actuated by the difference in pressure between static tubes mounted near the wing tips equidistant from the plane of symmetry and in a plane parallel to the lateral axis.

sta′tion-a-ry en′gine (*Engin.*) An engine located on a fixed foundation, as distinguished from a portable engine.

sta-tis′tics. The science of the arrangement of facts.

sta′tor (*Elec.*) The fixed part in an a.c. motor or generator; that part which does not rotate.

stat′o-scope (*A e r o.*) An instrument for detecting slight changes of altitude of an aircraft.

stay (*Aero.*) A wire or other tension member, as the stays of the wing and body trussing. (*Bldg.*) A prop or a guy for supporting canopies, steel chimneys, etc. A bar for holding parts together.

stay bolt (*Engin.*) A rod threaded at both ends; used to prevent bulging of the plates or parts through which it passes.

stay–bolt tap (*Mach.*) A type of combination reamer and tap used extensively in locomotive-boiler work.

stead′y rest (*Mach.*) A rest attached to the ways of a lathe for supporting long, slender work while it is being machined.

steam. Water vapor.

steam bronze (*Metal.*) Used for making valves and fittings. It is an alloy of about 85 per cent copper, 5 per cent zinc, 5 per cent lead, and 5 per cent tin.

steam ham′mer. A heavy hammer, moving between vertical guides, actuated by steam pressure.

steam main (*Mech. Engin.*) A horizontal pipe for carrying live steam from a boiler to radiators, a steam engine, or other steam consuming device.

steam plate (*Plast.*) Mounting plate for molds, which is cored for circulation of steam.

steam ta′ble (*Print.*) Table for drying the matrix used in stereotyping.

steam tur′bine (*Engin.*) A steam engine in which the steam acts on a rotating turbine instead of on a piston.

steel (*Metal.*) A very general term including the low carbon nontemperable steels, the high carbon steels which can be tempered, and alloy steels which are used for a wide variety of purposes.

steel al-loys (*Engin.*) Special steels for special purposes, in which certain ingredients are used, such as manganese for strength, nickel for strength and toughness, tungsten as a hardener and heat resister, chromium for resisting shocks, vanadium as a fatigue resister, etc. After being machined, alloy steel must be "heat treated" to bring it to its maximum strength.

steel belt (*M a c h.*) Thin, flat, steel belts varying from 0.008 to 0.035 in. in thickness and from $7/8$ to 8 in. in width have been successfully used. The pulleys should be faced with a thin layer of cork. Steel belts can be run at speeds as high as 10,000 feet per minute. It has been claimed that a 4-in. steel belt will transmit as much power as a 19-in. leather belt.

steel cast'ing (*Engin.*) Castings made of steel, for machine parts which are subjected to shock or particularly rough usage in places where cast iron, owing to its granular structure, would not "stand up."

steel con-vert'er (*Engin.*) The retort, lined with refractory material, in which cast iron is converted into steel, as by the Bessemer process.

steel–draul'ic brakes (*Auto. Mech.*) A mechanical brake system by which the brake pedal transmits effective braking force to the brake shoes by means of cables enclosed in protective armor, to each wheel.

steel en-grav'ing (*Print.*) (1) The act or art of cutting a design on a steel plate; (2) an engraved design on steel; (3) a picture printed from an engraved steel plate.

steel gird'er (*Engin.*) A built-up steel beam, receiving a vertical load and bearing vertically on its supports.

steel pul'ley (*Mach.*) Usually of the split type made of sheet steel. Light in weight and satisfactory in operation.

steel rule (*Mech.*) A flexible or rigid measuring strip of steel. These rules are available in various lengths. They are graduated in inches and fractions of an inch.

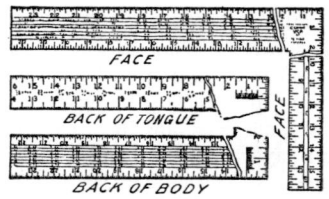

Carpenter's Steel Square

steel square (*Carp.*) The ordinary steel try square used by machinists; also the large square used by carpenters.

steel wool (*Shopwk.*) Fine threads of steel matted together into a mass; used principally for polishing or cleaning surfaces of wood or metal.

steel'yard. A weighing device consisting of a long lever with two arms of unequal length. In use a sliding weight can be moved on the longer graduated arm to balance the object to the weight which is suspended from the shorter arm.

stee'ple (*Arch.*) A spire; a tall structure rising above the body of a building, as a church steeple.

stee'ple jack. One who works on steeples, flagpoles, etc.

steer'ing col'umn (*Auto.*) The column or post on which is mounted the steering wheel, connected to various members by which steering motion is carried to the front wheels.

steer'ing gear (*Auto. Mech.*) A term applied, generally, to all that assemblage of parts from steering wheel to axle, by means of which steering is accomplished.

steer'ing–knuck'le arms (*Auto.*) Two irregular-shaped forgings, one left and one right, attached to the steering knuckles in order to make connection with the steering mechanism.

steer'ing wheel (*Auto. Mech.*) The hand wheel on an automobile, which through a system of gears and levers connecting it with the front wheels makes possible the steering control of the car.

stel'lite (*Engin.*) A trade name for an alloy containing chromium and cobalt with a small amount of molybdenum or tungsten. Used for tools and cutters. Stellite can be cast but cannot be forged, or machined except by grinding.

sten'cil. A thin plate of metal or other material, with letters or pattern cut out, used for marking. When placed on a surface and color is laid on, a certain figure or design is made.

step (*Aero.*) A break in the form of the bottom of a float or hull designed to reduce resistance when under way by rapidly reducing the wetted surfaces as speed increases. It also serves to eliminate suction effects.

step block or step bear'ing (*Mach.*) A bearing which takes the end thrust of vertical shafts.

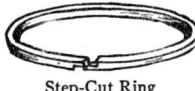
Step-Cut Ring

step–cut ring (*Auto.*) A piston ring with the ends cut to a rabbet or half-lap joint.

step–down trans-form'er (*Elec.*) A transformer which changes the supply or line voltage to a lower value.

step'ping round (*Mech. Draw.*) Trial process by which an arc, curve, or circle is divided into a number of parts by use of steppers or dividers; used in laying off a gear wheel.

step tap (*Metalwk.*) A tap with steps or sections of varying diameters to make easier the cutting of heavy internal threads. The end of the tap starts the thread, and each succeeding step removes more material.

ster'e-o-phon'ic (*Rad.*) A technique of sound reproduction, whereby the sound eminating from two separated areas of origin is reproduced by a system having two separate units reproducing the corresponding two originating sound areas. This method produces depth, richness, and added reality to the sound reproduced.

ster'e-o-type' (*Print.*) A cast plate of metal, made from a matrix of paper or plaster of Paris, reproducing the surface from which the matrix was made.

ster'e-o-typ'ing (*Print.*) The process of duplicating, in solid metal, cuts and type composed for printing. There are three methods, of which the papier-mâché or hot process is most generally used. The earlier clay process and the plaster process are now obsolete.

stern–droop (*Aero.*) A deformation of an airship in which its longitudinal axis bends downward at the after end.

stern'heav'y (*A e r o.*) The condition in which, in normal flight, the after end of an airship tends to sink and which requires correction by means of the horizontal controls.

stet (*P r i n t.*) A proofreader's term. When written on a proof, it means "do not take out the part marked."

stick (*Print.*) A small hand frame in which a compositor sets type.

stick'ful (*Print.*) A composing stick filled to the limit of its capacity.

stick'ing of valves (*Auto. Mech.*) Failure of the valves to open and close properly, caused by poor lubrication or by carbon deposits.

stick shel-lac' (*F u r n.*) Shellac in stick form used in refinishing, to fill in cracks, scratches, etc.

stif'fen-er (*Engin.*) Any angle, plate, channel, or other shape riveted to a member to increase rigidity.

stile (*Arch.*) An upright piece in framing or paneling.

Stillson Wrench

Still′son wrench (*Plumb.*) The pipe wrench of common use, named for its inventor.

stip′ple. To draw or engrave by means of dots instead of lines.

stip′pler (*Leather.*) A tool used in producing background effects.

stir′rup (*E n g i n.*) A strap or loop which supports a beam, rod, or spindle, or any similar object.

stir′rup or hang′er (*Bldg.*) A drop support attached to a wall or girder to carry the end of a joist or beam.

stitched edge (*Uphol.*) A padded edge formed by stitching a stuffed burlap roll to the edge of the seat or arm of a piece of furniture.

sto′a (stō′ȧ) (*Arch.*) A covered cloister, portico, or colonnade.

stock (*Mach.*) A general term referring to material to be worked on, especially shafting and bars as round stock or bar stock. (*Print.*) Paper used in a print shop.

stocks and dies (*Metalwk.*) The threaded blocks or dies together with levers with which they are operated; used for cutting male threads.

stone bruise (*Auto.*) A tire injury which results in broken fabric; frequently caused by running the car against a curb when turning around. Such an injury seldom causes immediate failure.

stone hand (*Print.*) One whose duty it is to arrange and to lock into forms the different pages of type matter so that they will print in proper position on the sheet.

stone′ma′son (*Masonry*) One who builds foundations, walls, etc., of stone.

stool (*Arch.*) The wood shelf inside of and across the bottom of a window.

stoop (*Arch.*) A platform or step at the door of a house.

stop (*Mech. and Arch.*) A piece attached to some part to prevent motion beyond a certain point, as on a machine in shopwork, or as a doorstop in a building.

stop′cock (*Plumb.*) A type of valve which consists of a body having a tapered opening, into which is fitted a plug of corresponding taper. By turning the plug through an arc of 90 deg., the flow of water is turned on or off.

stop lead′er (lēd′ẽr) (*Tel.*) A length of motion-picture film used between portions of subject film when the projector is to be stopped between subjects.

stopped mi′ter (*Woodwkg.*) A combination miter and butt joint; often used when the pieces being joined are not of the same thickness.

Stopped Miter

stop watch. A watch which can be started or stopped by pressure on the stem, used in timing races, etc.

stor′age bat′ter-y (*Elec.*) A combination of storage cells, each cell containing positive plates and negative plates, immersed in an electrolyte of dilute sulphuric acid.

stor′age cell (*Elec.*) One of the sections of a storage battery.

stor′age life (*Plast.*) Called also shelf life. The period of time during which a resin can be stored without loss of properties or of fluidity, depending upon a specified storage temperature.

stored en'er-ǵy weld'ing. A resistance-welding process wherein the electrical energy required to produce the weld is accumulated in a suitable storage reservoir, usually at a low rate, prior to its delivery to the weld usually delivered at a high rate.

storm door (*Arch.*) An extra outside door used in winter to avoid chilling the interior of a building and to lessen the effects of rain and wind at an entrance.

storm sash (*Arch.*) An extra or outer sash used as a protection from severe winter weather.

stove bolt. When supplied without a nut it is called machine screw: with a nut it is a stove bolt. Stove bolts formerly had a coarser thread pitch than machine screws.

strad'dle mill'ing (*Mach.*) The use of two or more milling cutters, with spacers between, mounted on the same arbor to permit simultaneous finishing of opposite faces.

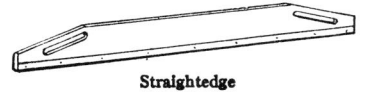

Straightedge

straight'edge (*Mech.*) A parallel, straight strip of wood or metal used for gauging the linear accuracy of work.

straight–eight en'ǵine (*Auto.*) Has all cylinders vertical and in a straight line.

straight flut'ed drill (*Metalwk.*) See FARMERS' DRILL.

straight mat'ter (*Print.*) Uniform type matter in which display lines are not used.

straight nee'dle (*Uphol.*) A large double-pointed needle from 6 to 20 in. long, used to sew webbing to springs, stuffing to burlap, etc.

straight–peen ham'mer (*Shopwk.*) One end of the head is wedge-shaped, with rounded edge. This peening edge is parallel with the handle.

straight–shank drill (*Shopwk.*) A drill with a round, parallel shank, used in self-centering chucks. These drills are not usually made in large sizes.

straight–shank mill'ing cut'ter (*Mach.*) Used in a profiling machine for die work, routing, etc.

strain (*Engin.*) To stretch beyond its proper limit. To act upon so as to cause change of form or volume.

strake (*Metalwk.*) In heavy metal plate construction, a continuous row of plates.

strand'ed wires (*Elec.*) Wires or cables made up of a number of small wires braided or twisted together; differing from flexible wire in that it has fewer strands than flexible wire.

Stranded Wires

strap'work (*Furn.*) (1) Decorative design consisting of narrow fillet or band with crossed, folded, or interlaced ornament. (2) An ornamental railing of wood or metal along the edge of a table, desk, or sideboard.

stra'ta. Plural of stratum. Layers either artificial or natural.

stra'to-sphere (strā'tŏ-sfēr) That portion of the earth's atmosphere which begins at an altitude of about seven miles and extends upward indefinitely.

straw'board (*Papermkg.*) A grade of board made entirely of cooked straw pulp. It is sometimes made as a combination board with liners of superior material.

streak'ing (*Paint and Lacquer*) In spray coats of paint or lacquer, light and dark streaks are caused by failure to lap the wet edges of the spray, or by using a spray nozzle that is out of line or adjustment.

stream feed'ers (*Print.*) An automatic method of feeding sheets to presses or folding machines.

stream'line (*Aero.*) The path of a small portion of a fluid relative to a solid body with respect to which the fluid is moving. The term is commonly used only of such flows as are not eddying.

stream'line flow (*Aero.*) A fluid flow in which the streamlines, except those very near a body and in a narrow wake, do not change with time.

stream'line form (*Aero., Auto.*) The form of a body so shaped that the flow about it tends to be a streamline flow.

strength of cur'rent (*Elec.*) The number of amperes flowing through a circuit. It may be likened to the flow of gallons per minute in a water pipe.

strength of ma-te'ri-als (*Engin.*) The science that treats of the effects of forces in causing changes in the size and shape of bodies.

stress (*Engin.*) An internal force which resists change in the shape or size of a body.

stress ac-cel'er-at'ed cor-ro'sion (*Metal.*) With an increase in stress, the corrosion of metal is accelerated. It is greater in steel than in some of the alloys.

stretch (*Tel.*) To slow up action.

stretch'er. Brick or stone lying lengthwise in a course.

stria (pl. striae) (strī'å) (*Plast.*) Surface or internal threadlike flaws in homogeneity of transparent plastic.

strik'ing off (*Fdry.*) Leveling of the surface of a foundry mold with a bar of wood or metal.

string (*Arch.*) One of the inclined sides of a stair supporting the treads and risers.

string course or sail'ing course (*Arch.*) It consists of a course of brick or stone, projecting from a wall horizontally, for decorative purposes, or to break the plainness of a large expanse of wall.

string'er (*Arch.*) A heavy plank or timber generally in horizontal position in a structure.

string mill'ing (*Mach.*) A milling operation in which a number of parts to be machined are mounted in a straight line so the same cut will be taken on each in turn.

strip (*Mach.*) To break, tear, or strip off the threads of a bolt or nut. (*Bldg.*) A long narrow piece of wood.

stripe (*Paint.*) A long narrow painted line, usually for decoration as on an automobile body.

strip'per (*Mach.*) A device used on presses to prevent the punched metal from lifting with the punch.

strip'ping–plate ma-chine' (*Fdry.*) A very easily operated molding machine on which a pattern is stripped through a plate.

stroke (*Auto. and Engin.*) The motion of a piston accomplished by the "throw" of the crankshaft.

strong sand (*Fdry.*) New sand, or sand which has not lost its good qualities by being used too often.

struc′tur-al load (*Engin.*) The load due to the structure itself as distinguished from the imposed load.

struc′tur-al steel (*Engin.*) The various shapes used by engineers in the erection of bridges, buildings, etc., as I beams, H beams, Z bars, channels, etc.

strut (*Aero., Engin.*) A compression member of a truss frame; e.g., the vertical members of the wing truss of a biplane (interplane struts) and the short vertical horizontal members separating the longeron in the fuselage.

strut gir′der. A lattice girder whose top and bottom members are connected by vertical struts and braced by diagonal braces or by counterbracing.

strut ten′on (*Woodwkg.*) A tenon, such as is used on a diagonal piece or strut, usually on heavy timbers.

stub gear tooth (*Mach.*) A type of involute tooth frequently used in automobile drives. Both addendum and dedendum are shorter than in the standard tooth and the pressure angle is 20 deg. instead of 14½ deg.

Stub's gauge (*Engin.*) A gauge for measuring the size of wire. Also known as "Birmingham gauge."

stub ten′on (*Carp.*) A short tenon.

stuc′co (*Masonry*) Plaster or cement used for external surfacing of walls.

stuck mold′ing (*Masonry*) A molding which is built to a form, on the floor, or on a table, and "stuck" in position when finished.

stud (*Arch.*) An upright beam or scantling as in the framework of a dwelling.

stud bolt. A bolt threaded at both ends with blank space between to permit gripping with a pipe wrench.

stud gear (*Mach.*) A gear mounted on a stud; an intermediate gear.

stuff′ing box (*Mach.*) A recessed chamber through which piston rods or valve stems pass, surrounded therein with packing, and used to prevent leakage.

stuff′ing reg′u-la′tor (*Uphol.*) A tapered, needlelike tool from 6 to 10 in. long which is used to even out all irregularities in stuffing.

stunt or dunt (*Pot.*) To crack or split on cooling.

style (*Furn.*) A definite form or design characteristic of a certain school or period.

sub′base (*Arch.*) The lowest part of a base.

sub′cloud car (*Aero.*) An observation car which may be lowered from an airship to a position below the clouds.

sub′con-trac′tor (*Engin.*) One who contracts to do a portion of a job, receiving his directions from and being responsible to the contractor of the whole.

sub′floor (*Bldg.*) A wood floor which is laid over the floor joists and on which the finished floor is laid.

sub′frame (*Auto.*) An auxiliary frame placed inside the main frame to support the power plant.

sub′head (*Print.*) A secondary title or head.

sub′let (*Engin.*) To engage a subordinate contractor to handle a piece of work.

sub′rail (*Arch. and Bldg.*) A molded member or shoe planted on the top

edge of a stair string to carry the lower end of the baluster.

sub'stance (*Papermkg.*) The basic weights selected as standard numbers for regular sizes of all types of paper. The weight of book paper can be determined on the basis of ream 25 by 38 in.; the weight of writings, on the basis of 17 by 22 in. A ream 25 by 40 in. is the last substance standard to be suggested. While formerly substance represented the weight of only one ream of paper, in certain papers it now represents the weight of paper per thousand sheets.

sub-stra'to-sphere (sŭb-strā'tŏ-sfēr). That layer of the earth's atmosphere just beneath the stratosphere where high-altitude transport operations are carried on.

sub-struc'ture (*Arch.*) The lower portion of a structure upon which something else is built up.

suc'tion (*Plaster.*) The manner in which certain kinds of plaster "pull" when worked with a trowel. The adhesion.

suc'tion stroke (*Auto.*) The intake stroke on which the fuel mixture is drawn into the cylinder.

suede calf'skin (swāde) (*Leather.*) A higher grade leather than suede lambskin. Used for the finer quality of linings.

suede fin'ish (*Leather.*) A lusterless, naplike finish.

suede lamb'skin (*Leather.*) A soft, pliable, velvet-finished leather used for ladies' handbags, etc.

sug'ar pine (*Wood*) *Pinus lambertiana.* A very large species of pine native in California and Oregon. Its diameter may be as great as 15 ft. and its height 200 ft. The wood is clear and light in color and easily worked. Much used for building trim, interior and exterior.

sul'phat-ed bat'tery (*Auto.*) Storage-battery plates that have become covered with a coating of white sulphate due to lack of charging, or to low water level, or to both of these conditions. If the sulphated condition has not progressed too far, the battery may be brought back by a recharging at a very slow rate.

sul'phate pa'per (*Papermkg.*) A paper made entirely of sulphate or "kraft" pulp. It is sometimes bleached white, unbleached, or dyed.

sul'phite bond (*Papermkg.*) A hard-sized bond paper which is made in four grades. The two higher grades may be watermarked according to Writing Paper Manufacturers' trade customs.

sul'phite pulp (*Papermkg.*) A pulp made from spruce and similar woods by the sulphite process.

sul'phur (*Chem.*) Symbol, S. Its presence in iron or steel always has an undesirable effect. In very small quantities, it makes cast iron hard and white. In wrought iron or steel, a mere trace will produce red-shortness.

sul-phu'ric ac'id (*Chem.*) H_2SO_4. Oil of vitriol. Made by roasting sulphur or roasting iron pyrites or other sulphide, then adding oxygen to the resulting dioxide and uniting the product with water. Widely used in the arts and industries in making "pickle," storage-battery electrolyte, refining lubricating oils, etc.

sump. A depression in a roof, etc., to receive rain water and deliver it to the downspout.

sun com′pass (*Aero.*) A compass in which the direction of the sun is utilized instead of the direction of the magnetic north or south pole.

sunk mold′ing (*Arch.*) Any molding which is recessed below the level of adjoining surfaces.

sunk pan′els (*Bldg.*) Panels recessed below the surrounding surface.

sunk spot (*Plast.*) Depression in a finished molding piece caused by shrinkage or contraction in the volume of the thick or nonuniform cross sections of the casting.

su′per-bronze (*M e t a l.*) Corrosion-resistant, high-tensile-strength brasses, containing both aluminum and manganese.

su′per–cal′en-dered (*P a p e r*) Paper stock to which a high finish is given by passing through calender rolls.

su′per-charge′ (*Aero.*) To supply an engine with more air or mixture than would be inducted normally at the prevailing atmospheric pressure.

su′per-charged en′gine (*Aero.*) A reciprocating engine equipped with a supercharger, an engine provided with a high degree of supercharging for operation at high altitudes.

su′per-charg′er (*Aero.*) A mechanical device for supplying the engine with a greater weight of charge than would normally be induced at the prevailing atmospheric pressure and temperature. There are several types, viz., centrifugal, positive drivers, rotary blower, and turbo. (*Auto.*) A mechanical device designed to give positive fuel mixture to racing motors and airplane motors. The mixture is put into the motors much more rapidly than is done in stock carburetion.

su′per–fines (*Papermkg.*) A high grade of flat writing paper having a more or less high finish.

su′per-heat′ed steam. Steam at a temperature higher than the temperature corresponding to the pressure of the boiling point at which it was formed.

su′per-het′er-o-dyne′. A radio receiving circuit which depends on the principle of superimposing upon the incoming high-frequency wave a similar wave of different frequency.

su′per-im′po-si′tion (*Tel.*) The overlapping of an image by one camera with the image from another camera; a blending or merging of images to any desired amount.

su-pe′ri-or fig′ures or let′ters (*Print.*) Small-type figures or letters set at the top of a line; e.g., B^3, C^n.

su′per-struc′ture. Anything built up or founded on something else.

sup′ple-ment′ed. Additions made to; something added.

sup′ple-ment of an an′gle. Its difference from 180 degrees.

sur′base (*Arch.*) A molding or border above a base, as above a baseboard in a room.

surd (*Algebra*) An irrational number or quantity; particularly an indicated root that cannot be extracted.

sur′face ac′tion (*Phys.*) Any kind of action which affects a surface; e.g., action of smoke fumes, moisture, etc., on a painted surface.

sur′face blow′off′ (*Engin.*) A valve or plugged connection in a boiler, located just above the water line and used to draw off grease, oil, and dirt.

sur′faced-sized (*Papermkg.*) Often used synonymously with tub sized. However, certain papers are surface sized not after immersion in a tub of size but by passing between rubber-covered rollers.

sur′face gauge. A machinist's gauge for scribing and lining up work.

sur′face grind′ing (*Metal Fin.*) The operation of grinding plane or flat metal surfaces.

sur′face har′den-ing (*Metal.*) (See CASE HARDENING.)

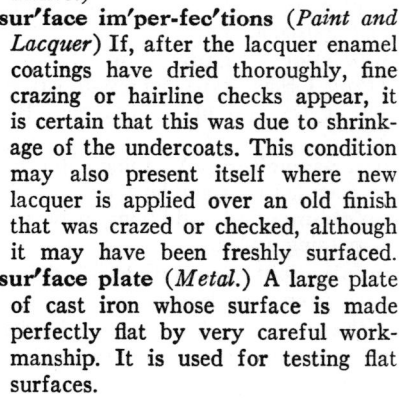

Surface Gauge

sur′face im′per-fec′tions (*Paint and Lacquer*) If, after the lacquer enamel coatings have dried thoroughly, fine crazing or hairline checks appear, it is certain that this was due to shrinkage of the undercoats. This condition may also present itself where new lacquer is applied over an old finish that was crazed or checked, although it may have been freshly surfaced.

sur′face plate (*Metal.*) A large plate of cast iron whose surface is made perfectly flat by very careful workmanship. It is used for testing flat surfaces.

sur′face speed (*Mech.*) The rate of movement of the surface in feet per minute. It may refer to a surface moving in a straight line, or to a cylindrical surface. In calculating the surface speed of a wheel, for instance, multiply the circumference in feet by the number of revolutions the wheel makes per minute.

sur′fac-ing of lum′ber (*Woodwk.*) Indicated by symbols such as S1E, surfaced on one edge; S1S, surfaced on one side; S2S, surfaced on two sides, etc.

sur-vey′ing. The science of measuring land.

sur-vey′or's a′re-a meas′ure.
625 square links = 1 square pole or square rod (sq. li.)
16 square poles = 1 square chain (sq. ch.)
10 square chains = 1 surveyor's acre (A.)
640 acres = 1 square mile (sq. mi.)
36 square miles = 1 township

sur-vey′or's com′pass (*Surv.*) An instrument for determining the difference in direction between any horizontal line and a magnetic needle.

sur-vey′or's meas′ure.
7.92 in. = 1 link
100 links = 66 ft. = 22 yd. = 4 rods = 1 chain
220 yd. = 10 chains = 1 furlong
80 chains = 8 furlongs = 1 mile

sus-pen′sion (*Chem.*) A turbid or cloudy mixture of two or more substances. A suspension will generally settle on standing; the suspended matter forming a layer at the bottom of the container.

swab (*Fdry.*) A piece of waste or a sponge used to wet the sand around a pattern prior to its withdrawal from the sand.

swag (*Furn.*) A festoon design, characteristic of the Adam style.

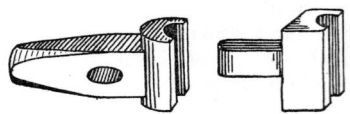

Top and Bottom Swages

swage (swāj) (*Forg.*) A form of die used by blacksmiths as an aid in forming forged work. It usually consists of two parts; the upper is a handled tool held by the smith, the lower has a square shank which fits into the hardy hole of the anvil.

swage block (*Smithing*) A large rectangular block of cast iron used by a blacksmith. It is pierced through with numerous holes, both round and square in section, for the reception of work which requires shouldering.

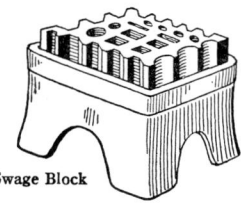
Swage Block

swash let′ters (*P r i n t.*) Ornamental letters with prolonged strokes; especially of the italic type.

sweat (*Engin.*) To coat with solder the surfaces to be joined, then causing the surfaces to adhere by the application of heat, as opposed to the common method of making a joint by direct application of the soldering iron.

sweat′ing (*Metal.*) When parts to be soldered are tinned, and then heated sufficiently to melt the solder without the use of a soldering iron, the process is called "sweating."

Swed′ish de-tail′ rul′ing pen. A ruling pen with blades much wider than those of a regular ruling pen in order to carry sufficient ink for long, heavy lines.

Swed′ish i′ron (*Metal.*) An iron of highest quality due to the freedom from phosphorus and sulphur of the Swedish ore.

sweep (*Tel.*) The motion of the electron beam in a picture or camera tube.

sweep′back (*Aero.*) The backward slant from root to tip (or inboard to outboard end) of an airfoil, or of the leading edge or other reference line of an airfoil.

sweep′ing (*Fdry.*) A system of making large cores without the aid of a core box; used when only a few cores are needed.

sweet gum (*Wood*) *Liquidambar styraciflua.* Also known as "Red gum." (See GUMWOOD.)

sweet oil (*Chem.*) A low-grade, heavy-bodied olive oil, used medicinally, for culinary purposes, and as a lubricant.

sweet or red gum (*Wood*) *Liquidambar styraciflua.* A tree of large growth whose wood is soft but tough. It takes a very beautiful finish, but has a great tendency to warp.

swell (*Fdry.*) Bulged place on a casting caused by too soft ramming of the mold.

swing of a lathe (*Mach.*) The largest diameter of work which can be carried between the centers of a lathe. In England, the swing refers to radius.

swing saw (*Woodwk.*) A circular saw mounted on a hinged frame suspended from above. The work remains stationary while the saw is pulled toward it.

switch (*Elec.*) A device for opening and closing an electric circuit.

switch′board (*Elec.*) A vertical board or panel of slate or marble, on which are mounted the main knife switches, the circuit breakers, and the meters for a large electrical installation.

switch box (*Elec.*) An iron box or case to protect the switch mechanism and to prevent accidental contact with current-carrying parts.

swiv′el (*Mech*.) A coupling device that permits either half of a mechanism to rotate independently of the other.

swiv′el vise (*Shopwk*.) A bench vise which may be rotated on its base to bring the work which it holds into better position.

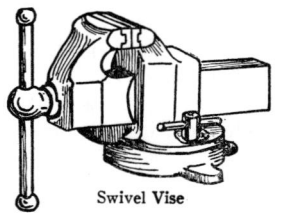

Swivel Vise

S wrench (*Mach*.) A wrench shaped like the letter S having either fixed or adjustable openings.

syc′a-more (*Wood*) *Platanus*. The buttonwood tree. A very large tree attaining height as great as 150 feet. Wood moderately hard, very difficult to split; weight 38 pounds per cu. ft.; light to brownish color, often beautifully marked; takes fine finish; used extensively in furniture manufacture, interior trim, and in the form of plywood in airplane construction.

sym′bol. A mark or character used as an abbreviation.

sym-met′ri-cal. Having corresponding parts; harmonious in proportion; balanced.

syn′chro-mesh trans-mis′sion (*Auto*.) A mechanical device designed to make gear shifting easy and silent. It eliminates clashing of gears and permits the driver to shift from second to high gear or from high to second gear without regard to engine or car speed.

syn′chro-niz-a′tion (*Tel*.) The process of keeping the moving beam of electrons in a picture tube in a receiver in step with the beam in the studio camera tube so that both move in synchronism.

syn′chro-nize. To cause to agree in time; happen simultaneously.

syn′chro-nous mo′tor (*Elec*.) One whose speed remains constant as long as the speed of the generator supplying it remains constant.

syn′the-sis (*Chem*.) Formation of a compound from its elements or from simple compounds.

syn-thet′ic (*Plast*.) Chemical compound made from elements or simpler compounds, applied particularly to substances that duplicate other substances occurring in nature.

syn-thet′ic res′in (*Plast*.) A plastic compound produced by chemical reaction with the use of simple components, in the hard state resembling natural resins, but differing widely in their chemistry and in their behavior with reagents. (See PLASTICS.)

T

tab (*Aero.*) An auxiliary airfoil attached to a control surface for the purpose of reducing the control force or trimming the aircraft.

tab′er-na-cle (*Arch.*) (1) A church or place of worship. (2) A niche, or recess, in which an image may be placed.

tab′o-ret (*Furn.*) A small stool or low table, frequently used as a stand for plants, ornamental objects, etc.

tab′u-lar mat′ter (*Print.*) Composition, mostly in figures, set in columns.

tab′u-late. To arrange items or data in a table or list.

ta-chom′e-ter (tȧ-kŏm′ê-tẽr) (*Engin.*) An instrument by means of which the speeds of shafts are indicated in revolutions per minute.

tack (*Print.*) The sticky condition of printing ink caused by the stiff varnish which it contains.

tack′le (*Mech.*) The chain, rope, and pulleys, or blocks, used for hoisting purposes in the erection of heavy work.

tæ′ni-a (tē′nĭ-ȧ) (*Arch.*) The flat band between the architrave and the frieze of the Doric order.

tail (*Aero.*) The rear part of an airplane, usually consisting of a group of stabilizing planes or fins, to which are attached certain controlling surfaces such as elevators and rudders; also called "empennage."

Tackle Block

tail beam or tail joist (*Arch.*) A joist or beam which abuts against the header joist.

tail boom (*Aero.*) A spar or outrigger connecting the tail surfaces and main supporting surfaces.

tail′-heav′y (*Aero.*) The condition in a heavier-than-air craft, in which, in normal flight, the tail sinks if the longitudinal control is released, i.e., the condition in which the pilot has to exert a push on the control stick to keep the given altitude.

tail′ing (*Bldg.*) The part of a projecting brick or stone inserted in a wall.

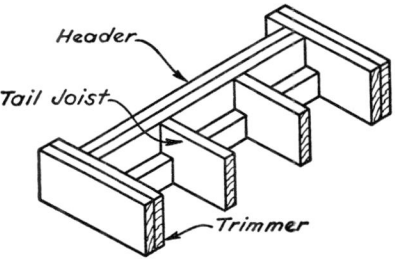

tail joist (*Bldg.*) A joist which has one end terminating against a header joist.

tail′less air′plane (*Aero.*) An airplane in which the devices used to obtain stability and control are incorporated in the wing.

tail light (*Auto. Mech.*) A signal light, required by law to be carried on the rear of every automobile, and lighted when the car is driven at night.

tail′piece (*Print.*) An ornament placed at the end of a chapter in a book, or at the bottom of a piece of printing.

tail print (*Patmkg.*) An extension on a core print to permit an easy with-

---

sāle, surfȧce, grăm, humȧn, mȧsk, solȧr, bär, bâre; mē, êdition, lĕnd, momĕnt, bakẽr; kīnd, fĭt; lōde, ômit, ŏlive, cŏnsume, sôrt; dūty, ûtility, nŭt, alȧm, bûrn.

drawal of the pattern from the mold; also to provide for easy setting and support of the core.

tail screw (*Wood Turn.*) The screw which operates the spindle of the tailstock on a lathe.

tail skid (*Aero.*) A skid for supporting the tail of an airplane on the ground.

tail slide (*Aero.*) Backward and downward motion, tail first, which an airplane may take after being brought to a stalling position following a steep climb.

tail′stock (*Mach.*) The movable head of a lathe as distinguished from the headstock which is fixed.

tail′stock′ spin′dle (*M a c h.*) The sleeve or spindle which carries the dead center in a lathe tailstock.

tail sur′face (*Aero.*) A stabilizing or control surface in the tail of an aircraft.

tail u′nit (*A e r o.*) Includes all the stabilizing and control surfaces at the rear end of an aircraft; stabilizer, fin, rudder, and elevator.

tail wheel (*Aero.*) A wheel used to support the tail of an airplane when on the ground. It may be steerable or nonsteerable, fixed or swiveling.

take (*Print.*) That portion of copy which a compositor has at one time.

take–off dis′tance (*Aero.*) The distance in which an airplane will finally break contact with the land or water, starting from zero speed. Take-off distance is considered in a calm or at a specified wind velocity.

take–off speed (*Aero.*) The air speed at which an airplane becomes entirely air-borne.

take′–up (*Shopwk.*) Any device for taking up slack or removing the looseness of parts due to wear or other cause.

tak′ing up (*Shopwk.*) Relates to the making of adjustment for wear, as in machinery.

talc. Soapstone; used in making paper, lubricants, and toilet preparations.

tal′low. Made from animal fats. The best grade is used in making oleomargarine. A large quantity is used in the manufacture of lubricating greases and leather dressings.

tam′bour (*Arch.*) A ceiled vestibule.

Tam′o, Japanese Ash (*W o o d*) *Fraxinus mandschuria.* Varies greatly both in color and marking. Used in large quantities for furniture and paneling. Very unusual grain effects are obtained with Tamo veneer.

tamp′ing (*Engin.*) Ramming down, as of ballast. (*Fdry.*) A molder's term, which means the ramming up of the sand around a pattern.

tan′bark. The bark of a tree containing tannin, as the bark of the oak. After being used for tanning, it has some use as fuel.

tan′dem air′plane (*A e r o.*) An airplane which has two or more sets of wings, one in front of the other and on about the same level.

tang. The shank of a cutting tool, or that portion which is driven into the handle.

tan′gent. Touching a line or surface at a point without intersecting.

tan′gent of an an′gle (*Math.*) The quotient of the opposite side divided by the adjacent side.

tan′gi-ble (tăn′jĭ-b'l) Evident; real.

tank (*Auto. Mech.*) The container for gasoline on an automobile.

tan′nin or **tan′nic acid** (*Chem.*) A lustrous, faintly yellowish, amorphous powder ($C_{14}H_{10}O_9$), obtained in the form of brownish white shining scales from gallnuts, sumac, tea, etc. Used in dyeing, tanning, etc., and in medicine as an astringent.

tan′ta-lum (*Metal.*) A ductile, acid-resistant, white lustrous metal obtained from tantalite. Much used as a filament in electric-light bulbs and radio tubes. Marketed in the form of wire and rods.

tap. The process of cutting threads with a tap. (*Mach.*) A fluted, threaded tool for cutting female or inside threads. (*Mech. Drg.*) An indication that a hole is to be tapped. It is usually indicated thus: 1½″—6 NC—2, which means that the hole is to be tapped with a 1½-in. tap, 6 National Coarse threads per inch, to a class 2 fit.

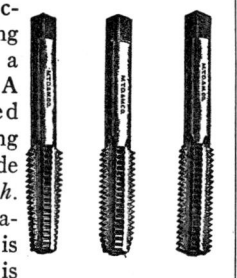

Taper, Plug, and Bottoming Taps

tap bolt (*Mach.*) A bolt usually threaded for its entire length. It is finished only on the point and the underside of the head. Tap bolts are made with both square and hexagon heads.

tape (*Engin.*) A flexible, measuring scale made of thin steel, or of linen or cotton, usually contained in a circular case into which it may be rewound after use.

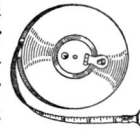

Steel Tape

ta′per (*Mech.*) A gradual and uniform decrease in size, as a tapered socket, a tapered shaft, a tapered shank.

ta′per at-tach′ment (*Mach.*) That adjustable mechanism attached to a lathe, which permits accurate taper turning.

ta′pered–shank drill (*Mach.*) A drill, twist or otherwise, whose shank is tapered, for use with the ordinary drill spindle or socket.

ta′pered spindle (*Mach.*) A spindle containing a tapered recess for the reception of a center or a tapered-shank tool.

ta′per gauge (*Mach.*) A gauge for testing the accuracy of tapers, either inside or outside.

ta′per per ft. (*Mach.*) The manner of expressing the amount of taper; that is the Jarno taper is .6 in. per ft., and Brown and Sharpe is .5 in. per ft. except for number 10.

ta′per pin (*Mech. Engin.*) Made of round stock, used for fastening some part to a shaft. It is graded in size by numbers from 1 to 10. No. 1 is .156 in. diameter at the large end, and is from ¾ to 1 in. long. No. 10 is .706 in. diameter at the large end, and 1½ to 6 in. long.

ta′per–pin drills (*Metalwk.*) Drills tapered ¼ in. per ft. and having serrated edges; designed for drilling holes for taper pins direct from solid metal.

ta′per ream′er (*Mach.*) Reamer of the ordinary fluted type for reaming tapered holes; as a reamer used to prepare a hole for a tapered pin.

ta′per tap. A tap tapered in the direction of its length, in order to afford ease in cutting when commencing a screw thread in a drilled hole.

ta′per turn′ing (*Mach.*) Lathe turning by setting over the tailstock or by the use of a taper attachment.

tap′es-try (*Furn.*) An ornamental fabric used for hangings and for furniture coverings.

tap, hob, Sell′ers (*Mach.*) A long tap, threaded only along the central portion of its length and containing many flutes; it is used for threading dies and "chasers."

tap hole (*Fdry.*) The hole in the breast of a cupola through which the molten metal is drawn.

tapped face′plate (*Shopwk.*) A faceplate having tapped holes instead of, or in addition to slots.

tap′per tap (*Mach.*) Special tap used for tapping nuts in tapping machines.

tap′pet (*Auto.*) A reciprocating part between the cam and the valve.

tap′pet valve (*Auto.*) Valve with a disk head from which extends a spindle to serve as a pilot. Commonly used in internal-combustion engines.

tap′ping (*Metalwkg.*) The threading of a hole by means of a tap, either by hand or by machine.

tap′ping bar (*Fdry.*) An iron rod from 3/4 to 1 1/4 in. diameter and from 3 to 10 ft. long; used to open the cupola so that molten iron may be drawn off.

tap′ping ma′chine (*Shopwk.*) A machine frequently used in production work on small parts. It has a forward motion for running a tap into a hole, and a reverse motion for backing it out.

tap re-mov′er (*Shopwk.*) A tool for gripping a broken tap in order that it may be backed out of the hole in which it was broken.

tap splice (*Elec.*) (See BRANCH SPLICE.)

tap wrench (*Mach.*) The double-armed lever with which a tap is gripped and operated during the process of tapping holes.

Tap Wrench

tar′nish. Loss of luster. To become dull.

tar-pau′lin. A stout waterproof covering of canvas.

taut. Tense, tight; as a rope pulled taut, thus eliminating sag.

taw′ing (*Leather.*) The tanning of leather with alum or salt.

tax′i (*Aero.*) To run an airplane over the ground, or a seaplane over the water, under its own power.

tax′i-me′ter (*Mech.*) A device for measuring the distance traveled by a taxicab; also computes fares.

tax′i-way (*Aero.*) A specially prepared area over which airplanes may taxi to and from the landing area of a landing field.

T bevel. A woodworker's tool. (See BEVEL.)

T bolt (*Mach.*) A bolt shaped like the letter T, the head being a transverse piece, which fits into the recessed undercut T slots, as on the table of a milling machine or planing machine.

teak (*Woodwkg.*) An East Indian tree of large size. The wood is very durable, and is highly prized for shipbuilding and for furniture.

tears (tāres) (*Tel.*) The horizontal disturbance in a television picture caused by noise which makes the picture appear to tear apart.

tech′ni-cal. Pertains to some partic-

ular art, science, trade, or occupation, as technical school, term, etc.

tech'ni-cal di-rec'tor (*Tel.*) Supervisor of technical devices and personnel in studio.

tech-nol'o-gy. The branch of knowledge that deals with the industrial arts.

tee (*Piping*) A fitting for connecting pipes of unequal sizes, or for changing direction of pipe runs. A bullhead tee is one with outlet larger than opening on run; straight tee has all openings of same size.

tel'e-cast (*Tel.*) A television program or a television broadcast.

tel'e-graph (*Elec.*) A means of transmitting to, and receiving from distant points, messages, by a series of electrically transmitted signals.

tel'e-phone (*Elec.*) An instrument for the electrical transmission of the voice over long distances.

tel'e-phone drop (*Elec.*) On a switchboard, one of the annunciator drops which, by falling, attracts the attention of the operator when a subscriber wishes a connection.

tel'e-phone ex-change' (*Elec.*) A central station equipped with switchboards for making connections between subscribers in its section and through other exchanges with any other line in the system.

tel'e-phone hook switch (*Elec.*) The switch controlled by a forked lever which holds and operates by the weight of the receiver. Used to control the operation of the ringing and talking circuits.

te-leph'o-ny. Operation of a telephone or system of telephones.

tel'e-pho'to lens (*Tel.*) Lens of very narrow angle used to provide large-size images at extreme distances.

tel'e-scope (*Phys.*) An optical instrument used in obtaining an enlarged, clearer view of some distant object.

tel'e-vi'sion (*Tel.*) Literally, seeing at a distance. A system of communications in which a picture scene is transmitted by dividing it, by a scanning process, into a great number of minute electrical signals. The electrical signals are received and changed back into light and shade to correspond with the original picture as seen by the television camera.

tel'e-vi'sion cam'er-a tube (*Tel.*) An electronic tube used to convert the light and shade of a scene into electrical signals.

tell'tale (*Mech.*) Usually a makeshift device attached to a machine or piece of work, for the purpose of indicating to the workman that a certain operation is completed, or that the direction of motion should be reversed, etc. A homemade indicator.

tem'per-a-ture (*Phys.*) Degree of heat possessed by a body.

tem'per-ing (*Forg. and Mech.*) The treatment of steel to bring it to the degree of hardness necessary for the work to be done. In carbon steels, this is accomplished by heating the piece to a cherry-red color, quenching it in oil or water temporarily, then, after an inspection of the color, giving it a final quenching. The hardening of special steels is accomplished by "heat treatment."

tem'per-ing sand (*Fdry.*) The mixing of foundry sand with water to bring it to the proper degree of dampness for molding purposes.

tem′plate (*M e c h.*) Any temporary pattern, guide, or model, by which work is either marked out, or by which its accuracy is checked.

tem′ple or ten′ter-hook′ (*Textile*) A device for keeping cloth stretched to an even width in hand weaving.

te-nac′i-ty (tĕ-năs′ĭ-tĭ) That property by which a material resists forces tending to tear it apart.

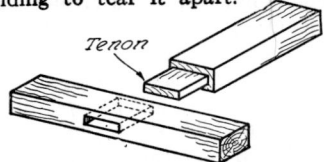

ten′on (*C a r p.*) A tongue projecting from the end of a piece of timber, which, with the mortise into which it fits, constitutes a mortise-and-tenon joint.

ten′on saw (*Woodwkg.*) An ordinary backsaw used by woodworkers on the bench.

ten′sile (*Engin.*) Of, or pertaining to extension or tension, as tensile action, tensile strength; capable of being stretched or drawn out.

ten′sile strain (*Engin.*) A strain or pull in a longitudinal direction; the reverse of a crushing strain.

ten′sile strength. The strength necessary to enable a bar or structure to resist a tensile strain. (*Phys.*) The amount of directly applied pull which a part will stand before it breaks. It is expressed as the number of pounds of force required to break a bar 1 sq. in. in area.

ten′sile stress (*Engin.*) The stress to which a bar or structure is subject when in tension.

ten′sion. A pulling force; the opposite of compression.

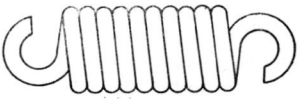
Tension Spring

ten′sion spring (*Mech.*) Any spring designed to be operated under a pulling strain.

ter′mi-nal (*Arch.*) The finish to a newel or standard. (*Elec.*) A point at which a connection is made between an electrical apparatus and the external circuit.

term of pat′ent. The length of time during which full protection is given one's rights in a patent. The term is seventeen years with no extensions allowed.

ter′na-ry steel (*M e t a l.*) A general term which includes all alloy steels composed of iron, carbon, and one other special element.

terne′plate (*Metal.*) Ordinary black, soft steel plate, coated both sides with an alloy of 80 per cent lead and 20 per cent tin.

ter′race (*Arch.*) A raised level space as a lawn, having at least one vertical or sloping side.

ter′ra cot′ta (*A r c h.*) A burned-clay product widely used for ornamental work on the exterior of buildings.

ter-raz′zo floor′ing (tĕr-rät′sō) (*Bldg.*) A flooring of the granolithic type with polished surface; the body consists of fragments of colored stone imbedded in neat cement.

ter′ti-a-ry col′or (tûr′shĭ-å-rĭ) A color obtained by mixing the secondary colors, orange, green, and violet, in pairs. The hues thus made are olive, citrine, and russet.

Tes′la coil (*Elec.*) A type of induction coil for obtaining high voltages and frequencies. Its primary winding consists of a few turns of heavy wire excited by a high voltage and controlled by a rotary spark gap and the secondary winding is of fine wire.

tes′ser-a (tĕs′ẽr-à) (*A r c h.*) A small square stone or tile used in making mosaic pavements, walks, etc.

test bar (*Fdry.*) The tests on gray cast iron are for transverse strength, flexure, shrinkage, chill, and hardness. The bars on which the tests are made are usually about 1¼ in. diameter and 15 in. long.

test bench (*Auto. Elec.*) A bench or table fitted with various instruments and gauges for testing automotive electrical equipment.

tes′ter (*Furn.*) A canopy over a bed supported by the bed posts.

test′ing (*Mech.*) A procedure for determining whether mechanical devices or electrical equipment is in proper workable condition.

test′ing machine (*E n g i n.*) A machine used for testing the strength and elasticity of materials.

test′ing set (*Elec.*) Those instruments or devices used for determining whether wiring or equipment is in perfect working order.

test lamp (*Elec.*) An ordinary lamp in a weatherproof socket.

test pat′tern (*Tel.*) A drawing containing a group of lines and circles, etc., transmitted for receiver adjustment and transmitter test purposes.

tet′ra-eth′yl lead (*Chem.*) A poisonous, volatile liquid added in small quantities to gasoline to reduce engine knock.

text (*Print.*) The body matter of a book or other piece of printing.

text type (*Print.*) A term applied to any black letter or Old English type.

T–head en′gine (*Auto.*) A cross section of the motor block resembles the letter T. Valves are arranged on both sides of the engine, requiring two camshafts and two camshaft-drive gears. An expensive type of construction.

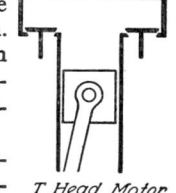

T Head Motor

the′o-rem. A truth capable of demonstration. A proposition to be proved.

the′o-ret′i-cal. Pertaining to or depending on an abstract principle; speculative; hypothetical.

the′-o-ry (*Science*) An attempt to account for a number of closely related observations or phenomena.

ther′lo (*Metal.*) An alloy of copper, aluminum, and manganese, used for instrument shunts and coils. It has a low temperature coefficient, and its thermoelectric power against copper is very low.

ther′mal con′duc-tiv′i-ty (*W e l d.*) The ability of a metal to transmit heat through its mass. The rapidity with which a metal conducts heat should be taken into consideration both in preheating and in the size of the blowpipe selected.

ther′mal jet en′gine (*Aero.*) A jet engine that utilizes heat to expand gases for rearward ejection. This is the usual form of aircraft jet engine.

ther′mal re-ac′tion (*Plast.*) Heat generated within the plastic by chemical reaction during its solidification.

ther′mal u′nit (*Phys.*) A unit chosen for the comparison or calculation of quantities of heat; used as a standard for comparison of other quantities.

ther'mit (*Engin.*) A mixture of powdered aluminum, and a metallic oxide as iron, chromium, or manganese oxide. It is used extensively in welding by the thermit process.

ther'mit (pres'sure) weld'ing. A pressure-welding process wherein the heat is obtained from liquid products of a thermit reaction.

ther'mit weld'ing. A nonpressure (fusion) welding process wherein the heat is obtained from liquid steel produced by a thermit reaction, and the filler metal is supplied by the steel produced in this reaction.

ther'mo-cou'ple (*Elec.*) An electrical generator made by the welding together, at one end, of two dissimilar metal rods or wires, which produce electricity at the free ends when the weld is heated; used in pyrometers for measuring extreme heat.

ther'mo-dy-nam'ics (*Engin.*) The science which treats of heat as a form of energy or mode of work.

ther'mo-e-lec'tric met'als. Metals or alloys used in thermocouples for measuring high temperatures. Platinum, nickel, copper, rhodium, etc., are much used.

ther'mo-graph (*Aero.*) An instrument for recording temperature.

ther-mom'e-ter. An instrument for measuring variations in temperature.

ther'mo-nu'cle-ar re-ac'tion (*Chem.*) A reaction in which two light nuclei combine to form a heavier atom, and thus releasing a large amount of energy.

ther'mo pile (*Elec.*) A group of dissimilar materials arranged alternately in such a manner that the junctions can be heated to produce an electric current.

ther'mo-plas'tic (*Plast.*) A plastic division in the families of plastics. (See PLASTICS.) A resin product in these families can be repeatedly softened by heat and changed in form. It hardens on cooling.

ther'mo-set (*Plast.*) A second plastic division. (See PLASTICS.) The resins in the families under this category take a form in a mold where they are chemically changed by the reaction of heat and pressure, which sets the material and reduces it to an infusible state.

ther'mo-si'phon sys'tem (*A u t o.*) This type of cooling system is based on the fact that hot water rises and cooler water settles in the system. Water heated by the engine rises within it and flows to the top of the radiator where it is cooled; by the time it reaches the bottom of the radiator it is relatively cool and starts on its round again.

ther'mo-stat. A device for automatic regulation of temperature.

ther'mo-stat'ic (*Heating*) In steam heating systems, device for draining air and condensation from radiators, etc., without permitting the passage of steam. The discharge valve is operated by means of a diaphragm filled with a volatile liquid which causes the rapid expansion or contraction.

ther'mo-stat'ic el'e-ment. An element or device which, when it receives the degree of heat for which it is constructed to operate, will cause the opening or closing of valves, switches, or other parts. A common form is a coil of hollow, metal tubing filled with ether or some other liquid and sealed at both ends. A less used form consists of a bimetal arm which, by contraction and expansion, operates a butterfly valve.

thick′ness gauge or feeler (*Mech.*) It is shaped somewhat like a pocket-knife, and has blades varying in thickness by thousandths of an inch. It is used in adjusting parts with a desired amount of clearance, as the valves of an automobile motor.

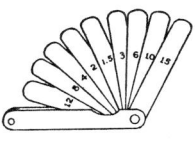

Thickness Gauge

thick′ness ra′tio (*Aero.*) The ratio of the maximum thickness of an airfoil section to its chord.

thick space (*Print.*) Spaces cast three to an em of any particular body.

thim′ble (*Mech.*) (1) A short tube, usually metal, to slip in, over, or about something, as over a bolt, pin, etc. (2) A grooved ring set in the eye of a rope or cable to prevent chafing and deformation.

T hinge (*Bldg.*) Consists of a strap with a "butt" at right angles to it. Used mainly for outside work on gates, doors, etc.

thin space (*Print.*) Spaces cast five to an em of their own body.

third–an′gle pro-jec′tion (*Draft.*) Projection of different views in mechanical drawing as practiced in the United States; usually a plan or top view, a front view, and a side or end view. Each view is taken with reference to the near side of the view from which it is projected.

third brush (*Auto.*) An auxiliary brush which regulates the current output of the generator by increasing or decreasing the field-coil current.

third–class lev′er (lĕv′ẽr)(*Mech.*) A lever with the power applied between weight and fulcrum.

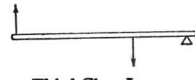

Third-Class Lever

thix-ot′rop-ic (*Plast.*) Liquid plastics which contain suspended solids, such as finely divided silica, are gel-like at rest, but fluid when applied. A thixatropic resin remains more or less fixed on an inclined surface, inhibiting its flow downward.

thix-ot′ro-py (*Chem. Plast.*) The property by which some compositions become solid at rest but liquify again on agitation.

thread. A fine cord or filament, usually of nonmetallic material, as silk, cotton or wool. Also see SCREW THREAD.

thread–cut′ting screws (*Mach.*) The entering end of such screws contains a slot with serrated cutting edge which makes the use of a tap unnecessary. The screw cuts its own threads. The use of thread-cutting screws is indicated for sheet metals, softer alloys, plastics, etc.

thread′ed sleeve (*Shopwk.*) A shell of metal, usually cylindrical and threaded internally; used for connecting two pieces of pipe or rods.

thread gauge (*Metalwk.*) A gauge for checking the pitch of screw threads.

thread′ing. The cutting of screw threads, either internal or external.

thread mil′ler (*Mach.*) A milling machine designed for thread and worm cutting.

thread plug (*Plast.*) A part of a mold that shapes an internal thread which must be unscrewed from the finished piece.

thread–roll'ing (*Mach.*) The formation of screw threads by hardened rolls or dies which roll grooves into a blank and raise enough metal above the surface of the blank to form a thread; such threads are stronger and less expensive than cut threads.

threads per inch (*Mach.*) Refers to thread size. Standard practice fixes the number of threads per inch for any diameter; that is ½-in. diameter, 13 threads per inch.; 1-in. diameter, 8 threads per inch, etc. The purposes of threads are: (*a*) to hold parts together, i.e., screws, bolts, nuts, etc.; (*b*) to tighten parts together to withstand the pressure of liquids or gases, i.e., pipes, fittings, etc.; (*c*) to transmit power as through jack screws, worm drives, etc.; (*d*) to adjust with great accuracy the parts of such instruments as calipers, micrometers, etc.

thread tool (*Mach.*) A lathe tool ground to the shape of the profile of the thread it is to cut.

three-and-four-flut'ed drills (*Metalwk.*) Often used in place of roughing reamers. They are not suited to drilling from the solid, but are used to enlarge cored or punched holes.

three'–phase (*Elec.*) Three a.c. windings or circuits differing in phase by 120 electrical degrees.

three ply (*Furn.*) Plywood built up, using three separate plies.

three-point sus-pen'sion (*Auto.*) A system of automobile-engine mounting in which the weight is carried at only three points.

three–quar'ter bind'ing (*Bookbndg.*) Similar to half binding but with more leather showing.

three–quar'ter float'ing ax'le (*A u t o.*) The rear-axle housing extends into the hubs of the wheels. The outer ends of the axle shafts are welded or keyed to the hub flanges, and the flange is bolted to the wheel hub. Only one bearing is used on each wheel hub and it is mounted on the axle housing.

three–square file (*Mech.*) A term commonly applied to a three-cornered file; used for saw sharpening.

three–way switch (*Elec.*) A switch which provides for the control of a light, or set of lights, from two different points.

three–wire cir'cuit (*Elec.*) A circuit of three wires giving a potential difference between the center or neutral wire and either of the outside wires of 125 volts, and 250 volts between the two outside wires. Built on the principle of two generators in series with a tap.

three–wire meth'od. A method of measuring the pitch diameter of screws as recommended by the U. S. Bureau of Standards. See handbooks for application.

three–wire trans-form'er (*Elec.*) A transformer having the secondary tapped at its center in order to have equal voltage between it and either outside ends or connections, and double this voltage between the two outside or end connections.

thresh'old (*Arch.*) (1) The entrance

to a building. (2) The plank, stone, or piece of timber under a door.

throat (*Arch.*) The opening from the fireplace into the smoke chamber. (*Mach.*) The gap in the frame behind the tool in a punching machine, the size of work taken being limited by the depth of the gap.

throt'tle (*Mech.*) To shut off or regulate, as steam. A device for accomplishing the same.

throt'tle valve (*Mech.*) (1) A thin, flat disk valve placed in a pipe or opening for the purpose of closing it partly or entirely, as in controlling the flow of air to be mixed with gas in an automobile motor. (2) A valve in a steam line for controlling the flow.

through bolt (*Mach.*) A bolt which passes through clearance holes in the pieces to be joined. Clamping actions are secured entirely by use of a nut.

Through Bolt

through shake (*Wood*) A shake, or separation of wood between annual rings, which extends between two faces of a timber.

throw (*Mech.*) The amount of eccentricity, as in the crankshaft of an engine. The throw is equal to half the length of the stroke of the piston.

throw'ing (*Ceram.*) The shaping of ware on a potter's wheel.

throw' out col'lar (*Auto.*) A steel ring or collar mounted on an oilless bearing. Used to engage and disengage the clutch.

thrust bear'ing or thrust block (*Mach.*) The bearing which receives the longitudinal thrust or pressure of a shaft.

thrust col'lar (*Mach.*) A collar turned on the body of a shaft or attached to it, for the purpose of absorbing or reducing end play of the shaft or parts mounted on the shaft.

thumb nut (*Mach.*) A wing nut or one so shaped that it can be operated by thumb and forefinger.

thumb plane (*Woodwkg.*) A name occasionally applied to a small plane 4 or 5 in. long, having a bit about 1 in. in width.

thumb screw (*Mech.*) A screw to be turned with the thumb and finger.

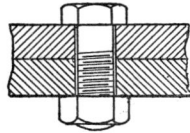

Thumb Screw

thumb'tack' (*Draw.*) A sharp pointed tack with relatively broad head; used by draftsmen for fastening down drawing paper.

thurm (*Cabwk.*) To work with saw and chisel across the grain, producing in upright square members, patterns like those produced by turning.

tie (*Arch.*) A piece inserted or attached to other pieces to hold them in position.

tie beam (*Arch.*) A beam which ties together or prevents the spreading out of the lower ends of the rafters of roof trusses.

tie dye'ing (*Textile*) Certain parts of the fabric to be tied are wound tightly with string to prevent the material from taking the dye. The pattern appears when the string is removed.

tie piece (*Wood Patmkg.*) A stiffening piece used on a pattern. It is not indicated on the drawing, and it need

tier. not be reproduced in the casting.

tier. To pile up one above another, as a tier of boxes.

tier'ing machine. A labor-saving machine, used for stacking up or tiering work or materials.

tie rod (*Auto. Mech.*) The transverse rod connecting the front wheels of an automobile in order to permit them to act as a unit in steering.

tie'-up ma·te'ri·al (*Print.*) An expression which includes all the material used in tying up composed types.

tight fit (*Mech.*) A fit made with light pressure.

tight pul'ley (*Mach.*) A pulley attached to its shaft; as opposed to a loose pulley which runs free on its shaft.

tile (*Arch.*) Terra cotta, cement, or glass pieces used for roofing; also made in artistic designs and finishes for floor and wall covering.

tilt'-top' ta'ble (*Furn.*) A pedestal table with the top so hinged that it can be swung from a horizontal to a vertical position.

tim'ber. Trees in the forest, trees when cut into logs or when sawed into large squared sizes. Specifically, lumber 5 inches or more in the least dimension.

tim'ber trestle (*Engin.*) Name applied to such wooden structures as are used for carrying railroad tracks across a stream or ravine.

time meas'ure.

```
60 seconds (sec.) = 1 minute (min.)
60 minutes       = 1 hour (hr.)
24 hours         = 1 day
 7 days          = 1 week (wk.)
28, 29, 30, or 31
   days          = 1 calendar month (mo.)
30 days          = 1 month in computing
                       interest
52 weeks         = 1 year (yr.)
365 days         = 1 year (yr.)
366 days         = 1 leap year
```

tim'er (*Auto.*) A device used on automobiles to break primary ignition circuit at the proper time for the spark to occur in cylinders.

time switch (*Elec.*) A clock-controlled switch.

tim'ing (*Auto. Mech.*) (1) The adjustment of valves and crankshaft of an engine in their relative position to produce the greatest effective output in h.p. (2) The point at which ignition breaker is set in relation to top dead-center position of the piston to secure the greatest effective expansive force upon head of piston.

tim'ing gear (*Auto.*) The gears that drive the camshaft so that the valves operate in correct time with the pistons. Since the camshaft has to turn once for every two revolutions of the crankshaft, these gears must be in the ratio of 2 to 1.

tim'ing marks (*Auto.*) *Ignition:* Marks on engine flywheel or dynamic balancer that align with a pointer at the instant No. 1 cylinder is ready to fire. *Valve:* Marks on timing gears or sprockets to enable mechanics to quickly and accurately time valves to piston position.

tin (*Metal.*) A silvery-white metal with specific gravity 7.3. It is of very great value in the industries, chiefly in the making of alloys.

tinc'ture (*Wood Fin.*) The finer and more soluble parts of a substance separated by a solvent.

tin'der. Any dry inflammable material such as might be used for kindling a fire.

tin'ning (*Metal.*) (1) The process of coating iron plates with tin, in tin-plate manufacture. (2) The coating of a soldering iron with solder previous to its use.

tin'-plate' (*Metal.*) A thin sheet of steel coated with tin.

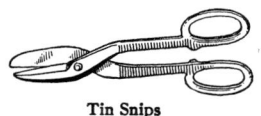

Tin Snips

tin'smith'. One who makes articles from tin plates.

tin snips (*Sheet-Met. Wk.*) The ordinary hand shears used by sheet-metal workers.

tint block (*Print.*) A flat plate or electrotype used for printing a solid color. Usually the color is light or in contrast to the base color.

tints (*Paint.*) Light colorings, especially colors containing some white.

tip ra'dius (*Aero.*) (Or propeller radius.) The distance of the outermost point of a propeller blade from the axis of rotation.

tire bolt. A bolt having a flat unslotted head; used for attaching the metal tire to the felloe of a wheel.

tire tool (*Auto.*) A flat bar of iron or steel commonly spoken of as tire iron used for applying and removing tires. Any tool used for the same purpose can be considered a tire tool.

tis'sue ma-nil'a (*Papermkg.*) Manila-colored tissue made of strong fiber.

tis'sue pa'per (*Papermkg.*) A general term used descriptively with reference to different grades of very thin paper.

ti-ta'ni-um (tī-tā'nĭ-ŭm) (*Metal.*) A metallic element of the carbon group. Used in alloys with copper, bronze, and other metals. Titanium oxide is one of the most important of the white pigments. Paints made from it have exceptional qualities.

ti'tle block (*Draft.*) The outlined space usually in the lower right corner, or in strip form across the bottom of a drawing, containing name of company, title of drawing, scale, date, and such other information as may be considered necessary.

ti'tle–page (*Print.*) That page, at the beginning of a book, which contains the title, the name of the author, and the name of the publisher.

T joint (*Forg.*) A type of welded joint used for uniting two pieces of iron at right angles to each other. (*Plumb.*) The ordinary three-way pipe fitting, in which one branch is at right angles to the other two and midway between them.

T.N.T. tri-ni'tro-tol'u-ol (trī-nī'trô-tŏl'û-ōl) (*Chem.*) ($C_7H_5(NO_2)_3$) Obtained by nitrating toluol. Melting point 80 deg. C. An explosive not particularly sensitive to shock, which makes it relatively safe to handle.

to'bin bronze (*Metal.*) A trade name for an alloy of copper, zinc, tin, iron, and lead. It has a high tensile strength and resistance to corrosive action of salt water, which makes it desirable for ship fittings.

toe (*Metalwk.*) The edge of a flange on a bar.

toe–in (*Auto.*) Relates to the setting of the front wheels so that they will be from $\frac{1}{8}$ to $\frac{1}{4}$ in. closer together at the front than at the rear. This is necessary in order to reduce tire wear to a minimum. It also makes the car easier to steer and compensates for the tendency of the wheels to spread when the car is being operated at high speed.

toe'ing (*Woodwkg.*) The driving of nails or brads obliquely, near the end of one piece, to attach it to another.

toe'nail'ing (*Woodwk.*) The driving of nails slantwise as in floor laying to avoid having nailheads show on the surface.

toe switch (*Auto.*) That switch, attached to the floor boards of the car, which, when pressed by the foot, causes the starter to operate.

tog'gle (*Mech.*) A double joint having a central hinge like an elbow.

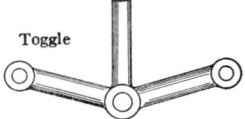
Toggle

tog'gle bolt (*Elec.*) Used for attaching articles to a hollow-tile wall. It consists of a screw with a swivel piece attached near the end. This piece may be swung into a lengthwise position while the bolt is being inserted, after which it swings to a right-angle position, thus permitting "pulling up" on the bolt.

tog'gle switch (*Elec.*) A switch which opens or closes electrical contacts with a quick movement when the knob or projecting arm is pushed up or down or to one side or the other.

Toggle Switch

tol'er-ance (*Mach.*) Allowable inexactness or error in the dimensions of manufactured machine parts. (*Mech.*) Also called limit or allowance.

tol'u-ene (tŏl'ū-ēn) (*Chem.*) ($C_6H_5CH_3$) A coal-tar product. Its principal uses are in the manufacture of dyestuffs and T.N.T.

ton'can met'al (*Metal.*) A trade name for a highly refined, low-carbon steel or iron much used for sheet-metal work because of its corrosion-resistant qualities.

tone (*Color*) The shade, hue, or degree of color, as a dark or light tone.

tongs (*Forg.*) A two-legged instrument used for picking something up or for holding material while it is being worked. Also called a pair of tongs.

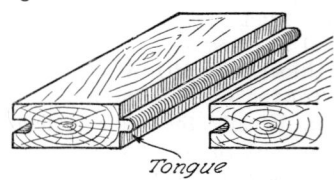
Tongue

tongue (*Arch.*) A projecting bead so cut on the edge of a board that it may fit into a corresponding groove on the edge of another piece.

tool bit (*Mach.*) A small piece of high-speed steel mounted in a tool holder and used as a cutting tool.

tool box or tool head (*Mach.*) On planing machines, that assemblage of parts attached to the cross side which carries the tool. It is so constructed that feed may be imparted to the tool.

tool hold'er for lathe or plan'er (*Shopwk.*) A bar, or piece of steel, into which a cutter is inserted, permitting the use of small pieces of expensive steel. The cutter may be removed for sharpening or renewal without moving the holder.

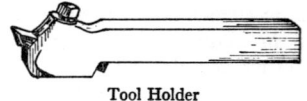
Tool Holder

tool′ing calf (*Leather.*) A bark-tanned leather, excellent for tooling work.

tool′ing sheep′skin (*Leather.*) An inexpensive leather obtainable in colors. Adapted to the making of small articles, such as coin purses, cardholders, key cases, etc.

tool′ing up. The preparation and assembling of special tools, fixtures, etc., which enable a manufacturer to use mass-production methods in putting out a product.

tool, knurl′ing (nûr′lĭng) (*Shopwk.*) A tool, containing knurls, which is held firmly against a piece of revolving work to produce a milled surface, both for ornamentation and to provide a better grip.

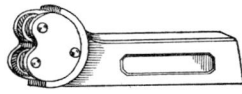

Knurling Tool

tool′ mak′er (*Mach.*) A workman skilled in the making of jigs, fixtures, gauges, etc.

tool′mak′er's clamp. An all-metal clamp similar in design but smaller than a woodworker's handscrew or screw clamp.

tool post (*Mach.*) A circular post attached to the top of a lathe slide rest for the clamping down of the cutting tools.

tool–post′ ring (*Mach.*) The dish or ring, with concave upper face which forms a seat for the tool-post rocker.

tool–post rock′er (*Mach.*) The fingerlike part of steel inserted in the slot of the tool post to give proper adjustment for height of the cutting tool with regard to the work.

tool′room′ (*Mach.*) A room in which tools and parts are stored and from which they are issued to workmen; a shop where jigs, fixtures, etc., are made, stored, and repaired.

tools, in-sert′ed cut′ter (*Shopwk.*) Before the invention of the high-speed steels, which are quite expensive, practically all tools for machine work were made in one piece of carbon steel. Later, the difficulty of working the high-speed steels, and their high cost, brought on the market tool holders, for which small cutters or blades, already formed to the desired shape, can be easily obtained.

tool steel (*Metal.*) Any of the carbon steels or the high-speed steels suitable for use as cutters.

tool tip (*Mach.*) A small cutting piece of cemented carbide, welded or brazed on a solid shank of carbon steel. See TUNGSTEN CARBIDE.

tooth (*Papermkg.*) A term used with reference to a paper finish denoting that it is suitable for crayon or pencil drawing.

tooth face (*Mach.*) The surface of a machine-tool cutter on which the chip impinges as it is cut from the work.

tooth′ing (*Masonry*) Leaving a section of brickwork toothed so that the brickwork to follow can be bonded into it. It consists of allowing alternate courses to project a sufficient distance to assure a good bond with the portion to be built later.

tooth or′na-ment (*Arch.*) One of the peculiar marks of the early English period of Gothic architecture, generally inserted in the hollow moldings of doorways, windows, etc.

top (*Textile*) The long wool fibers for worsted yarn prepared by the combing process.

top dead cen'ter (*Auto.*) The extreme top position of the No. 1 piston in its cylinder. This position is indicated by a mark on the flywheel. All adjustments for engine efficiency are made with relation to this position as a basis.

top'ping (*Textile*) Slipping a dyed material into a bath of another color.

torque (tôrk) (*E l e c.*) The turning effort of a rotor. (*Engin.*) The turning effort or twist which a shaft sustains when transmitting power.

torque arm (*Auto.*) An arm or pair of arms used to prevent any turning of the rear-axle housing when power is applied to the rear axle.

torque converter (*Auto. Mech.*) A specially designed transmission used to increase torque at the rear wheels, providing a quicker pick-up.

torque stand (*Aero., Auto.*) A test stand on which the engine torque is measured.

torque wrench (*Mech.*) A wrench designed to disengage when the torque required to turn a bolt or nut increases beyond a certain point; also a wrench with a gauge that shows pressure exerted.

tor'sion (*Engin.*) The act of twisting. The tendency to deform, as a rod, by twisting.

tor'sion-al strength (*E n g i n.*) The strength necessary to enable a bar or structure to resist a torsional strain. The strength of a shaft to resist torsion varies as the cube of its diameter.

tor'sion bal'anc-er (*Auto. Mech.*) A device mounted on the end of the crankshaft to reduce vibration set up by piston impulses.

tor'sion spring. A helical spring which operates when both ends are fastened, producing a coiling and uncoiling motion as in a door spring.

tor'so (*Arch.*) (1) A term applied to columns with twisted shafts. (2) A damaged statue of which only the trunk remains.

to'rus (*Arch.*) A large convex molding of nearly semicircular section, largely used as a base molding.

Torus

tote box'es or pans (*Shopwk.*) Boxes or pans, generally of metal, used in industrial establishments for carrying or storing small parts. They are usually slightly tapered on the sides so that, when empty, they can be stacked.

tough'ness (*Engin.*) The resistance of a metal to begin permanent deformation and the further resistance to failure after permanent deformation has begun.

tour'ing car (*Auto.*) An obsolete term for a car body of open design, suitable for five or seven passengers. See "phaeton."

tow'er (*Arch.*) A structure larger than a pinnacle and less tapering than a steeple; frequently a part of a large building.

T plate (*Bldg. and Furn.*) A metal plate shaped like a letter T used for strengthening a joint where the end of one and the side of another meet.

T Plate

trace (*Draw.*) To follow as with a pencil; sketch; map out. To copy, as a drawing on tracing linen or tracing paper.

trac'er. An apprentice or subdraftsman who prepares tracings from the

drawings made by a draftsman called the detailer.

trac′er-y (*Arch.*) The ornamentation of panels, circular windows, window heads, etc.

tra-che′li-um (trȧ-kē′lĭ-ŭm) (*Arch.*) The neck of a Greek Doric column between the annulets and the grooves or hypotrachelium.

trac′ing (*Draw.*) Sketching; designing; drawing. Usually the linen, paper, or other transparent material on which a drawing has been made for quantity reproduction.

trac′ing a cir′cuit (*Auto. Elec.*) (1) Identifying a particular circuit from source to point of operation, visually, by means of meters, or by a bell-ringing generator, in order to locate faults or to add to the circuit. (2) Identifying a circuit by means of colored threads woven into the wire covering.

trac′ing lin′en (*Draw.*) A linen coated with a sizing on which drawings are made for reproduction.

trac′ing pa′per (*Draw.*) Thin semi-transparent paper on which drawings are made for blueprinting. It is much less expensive than tracing linen, and, when not to be used too frequently, serves almost equally well.

trac′ing tool (*L e a t h e r.*) A small, pointed tool, used both for tracing and finishing designs on leather.

trac′tion. Adhesive or rolling friction as of wheels on a road.

trac′tor air′plane (*Aero.*) An airplane with propeller or propellers forward of the main supporting surfaces.

trac′tor pro-pel′ler (*Aero.*) A propeller mounted on the forward end of the engine or propeller shaft.

trade′-un′ion. An alliance of workmen organized for the purpose of securing standardized privileges for all its members.

traf′fic beam (*A u t o. M e c h.*) An automobile headlight beam aimed downward to prevent the beam from blinding an oncoming driver. This beam is for use in city driving and for passing in country driving.

traf′fic-con-trol′ pro-jec′tor (*Aero.*) A projector designed to give light signals to an aircraft pilot.

trail′ing edge (*Aero.*) The rear edge of an airfoil or of a propeller.

train (*Shopwk.*) An arrangement of gears meshed together for the purpose of transmitting power and varying speed.

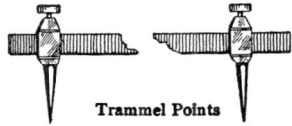

Trammel Points

tram′mel (*Draw. and Shopwk.*) A beam compass, in which the head slides along a straight bar. It is tightened by setscrews, and is used to strike radii too large for the capacity of an ordinary compass.

tran′sept (*Arch.*) That portion of a church which passes transversely between the nave and choir at right angles, and so forms a cross on the plan.

trans′fer. To remove from one place to another.

trans′fer cal′i-pers (*Mach.*) Used in measuring recesses and in places where the adjustment made must be shifted in order to remove them

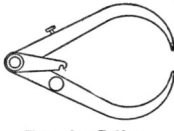

Transfer Caliper

trans′fer mold′ing (*Plast.*) Another name for injection molding of thermosetting materials.

trans′fer pa′per (*Papermkg.*) A specially finished paper of tissue substance used for making lithograph transfers and the like.

trans-form′er (*Elec.*) An instrument by means of which electrical currents are changed in regard to voltage and amperage from high to low or vice versa.

tran-sis′tor (*Elec.*) A compact unit performing many of the functions of vacuum tubes in electronic circuits with the advantage of small size and cool instantaneous operation; an active semiconductor device with three or more electrodes.

tran-sis′tor ra′dio (*Rad.*) One in which transistors are used instead of vacuum tubes. These are miniature components employed throughout the circuitry and power supply, usually small batteries in place of house current. The low power requirement of the transistors results in long battery life and their relatively small size permits compact design.

trans′it. Consists principally of (*a*) a telescope for sighting, (*b*) graduated arcs and a vernier for measuring horizontal and vertical angles, (*c*) a level, (*d*) a tripod with leveling screws. (*Surv.*) An instrument commonly used by surveyors and engineers for measuring angles, determining bearings, and also for leveling.

trans′ite (trăns′īt) (*Metal.*) A trade name for a material of asbestos fiber and Portland cement molded under high pressure. Used for fireproof walls, roofing, and in lining ovens, etc.

tran-si′tion strip (*Aero.*) A section of a landing area adjacent to a runway or other hard-surfaced area, constructed of crushed stone or other suitable material, properly bound, to insure safe landing and taxiing of an airplane across such a runway or area in any direction.

trans′it-man. One who operates a surveyor's transit. He need not necessarily be a graduate engineer.

trans-lu′cent (trăns-lū′sĕnt) Semitransparent. (*Papermkg.*) A coated cardboard having a glossy finish.

trans-mis′sion (*Auto.*) The name given to the arrangement of gears, contained in a housing attached to the rear end of the motor, by which variations of speed ratios and forward and reverse motion are obtained.

trans-mit′ter (*Elec.*) (1) In telephony, that part of the instrument into which one speaks. It consists of two flat carbon electrodes, one mounted on a vibrating diaphragm, and the other stationary. Between them is a mass of granular carbons. (2) In telegraphy, the key for sending signals.

trans-mit′ting set (*Radio*) A set consisting of apparatus employed in the generation of a modulated or continuous radio carrier wave at a certain frequency.

trans′mu-ta′tion (*Elec.*) The changing of one element into another. (See ALCHEMY.) In recent years transmutation has been accomplished by bombarding elements with particles given off by a radium preparation. Another method makes use of the cyclotron.

tran′som (*Arch.*) A small window over a door, or other window.

tran′som bar (*Arch.*) The horizontal member which divides an opening into two parts usually between top of a doorway and a transom above.

trans-par′ent. Transmitting light so that objects may be distinctly seen. Clear; luminous; bright.

trans-pose′ (*Algebra*) To transfer from one side of an equation to the other, with changed signs, so as to retain the equality of the members.

trap (*Engin.*) In steam heating systems, a device for draining condensation and air from radiators, piping systems, etc., without passing steam.

trap door (*Arch.*) A door or cover used to close off an opening in floor, ceiling, or roof.

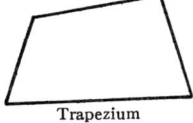
Trapezium

tra-pe′zi-um (*Geom.*) A quadrangular figure which has no sides parallel.

trap′e-zoid (*Geom.*) A quadrangular figure which has two parallel sides. (*Math.*) Area = half the sum of parallel sides × perpendicular height.
Trapezoid

trap rock. A very hard, durable rock, difficult to quarry; widely used for roads and railroad ballast.

trass (*Plaster.*) A kind of gray, yellow, or whitish earth common in volcanic districts, used in the making of a hydraulic cement.

trav′e-ling crane (*Fdry.*) A crane operated by steam or electric power, and so geared that it may travel longitudinally or transversely. The crane, usually of the overhead type, is mounted on a cross beam whose ends are carried on parallel rails.

trea′cle stage (*Plast.*) A thermosetting resin in liquid form.

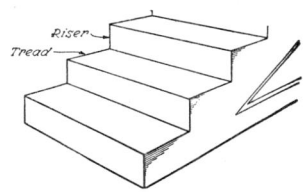

tread (*Arch.*) The flat portion of a step, as that portion on which the foot is placed when mounting the stairs.

trea′dle (*Mach.*) That portion of a machine operated by the foot.

tre′foil (*Arch.*) A three-lobed ornamental unit.
Trefoil

treil′lage (trĕl′åj) (*Arch.*) A trellis; latticework for supporting vines.

trel′lis (*Arch.*) An ornamental lattice made up of wooden strips to support vines; a summerhouse or the like made of latticework.

trench (*Engin.*) A long narrow excavation in the ground, as a trench dug for the laying of pipes.

trend. General tendency.

tre-pan′ (trĕ-păn′) (*v.*) (*Mach.*) To cut a circular groove around a hole.

T rest. The tool support on a wood-turning lathe. Also a support for work being ground by an abrasive wheel.

tres′tle (*Arch.*) Usually a horizontal beam with four braced legs, used in pairs to support a horizontal board. (*Engin.*) Timberwork supporting a road or railroad over a depression. (*Furn.*) A braced frame forming the support of a table top. (*Uphol.*) A sawhorse with a wider top with a stuffed roll around the outer edges.

tres'tle ta'ble (*Draw.*) A large drawing board carried on trestles.

tri'an'gle (*G e o m.*) A figure having three sides and three interior angles. A right triangle is one having one right angle; an equilateral triangle has equal sides and angles. Area = base x half perpendicular height.

tri-an'gu-lar scale (*Draw.*) A draftsman's scale having three faces and six graduated edges, one edge with full-size measurements and the others with various reductions in scale.

Triangular Truss

tri-an'gu-lar truss. A very popular truss for short spans especially for roof support.

tri-an'gu-la'tion (*Surv.*) The use of a series of triangles formed by lines which connect points of observation, for measuring distances on, and areas of, land and water.

trick'le charge (*E l e c.*) A rectifier changing alternating current to direct current, and delivering the same to a storage battery for 24 hours per day, usually at a very minute rate.

tri-fio'ri-um (*A r c h.*) The space between the sloping roof over the aisle and the aisle vaulting in a church.

tri'glyphs (trī'glĭfs)(*Arch.*) The flats of the Doric frieze which contain three vertical channels.

trig'o-nom'e-try (*Math.*) The science of measuring the sides and angles of triangles.

trim (*Arch.*) Ornamental parts of wood or metal; used to cover the joints between jambs and plaster wall around a door or window. (*Papermkg.*) The greatest width of finished paper which can be made on a paper machine allowing for trimming off the two deckle edges .

trim (air'plane)(*Aero.*) The attitude with respect to wind axes at which balance occurs in rectilinear flight with free controls. (*Arch.*) Moldings and other finishings about a door, window, etc., either internal or external.

trim an'gle (*A e r o.*) The angle between the horizontal and the longitudinal base line of a seaplane float or flying-boat hull. It is positive when the bow is higher than the stern.

trim'mer arch (*Arch.*) The rather flat arch such as is used to support a hearth.

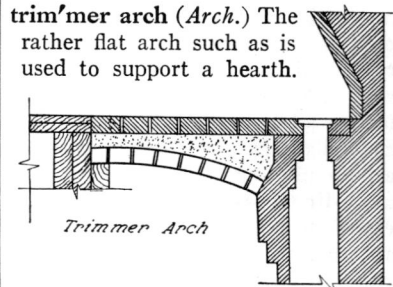
Trimmer Arch

trim′mers (*Arch.*) (See TRIMMING JOISTS.)

trim′ming dies (*Mach.*) Dies used to remove the superfluous metal left around the edges of many kinds of drawn or formed work.

trim′ming joist (*Arch.*) A joist which supports a header joist.

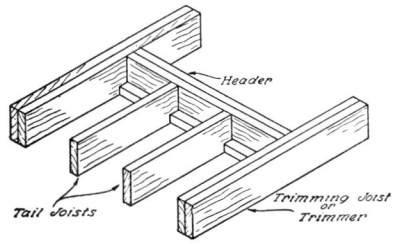

trip ham′mer (*Mach.*) A power hammer operated by a tripping mechanism which causes the hammer to drop.

tri-phib′i-an (*Aero.*) An airplane equipped with a gear for taking off and landing on land, water, snow or ice.

tri′plane (*Aero.*) An airplane with three main supporting surfaces, one above another.

tri′ple case (*Print.*) A type storage case spaced to hold three fonts of type.

tri′plex steel (*Metal.*) A steel produced by a combination of the Bessemer, basic open hearth and the electric processes.

trip′o-li. Rottenstone or decomposed limestone used for polishing.

trip′per (*Shopwk.*) A mechanism or part that suddenly releases another part. A "throw-out" or "shut-off" device operated either by hand or by power.

tri-sect′ (*Draw.*) To divide into three equal parts.

trol′ley (*Elec.*) A small wheel or a sliding contact usually at the end of a pole, used for the transfer of current for the operation of equipment. (*Mech.*) The head which supports a chain hoist and which is equipped with wheels to permit its motion on the beam or track which carries it.

trou′ble lamp (*Elec.*) An electric lamp at the end of a long extension cord used for bringing light to the source of trouble on repair jobs, etc.

trow′el (*Fdry.*) Foundry trowels are small and narrow, usually about 1½ in. wide and 5 or 6 in. long.

troy weight. A weight of 12 ounces to the pound, used by goldsmiths and jewelers.

24 grains (g.)	= 1 pennyweight (dwt.)
20 pennyweights	= 1 ounce (oz.)
12 ounces	= 1 pound (lb.)

true air′speed me′ter (*Aero.*) A type of anemometer which measures the true speed of an aircraft with relation to the air.

trun′nion (*Mech.*) One of two opposite cylindrical supporting lugs or projections from the side of an object, which allows it to be turned as on an axis.

truss (*Arch.*) A built-up framework of triangular units for supporting loads over long spans. (*Furn.*) A rigid frame, used in pairs to support the ends of a piece of furniture. These trusses are usually connected with some form of stretcher.

trussed ax′le (*Auto.*) An axle stiffened by the use of a truss rod. (See truss rod.)

trussed beam (*A r c h.*) A beam stiffened by a truss rod.

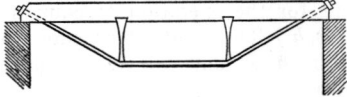

Trussed Beam

truss rod (*Engin.*) A rod attached to the ends of a trussed beam, through which the strain due to downward pressure is transmitted.

try square (*Mech.*) A small square used by mechanics in testing squareness of their work; also used to lay off right angles.

Try Square

T slot (*Mach.*) A recessed, undercut slot made in the table of a milling, planing, or other machine, to receive the head of a T bolt. The slot permits the easy adjustment of the bolt to the position desired.

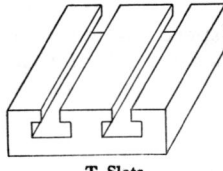

T Slots

T–slot cut′ter (*Mach.*) A milling cutter for finishing the wide portion of T slots.

T square (*Arch.*) A draftsman's tool, consisting of a blade from 2 to 3 in. wide and from 1 to 5 ft. long, attached at right angles to a head, which is at least twice as thick as the blade; used for ruling parallel, horizontal lines.

tube (*Elec.*) A general term including the devices used as a part of the apparatus for amplifying and detecting radio and other small currents and rectifying a.c. to d.c.

Tube Punch

tube punch (*Leather.*) A hand punch shaped somewhat like a pair of pliers and having a hollow tube or tubes for punching holes for snaps, eyelets, etc.

tub–siz′ing (*Papermkg.*) A process of surface sizing in which the web of paper is placed in the size vat.

tu′bu-lar ax′le (*Auto.*) Axle made of steel tubing.

tu′bu-lar ra′di-a′tor (*Auto.*) A radiator made up of many tubes through which the water of the cooling system circulates.

Tu′dor style (*Arch.*) The architecture of England during the reign of the Tudors. General reference is to the time of Henry VIII.

tuft′ing (*Uphol.*) Sewing through both stuffing and outer covering in order to hold stuffing in place. Each tuft is usually marked by a button to improve appearance and to prevent the twine from cutting through the covering.

tu′lip tree (*W o o d*) *Liriodendron tulipifera.* Commonly spoken of as poplar or tulip poplar. Wood is light yellow in color, soft, and easily worked; it has a wide variety of uses, many similar to white pine.

tum′ble (*Fdry.*) To clean castings or forgings in a rotating drum by means of friction.

tum′bled (*Print.*) When a printed sheet is backed up by turning it from top to bottom, instead of from right to left, it is said to be tumbled. This should be avoided if possible.

tum′bler gear (*Shopwk.*) An intermediate gear in a train of gears serving to reverse the direction of the driven gear.

tum′ble sheet (*Print.*) A sheet that is tumbled when backed up, i.e., fed to the same side guides but opposite gripper edge.

tun′er (tūn′ēr) (*Radio*) A coil-condenser circuit which can be adjusted to select a desired radio signal and reject others.

tung oil (*Paint.*) Obtained from the seed of a tree native to China and Japan; used in the manufacture of varnishes, linoleum, and varnish driers. Also called "Chinese wood oil."

tung′sten (*Chem.*) This metal is found in certain minerals, principally wolframite. In the metallic state, it is used with iron in making high-speed steel. In colloidal form, it is used in making electric-lamp filament, and in the form of sodium tungstate (Na_2WO_4) as a fireproofing on wood and fabrics.

tung′sten car′bide. An iron-gray powder produced by carbonizing incandescent tungsten in a methane or hydrocarbon vapor. It is used as an abrasive, or it is briquetted with cobalt or other binders into tools for high-speed cutting of metal. It is sold under such trade names as Widia metal, Carboloy, and Phoran. Its use for cutting tools makes possible an increase of from 3 to 5 times the former cutting speeds. While very expensive, many shops feel the additional expense justified. In many cases feed and depth of cut are limited only by the ability of the machine to stand the strain.

tung′sten lamp (*Elec.*) A type of incandescent lamp having a filament of fine tungsten wire.

tung′sten steel (*Metal.*) An alloy steel much used for cutting tools.

tun′ing (*Elec.*) The act of changing electrical characteristics of a radio receiving circuit so that desired incoming signals will have greatest clearness and strength.

tun′nel en′gi-neer′ (*Engin.*) One who plans the specifications, design, and supervises the construction of tunnels under streams and through mountains, usually to improve transportation facilities.

tur-bid′i-ty. The degree of cloudiness of water as compared to perfectly clear water; due to silt, etc.

tur-bine (*Mach.*) A type of steam engine in which all driving parts rotate.

tur′bo-pro-pel′ler en′gine (*Aero.*) An aircraft engine of the gas turbine type in which the turbine power is used to drive both a compressor and a propeller. Often called a "turboprop."

tur′bu-lence (*Auto.*) A swirling motion given incoming fuel charges by the shape of the cylinder head. This condition is desirable as a means of reducing knocking and pinging.

tur′bu-lent flow (*Aero.*) Any part of a fluid flow in which the velocity at a given point varies more or less rapidly in magnitude and direction with time.

turf or peat. (See PEAT.)

turn–and–bank in′di‑ca′tor (*Aero.*) An instrument combining in one case a turn indicator and a lateral inclinometer.

turn′buck′le (*Mech.*) A form of coupling threaded so as to regulate tension in the rods which it connects.

Turnbuckle

turned sort (*Print.*) Type purposely placed face downwards so that the black foot prints.

turn in′di‑ca′tor (*Aero.*) An instrument for indicating the existence of an angular velocity of turn of an aircraft about its normal axis. In horizontal flight it indicates the presence of a yawing velocity.

turn′ing gouge (*Woodwkg.*) A gouge used for roughing down woodwork in a lathe. Such gouges are made in widths from ¼ to 1½ in.

turn′ing ma-chine′ (*Sheet-Met. Wk.*) A machine used to prepare the edge of a cylindrical or flaring body, such as the edge of a pail or a funnel, to receive a wire.

turn me′ter (*Aero.*) An instrument that measures the rate of turn of an aircraft about any predetermined axis.

tur′mer‑ic (*Chem.*) A plant obtained from China, East India, and many tropical countries. Used as a yellow dye in the manufacture of turmeric paper which is used as a test for alkaline substances, which turn it from yellow to brown. Also used for medicine, coloring foodstuffs, dyeing textiles, etc.

tur′pen-tine (*Paint.*) The distilled sap of the long-leaf pine. Used in mixing paint to make it spread easier.

tur′ret (*Arch.*) Small tower at one of the angles of a large building, rising from the ground or built on corbels. (*Tel.*) A multiple lens holder enabling a camera man to select from as many as four lenses on one camera.

tur′ret lathe. A lathe with revolving tool head, making possible several operations without removing the tools from the machine.

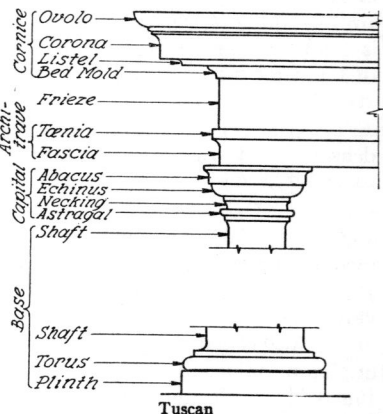

Tuscan

Tus′can (*Arch.*) The plainest of the five orders of classic architecture.

tu′yère′ (twē′yâr′) (*Fdry.*) An opening through which the air passes from the "wind box" into the cupola.

tweez′ers (*Print.*) Small pick-up pincers used for removing type when making corrections.

twin ig-ni′tion (*Auto.*) An ignition system having two sets of breaker points arranged to fire either simultaneously or alternately.

twin–six en′gine (*Auto.*) Consists of two sets of six cylinders placed at an angle of 60 deg.

Twist Bit

twist bits (*Wood Patmkg.*) Similar to the twist drills used for drilling metal, but ground at a sharper angle; used principally for boring holes for screws in wood.

twist drill (*Mach.*) A drill made from round stock, having two helical grooves extending through its effec-

Twist Drill

tive length. Twist drills are made for use on both metal and wood, with straight, square, or taper shank. Those for use on wood are called "twist bits."

twist'ed ca'ble (*Elec.*) A cable consisting of two or more conductors twisted together.

two–fil'a-ment bulbs (*Auto. Elec.*) See DOUBLE FILAMENT LAMP.

two–line let'ter (*Print.*) An initial letter as high as two lines of the text.

two–on (*Print.*) The use of two or more forms arranged for printing in duplicate.

two'–phase (*Elec.*) Or quarter phase. Two windings or circuits with a phase displacement of 90° (electrical).

two–phase al'ter-na'tor (*Elec.*) Polyphase a.c. alternator wound to deliver two sets of current differing in phase displacement by 90 deg.

two–speed rear ax'le (*Auto. Mech.*) In this type, two speeds are incorporated in the axle, giving twice the number of speeds obtainable with the single-speed axle. Especially adapted to trucks, making possible a saving in wear and tear on the engine and in gasoline consumption.

two–tone steer'hide (*Leather.*) An inexpensive leather suitable for book covers, cases, etc. It is supplied in natural and mottled effects.

two–way ra'dio. Radio communication carried on between several localities with portable equipment which contains the means of receiving and transmitting radio energy.

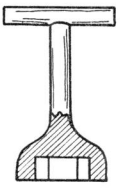

T Wrench

T wrench. A socket wrench shaped like the letter T.

tym'pan (*Print.*) One or more thicknesses of paper on the impression surface of a printing press to improve the quality of the presswork.

tym'pa-num (*Arch.*) The terms *tympanum* and *pediment* are often used interchangeably. The triangular space bounded by cornice, contains the pediment.

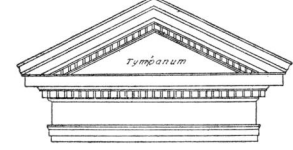

type (*Print.*) A metal character .918 in. in height; used in printing.

type cast'er (*Print.*) A type-casting machine.

type gauge (*Print.*) A graduated strip of wood or metal used for measuring the number of lines in a piece of matter.

type high (*Print.*) The height varies slightly in different countries. In the United States it is .918 in. high.

type met′al (*Print.*) An alloy of one part tin, two of antimony, and five of lead.

type plan′er (*Print.*) A solid wooden block with a smooth surface, used to plane down the type form before it is locked in the chase.

ty-pog′ra-pher (*P r i n t.*) A master printer or typographic designer.

ty′po-graph′ic (*Print.*) Pertaining to the art of printing.

ty-pog′ra-phy (*Print.*) (1) Typesetting or the arrangement of parts in a piece of type composition. (2) The art of printing.

U

U bolt (*Mech.*) A bolt shaped like the letter U threaded at both ends; called a "clip" as a spring clip on an automobile.

U clamp (*Mach. Shop*) A clamp shaped like the letter U; used for clamping down work on planer beds, etc.

u-dom′e-ter (*Phys.*) A rain gauge.

ul′ti-mate set (*Engin.*) The difference between the length of a specimen plate, or bar, before testing and at the moment of fracture, and given in percentage of the length.

ul′ti-mate strength (*E n g i n.*) The highest unit stress that can be sustained, this occurring just at or just before rupture.

ul′tra-ma-rine′ (*Paint.*) A light-blue to deep-blue pigment originally made from the powdered mineral lapis lazuli, but now made from kaolin, soda, charcoal, and sulphur.

ul′tra–speed weld′ing. A resistance welding process, wherein two or more welding electrodes are in simultaneous contact with the material to be welded, with the welding current commutated successively between the welding electrodes by means of a commutating device in the secondary welding-current circuit.

ul′tra-vi′o-let. Zone of invisible radiations beyond the violet end of the spectrum of visible radiations. Waves are shorter than those of light and characterized by chemical action.

um′ber (*P a i n t.*) A chestnut-brown hydrated ferric oxide containing manganese oxide and clay. Burnt umber produces a reddish-brown color. Both are used as pigments.

un′con-trolled′ spin (*Aero.*) A spin in which the controls are of little or no use in effecting a recovery.

undercoating (*Auto. Mech.*) The spraying of a plastic material on the exposed underparts of an automobile to retard corrosion and to deaden noise.

un′der-cut′ (*Mach.*) Teeth on small gear wheels are said to be undercut when they "thin down" as they approach the root line. (*Patmkg.*) The reverse of draft on a pattern; i.e., a pattern having proper draft will draw from the sand freely, while, if a surface is undercut, it will pull the sand and break the mold.

un′der-ground ca′ble (*E l e c.*) A single or multiple conductor cable sheathed in lead or other waterproof materials, carried in a duct beneath the surface of the ground.

un′der-lay′ (*P r i n t.*) The process of equalizing the impression on the press by means of inserting spots of paper beneath the type form.

un′der-pin′ning (*Engin.*) Excavating under walls or erections, and filling the space with concrete or timbering

un′der-shot′ wheel (*Engin.*) A water wheel which receives its power from water applied at its bottom.

un′der-slung′. Having the springs attached to the underside of the axles instead of resting on them, as an underslung wagon or automobile.

un′der-writ′er (*Elec.*) Name given to representative of an inspection organ-

---

sāle, surfâce, grăm, humăn, màsk, solɑr, bär, bâre; mē, êdition, lĕnd, momĕnt, bakēr; kīnd, fĭt; lōde, ômit, ŏlive, cŏnsume, sôrt; dūty, ûtility, nŭt, alŭm, bûrn.

ization who examines electrical installations for life and fire hazards.

un′du-la-to′ry move′ment (*Aero.*) A rising and falling as if on waves.

u′ni-form load (*Engin.*) Includes the weight of the structure itself and any load evenly spread over it.

u′ni-lat′er-al tol′er-ance. An allowable variation plus or minus from a basic dimension, but not both, e.g., 5.250″ — .002″.

un′ion (*Plumb.*) A coupling or connection for pipes.

u′nit mag-net′ic pole (*Elec.*) One which will repel an equal and like pole with a force of one dyne at a distance of 1 cm. A dyne is the force which, acting upon a mass of 1 gram during 1 second, gives the mass a velocity of 1 cm. per second.

u′nit of ca-pac′i-ty (*Elec.*) (See FARAD.)

u′nit of E.M.F. (*Elec.*) (See VOLT.)

u′nit of il-lu′mi-na′tion (*Elec.*) Candle power — The brightness of a lamp. Mean spherical candle power is candle power averaged over all directions from the center of the lamp. Mean horizontal candle power is average candle power in a horizontal plane through the luminous center of a lamp.

u′nit of mag-net′ic flux (*Elec.*) The total number of lines of force set up in a magnetic substance. Treated as a magnetic current flowing in a magnetic circuit.

u′nit of mag-net′ic in-ten′si-ty (*Elec.*) Magnetomotive force (M.M.F.) Magnetic pressure which drives lines of force through a magnetic circuit.

u′nit of mag-net′ic re-luc′tance (*Elec.*) Oersteds. Magnetic resistance. The resistance offered to the magnetic flux by the substance magnetized.

u′nit pow′er plant (*Auto.*) Consists of the complete motor and transmission and all motor accessories.

u′nit stress (*Engin.*) The stress on a unit of section area, usually expressed in pounds per square inch.

u′ni-ver′sal. General; all-reaching; total; entire.

u′ni-ver′sal chuck or con-cen′tric chuck (*Mach.*) A jaw chuck whose jaws are so arranged as to permit simultaneous movement for quick centering of the work.

u′ni-ver′sal grind′ing ma-chine′ (*Shopwk.*) A grinding machine provided with a swivel table, a swivel headstock, and a swivel wheel head, used for external and internal cylindrical grinding, surface grinding, face grinding, etc.

u′ni-ver′sal joint (*Mach.*) A type of coupling which permits the free rotation of two shafts whose axes are not in a straight line.

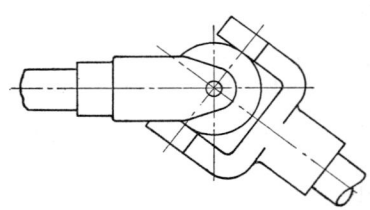

Universal Joint

u′ni-ver′sal mill′ing ma-chine′ (*Mach.*) A machine tool having both transverse and longitudinal feed. The work is fed against a revolving cutter. It is similar in appearance to the plain milling machine, the principal difference being that the universal machine has a swivel table.

u′ni·ver′sal saw ta′ble (*Carp.*) A saw table that may be tilted to permit sawing at a bevel.

un·lim′it·ed ceil′ing (*Aero.*) Perfect flying weather with cloud level higher than 9000 ft.

un·shield′ed car′bon arc weld′ing. A carbon-arc-welding process wherein no shielding medium is used.

un·shield′ed met′al arc weld′ing. A metal-arc-welding process wherein the electrode used is a bare or lightly coated wire or rod.

un·sound′ knot (*Wood*) A knot which is not as hard as the wood it is in.

un′sta′ble os′cil·la′tion (ŏs′ĭ-lā′shŭn) (*Aero.*) An oscillation whose amplitude increases continuously until an attitude is reached from which there is no tendency to return toward the original attitude, the motion becoming a steady divergence.

up·hol′ster·er's bench. A trestle, usually 36 in. long, 30 in. high, and topped with a padded board 8 in. wide.

up·hol′ster·er's ham′mer. A double-pointed hammer having a head 5½ in. long, with faces 5/16 to ½ in. in diameter, making it possible to tack in places which could not be reached with a hammer of a different type.

up·hol′ster·er's pin or skew′er. A needlelike tool about 3½ in. long, having a ring formed at one end. It is used as a temporary basting for covers. It serves as an aid in getting covers in proper position before sewing or tacking.

up·hol′ster·y (*Furn.*) The act of fitting covering to furniture, cushioning, etc. The material used for the same.

up′keep (*Auto.*) The cost of operation and maintenance.

up′per case (*Print.*) Capital letters as distinguished from lower-case, small letters.

up′per sur′face ai′le·ron (ā′lê-rŏn) (*Aero.*) A split flap forming the rear upper surface of a wing, deflected for lateral control.

up′right (*Arch.*) Something standing upright, as a piece of timber in a building. (*Furn.*) An extension of back legs supporting a chair back.

up′right′ grain (*Print.*) A type of base used when printing unmounted plates, using tacks or catches for fastening.

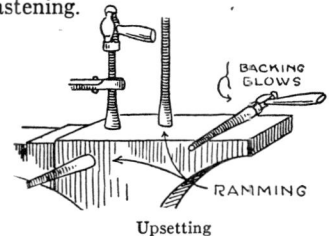

Upsetting

up′set (*Forg.*) To shorten or thicken metal by hammering or by pressure.

up′set butt weld′ing. A resistance-butt-welding process wherein the potential is applied after the parts to be welded have been brought in contact and where the heat is derived principally from resistance.

u·ra′ni·um (*Metal.*) A hard malleable metal used to increase strength and toughness of high-speed steels. Also used in small quantities in cast iron. Two principal isotopes are found in natural uranium are U-235 and U-238. Only U-235 is readily fissionable and only 1 part in 140 of natural uranium is U-235.

u·re′a (*Plastics*) A soluble, white

crystalline substance obtained from urine. It is used as a base for urea-formaldehyde resinoids. Also made synthetically.

u·re′a res′in (*Plast.*) A plastic in the aminos (urea and melamine) family. It is derived from the reaction of urea with formaldehyde or its polymers. Its mar resistance, oil resistance, and surface hardness recommends it for such uses as electric mixer housings, buttons, etc. It is also used in the familiar plywood adhesive and lumber laminating field, and for hard-finish coatings. (See PLASTICS.)

use′ful load (*Aero.*) The crew and passengers, oil and fuel, ballast other than emergency, ordinance, and portable equipment.

U.S.F. thread (*Mach.*) The United States Form thread has the same shape as the National Coarse, U.S.S. thread but differs in pitch.

u·til′i·ty. The quality or state of being useful, especially for some practical purpose; also, that which is of practical use.

V

V's (*Mach. Shop*) Ways shaped like a V, either raised or sunken, to serve as a guide for a movable table or carriage.

vac′u-um (*Phys.*) A space from which the air or any matter has been exhausted. (*Steam. Heat.*) A pump used to remove condensation and air from the return main of a heating system in order to (*a*) create a vacuum and (*b*) return the condensate to the boiler or to a receiving tank.

vac′u-um brake (*A u t o.*) A system particularly desirable for heavy passenger cars. The mechanical braking system is operated by a vacuum taken from the intake manifold or carburetor at a point just above the throttle valve.

vac′u-um clean′er. A motor-driven fan machine used for sucking up dirt and dust from rugs, etc.

vac′u-um con-trol′ (*Auto.*) The term may apply to any automobile devices such as brakes, clutch, etc., controlled by manifold vacuum.

vac′u-um form′ing (*Plast.*) Also known as sheet forming, and heat forming. An important fabricating operation in which thermoplastic sheet is heated until plastic, when it is clamped into a forming fixture under a frame, and drawn down over a shaped mold by vacuum. There are many variations of the process: some in which sheets are blown upward or downward into molds by air pressure, and some which compensate for the thinning of stretched areas by a step procedure. Forming is widely used in display signs (notably for oil stations) and in airplane covers.

vac′u-um fu′el sup-ply′ (*A u t o.*) Depends upon the use of a vacuum tank to raise the gasoline from the main tank to the higher level of the engine. When the engine is running, a partial vacuum is maintained in the vacuum tank by utilizing the vacuum created at the carburetor.

vac′u-um gauge (*Auto.*) An instrument calibrated in atmospheric inches to test the vacuum produced in the intake manifold of an engine or in the fuel line.

vac′u-um met′al-iz′ing (*Plast.*) A process by which plastic parts are thinly coated with vaporized metal (aluminum). This is done in a vacuum tank, the vaporizing being accomplished by means of an electric element. The metal is lacquer sprayed to gold, brass, or copper color. Products may also be partially metalized.

vac′u-um spark ad-vance′ (*Auto. Elec.*) A metal diaphragm connected by a rod to the breaker-point plate. The diaphragm is actuated by the intake manifold vacuum which varies with the throttle opening, causing an advance of the spark by rotation of the breaker-point plate.

vac′u-um tube (*Elec.*) An electron tube evacuated to such a degree that its electrical characteristics are essentially unaffected by the presence of residual gas or vapor.

va′lence (vā′lĕns) (*C h e m.*) That property possessed by elements of radicals of combining with or replacing other elements or radicals in definite and constant proportion.

val′ley (*Arch.*) (1) The gutter or angle formed by the meeting of two roof slopes. (2) The space between vault ridges viewed from above.

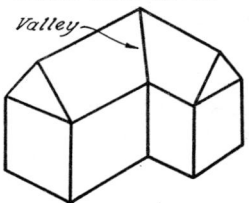

val′ley raft′er (*Arch.*) The rafter extending along and under a valley.

val′ue (*Color*) The quality of lightness or darkness of a color.

valve. A device for regulating the flow of a liquid or gas through pipes.

valve ac′tion (*Auto.*) Those parts controlling the opening and closing of the valves, namely, timing gears, chain, camshaft, valve lifters, and valve assembly.

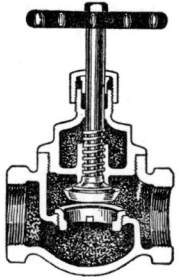

Globe Valve

valve face (*Auto.*) The beveled part of the valve head which mates with the valve seat.

valve keep′ers (*Auto.*) Keys to maintain the spring tension on the valve stem, usually placed below the spring washer on the valve stem.

valve lap (*Auto.*) The amount of lap between the opening of the intake and the exhaust, indicated by marks on the flywheel in degrees or number of teeth. Opening of the intake valve prior to closing of the exhaust valve is called "positive lap." When the intake valve opens after the closing of the exhaust valve it is called "minus lap."

valve lift′er (*Auto.*) (1) Same as valve plunger or valve tappet. (2) A hand tool for relieving spring pressure when removing or replacing valves.

valve–lift′er as-sem′bly (*Auto.*) The various parts, guides, tappets, adjusting screws, etc., which operate between the camshaft and the poppet valves to regulate valve action. These parts are sometimes mounted in a housing bolted to the crankcase.

valve port (*Auto.*) Opening into or from the combustion chamber which provides a channel for the passage of gases and a seal for the head of the valve.

valve push rod (*Auto.*) See PUSH ROD.

valve re-tain′er (*Auto.*) Same as "keeper." It may also apply to any locking device which keeps the valve and spring in position.

valves (*Auto.*) Those devices which control the flow of intake and exhaust gases to and from the engine cylinders. On automobile engines, they are called poppet valves.

valve seat (*Auto.*) That part of the

engine block machined to receive the poppet valve and provide a seal against leakage of gases.

valve-seat in'serts (*Auto.*) Rings of alloy steel pressed in position in the valve ports to increase the life of the valve seats.

valve spring (*Auto.*) A compression-type spring exerting pressure of 40 to 90 pounds to keep valves in closed position.

valve stem (*Auto.*) The shank of a poppet-type valve.

valve-stem clear'ance (*Auto.*) Distance between lower end of valve stem and valve tappet. Its purpose is to care for expansion due to heat.

valve tim'ing (*Auto.*) Proper setting of valve actions with reference to piston position.

va-na'di-um (vá-nā'dĭ-ŭm) (*Metal.*) A rare silver-white metallic element, valuable in the making of an alloy steel. Vanadium steel is used in parts subject to shock, as automobile axles.

va-na'di-um steel (*Metal.*) Generally contains between 0.10 to 0.15 per cent of vanadium. Such steel can be forged readily but must be heated gradually. Chrome vanadium or nickel vanadium steels are used more than plain vanadium steels.

Van-dyke' brown (*Paint.*) A native earth, being a clay stained with a bituminous compound. It is used in mixed paints on account of its deep shade.

Van-dyke' pa'per (*Draw.*) Is a sensitized paper which is printed in the same manner as blueprint paper, except that the tracing is put in the printing machine with the ink lines toward the paper. This produces a negative with brown background and white lines. This negative is used like a tracing to produce a print which has white background and brown lines. Blueprints can also be made from such a negative, in which case the background is white and the lines blue.

vane (*Arch.*) A weathercock for indicating the direction of the wind.

vane-type pump (*Auto.*) Consists essentially of a circular impeller, set off center in a body casting, having two vanes or wings. Oil is drawn in after one vane and carried on ahead of the next vane until it is forced out through the feed lines.

vane-type su'per-charg'er (*Aero.*) A positive-displacement rotary blower having an eccentrically located rotor provided with one or more vanes.

van'ish-ing point (*Draft.*) A term used in perspective to designate the point toward which all parallel receding lines converge or meet.

va'por (*Auto.*) Gas, steam, or mixture of gasoline and air.

va'por heat'ing (*Bldg. and Engin.*) Broadly a type of warming buildings consisting of a two-pipe gravity return system of steam circulation in which provision is made to retard or prevent the passage of steam from the radiator into the return main, and in which the air from the system, as well as the condensed water, is carried back to a point near the boiler. At this point the air is expelled from the mains and the water is returned to the boiler.

va'por-ize (*Chem.*) To convert into a state of gas or vapor.

va'por-iz'er. An early type of carburetor.

va′por lock. A stoppage or diminution in the fuel flow of an engine caused by fuel vapor accumulating in the fuel lines.

var′i-sor (*Elec.*) A two electrode semiconductor device having a voltage-dependent nonlinear resistance.

va′ri-a-ble (vā′rĭ-á-b'l) (*Algebra*) A quantity which may change in value while that of others remains constant.

var′i-a-ble con-dens′er (*Elec.*) Type of condenser in which the capacity can be varied within certain limits.

var′i-a-ble in-duc′tor (*Elec.*) Usually a single coil with some means of varying its properties of self-induction.

va′ri-a-ble mo′tion (*Engin.*) When a body moves over equal spaces in unequal times the motion is said to be variable.

va′ri-a-ble–pitch pro-pel′ler (*Aero.*) A propeller whose blades are so mounted that they may be turned about their axes to any desired pitch while the propeller is in rotation.

va′ri-a-ble re-sist′ance (*Elec.*) A resistance that can be adjusted or changed to different values.

var′nish (*Paint.*) A solution of certain gums, in alcohol or oil, used for producing a hard, shiny finish on a surface. Varnishes are either clear or colored.

var′y-ing du′ty (*Elec.*) That demand which requires operation of loads of varying quantity for intervals of time, both of which may be subject to wide variation.

va′ry-ing speed mo′tor (*E l e c.*) A motor in which the speed varies with the load, ordinarily decreasing as the load increases. Note: This is not the same as an adjustable speed motor.

vault (*A r c h.*) An arched ceiling or roof; a laterally conjoined series of arches; a room or space covered by a vault.

V belt. A belt with a V section for use on grooved pulleys. Such belts have less tendency to slip or to leave the pulley than do flat belts.

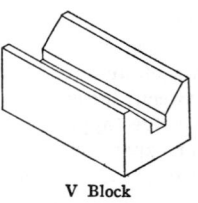

V Block

V blocks (*Mach.*) Metal blocks cut V shaped on one side to permit holding cylindrical work while machining or testing.

vec′tor (*Elec.*) Graphic representation of the component parts which act together in an alternating circuit.

vee ra′di-a′tor (*A u t o.*) A type of radiator made in two sections joined at the middle at an angle less than 180 deg.

veg′e-ta-ble tannage (*Leather.*) Tanning leather by the use of vegetable substances containing tannic acid.

ve′hi-cle (*Chem.*) A liquid medium by which a varnish or lacquer is applied.

vel′lum (*Paper*) Paper made in imitation of parchment.

ve-loc′i-ty (vĕ-lŏs′ĭ-tĭ) (*Mech.*) It is distance divided by time, and is expressed in feet per second or per minute. (*Phys.*) The rate of movement of a body.

velox paper (*Photography*) A trade

name for a certain type of photographic paper.

ve-neer′ (*Arch. and Wood Fin.*) A thin layer of wood or other material placed on a commoner surface to secure a superior effect or to reduce cost.

ve-neer′ press (*Woodwk.*) A large heavy-duty press for gluing up plywood or panels.

ve-neer′ saw (*Woodwk.*) A special type of circular saw used for cutting veneers.

Ve-ne′tian blind (*Arch.*) A type of window shade consisting of a series of slats held together by tapes and adjustable by means of pull cords.

Ve-ne′tian red (*P a i n t.*) (Fe_2O_3) A very brilliant, red pigment made by heating ferrous sulphate in the presence of lime.

vent (*Fdry.*) A small hole made in a foundry mold to permit the escape of gases.

ven′ti-la′tion (*B l d g.*) The act or method of supplying with fresh air.

ven′ti-la′tor (*Bldg.*) A device for providing fresh air to a room or other space by (*a*) introducing outside air, or (*b*) exhausting foul air.

vent′ing (*F d r y.*) The making of a channel or vent in a mold for the escape of air, steam, and gas.

vent pipe (*Arch.*) Any small ventilating pipe running from various plumbing fixtures to the vent stack.

vent stack (*Arch.*) The vertical pipe connecting with the vent pipes and extending through the roof. It carries off gases, and aids in maintaining a water seal in the trap.

Ven-tu′ri tube (věn-tōō′rē) (*Aero.*) A short tube with flaring ends and a narrow or constricted section between them, into which a side tube opens. When fluid flows through the Venturi, there is a reduction of pressure in the constricted section, the amount of the reduction being a function of the velocity of flow.

vent wire (*Fdry.*) To provide for the escape of steam and gas, vents are made with a wire before the pattern is removed from the mold.

ve-ran′da (*Arch.*) An open portico extending along the outside of a building.

ver′di-gris (vûr′dĭ-grēs)(*Chem.*) The oxidation on the surface of copper. Verdigris is also formed by treating copper with acetic acid. Used principally as a pigment and in dyeing.

verge (vûrj) (*Arch.*) The edge of the tiling, slate, or shingles projecting over the gable of a roof.

verge boards (*A r c h.*) Boards suspended from the verge of a gable. During the last quarter of the nineteenth century, verge boards were made of highly ornate scroll-saw work.

ver-mic′u-lat′ed (*Arch.*) Stones, etc., worked so as to have the appearance of having been eaten into by worms.

ver-mil′ion (vẽr-mĭl′yŭn) (*Paint.*) This red pigment is used in enormous quantities. It is usually made from mercuric sulphide (HgS), tinted with puranitraniline.

ver′ni-er (vûr′nĭ-ẽr)(*Mech.*) A small movable auxiliary scale for obtaining fractional parts of the subdivisions of a fixed scale. The complete instrument.

ver′nier depth gauge (*Mach.*) A rod type gauge fitted with a vernier and used for checking narrow recessed portions, and shoulders or steps of a machine part.

ver′ti-cal. Plumb, perpendicular, upright.

ver′ti-cal bor′ing mill (*Mach.*) A machine tool, with revolving table which carries the work, and a slide arrangement which permits both vertical and horizontal feed of the tool. It is especially adapted to a class of work that cannot be easily "set up" on a lathe.

ver′ti-cal cen′ter-ing (*Tel.*) The control which regulates the position of the picture vertically on the screen of the receiver tube.

ver′ti-cal flash ring (*Plast.*) The clearance between the force plug and the vertical wall of the cavity in a positive or semipositive mold; also the ring of excess material which escapes from the cavity into this clearance space.

ver′ti-cal lathe (*Mach.*) A type of vertical boring mill which carries a side head.

ver′ti-cal tail a′re-a (*Aero.*) The area of the actual outline of the rudder and the fin projected in the vertical plane, the fairings and fillets being ignored.

ver-tim′e-ter (*Aero.*) A device for indicating the rate of rise and fall of an aerostat, usually a special form of statoscope. A rate of climb meter serves the same purpose, although of a different form.

ves′ti-bule (*Arch.*) A small entrance room, either to a building or to a room within the building.

vi′a-duct (*Engin.*) A large masonry, bridgelike structure for carrying a roadway or railroad over a valley, gorge, or the like.

vi′brat-ing bell (*Elec.*) An electric device having a clapper or hammer which strikes a bell rapidly when an electric current flows through it. It operates on the principle of electromagnetic attraction.

vi-bra′tion damp′en-ers (*Auto.*) Counterweights or balancers on a crankshaft for the purpose of reducing vibration.

vi′bra-tor coil (*Elec.*) An induction coil so constructed that the magnetism of the core operates the make and break or vibrator of the primary circuit.

vi′de-o (I see) (*Tel.*) That portion of the television signal which contains the picture information. Video is also loosely used as a synonym for television.

view′ing mir′ror (*Tel.*) A mirror used to reflect the image formed on a picture tube in indirect-view receivers at a convenient viewing angle.

vi-gnette′ (vĭn-yĕt′) (*Arch.*) A vinelike ornament. (*Print.*) (1) A halftone cut whose lines fade away until they vanish on the surface of the paper. (2) A small decorative design used before the title-page, or at the beginning or end of a chapter.

vi-gnet′ted halftone (*Print.*) A halftone on which one or more of the edges of the object are shaded from dark tones to pure white.

vi′nyl ac′e-tal res′ins (*Chem. Plast.*) Prepared from polyvinyl acetate. Used as an interlayer in safety glass and as a bonding resin. Properties are toughness, adhesiveness, imperviousness to moisture, stability toward light and heat.

vi′nyl-es′ter res′ins (*Chem. Plast.*) Much used in the form of sheet materials, surface coatings, adhesives and molding compounds; odorless, tasteless, light in weight and slow burning.

vi-nyl'i-dene chlo'ride res'ins (*Chem. Plast.*) The raw materials for this class of resin are crude oil and brine. Properties are high tensile strength, resistance to abrasion, noninflammable, easy to machine, good color range. Used for car seats, fish leaders, and as a bonding agent for abrasive wheels.

vi-nyl' res'in (*Plast.*) An important family of resins. (See POLYVINYL and PLASTICS.)

vis'cid (vĭs'ĭd)(*Phys.*) Mucilaginous, sticky, or adhesive.

vis-cos'i-ty (vĭs-kŏs'ĭ-tĭ) (*Plast.*) The friction of a liquid substance against its carrier, and its resistance to flow. Said of oils or resins. (*Phys.*) The density of fluid, gauged by the rate at which it flows through a gauge pipe of standard length and diameter.

vis'cous (*Chem.*) Refers to thick or slow-flowing liquids.

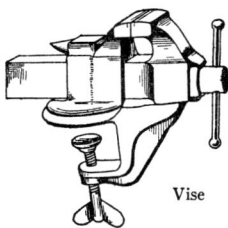
Vise

vise (*Shopwk.*) A mechanical contrivance for holding a piece of wood or metal while it is being worked on. It consists essentially of two jaws, one fixed and one movable, the movable jaw being operated by a screw by means of which clamping action is secured. There are many forms of vises for different purposes.

vise clamps (*Mach.*) False jaws for a vise. They are made of brass or copper, and are used over the faces of the hardened steel jaws to prevent bruising the work.

vis'i-bil'i-ty (*Aero.*) The greatest distance at which conspicuous objects can be seen and identified.

vis'ta (*A r c h.*) A view, as along an avenue.

vis'u-a-lize. To make visible; to form a mental picture or image.

vit're-ous (*Chem.*) Glassy; pertaining to glass, or having some of the properties of glass.

vit'ri-fi-ca'tion. The state of a substance which is fused together by burning.

vit'ri-fied brick (*Masonry*) A very hard paving brick burned to the point of vitrification and toughened by annealing.

vix'en file (*Shopwk.*) A flat file with curved cuts, particularly efficient on soft metals and for filing round work in a lathe.

voids (*Engin.*) Vacant spaces such as occur between broken particles of a substance, as stone, coal, etc.

vol'a-tile (*Chem.*) Capable of being rapidly vaporized.

vol'a-tile liq'uid. A liquid which vaporizes readily.

volt (*Elec.*) The unit of electromotive force; electrical pressure.

Volta, Alessandro (1745–1827). Italian physicist. The unit of electrical pressure, the volt, was given his name in honor of his discoveries and inventions in electricity.

Vol'ta's law (*Elec.*) The difference of potential between any two metals is equal to the sum of the differences of potentials between the intervening metals in the contact series.

volt′age am′pli‑fi‑ca′tion (*R a d i o*) The type of amplification of the radio signal attained in the R.F. (radio frequency) amplifier stages, which stresses the voltage amplification rather than power amplification as in A.F. (audio frequency) amplifier stages. Amplification of strength of signal before detection.

volt′age di‑vid′er (*Elec.*) Usually a resistor that can be tapped or adjusted to provide variations of voltages between its ends.

volt′age drop (*Elec.*) The voltage consumed in forcing a current through a certain resistance or group of resistances connected in a single circuit.

volt′age reg′u‑la′tor (*Auto.*) A device of electromagnetically operated contact points and a resistance unit which, when connected in series with the field of an auto generator, reduces the generator's output when the battery reaches a predetermined voltage.

vol‑ta′ic cell (*E l e c.*) Primary cell. Name given to the cell first discovered by Volta. Sometimes called a galvanic cell. It is a cell in which two dissimilar metals are immersed in a solution which is capable of acting chemically more upon one than on the other, to produce a difference of potential (voltage) across the metals.

volt′me′ter (*E l e c.*) An instrument for determining voltage.

vo‑lute′ (*Arch. and Furn.*) The spiral ornament of Ionic and Corinthian capitals.

vo‑lute′ with ease′ment (*Arch. and Bldg.*) A spiral part of a handrail, supplanting a newel post. The volute or spiral is in a horizontal plane, and the ramp slopes to connect with the rising slope of the handrail.

vos‑soir′ (vōō‑swär′) (*Arch.*) One of the wedge‑shaped blocks of stone of which an arch is composed.

V thread (*Mach. Shop*) A screw thread whose section is V shaped, the included angle being 60 deg. It is similar to the U.S.S. thread, except that the V thread is sharp at the top and bottom, where the U.S.S. or National thread has a flat equal to one‑eighth pitch.

V–type en′gine (*Auto.*) An engine with cylinder blocks arranged in a V shape. One crankshaft serves both banks of cylinders.

vul′ca‑nite (*Chem.*) A compound of India rubber and sulphur, widely used in the industries. Nonelastic, hard rubber.

vul′can‑iz′ing (*Chem.*) (1) Treating crude India rubber with sulphur at a high temperature, thus increasing its strength and elasticity. (2) The joining of two pieces of rubber by the application of cement and heat, as in patching an automobile tire.

W

wain′scot (wān′skŏt) (*Arch.*) A lining of interior walls, usually paneled.

wain′scot-ing (*Arch.*) Lining or paneling interior walls with wood.

wain′scot-ing cap (*Arch.*) The molding at the top of a wainscoting.

wall bed (*Arch.*) Any one of the various types of beds which swing or fold into the wall or closet when not in use. Commonly used in small apartments.

wallboard (*Arch.*) A general term applied to any of the many building boards used in place of plaster on interior walls and ceilings.

wall brack′et (*Mech.*) Frequently a shaft hanger attached to a wall or post; in general, any bracket attached to a wall and used as a support.

wall plate (*Masonry*) A horizontal timber on a wall for bearing the ends of joists, girders, etc., and for distributing the weight.

wall sock′et (*Elec.*) An electric outlet located in or on the wall for the purpose of providing a source of current.

wane (*Wood*) Wane is a defect in a timber or plank.

ward′ing file (*Mech.*) A very thin, flat file used principally by locksmiths.

warp (*Aero.*) Twisting the surface of an airplane wing to change its form. (*Textile*) The threads running lengthwise of a fabric. (*Woodwkg.*) To permanently distort or twist out of shape as by moisture or heat.

warp′ing (Fdry.) A distortion or twisting of a casting due to unequal strains in cooling.

wash (*Aero.*) The disturbance caused in the air by the passage of the wings and propeller of an airplane.

wash′er (*Mech.*) A small, flat, perforated disk, used to secure the tightness of a joint, screw, etc.

Washer

wash′er cut′ter. A device having a fixed center and either one or two adjustable cutting points for cutting washers from leather, rubber, etc.

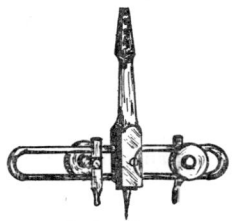
Washer Cutter

wash′in (*Aero.*) Permanent warping of a wing which results in an increase in the angle of attack near the tip.

wash′out (*Aero.*) Permanent warping of a wing which results in a decrease in the angle of attack near the tip.

waste (*Shopwk.*) Cotton waste is the refuse of cotton mills, used in shops for cleaning machinery. It consists of fine, soft, cotton fibers matted together.

waste lu′bri-ca′tion (*Mach.*) Consists of packing oil-soaked waste in a journal box. Such lubrication is common practice on railway cars.

---

sāle, surfâce, grăm, humăn, màsk, solàr, bär, bâre; mē, êdition, lĕnd, momĕnt, bakēr; kīnd, fĭt; lōde, ômit, ŏlive, cŏnsume, sôrt; dūty, ûtility, nŭt, alŭm, bûrn.

wa′ter bar (*Bldg.*) A bar or strip inserted in a joint between wood and stone sills of a window to prevent passage of water.

wa′ter cool-ing (*Engin.*) When the heat generated by an internal-combustion engine is carried off by water circulating through the water jacket and radiator.

wa′ter gas (*Chem.*) Made by passing steam over very hot coal or coke, which is enriched with liquid hydrocarbons; sometimes used for fuel or illuminating gas.

wa′ter glass (*Chem.*) A solution of sodium or potassium silicate made by fusing quartz sand with potash or sodium hydrate. It is a heavy oily liquid; used as an adhesive, protective coating, and as fireproofing agent.

wa′ter ham′mer. Sounds like the blows of a hammer occurring when the flow of water in a pipe is suddenly checked.

wa′ter jack′et (*E n g i n.*) The outer casing of a motor block and head, so constructed as to permit a circulation of water between it and the cylinder walls, for the purpose of carrying off heat from the motor.

wa′ter-mark′ (*Papermkg.*) A marking produced in paper by the pressure of a raised design on the dandy roll or in the mold which can be seen when the paper is held up to the light.

wa′ter-proof′ing walls (*Concrete*) Making them impervious to water or dampness, by mixing a compound with the concrete, or by applying the compound to the surface.

wa′ter pump (*Auto.*) A pump by means of which a forced circulation of the water in the cooling system is produced. These pumps are usually placed at the front of the cylinder block where they are operated in connection with the fan drive or generator drive.

wa′ter put′ty (*Woodwk.*) A powder which, when mixed with water, makes an excellent filler for cracks, nail holes, etc. Not suitable for glazing.

wa′ter re-cov′er-y ap′pa-ra′tus (*Aero.*) Apparatus carried on an airship for condensing and recovering the water contained in the exhaust gases of internal-combustion engines.

wa′ter sof′ten-er (*Plumb.*) A device for eliminating from domestic water supplies the calcium and magnesium sulphates or bicarbonates which render soap valueless for cleansing purposes; also any chemical added to water to accomplish this purpose.

wa′ter spots (*Paint and Lacquer*) Water spots are slight discolorations that appear in the film of lacquer enamels and oftentimes appear to go down very deep into the film. Usually caused by sealing in moisture.

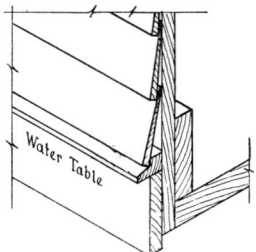

wa′ter ta′ble (*A r c h.*) A projecting, sloping member around a building to throw rain water away from the wall.

watt (*E l e c.*) An electrical unit of power; equals volts multiplied by amperes.

watt hour (*Elec.*) A unit of measure of electrical work, equal to one watt expended for one hour.

watt′less cur′rent (*Elec.*) That component of an alternating current which does not combine with the voltage to produce power; the idle component as distinguished from the active component.

watt′me′ter (*E l e c.*) An instrument for measuring electric power in watts; the unit of electrical energy, volt times amperes, combining therefore the functions of a voltmeter and an ammeter.

watt sec′ond (*Elec.*) A unit of measure of electrical work equal to the rate of one watt expended for one second of time.

watts per candle (*Elec.*) Term used commercially to denote the consumption of a lamp in watts per mean horizontal candle power produced.

wave form of al′ter-nat′ing cur′rent (*Elec.*) The sine wave produced by an alternating current designating its values (instantaneous, effective, and maximum) and its polarities, for a given period of time. A sine wave showing all the characteristics of that current.

wave length (*Elec.*) The length in meters of one complete sine wave of an alternating current. In radio, the distance in meters between the maximum points of two successive magnetic waves sent out by a transmitter.

wave trap (*Radio*) A combination of coil and condenser (tuner) that can be adjusted to filter out a signal at a certain frequency.

wav′i-ness (*Plast.*) Wavelike unevenness or out-of-plane; may be on the surface.

wax (*Chem.*) An organic salt (ester) of a high monotomic alcohol and a high fatty acid; e.g., beeswax.

wax en-grav′ing (*Print.*) A process of making printing plates by engraving on a wax-coated copper plate, building up the background, and making an electrotype from the plate.

wax fin′ish (*Woodwkg.*) A very smooth finish secured by polishing a wood surface with wax prepared for the purpose.

ways (*Shopwk.*) Longitudinal guides, upon which the work or a table bearing the work may slide, as the ways of a lathe or planer.

weak sand (*Fdry.*) Sand that will not hold together due to the small percentage of clay which gives it but little strength at the usual temper and hardness.

wear and tear. Depreciation in value due to use.

weath′er. To season, dry, injure, or alter in any way the condition of wood, stone, or other material through exposure to the weather.

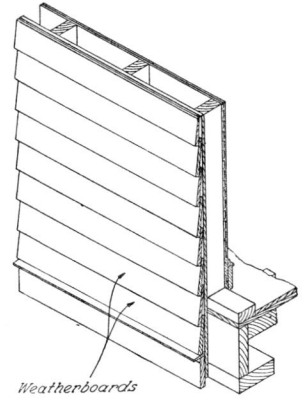

Weatherboards

weath′er-boards (*Arch.*) Boards used

as an outside covering of buildings, nailed on so as to overlap and shed the rain.

weath′er-ing (*Arch.*) The slope given to offsets, buttresses, and the upper surface of cornices and moldings, to throw off rain. (*Wood*) The wearing away of the surface of timbers caused by exposure to the elements.

weath′er strip (*Arch.*) A strip of metal, wood, or other material such as is used around doors and windows to prevent draughts.

web (*Mech.*) A thin plate connecting two parts of a casting, forging, etc. (*Papermkg.*) Paper in the process of being formed or having been on the paper machine.

web′bing (*Uphol.*) Made from jute fiber in the standard width of 3, 3½, and 4 inches with 72 yards to the roll. Used mainly as a spring support on furniture frames.

web′bing stretch′er (*Uphol.*) A device for stretching webbing across the openings of furniture frames. It consists of a small, flat piece of wood, padded at one end, with several sharp steel points inserted in the other end to engage the webbing.

web-cal′en-dered (*Papermkg.*) Paper calendered from a roll of paper as distinguished from paper which is calendered in the sheet.

web of drill (*Mech.*) The thickness of a drill at the bottom of the flutes.

wedge (*Mech.*) A piece of wood, or metal, V shaped in longitudinal section, used for producing strong pressure, or for splitting a substance apart.

wedg′ing (*Ceram.*) The working of clay to get it into proper condition for use.

weft or woof (*Textile*) The threads running crosswise of a weave.

weight (*Papermkg.*) A term applied in general to the weight of a ream of paper or to the weight of 1000 sheets of paper.

weight font (*Print.*) Type sold by weight as opposed to type sold by characters.

weight′ing (*Textile*) Giving body or weight to silk by the addition of mineral salts or other substances.

weir (wēr) (*Engin.*) A dam or barrier by means of which the water of a stream is held back in order to provide a sufficient head of water for power purposes.

weld′ing(*Mech.*) Uniting of pieces of iron or steel by fusion accomplished by the oxyacetylene, electric, or hammering (forging) process.

weld′ing rod (*Weld.*) Usually 24 in long and ¼, ⅜, or ½ in. in diameter; used for flowing into the joint to be blowpipe welded. Welding rods are of different composition according to the class of work on which they are to be used.

weld′ing trans-form′er (*Elec.*) A step-down transformer used to produce sufficient instantaneous current to fuse the metals, in contact, through which it is flowing.

weld-mark (*Plast.*) Mark formed by the incomplete union of two or more streams of plastic material flowing together.

weld pe′ri·od. The time required to go through one complete cycle of a welding operation.

weld time. The interval during which current is allowed to flow through the work during the performance of one weld. In pulsation welding, the weld period includes the "cool-time" intervals.

well′hole (*Arch. and Bldg.*) The small space enclosed on three sides by three flights of a stair.

Welsh plugs (*Auto.*) Small disks of sheet metal used to seal the holes left by core prints in the cylinder casting.

welt′ed edge (*Uphol.*) An edge made by inserting a covered cord between the edges of the covering when they are sewed together.

west′ern frame con·struc′tion (*Bldg.*) A type of framing in which the studs extend from the top of each tier of joists to the next tier above; i.e., studs have a length only equal to the height of one story.

Western Union Splice

Western Union splice (*Elec.*) The electrical connection made by paralleling the bared ends of two conductors and then twisting these bared ends, each around the other.

wet end (*Papermkg.*) That part of the paper machine beginning at the place where the web is begun and extending up to the first dryer.

wet rot (*Wood*) Decay of lumber, due to moisture and warmth.

wet steam. Saturated steam which contains entrained moisture.

Wheat′stone's bridge (*Elec.*) A method of measuring resistances by the proportion existing between the resistance of three known adjustable resistances and the one to be found, all forming the arms of the bridge.

wheel and ax′le. An elementary mechanical principle for raising heavy weights. Power is applied to the circumference of the wheel which is mounted on an axle. The weight is attached by chain or rope to the axle which serves as a drum.

wheel base. The distance from the center of a front wheel to the center of a rear wheel, as on an automobile or wagon.

Wheel Dresser

wheel dress′er (*Mech.*) A tool for cleaning, resharpening, and truing the cutting faces of grinding wheels.

wheel hub. The boss or center of a wheel from which spokes radiate, and is bored to receive the axle.

wheel lathe (*Mach.*) A special lathe with a short bed and a deep gap for use in machining wheels.

wheel pull′er (*Auto.*) A device used for pulling automobile wheels from the axles.

wheel tru′ing (*Mech.*) Any operation on any part of a grinding wheel to balance it or to change its shape so as to improve its grinding or cutting qualities.

wheel win′dow (*Arch.*) A circular window with mullions or arms radiating from the center as the spokes of a wheel.

wheel′wright′. One who builds or repairs wagons or the like.

whet′ting (*Mech.*) The "rubbing up" of a tool on an oilstone for the purpose of improving its cutting edge.

whirl′er (*Ceram.*) A revolving device used when banding or decorating ware.

white an′ti-mo-ny (*Paint and Lacquer*) Sb_2O_3. A nonpoisonous, white pigment used in paint manufacture. Produces a slow-drying paint with properties similar to those of titanium oxide paint.

white ce′dar (*Wood*) *Chamaecyparis thyoides*. Height usually 30 to 50 ft., diameter 1 to 2 ft. Wood is light, soft, very durable. Used for shingles, boat building, fence posts, and wooden ware.

white coat (*Plaster.*) The hard, white top coat of a plastered wall. It is a composition of plaster of Paris and lime putty, to which marble dust is sometimes added. Gypsum plasters are also used for top coating.

white i′ron (*Metal.*) An extremely hard cast iron, resulting when the casting is chilled in a metallic mold.

white lead (*Chem. and Paint.*) Hydrated carbonate of lead, used in paintmaking.

white–met′al al-loys′ (*M e t a l.*) A mixture of zinc, tin, and copper, much used for the die casting of automobile hardware.

white oak (*Woodwkg.*) The hardest of American oaks. It is heavy and close-grained, and is used where strength and durability are required.

white pine (*Woodwkg.*) A straight-grained softwood, light in color; used extensively by patternmakers and joiners.

white space (*Print.*) Unprinted area on a sheet.

white spots (*Paint and Lacquer*) White dots or specks appearing in the final film are due to too much haste in rushing the job through or the sealing in of moisture. Also due to cheap, improperly formulated thinner.

white spruce (*Woodwkg.*) An inexpensive wood largely used for framing, flooring, etc.

white′wash (*B l d g.*) Lime slaked in water and applied with a brush or as a spray. Salt is sometimes added to make it adhere better, and bluing may be added to give a whiter tone.

whit′ing (*Chem.*) Pulverized chalk; when mixed with oil into a paste form, it becomes putty.

Whit′ney keys (*Mach.*) Square bar keys rounded at both ends.

Whitworth Thread

Whit′worth thread (*M a c h.*) The standard English thread, having rounded tops and bottoms and an included angle of 55 degrees.

whole depth (*Gear.*) The total depth of a tooth, from addendum line to root line.

whorl (hwûrl) (*Furn.*) A spiral scroll design.

wick′et (*Arch.*) A small door set within a larger door.

wick–feed oil′ers (*Mach.*) Those in which lubrication is accomplished by means of a wick immersed in a reservoir of oil. Oil absorbed by the wick is carried to the bearing.

wig'gler (*Mach.*) A device used on accurate work for exactly locating a center-punch mark on work to be drilled, directly in line with the center line of the drill spindle. Used also for accurately truing up work in a chuck.

wild black cherry (*Wood*) *Padus serotina*. Usual height 50 to 75 ft., diameter 2 to 3 ft. Wood is reddish brown, moderately heavy, hard, strong, and does not warp or split in seasoning; much used in furniture, fine panels, etc.

William and Mary, 1689–1702 (*Furn.*) This style, named after the English monarchs, succeeded the late Jacobean; it is characterized by lighter and more graceful designs with outlines combining the straight line and the curve; turned uprights and underpinnings, woven cane surfaces, and club-shaped foot.

winch (*Mech.*) A windlass.

wind (wīnd) (*Shopwk.*) The warp or twist in a piece of wood is frequently spoken of as wind.

wind cone (*Aero.*) A tapered fabric sleeve pivoted on a standard to indicate the wind direction.

wind'ers (wīn'dērs) (*Bldg.*) Treads of steps that are wider at one end than at the other. Used where steps are carried around curves or angles.

wind in'di-ca'tor (*A e r o.*) A device that indicates the direction and velocity of the surface wind.

wind'ing stair. A stair which changes directions by means of winders or a landing and winders. The wellhole is very wide and the balustrade follows the curve with only a newel at the bottom.

wind'lass. A machine for hoisting or hauling.

wind load (*E n g i n.*) The load on a structure due to wind pressure.

win'dow (*Arch.*) An opening in the wall of a building closed with transparent material inserted in a frame, placed so as to admit light, and made to open for air.

win'dow-head (*A r c h.*) The upper portion of a window frame.

win'dow jack. A small portable platform which fits over a window sill and projects outward beyond it. Used principally by painters.

win'dow seat (*Bldg.*) A seat built below, or in the recess of a window.

wind shake (*Lumber*) A split in lumber caused by the effect of wind before the tree was cut.

wind'shield wip'er (*Auto.*) A device operated mechanically, electrically, by manifold vacuum, or by hand, usually having a rubber blade which sweeps rain or snow from the glass of the windshield.

wind tee (*Aero.*) A large T-shaped weather vane located on a landing field or on top of an adjacent structure to indicate direction of wind.

wind tun'nel (*Aero.*) An apparatus producing an artificial wind or air stream, in which objects are placed for investigating the air flow about them and the aerodynamic forces exerted on them.

wing (*Aero.*) Refers to the main supporting surfaces of an airplane, left wing, right wing, upper wing, or lower wing. (*Arch.*) A section of a building extending out from the main part.

wing a're-a (*Aero.*) Wing area is

measured from the projection of the actual outline on the plane of the chords, without deduction for area blanketed by fuselage or nacelles. That part of the area so determined, which lies within the fuselage or nacelles, is bounded by two lateral lines that connect the intersections of the leading and trailing edges with the fuselage or nacelle, ignoring fairings and fillets. For the purpose of calculating area, a wing is considered to extend without interruption through the fuselage and nacelles. Unless otherwise stated, wing area always refers to total area including ailerons.

wing ax′is (*Aero.*) The locus of the aerodynamic centers of all the wing sections.

winged di-vid′ers. Dividers having a flat metal wing attached to one leg and projecting through the other. A setscrew on the slotted leg permits locking the dividers at a desired dimension.

wing heav-y (*Aero.*) The condition of an airplane whose right or left wing tends to sink when the lateral control is released in any given attitude of normal flight.

wing load′ing (*Aero.*) Gross weight fully loaded, divided by supporting surface area.

wing nut (*Mech.*) A form of nut which is tightened or loosened by two thin flat wings extending from opposite sides; a thumb nut. Wing Nut

wing–o′ver (*A e r o.*) A maneuver in which the airplane is put into a climbing turn until nearly stalled, at which point the nose is allowed to fall while continuing the turn, then returned to normal flight from the ensuing dive or glide in a direction approximately 180 deg. from that of the start of the evolution.

wing pro′file (*Aero.*) The outline of a wing section.

wing rib (*Aero.*) A fore-and-aft member of the wing structure of an airplane, used to give the wing section its form and to transmit the load from the fabric to the spars.

wing sec′tion (*Aero.*) A cross section of a wing parallel to the plane of symmetry or to a specified reference plane.

wing skid (*Aero.*) A skid placed near the wing tip to protect the wing from contact with the ground.

wing spar (*A e r o.*) The principal, transverse, structural member of the wing assembly of an airplane.

wing tip (*Aero.*) The outer end of an airplane wing.

wing–tip flare (*Aero.*) A pyrotechnic device attached to an aircraft for illuminating the ground while landing.

wing truss (*Aero.*) Consists of struts, tie rods, wires, cables, and spars; forming the truss by which wing loads are transmitted to the fuselage.

wiped joint (*Plumb.*) A lead joint in which molten solder is poured upon the two pieces to be jointed until they are of the right temperature. The joint is then wiped up by hand with a moleskin or cloth pad while the solder is in a plastic condition.

wip′er (*Mech.*) A form of cam having a sliding or wiping motion.

wire bar (*Metal.*) Copper bars, for rolling into rods, tapered at the ends to permit easy entrance to the rolls.

wire brush. A hand brush fitted with wire or thin strips of steel instead of bristles. Used for removing rust, dirt, or foreign matter from a surface.

wire cloth. A fabric made of wire. The size of mesh is made to suit the purpose for which it is to be used.

wired edge (*Sheet-Mt. Wk.*) An edge which is strengthened by being closed over a piece of wire.

wire draw'ing. The process by which wire is made; as by drawing metal through a hole in a steel plate.

wire gauge (*Mech.*) A notched plate having a series of gauged slots, numbered according to the sizes of the wire and sheet metal manufactured; used for measuring the diameter of wire. Most widely used in the United States is the United States Standard Steel Wire Gauge, which name has official sanction, without legal effect. The Birmingham gauge is recognized in acts of Congress for tariff purposes. American Gauge or Browne and Sharpe's gauge are used for copper wires and all nonferric metal wires.

wire glass (*Bldg.*) A type of window glass in which is imbedded wire of coarse mesh, to prevent scattering of fragments should the glass be broken.

wire mark (*Papermkg.*) The marking in a web of paper caused by the wire of a Fourdrinier machine or the covering of a mold of a cylinder machine.

wire nails (*Papermkg.*) Nails made of wire. They are to be had in all sizes and head shapes suited to their purpose. Such nails have almost entirely replaced the cut nails formerly used.

wir'ing ma-chine' (*Sheet-Met. Wk.*) Used to crimp in the edge of metal around the wire after it has been placed in the groove prepared for it by the turning machine.

withe (wĭth) (*Arch.*) The portion between flues in the same chimney.

wolf'ram-ite (wŏŏl'frăm-īt) (*Metal.*) A German alloy of aluminum and tungsten with a small percentage of copper and zinc. It has many of the qualities of duralumin.

wood al'co-hol (*Chem.*) (See METHANOL.)

wood'cut (*Print.*) A printing plate made of wood. The background is cut away, leaving the part to be printed in relief.

wood en'grav'ing (*Print.*) The art of making woodcuts.

wood fin'ish-ing (*Carp.*) Preparing the wood surface to receive a finish, and applying paint, stain, or varnish; also polishing when certain kinds of finish are desired.

wood flour. A finely powdered wood, generally of white pine, used as a filler in linoleum, flooring, and rubber.

wood pat'tern-mak'ing. The making of models or plans out of wood.

wood pul'ley (*Mach.*) Lighter than cast iron and will transmit probably 25 per cent more power with the same belt tension. Not suitable for use under conditions of excessive moisture.

Wood'ruff key (*Mach.*) A semicircular or semielliptical key flattened on the sides, for use in a keyway cut by bringing a rotary cutter against the material.

wood screws (*Shopwk.*) Made in oval-, round-, and flathead types. Length is measured from largest bearing diameter of head to the point of the screw. Gimlet points are standard, and screws are made bright galvanized and blued. Increment between sizes is 0.013 of an inch. They are made in sizes No. 0 to 30 and in length from ¼ in. to 6 in. The thread extends for seven tenths the length and the included angle of the head of flathead wood screws is 82 deg.

wood turn′ing. The art of shaping pieces of wood on a lathe.

wood′work. Things made of wood.

wood′work′ing. The trade in which things are made out of wood.

woof (*Textile*) The cross threads in fabric; those running opposite to the warp threads.

work. Work is measured, not in terms of time, but in terms of footpounds or inch-pounds. (*Phys.*) Force times the distance through which it acts.

work and turn (*Print.*) The printing of both sides of a sheet with the identical form. The sheet is fed to the same gripper edge both times but opposite side guides.

work hard′en-ing (*M e t a l.*) The hardening of metal while being worked, as in hammering. Two explanations are offered for this hardening; the amorphous cement theory and the slip interference theory.

work′ing depth (*Gear.*) The depth of a tooth from addendum line to clearance line; i.e., the total depth minus the clearance.

work′ing draw′ing (*Arch.*) A drawing which contains all dimensions and instructions necessary for successfully carrying a job to completion.

work′ing edge (*Wood Patmkg.*) In planing a piece of wood, one of the wide faces is first trued and called the "working face"; then an edge is trued square with the working face and is called the "working edge."

work′ing gaug′es (*Mach.*) A general classification of the gauges used in production.

work′ing load (*Engin.*) The ordinary load to which a structure is subjected; not necessarily the maximum load, but the average or mean load.

work′ing-u′nit stress (*Engin.*) The ultimate stress divided by the factor of safety.

work life (*Plast.*) The time a resin or an adhesive remains usable after it has been mixed with its catalyst and other ingredients.

works man′ag-er. The general superintendent in an industrial plant. In many establishments same as chief engineer.

worm-and-gear steer′ing (*A u t o.*) Consists of a worm on the lower end of the steering-gear shaft meshing with a worm gear on the cross shaft. Adjustment is usually well taken care of.

worm drive (*Auto.*) Drive by worm and wheel instead of bevel gear and pinion, or chain.

worm gear′ing (*Gear.*) Gearing composed of worms and worm wheels.

worm threads (*Mach.*) These threads are of the acme type, having an included angle of 29 deg., but are usually made deeper than the standard acme thread.

wove pa'per (*Paper*) Paper which does not have the watermark lines which can be seen in a laid paper.

wreath (*Arch. and Bldg.*) Section of a handrail curved in both vertical and horizontal planes and used to connect the side of a newel post with the ascending run of the handrail.

wreath piece (*Bldg.*) The curved section of the handrail string of a curved or winding stair. Also simple wreath.

wreck'ing bar (*Mach.*) A steel bar usually from 1 to 2 ft. in length, with one end drawn to a thin edge, the other curved to a claw.

wrench (*Mach.*) Common types are adjustable wrenches, monkey wrenches, double-end S wrenches, box wrenches, T wrenches, and socket wrenches. (*Mech.*) A tool for exerting a twisting strain, as in tightening a nut or bolt.

wring'ing fit (class 5) (*Mach.*) Also known as "tunking fit." A metal-to-metal fit usually not suitable for interchangeable parts.

wrink'ling (*Paint and Lacquer*) A gathered or wrinkled film is caused by applying heavy coats, abnormal heat or humidity, or the application of an elastic film over a surface.

wrist pin (*Mach.*) Sometimes applied to a crankpin or to any projecting pin which receives a connecting rod; in general, the pin connecting the rod to the crosshead in a steam engine, or connecting the connecting rod to the piston in a gasoline engine.

wrong font (*Print.*) Any letter of a kind different from that of the other letters of the word in which it is used.

wrong side (*Papermkg.*) Term applied to the wire side of a sheet of paper for it displays the impression of the wire more clearly than the "right" right which is also called the felt side.

wrought iron (*Metal.*) Iron which has had the major portion of its carbon, as well as the foreign elements which would effect its working value, removed.

wye (wī) (*Plumb.*) A fitting, either cast or wrought, that has one side outlet at any other angle than 90 deg. The angle is usually 45 deg. unless otherwise specified.

wye lev'el (*Surv.*) The spirit level is attached to the telescope which rests in two Y-shaped supports. These are fastened to a horizontal bar to which the vertical axis is attached. The telescope can be taken out of the Y's, turned end for end, and replaced when testing the bubble for adjustment.

X

X-braced chair (*Furn.*) A chair with X-shaped underbracing or stretchers.

X mem'ber (*Auto.*) A pressed-steel channel construction built in shape like the letter X, and placed within the main frame assembly of an automobile.

X-ray. Similar to gamma rays, and highly penetrating radiation, X rays do not come from the nucleus of the atom but from the surrounding electrons. These rays are produced by electron bombardment. The rays pass through most objects as though they were transparent. By means of these rays it is possible to see and to photograph shadows of bones, interior organs, etc., of the body. (*Phys.*) A popular name for Roentgen rays. A form of radiant energy sent out when the cathode rays of a Crookes tube strike upon the opposite walls of the tube or upon any object in the tube.

X-ray tube. A vacuum tube designed for producing X rays by accelerating electrons to a high velocity by means of an electrostatic field and then suddenly stopping them by collision with a target.

X-shaped chair (*Furn.*) A chair of ancient origin, the supporting structure of which is X shaped, often elaborately decorated, frequently folding.

---

sāle, surfâce, grăm, humăn, màsk, solár, bär, bâre; mē, êdition, lĕnd, momĕnt, bakēr; kīnd, fĭt; lōde, ômit, ŏlive, cŏnsume, sôrt; dūty, ûtility, nŭt, alŭm, bûrn.

Y

Yan'kee ma-chine' (*Papermkg.*) A Fourdrinier paper machine having a large single dryer with a highly polished surface. When the paper contacts this surface it assumes a glazed finish.

yard'age (*E n g i n.*) Relates to cubic yards of earth excavated.

yard'stick. A graduated, wooden, measuring scale 36 inches long. Such a scale made of metal would properly be called a 36-inch scale.

yaw (*Aero.*) A deviation from the line of flight by angular motion about the normal axis of an airplane.

yaw'me'ter (*A e r o.*) An instrument for measuring the angle of yaw.

Y con-nec'tion (*Elec.*) A branching connection applied to a three-phase circuit.

year ring (*Woodwkg.*) Also called "growth ring," or "annual ring." Rings of tubes or cells by means of which the sap is conveyed throughout a tree. They are clearly visible on a cross section of a log. Each ring represents a year of growth.

yel'low brass (*Metal.*) An alloy of 70 parts copper and 30 parts zinc. It is an inferior alloy used where strength is not essential.

yel'low o'cher (ō'kēr) (*P a i n t.*) A color derived from the mineral earth ocher, and used as a pigment.

yel'low pine (*Wood*) *Pinus palustris and P. echinata.* An evergreen of two principal varieties, long leaf and short leaf. The wood of the long-leaf pine is dense, heavy, and very strong; mostly used in the form of heavy timbers. The short-leaf pine is brittle, not nearly so strong, and is less expensive; used for studding, joists, cheap flooring, etc.

yew (yōō) (*Wood*) *Taxus.* A slow-growing, medium-size evergreen tree. The wood is close grained, hard, and flexible. Its color is orange red to brown.

yield point (*Engin.*) That unit stress at which the specimen begins to stretch without increase in the load.

yield strength (*Engin.*) The load required to produce a permanent stretch or elongation of a material.

yield val'ue (*Plast.*) The lowest pressure at which a plastic will flow. Below this pressure the plastic behaves as an elastic solid; above this pressure as a viscous liquid.

yoke (*Arch.*) The horizontal top member of a window frame. (*Tel.*) A set of coils used around the neck of an electronic camera or picture tube to produce the horizontal and vertical deflection of the electron beam.

Young's mod'u-lus (*Mech. Engin.*) Same as modulus of elasticity.

---

sāle, surfâce, grăm, humăn, màsk, soldr, bär, bâre; mē, êdition, lĕnd, momĕnt, bakēr; kīnd, fĭt; lōde, ômit, ŏlive, cŏnsume, sôrt; dūty, ûtility, nŭt, alŭm, bûrn.

Z

ze-bran-o (*W o o d*) *Distemonanthus benthamianus.* Zebrawood. A very large tree, native of the west coast of Africa. Wood is hard, heavy, and tough; its light-colored background and parallel dark-brown stripes make it valuable for unusual effects on fine furniture and paneling.

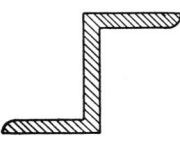

zee bar (*Engin.*) A structural-steel bar with cross section like the letter Z. Much used in ship construction as well as in other engineering fields.

ze′ro. The numeral 0; a cipher; the lowest point.

ze′ro ceil′ing (*Aero.*) Cloud level below 100 feet. Weather unfit for flying.

ze′ro lift an′gle (*Aero.*) The angle of attack of an airfoil when the angle of incidence is zero.

ze′ro lift line (*Aero.*) A line through the trailing edge of an airfoil parallel to the direction of the wind when the lift is zero.

zig′zag′ rule. Derives its name from the manner of opening and closing. Often referred to as a folding rule. Made up in 6-in. sections total from 2 to 8 ft.

zinc (*Metal.*) A bluish-white metal principally used in galvanizing and in making alloys.

zinc chlo′ride (*C h e m.*) $ZnCl_2$. A white, deliquescent salt, obtained by the solution of zinc, or zinc oxide, in hydrochloric acid, or by burning zinc in chlorine. Used as a soldering flux.

zinc en′grav′ing or etch′ing (*Print.*) A printing plate made of zinc. The background is etched and cut away leaving the design in relief.

zinc ox′ide (*Chem.*) (ZnO) A white powder derived by heating zinc carbonate. Used as a paint pigment, for medicines, and zinc salts.

zinc sul′phate (*Chem.*) ($ZnSO_4$) Made by dissolving scrap zinc in sulphuric acid. It is used in calico printing, dyeing, as a drier for linseed oil, in medicine, and for preserving wood and skins.

zinc white (*Paint.*) Zinc oxide used as a pigment.

zinox (*Paint.*) A hydrated oxide of zinc used in the manufacture of enamels.

zoom (*Aero.*) A short, steep climb during which the rate of climb is greater than that which can be maintained during steady flight.

---

sāle, surfâce, grăm, humăn, màsk, solȧr, bär, bâre; mē, ēdition, lĕnd, **momĕnt**, bakēr; kīnd, fĭt; lōde, ômit, ŏlive, cŏnsume, sôrt; dūty, ûtility, nŭt, alŭm, bûrn.